Drug Use and Abuse

FIRST CANADIAN EDITION

Stephen A. Maisto
Syracuse University

Mark Galizio
University of North Carolina at Wilmington

Gerard J. Connors
Research Institute on Addictions, University at Buffalo

Shannon Maheu
Fanshawe College

Anjanie McCarthy
Fanshawe College

NELSON EDUCATION

NELSON EDUCATION

Drug Use and Abuse, First Canadian Edition

by Stephen A. Maisto, Mark Galizio, Gerard J. Connors, Shannon Maheu, and Anjanie McCarthy

Vice President, Editorial Higher Education:
Anne Williams

Executive Editor:
Lenore Taylor-Atkins

Marketing Manager:
Ann Byford

Developmental Editor:
Leah Blain

Photo Researcher:
Melody Tolson

Permissions Coordinator:
Melody Tolson

Content Production Manager:
Christine Gilbert

Production Service:
Cenveo Publisher Services

Copy Editor:
Jessie Coffey

Proofreader:
Erin Moore

Indexer:
Robert Swanson

Manufacturing Manager—Higher Education:
Joanne McNeil

Design Director:
Ken Phipps

Managing Designer:
Franca Amore

Interior Design:
Dianna Little

Cover Design:
Dianna Little

Cover Image:
Ikon Images/Superstock

Interior Images:
Chapter opener pages throughout—Ikon Images/Superstock; Key Terms icon—Alex Staroseltsev/Shutterstock; "This is Your Brain..." box icon—iStockphoto; Contemporary Issue box icon—iStockphoto; Drugs and Culture box icon—iStockphoto; Essays/Thought Questions Icon—Jirsak/Shutterstock; Suggested Readings Icon—Tristan Paviot/Getty Images

Compositor:
Cenveo Publisher Services

Printed and bound in Canada
5 17 16

For more information contact Nelson Education Ltd., 1120 Birchmount Road, Toronto, Ontario, M1K 5G4. Or you can visit our Internet site at http://www.nelson.com

Library and Archives Canada Cataloguing in Publication

Drug use and abuse/Stephen A. Maisto...[et al.].—1st Canadian ed.

Includes bibliographical references and index.
ISBN-13: 978-0-17-651415-0

1. Drugs of abuse. 2. Substance abuse. I. Maisto, Stephen A

RM316.D764 2012
362.29 C2012-901179-7

ISBN-13: 978-0-17-651415-0
ISBN-10: 0-17-651415-5

To Sam
S.A.M.

To my parents, Joe and Audrienne,
and to my wife, Kate,
and to my daughter, Annie
M.G.

To Lana and Marissa
G.J.C.

To my husband, Norm, and our sons,
Ky, Nolan, and Josh for serenading me
and asking lots of questions
S.M.

To my husband, Robin, and our sons,
Garnett and Caelan,
who make me laugh every day
A.M.

ABOUT THE AUTHORS

Stephen A. Maisto received a PhD in experimental psychology from the University of Wisconsin—Milwaukee and completed a postdoctoral respecialization in clinical psychology from George Peabody College of Vanderbilt University. He is a professor of psychology at Syracuse University. He has been engaged in research, teaching, clinical practice, and clinical training in the assessment and treatment of substance-use disorders for 30 years. Dr. Maisto has published over 150 articles, 25 book chapters, and several books on substance use and substance-use disorders. His current research is supported by the National Institute on Alcohol Abuse and Alcoholism and the Department of Veterans Affairs. Dr. Maisto is a member of the American Psychological Association (Fellow, Divisions of Clinical Psychology and Addictive Behaviors), Association for Psychological Science, Research Society on Alcoholism, and the Association for Behavioral and Cognitive Therapies.

Mark Galizio received his PhD in experimental psychology in 1976, from the University of Wisconsin—Milwaukee, where he served as a research assistant at the Midwest Institute on Drug Abuse. He is chair and professor of psychology at the University of North Carolina at Wilmington, where he has taught and conducted research for over 30 years. He has published extensively in the areas of behavioural pharmacology and behaviour analysis and has served as associate editor of the *Journal of the Experimental Analysis of Behavior.* His research has been supported by grants from the National Institute on Drug Abuse, the National Institute of Neurological Disorders and Stroke, and the National Science Foundation. He is a fellow of the American Psychological Association (Divisions of Psychopharmacology and Substance Abuse, Behavior Analysis, Behavioral Neuroscience and Comparative Psychology, and Experimental Psychology), and is past president of the Division of Behavior Analysis.

Gerard J. Connors is director of the Research Institute on Addictions at the University at Buffalo. He earned his doctoral degree in clinical psychology from Vanderbilt University in 1980. Dr. Connors's research interests include substance use and abuse, relapse prevention, self-help group involvement, early interventions with heavy drinkers, and treatment evaluation. He is a fellow of the American Psychological Association (Divisions of Clinical Psychology and Addictions). Dr. Connors has authored or coauthored numerous scientific articles, books, and book chapters. His current research activities are funded by grants from the National Institute on Alcohol Abuse and Alcoholism.

Shannon Maheu is currently a full-time Professor of Psychology in the School of Language and Liberal Studies at Fanshawe College, London, Ontario. She has recently been awarded the President's Award for Teaching Excellence in 2011, which has subsequently led to her recognition as an effective leader in the classroom and among colleagues. She has successfully completed her Master's in Educational Psychology at the University of Western Ontario. Over the last six years she has been teaching a number of cognitive, social, and educational psychology courses, including Psychology of Addictions and Culture of Addictions. She has recently coauthored an Introductory Psychology textbook, *PSYCH,* has authored numerous book chapters, and written teacher and student resources to supplement college textbooks. She is pedagogically interested in student-centred learning and its subsequent outcomes on success.

Anjanie McCarthy is Coordinator of Social Sciences and Professor of Psychology at Fanshawe College. She has an undergraduate degree from the University of Toronto, and both a Master's and Doctorate Degree in Psychology from Queen's University, Ontario. She completed a post-doctoral fellowship at the University of Toronto before accepting a position at Fanshawe College. Her research interests include the development of nonverbal behaviours during interpersonal interactions. Her current research focuses on nonverbal communication in the classroom and ways to enhance communication between teacher and student.

BRIEF CONTENTS

CONTENTS

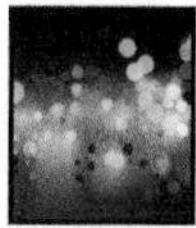

CHAPTER 12 Psychotherapeutic Medications 273

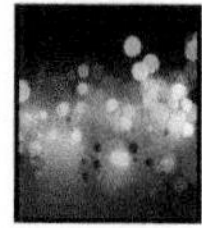

CHAPTER 13 Other Prescription and Over-the-Counter Drugs 314

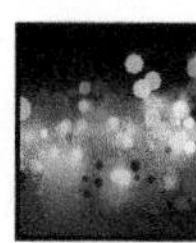

CHAPTER 14 Treatment of Substance-Use Disorders 336

In this first Canadian edition, we present relevant issues around drugs of use and abuse from a Canadian perspective. We present updated Canadian research findings, Canadian statistics, and information related to the culture of drug abuse and addiction in our society.

The central theme of this first Canadian edition is that a drug's effects are determined not only by its chemical structure and interaction in the body but also by the drug users' biological and psychological characteristics and the setting in which they use the drug. This central theme is reflected throughout the presentation of individual drugs or drug classes and in the discussion of prevention and treatment. The text examines the complexity of human drug consumption on biological, psychological, cognitive, and social levels. This scholarly text is written for students of varying levels of knowledge in the biological, behavioural, or social sciences.

The text also contains a number of pedagogical features designed to increase students' interest and learning. An engaging and informative **Did You Know?** section at the beginning of each chapter challenges students' preconceptions about drug use and abuse while drawing their attention to important concepts or facts that follow in the chapter. The **Margin Glossary** helps students identify and define important terms within the text. **Margin Quotations** highlight key information or concepts further discussed in the chapter. **Drugs and Culture boxes** highlight issues relevant or specific to Canadian drug use legislation, recent research, or 'hot topics' that influence the culture of Canadian society. **Contemporary Issue boxes** take a more global perspective on issues of drug abuse, treatment, and legislation and discuss current controversies involving drugs or drug use. Finally, **This is Your Brain on…** diagrams are included as visual learning tools that assist students in understanding the chemical reactions that occur in the brain while using drugs.

Instructor Supplements

The **Nelson Education Teaching Advantage (NETA)** program delivers research-based instructor resources that promote student engagement and higher-order thinking to enable the success of Canadian students and educators.

Instructors today face many challenges. Resources are limited, time is scarce, and a new kind of student has emerged: one who is juggling school with work, has gaps in his or her basic knowledge, and is immersed in technology in a way that has led to a completely new style of learning. In response, Nelson Education has gathered a group of dedicated instructors to advise us on the creation of richer and more flexible ancillaries that respond to the needs of today's teaching environments.

In consultation with the editorial advisory board, Nelson Education has completely rethought the structure, approaches, and formats of our key textbook ancillaries. We've also increased our investment in editorial support for our ancillary authors. The result is the Nelson Education Teaching Advantage, which includes a *NETA Assessment* component designed to improve Nelson's testing materials. Under *NETA Assessment*, Nelson's authors create multiple-choice questions that reflect research-based best practices for constructing effective questions and testing not just recall but also higher-order thinking. Our guidelines were developed by David DiBattista, a 3M National Teaching Fellow whose recent research as a professor of psychology at Brock University has focused on multiple-choice testing. All Test Bank authors receive training at workshops conducted by Prof. DiBattista, as do the copyeditors assigned to each Test Bank. A copy of *Multiple Choice Tests: Getting Beyond Remembering*, Prof. DiBattista's guide to writing effective tests, is included with every Nelson Test Bank package.

The NETA Test Bank written to accompany *Drug Use and Abuse* includes over 700 multiple-choice questions written according to NETA guidelines for effective construction and development of higher-order questions. Test Bank files are provided in Word format for easy editing and in PDF format for convenient printing whatever your system.

On the book's companion website, **www.druguseandabuse.nelson.com**, we provide PowerPoint Presentations for each chapter, chapter outlines, learning objectives, glossary terms and definitions, useful web links, and an image bank that provides figures and tables from the first Canadian edition that instructors can use as is or modify to create their own presentations.

Student Supplements

The companion website offers text-specific, interactive review and enrichment materials for students, including tutorial quizzes, flash cards, and useful web links.

Acknowledgements

This text could not have been completed without the help of a number of people. Foremost among these individuals are Lenore Taylor-Atkins, Executive Editor; Leah Blain, Developmental Editor; Christine Gilbert, Content Production Manager; Ann Byford, Marketing Manager; Vicki Gould, Director, Asset Management Services; Debbie Yea, Project Manager, Asset Management; and Melody Tolson, Permissions Researcher. Thanks also go to the production team, including Jessie Coffey, copyeditor; Erin Moore, proofreader; and Robert Swanson, indexer. Thank you as well to the composition team at Cenveo Publishing Services, led by Manisha Singh.

Many thanks also go to those who contributed time and energy to reviewing our manuscript. The following reviewers offered outstanding suggestions that helped us to produce a better book: Anastasia Bake, St. Clair College and University of Windsor; Sandra Bullock, University of Waterloo; John Conklin, Camosun College; Richard Dyck, University of Calgary; Evelyn Field, Mount Royal University; Margaret Forgie, University of Lethbridge; Kerry-Anne Hogan, University of Ottawa; Bruce McKay, Wilfrid Laurier University; Kelly McShane, Ryerson University; Tony Robertson, Vancouver Island University; and Nicole Vittoz, University of British Columbia.

We also wish to thank everyone else who has helped us along this journey, especially our family and friends. We would also like to thank each other for the unique support given as we worked together on this project.

Shannon Maheu
Anjanie McCarthy

CHAPTER 1

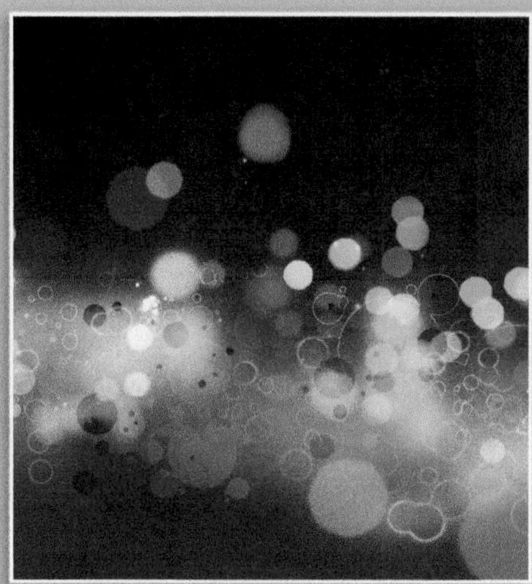

Drug Use and Abuse

Did You Know

?

- A drug's street name sometimes describes the actual effect of that drug.
- Drugs tend to have a greater effect on women than men because men have less body fat, not because they typically weigh more than women.
- Expectancies about alcohol's effects may be a more powerful determinant of its effects than is the pharmacological action of alcohol.
- People who have developed tolerance to one drug also will have tolerance to certain other drugs, even though they may never have taken those other drugs.
- The highest rates of alcohol and other drug use are found among 18- to 25-year-olds.
- Health Canada only recently began conducting an annual survey, called the Canadian Alcohol and Drug Use Monitoring Survey, on alcohol and drug use in Canada.
- A majority of Canadians believe that if you try drugs you are likely to become dependent.

There's no doubt that each of us knows someone or is someone who uses drugs. We see social depictions of drug use and abuse in the media and may even find ourselves confronted by drug use in our own personal lives. Although what we see and hear in the media often focuses on the negative consequences of drug use, drugs are popular all over the world because people perceive that they benefit from using drugs. For example, on an *individual* level, people say that drugs make them feel more relaxed, socialize more easily, feel sexier, escape boredom, and feel more confident and assertive. Drugs have also helped to ease a lot of suffering in humans and other animals when used for specific medical purposes. On a *group* or *community* level, drugs have been used for thousands of years as part of social and religious rituals. A drug used for such purposes has little to do with the drug's chemistry but rather with social or cultural factors. One society may condone the use of a drug—say, alcohol in North American and European countries—whereas another society condemns it, such as the Islamic countries of Iran and Saudi Arabia. The extended list of benefits and negative consequences of drug use provides us with a complex picture of human drug use and suggests that many different factors influence drug use.

"Food is good. Poison is bad. Drugs may be good or bad, and whether they are seen as good or bad depends on who is looking at them."

(Weil & Rosen, 1983, p. 10)

What influences drug use and how that use affects us is the subject of drugs and human behaviour and are what this text is about.

This introductory chapter defines the major terms associated with drug use and explains the drug classification systems. These topics set the stage for how the next sections of the textbook are organized and provides an overview of the key concepts that explain drug use and abuse.

Defining Drug Use and Abuse

Humans have used drugs for several thousand years, but the scientific study of drugs is more recent. The scientific study of drugs is called **pharmacology**, and it is concerned with all information about the effects of chemical substances (drugs) on living systems. Pharmacology is considered a part of biology and is allied with physiology and biochemistry (Blum, 1984). **Psychopharmacology** is an area within the field of pharmacology that focuses on the effects of drugs on behaviour. Psychologists recognize that understanding how drugs affect human behaviour requires knowledge about biological, personal, social, and environmental factors.

pharmacology
The scientific study of drugs concerned with all information about the effects of drugs on living systems.

psychopharmacology
The subarea of pharmacology that is concerned with the effects of drugs on behaviour.

drug
Broadly defined as any chemical entity or mixture of entities not required for the maintenance of health but that alters biological function or structure when administered.

drug abuse
Any use of drugs that causes physical, psychological, legal, or social harm to the individual user or to others affected by the drug user's behaviour.

Behaviour drugs are easy enough to talk about, or so it seems from the numbers and variety of people who do so; however, defining *drug* is not so simple. Although they have run into confusion along the way, experts have arrived at a workable definition. According to a World Health Organization (WHO) report published in 1981, **drug** is defined in the broadest sense as "any chemical entity or mixture of entities, other than those required for the maintenance of normal health (like food), the administration of which alters biological function and possibly structure" (p. 227). This definition remains useful today.

So then, what is drug *use* and what is drug *abuse*? People use drugs for a number of reasons. There are many instrumental uses of drugs in society, such as to manage pain or reduce anxiety. Other uses are recreational, such as to get high or to relax. These uses for drugs seem to be considered abusive if negative consequences are associated with their use. Generally, abuse has been referred to in different ways. However, experts tend to focus their definition of **drug abuse** as "any use of drugs that causes physical, psychological, legal, or social harm to the individual or to others affected by the drug user's behaviour" (Rinaldi et al., 1988).

If *abuse* is drug use with negative consequences, then drug *use* may be viewed as the larger category, with drug abuse as a subset. Drug consumption that does not meet the criteria for drug abuse is referred to as drug use.

Drug Classification

To make the definition useful for research and practical purposes, it is necessary to order the substances that fit the definition of *drug* into smaller categories. Pharmacologists have attempted to define drugs by creating classification systems for drugs. These classification systems are useful for research and practical purposes, and are based on the primary properties of drugs to communicate a drug's nature and the ways it can be used. Table 1.1 presents some of the major ways of classifying drugs.

TABLE 1.1 Drug Classifications

Classification System	General Classification Criteria	Details/Limitations	Example(s)
Origin	Distinguishes source of drug (e.g., plants)	May include many drugs that have different chemical actions	Opiates (derived from opium poppy)
Therapeutic Use	Similarities in how a drug is used to treat or modify something in the body	Outlines dosage and use for medical treatments, although some drugs are used differently from their therapeutic use (e.g., abuse of morphine or amphetamines)	Morphine is used for pain management Amphetamines are used for appetite-suppressant
Site of Drug Action	Where in the body the drug is causing physical changes	Limited when a drug affects several different body sites	Alcohol depresses the CNS Cocaine stimulates the CNS
Chemical Structure	Similarities in chemical structures, which derive synthetic compounds	Synthetic compounds form the chemical base of specific drugs	Barbiturates (e.g., Amytal) are derived from chemical structure barbituric acid
Mechanism of Action	How a drug produces its **drug effects**	Similar effects are used to categorize pharmacology May affect the same body site	Alcohol and nicotine depress the CNS and decrease appetite
Street Name	Comes from drug "subcultures" and the street drug market	Names typically reflect actual drug effects	Amphetamines are called 'speed' Barbiturates or depressants are called 'downers'

drug effects
The action of a drug on the body. Drug effects are measured in different ways.

psychoactive
Pertaining to effects on mood, thinking, and behaviour.

The specific drugs discussed in this text (Chapters 5 through 13) follow the general classification by drug effects, which include information on all the areas of classification discussed in Table 1.1. We focus on drug use and abuse of **psychoactive** drugs—those that affect moods, thinking, and behaviour. These drugs with psychoactive properties are the ones that people are most likely to use, often in ways that create serious problems for them. Some substances have been designated formally as psychoactive, such as alcohol, whereas others have not, such as aspirin.

Use of the DSM-IV

In Canada, the United States, and other countries, providers of care for physical and mental illness have handled problems of definition by developing systems of definitions of illnesses, which they call *diagnostic systems.* A diagnosis typically is based on a cluster of symptoms that is given a name (the diagnosis). The advantage is that, say, if two physicians are communicating about pneumonia in a patient and they are following the same diagnostic system, then each knows exactly what the referent of the other is when the term *pneumonia* is used; that is, a specific cluster of symptoms is being referred to. The American Psychiatric Association (APA) has published the *Diagnostic and Statistical Manual* (DSM), which provides formal criteria system for diagnosing and treatment psychological disorders. The most recent version (systems are revised because of ongoing research that provides new information about different disorders) was revised in 2000 and is called DSM-IV-TR. The DSM-IV-TR includes a category for "substance-related" (alcohol- or other drug-related) disorders, which differentiates between "substance dependence" and "substance abuse."

Table 1.2 lists the criteria for defining substance dependence and abuse according to DSM-IV-TR (APA, 2000). It is important to make a few comments about the criteria:

- Most generally, the same criteria are applied in defining dependence and abuse for all drugs and drug classes that people tend to use for nonmedical reasons (which includes all the drugs we discuss in this text).
- Dependence and abuse are considered separate diagnoses. A person could not be diagnosed with both dependence and abuse of a given substance, although it is possible to meet the criteria for dependence on one substance and for abuse of another.
- Provide clinicians, psychiatrists, psychologists, and others with consistent description and language regarding diagnoses for psychological disorders. This is important for both prescribing of medication and other treatment options.

Dependence, Tolerance, and Withdrawal

Substance Dependence

dependence
A strong compulsion or urge; in this case to continue taking a particular drug.

craving
A term that has been variously defined in reference to drug use; typically a strong or intense desire to use a drug.

According to the DSM-IV, substance **dependence**, a strong compulsion to continue taking a particular drug, is diagnosed when at least three of the seven criteria listed for dependence are present at any time in the same 12-month period.

There are two types of dependence:

- *Physical dependence*, which is based on the idea that drug-taking behaviours continue in order to avoid negative consequences associated with physical withdrawal symptoms (e.g., heroin user who presents hypersensitivity to pain and inability to sleep following cessation of the drug); and
- *Psychologial dependence*, which is based on the idea that drug-taking behaviours persist based on the **craving** for the positive effects associated with using the drugs.

TABLE 1.2 DSM-IV Diagnostic Criteria for Substance Dependence and Abuse

Substance Dependence

A maladaptive pattern of substance use leading to clinically significant impairment or distress, as manifested by three or more of the following occurring at any time in the same 12-month period:

1. Tolerance, as defined by either of the following:
   (a) Need for markedly increased amounts of the substance to achieve intoxication or desired effect
   (b) Markedly diminished effect with continued use of the same amount of the substance
2. Withdrawal, as manifested by either of the following:
   (a) The characteristic withdrawal syndrome for the substance
   (b) The same (closely related) substance is taken to relieve or avoid withdrawal symptoms
3. The substance is often taken in larger amounts or over a longer period than was intended
4. A persistent desire or unsuccessful efforts to cut down or control substance use
5. A great deal of time is spent in activities necessary to obtain the substance (e.g., visiting multiple doctors or driving long distances), to use the substance (e.g., chain-smoking), or to recover from its effects
6. Important social, occupational, or recreational activities given up or reduced because of substance use
7. Continued substance use despite knowledge of having had a persistent or recurrent physical or psychological problem that is likely to be caused by or exacerbated by the substance (e.g., current cocaine use despite recognition of cocaine-induced depression, or continued drinking despite recognition that an ulcer was made worse by alcohol consumption)

Specify if:

1. With physiological dependence: Evidence of tolerance or withdrawal (that is, either item [1] or [2] is present).

Substance Abuse

A maladaptive pattern of substance use leading to clinically significant impairment or distress, as manifested by one or more of the following:

1. Recurrent substance use resulting in a failure to fulfill major role obligations at work, school, or home (e.g., repeated absences or poor work performance related to substance use; substance-related absences, suspensions, or expulsions from school; neglect of children or household)
2. Recurrent substance use in situations in which it is physically hazardous (e.g., driving an automobile or operating a machine when impaired by substance use)
3. Recurrent substance-related legal problems (e.g., arrests for substance-related disorderly conduct)
4. Continued substance use despite having persistent or recurrent social or interpersonal problems caused or exacerbated by the effects of the substance (e.g., arguments with spouse about consequences of intoxication, physical fights)

Does not meet the criteria for substance dependence for this substance?

Source: Reprinted with permission from the *Diagnostic and Statistical Manual of Mental Disorders, Fourth Edition, Text Revision*, (Copyright © 2000). American Psychiatric Association.

Drug Tolerance

The DSM-IV criteria for dependence include the term *drug tolerance*, which was defined in parts (a) and (b) of criterion 1 in Table 1.2.

Drug **tolerance** is defined as the repeated administration of a given dose of a drug that often results in reduced response to the drug (O'Brien, 2001). In essence, over time an increased amount of a drug is needed to achieve its desired effects. There are three distinct types of tolerance involving different mechanisms: dispositional, functional, and behavioural.

tolerance
Generally, increased amounts of a drug needed to achieve intoxication, or a diminished drug effect with continued use of the same amount of a drug.

Dispositional tolerance occurs when the regular use of a given drug results to some degree in an increase in the metabolism rate of a drug so that users must consume greater quantities of the drug to maintain a certain level of it in their body.

© Bubbles Photolibrary/Alamy

Cocaine is a short-acting drug, and when the highly pleasurable effects of an initial dose begin to wear off, users are prone to taking another dose. However, the second administration—even when the same amount is taken—generally produces much less of a pleasurable high due to rapidly developing *acute tolerance*.

Functional tolerance, or pharmacodynamic tolerance, means that the brain and other parts of the central nervous system become less sensitive to a drug's effects. The two types of functional tolerance are acute and protracted. *Acute tolerance* (sometimes called tachyphylaxis) is measured within the course of action of a single dose or the first few doses of a drug. When a person takes a dose of a drug, the amount of drug in the body—measured as the amount of drug in the blood, or the blood level—rises to some peak level. With some drugs, at any point when the blood level is rising to peak, users may experience greater drug effects than at that same point when the blood level is falling. *Protracted tolerance* pertains to the effects of a given dose of a drug when it is administered more regularly or chronically. Protracted tolerance means that the individual consumes greater amounts of a drug to achieve an effect that was once achieved with a lesser dose.

Behavioural tolerance involves a behavioural adjustment by the person, which through experience in using drugs, compensates for its effects. For example, individuals who have had considerable experience with the effects of alcohol on motor coordination may learn to compensate for their intoxication by walking slowly or with a lower centre of gravity to keep from falling—even if they are quite drunk (for example, Vogel-Sprott, 1992).

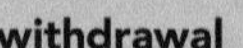

cross-tolerance
Tolerance to a drug (or drugs) never taken, which results from protracted tolerance to another drug (or drugs).

In some cases, tolerance to one drug may extend to other closely related drugs—this is called **cross-tolerance**. People who have developed tolerance to one drug also will have tolerance to certain other drugs, even though they may never have taken those other drugs.

Withdrawal

withdrawal
A definable illness that occurs with a cessation or decrease in use of a drug.

syndrome
In medicine, a number of symptoms that occur together and characterize a specific illness or disease.

Withdrawal is a definable illness that occurs with a cessation or decrease in drug use after the body has adjusted to the presence of a drug to such a degree that it cannot function without the drug. Not all drugs are associated with an identifiable withdrawal **syndrome** (also called *abstinence syndrome*). For any drug associated with withdrawal symptoms, the severity of those symptoms may change with the characteristics of the users and their history of use of that drug. Furthermore, psychological symptoms, such as anxiety, depression, and craving for drugs, are often part of withdrawal syndromes. These psychological symptoms strongly influence whether the individual can stop using drugs for any length of time.

It is critical to mention that both drug tolerance and withdrawal affect drug-use patterns. For example, if tolerance to a drug develops, the individual must consume increasing amounts of it to achieve a desired drug effect. Such a trend in use may affect how much time the person devotes each day to acquiring the drug and to using it. Furthermore, with increased tolerance of drug use, the person becomes more susceptible to experiencing various negative physical, social, or legal consequences.

Withdrawal symptoms from drug use also make a person more likely to continue or resume the use of a drug after a period of abstaining. Many studies have shown that relief from withdrawal is a powerful motivator of drug use. In this regard, drug withdrawal may begin when the level of drug in the blood drops. If the user takes more of the drug at this point, the withdrawal symptoms are relieved. Here the motivating force is the "turning off" of unpleasant withdrawal symptoms, which works to perpetuate a powerful cycle of drug use–drug withdrawal–drug use.

The Drug Experience

As we said earlier, people enjoy many of the experiences they have when they take drugs. This raises an important question: What causes the "drug experience"? Some perspectives of the drug experience have argued that the search for altered consciousness has been a human desire since our primitive beginnings (Butts, 1978). Learning theories offer a simple explanation for this: Actions that have pleasurable outcomes are increased or repeated. A drug user may be seeking relief from negative feelings or events in their life; if drugs provide this (temporary) relief, he or she is more likely to continue using drugs. Still, and not too long ago, the chemical actions of drugs have been viewed as the primary reason people experience psychoactive changes when they take different drugs. Today, research from different disciplines, such as pharmacology, psychology, and sociology, has shown that the drug experience is a product of more than just the drug's pharmacological action.

Generally, we can look at three sets of factors: 1) pharmacological factors; 2) characteristics of the drug user; and 3) social and environmental factors.

Pharmacological Factors

As presented in the drug classification table, the chemical properties and mechanism of action on the body of the drug used play a role in the drug experience. In addition, **drug dosage** (or dose), which is the measure of how much of a drug is consumed, and the **route of drug administration**, or the way the drug enters the body, affect the resulting drug experience. This is important because the route of administration affects how much of a dosage reaches its site(s) of action and how quickly it gets there. Chapter 4 discusses in detail major routes of drug administration and their effects on the drug experience.

drug dosage
A measure of the quantity of a drug consumed.

route of drug administration
The way that drugs enter the body (e.g., oral, or, intravenous).

Characteristics of the Drug User

Differences among people probably account for most of the differences in how they react to a given dose of a drug. Roughly, we can divide user characteristics into two types: biological and psychological.

Biological Characteristics

Inherited Differences in Reactions to Drugs Major differences in how people react to drugs are genetically based (Nies, 2001). For example, the way people are affected by their first dose of a drug is called their **initial sensitivity** to a drug. Differences in sensitivity are thought to be determined genetically. More generally, the role genetics plays in causing substance disorders is readily researched. Alcohol dependency in particular has received much attention. It is believed that inherited differences in how

initial sensitivity
The effect of a drug on a first-time user.

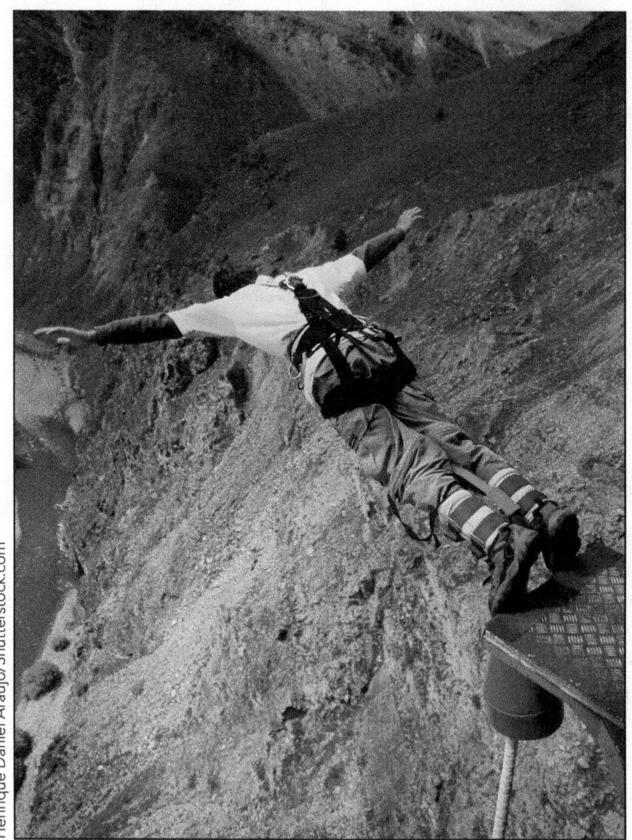

Henrique Daniel Araujo/Shutterstock.com

Individuals who enjoy bungee jumping probably would score high on a measure of sensation seeking, which is a constant personality characteristic associated with drug abuse.

alcohol is experienced (as a result of action in the brain) and metabolized may be of major importance in some individuals developing alcohol abuse or dependence (see Chapter 6).

Gender and Weight A specified dose of a drug administered to a man and a woman will, on average, have somewhat greater effects on the woman. One major reason for this difference is the tendency for women to have a higher percentage of body fat and therefore a lower percentage of body water than men do. (Chapter 4 explains how percentage of body fat influences drug effects.) Also, people who weigh more have more blood and other fluids, so for a given quantity of drug, they would have a smaller concentration of it than would people who weigh less.

Age Age can influence drug effects if the users are very young or old. Children are more sensitive to drugs because enzyme systems that metabolize drugs may not be fully developed. As a result, the drug stays active longer. In the elderly, these same enzyme systems may be impaired, with the same result of increased duration of drug action.

Psychological Characteristics

How an individual's psychological characteristics affect the drug experience has often been studied in research on personality and drug use. These characteristics are thought to be fairly constant, although variations occur in how a person acts in different situations. Nevertheless, personality characteristics are for the most part viewed as enduring.

sensation seeking
The need for varied, novel, and complex sensations and experiences and the willingness to take physical and social risks for the sake of such experience.

Personality One personality characteristic that has received a lot of attention regarding its relationship to drug use is **sensation seeking** (Zuckerman, 1979). A number of studies have shown a positive relationship between sensation seeking and frequency of drug and alcohol use and the variety of drugs that are used. The more sensation seeking a person is, the more the person tends to use alcohol and drugs and to use more kinds of drugs (Earleywine, 1994). One explanation for these findings is that sensation seeking represents the individual's higher degree of sensitivity to the pleasurable effects of drugs. That is, *sensation seeking* is a summary term for one source of the differences in how people experience drugs.

addictive personality
The hypothesis that particular personality characteristics are common to all people with substance abuse disorders.

What about an Addictive Personality? The notion of an **addictive personality** has generated a lot of research and discussion, and it remains a popular idea among people who treat individuals who have substance dependency. The addictive personality implies that people who have particular personality characteristics (e.g., sensation-seeking) experience a unique reaction to alcohol and drugs, or that they find alcohol and drugs especially valuable in coping with life's stressors (Nakken, 1996). As a result, people with an addictive personality would be more likely to develop substance abuse problems than people who do not have such personality characteristics.

Although the idea may have some appeal, it is important to note that people identified as having a substance abuse problem have considerable personality differences. But this research does suggest that some personality characteristics may interact with other factors, like stress, influences of peers, and quality of family life, to make it more likely that a person will develop problems with alcohol and drugs.

Drug Expectancies and Beliefs

Drug expectancies and beliefs can exert powerful influences on the drug experience. One factor that is prominent in this regard is what a person expects to achieve or to have happen when using a drug. This anticipation is called a **drug expectancy**.

A person's expectancies are based on previous experiences with a given psychoactive substance and its effects. These experiences could have been direct (that is, the person has used the substance) or indirect (the person has been exposed to the substance and its effects through instruction, friends' use, television, advertising, reading, and so on). These experiences provide a cognitive **psychological set** about a drug, which refers to knowledge, attitudes, expectations, and thoughts about how a substance influences the drug experience.

For example, researchers have investigated alcohol-related expectancies by conducting studies in which some participants are told they are drinking alcohol but actually receive a nonalcoholic "**placebo**" beverage. It was found that people who believed alcohol fosters aggression or enhances sexual arousal actually experienced those effects, at least partly because they expect that result, along with any specific pharmacological effect of alcohol. Expectancies may affect other kinds of behaviours, too. For example, one experiment showed that young adult men's beliefs about alcohol and skills on a motor task (for example, tracking a target moving on a rotating disk with a stylus) affected their performance on such tasks while they were under the influence of a dose of alcohol equal to about four 12-ounce beers in a 175-pound man (Fillmore & Vogel-Sprott, 1996). In this regard, as expected, alcohol did affect motor performance. However, the impairment was reduced in experienced drinkers who expected alcohol to have only mildly impairing effects on the task, even though they were told that alcohol would severely impair their performance.

drug expectancy
A person's anticipation of or belief about what he or she will experience upon taking a drug.

psychological set
An individual's knowledge, attitudes, expectations, and other thoughts about an object or event, such as a drug.

placebo
In pharmacology, a chemically inactive substance that is used in controlled research to study the effects of expectations or beliefs about a drug's effects (e.g., water or sugar pills).

Social and Environmental Factors

Although it has not always been the case, it now is generally accepted that the drug effects people experience are strongly influenced by social and environmental (setting) factors (Zinberg, 1984). There are many factors that relate to the drug environment, such as laws pertaining to drug use in the community where the drug is taken, the immediate physical environment where the drug is used, and whether other people are present at the time of drug use. Setting seems to be a particularly important influence on the effects of alcohol, marijuana, and hallucinogenic drugs. Pliner and Cappell (1974) demonstrated this point with alcohol. In their study, men and women drank moderate amounts of alcohol alone and with others. When subjects drank alone, they mostly reported experiencing physical changes, like fuzzy thinking, sleepiness, and dizziness. In contrast, subjects who drank the same amount of alcohol but with others said their mood changed to feeling friendly and more pleasant. Because subjects who drank an alcohol placebo beverage reported no changes whether drinking alone or with others, it seems that the social setting affects how you interpret the physiological changes that alcohol induces.

Another example of the influence of the setting involves reactions to marijuana. Carlin, Bakker, Halpern, and Post (1972) noted that, with lower doses of marijuana, smokers viewed others in the setting as more intoxicated than they actually were.

© Corbis

People use drugs in a variety of situations and experience different reactions to them. Alcohol consumption is often regarded as a recreational and social drug associated with enjoyment with friends and decreased inhibitions.

The experimenters were able to enhance or diminish the degree of reported marijuana intoxication by having an accomplice act "up" or "down." Setting was not so influential with higher doses of marijuana. Findings such as the above imply that what people experience when taking marijuana is influenced by their expectations about the drug's effects and by others' presence in the drug-taking setting.

Together, these three sets of factors influence what people experience when they take a drug. You may have guessed that the path to a drug experience is not always easy to chart. However, most of us have a strong desire to understand how drugs affect people and why people abuse drugs.

Drug Addiction

addiction
In reference to drugs, overwhelming involvement with using a drug, in which the person feels a need to have it, develops a tolerance to it and has a strong tendency to resume use of it after stopping for a period.

In society today, the term 'addiction' is applied to almost everything we do and everything that we consume. It is often used to describe anything for which we have a strong attraction. For example, "I am addicted to shopping," or "I am addicted to tattoos." As a result, the term **addiction** could be considered as one of the most misused (or overused) words in casual conversation today. However, when used appropriately, it applies to some of the most debilitating disorders we can encounter. Research in the field of addictions illustrates a variety of definitions that emphasize the common reference of 'compulsive drug use' as a major component of addiction (McMurran, 1980; Nakken, 1996; Peele 1985).

Together, these definitions have several common inferences with respect to addiction: compulsion, tolerance, withdrawal, and negative consequences. In essence, the individual's life centres on drug use and its procurement to the point of reduced attention to or outright neglect of other aspects of life. Similarly, drug use persists despite the risk of incurring serious consequences by doing so. Individuals with addictions also have an inability to stop or to reduce drug use for any length of time, if that is the intention.

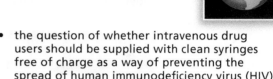

CONTEMPORARY ISSUE BOX 1.1

U.S. Society and Drug Use

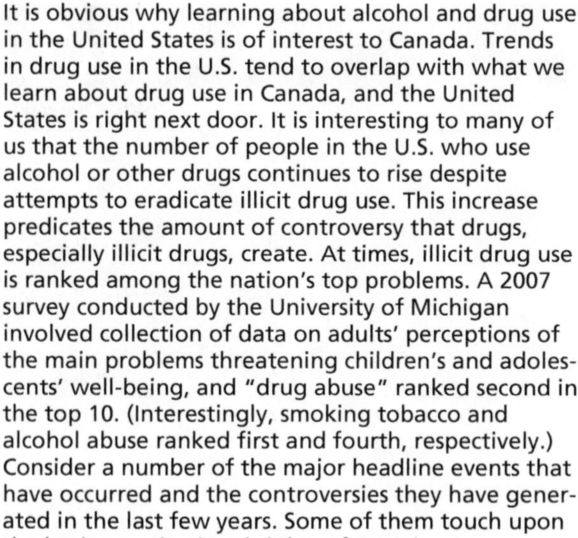

It is obvious why learning about alcohol and drug use in the United States is of interest to Canada. Trends in drug use in the U.S. tend to overlap with what we learn about drug use in Canada, and the United States is right next door. It is interesting to many of us that the number of people in the U.S. who use alcohol or other drugs continues to rise despite attempts to eradicate illicit drug use. This increase predicates the amount of controversy that drugs, especially illicit drugs, create. At times, illicit drug use is ranked among the nation's top problems. A 2007 survey conducted by the University of Michigan involved collection of data on adults' perceptions of the main problems threatening children's and adolescents' well-being, and "drug abuse" ranked second in the top 10. (Interestingly, smoking tobacco and alcohol abuse ranked first and fourth, respectively.) Consider a number of the major headline events that have occurred and the controversies they have generated in the last few years. Some of them touch upon the basic constitutional rights of Americans:

- the right of the federal government and other public and private employers to conduct urine screens (tests for drug taking) of employees as a way to control drug abuse in the workplace
- the question of whether intravenous drug users should be supplied with clean syringes free of charge as a way of preventing the spread of human immunodeficiency virus (HIV) infection
- the continuing debate about whether marijuana should be available as a prescription drug
- proposed legal penalties related to selling or using drugs—the requirement of life sentences for drug dealers who are convicted twice of selling drugs to teenagers and the imposition of the death penalty for dealers when a murder occurs during a drug deal
- the argument that drugs like marijuana and cocaine should be available legally to adults because the "war on drugs" has been lost

A majority of Americans use alcohol or other drugs on a regular basis. However, the country's attitudes toward such use, especially regarding illicit drugs, are far from permissive. Society's proposed and actual solutions to the war on drugs in the U.S. have far-reaching legal, social, and financial implications. Which stand out to you? Do these implications influence Canada's 'war on drugs' approaches?

Alcohol and Drug Use in Canada

In Canada, national and provincial survey studies of alcohol and drug use have involved interviewing a sample of Canadians (in this case, age 15 or older) across the country. The Canadian Alcohol and Drug Use Monitoring Survey (CADUMS) is an on-going general survey, sponsored by Health Canada, which interviews a random sample of Canadians about alcohol and illicit drug use. The survey is conducted by telephone, and targets approximately 10 000–16 500 Canadians each survey year (CADUMS, 2009). This brief review of the Canadian Alcohol and Drug Use Monitoring Survey (2009) will help you understand drug use patterns and related problems that exist within Canada, including perspectives of drug use and abuse.

The Canadian Alcohol and Drug Use Monitoring Survey (CADUMS)

In this section, we refer to findings from the 2009 survey (CADUMS, 2009). In 2009, telephone interviews were completed with 13 082 respondents, across all 10 provinces. In the 2009 CADUMS, a variety of data about drug use in Canada were collected. We first discuss data on the overall **prevalence** of use in the 12 months preceding the interview (conducted in January 2009) respectively for different drugs,

prevalence
The general occurrence of an event, usually expressed in terms of percentage of a population.

including alcohol. A comparison of prevalence data from the 2004 Canadian Addiction Survey (CAS) and the 2008 CADUMS are included where available. Several findings related to prevalence in Table 1.3 show that alcohol tops the use list, followed by marijuana. Prevalence of pharmaceutical use of pain killers, stimulants, and sedatives are non-significantly, but slightly lower in 2009. However, prevalence of

TABLE 1.3 Percentages of Individuals Aged 15 and Older Who Reported Use of Drugs for the Past Year, 2008 and 2009

	2008 Overall	2009 Overall
N=	16 640	13 082
Past Year Alcohol & Cannabis Use		
Alcohol use	77.3	76.5
Cannabis	11.4*	10.6*
Past Year Illicit Drug Use		
Cocaine/Crack	1.6	1.2
Speed	1.1	0.4
Hallucinogens (excluding salvia)	—	0.7
Hallucinogens (including salvia)	2.1	0.9±
Ecstasy	1.4	0.9
Past Year Pharmaceutical Use		
Pain Relievers	21.6	19.2
Pain Relievers (to get high)	0.3	0.4
Pain Relievers (to get high among users)	1.5	2.3
Stimulants	1.1	1.0
Stimulants (to get high)	0.3	0.1
Stimulants (to get high among users)	25.5	9.4
Sedatives	10.7	9.1
Sedatives (to get high)	0.2	0.2
Sedatives (to get high among users)	14ᵅ	1.7
Any pharmaceutical	28.4	25.0±
Any pharmaceutical (to get high)	0.6	0.6
Any pharmaceutical (to get high among users)	2.0	2.3

Notes:
N = Sample size
95% Confidence Interval

* Indicates that the difference between 2009 and 2004 is statistically significant
± Indicates that the difference between 2008 and 2009 is statistically significant
– No comparable estimates
ᵅ Estimate is qualified due to high sampling variability; interpret with caution

Source: Adapted from: Health Canada, *Canadian Alcohol and Drug Use Monitoring Survey*. Found at: http://www.hc-sc.gc.ca/hc-ps/drugs-drogues/stat/_2009/summary-sommaire-eng.php

abuse (to get high) by users is slightly higher in 2009 (except for stimulants, which is reported as lower in 2009). There is also a higher rate of abuse (to get high) among users than non-users in both 2008 and 2009 data.

Table 1.4 presents sex and age differences in drug use in the past year, as reported in the 2009 national survey. As you can see in Table 1.4, individuals aged 15–24 have

TABLE 1.4 Percentages of Individuals by Sex and Age Groups Who Reported Use of Drugs for the Past Year, 2009

	Males	Females	Age 15–24	Age 25+
N=	5260	7822	955	12 079
Past Year Alcohol & Cannabis Use				
Alcohol use	80.2	73.0	75.5	76.7
Cannabis Use	14.2[*]	7.2[*]	26.3[*]	7.6[*]
Past Year Illicit Drug Use				
Cocaine/Crack	1.5	0.9	3.0[Q]	0.9
Speed	1.3 (08)	0.8 (08)	3.7 (08)	0.6 (08)
Hallucinogens (excluding salvia)	0.7	0.8	3.7[Q]	0.3
Hallucinogens (including salvia)	1.1[±]	0.8	4.4	0.3
Ecstasy	1.1	0.7	3.6	0.4
Past Year Pharmaceutical Use				
Pain Relievers	18.3	20.2[±]	14.6	20.2
Pain Relievers (to get high)	0.5[Q]	0.4	1.2[Q]	0.3
Pain Relievers (to get high among users)	2.8	1.8	8.5	1.4
Stimulants	0.6	1.2	2.7[Q]	0.6
Stimulants (to get high)	0.2[Q] (08)	0.3[Q] (08)	1.2 (08)	0.1 (08)
Stimulants (to get high among users)	22.5[Q] (08)	27.8[Q] (08)	35.3 (08)	14.7 (08)
Sedatives	7.0	11.1	4.0	10.1
Sedatives (to get high)	0.1[Q] (08)	0.2[Q] (08)	0.8[Q] (08)	[S]
Sedatives (to get high among users	[S]	1.6[Q] (08)	14.4 (08)	[S]
Any pharmaceutical	22.3	27.6[±]	18.2	26.3
Any pharmaceutical (to get high)	0.7	0.4	1.7	0.3[±]
Any pharmaceutical (to get high among users)	3.3	1.5	9.5	1.3

Notes:
N = Sample size
95% Confidence Interval

[*] Indicates that the difference between 2009 and 2004 is statistically significant
[±] Indicates that the difference between 2008 and 2009 is statistically significant
[Q] Estimate is qualified due to high sampling variability; interpret with caution
[S] Estimate is suppressed due to high sampling variability

Source: Adapted from: Health Canada, *Canadian Alcohol and Drug Use Monitoring Survey*. Found at: http://www.hc-sc.gc.ca/hc-ps/drugs-drogues/stat/_2009/tables-tableaux-eng.php#t3

CONTEMPORARY ISSUE BOX 1.2

Survey Data on Drug Use: Are They Accurate?

There are compelling reasons for conducting national survey studies of drug use and its consequences. Such information can help a society formulate effective legal and social policies on the use of specific drugs. National survey data also may help to identify groups within a population that are at the greatest risk for experiencing health or other problems related to drug use, which could help in creating more effective prevention programs.

These and other benefits of national survey data on drug use are significant, but a big question is whether the information that is obtained reflects a society's *actual* drug use. That is, are the data accurate?

There are several reasons for asking this question. For example, even the largest surveys rarely collect data from every person in a target population, so it is possible that the sample of people chosen to participate in the survey is biased in some way. This means that the sample might not reflect the population's characteristics on sex of the respondent, race, religion, or education, all of which could be associated with the main behaviour of interest. In addition, because many of the drugs asked about are illegal for nonmedical use, or for any use at all, people may be reluctant to admit to a researcher that they have used a particular drug or have used it in particular amounts or frequency. Furthermore, as surveys typically ask about past behaviour, memory limits may interfere with the collection of accurate information, regardless of the respondent's intention to tell the truth.

These and other problems are real and must be addressed if national survey data on drug use are to have the utility that they are intended to have. Fortunately, the challenge to collect accurate survey information has been an active research area over the years, and methods of representative sampling and data collection to assure confidentiality or anonymity of responses have led to better survey design and procedures. These advances have resulted in data that meet high standards of reliability and accuracy. This is not to say that national survey data provide a literal picture of drug use in a population, but that the picture is getting clearer and more detailed as survey research methods continue to improve.

If you were designing a survey to study some behaviour, such as drug use, in a given population, what potential sources of bias in the data would you consider? How would you handle them?

reported highest prevalence of illicit drug use, with cannabis and ecstasy reported as most used. However, individuals 25 years of age and older have reported the highest prevalence of pharmaceutical use.

The CADUMS data of 2009 also differentiated prevalence of drug use among the provinces of Canada. Table 1.5 presents this data. It is important to note that Nunavut and Yukon Territories are not included in this survey data. As a result, one must recognize that the survey is not a complete representation of all Canadians. In addition, little data has been usable in such provinces as Newfoundland, New Brunswick, and Prince Edward Island because of sampling variability (unable to accurately report statistics). What stands out for you in Table 1.5?

Summary of Survey Data

Multiple Drug Use

polydrug use
The same person's regular use of more than one drug.

The person who is counted in the percentage of, say, marijuana users in a survey sample may be the same person who increases the percentage of alcohol users. Such multiple drug use (also called **polydrug use**) is extremely important because of the effects that drug combinations have on the body. We explore those effects in detail in Chapter 4. For now, it is important for you to know that polydrug use is a critical health and social problem.

TABLE 1.5 Percentages of Individuals, by Province, Who Reported Use of Drugs for the Past Year, 2009

	Canada	NL	PE	NS	NB	QC	ON	MB	SK	AB	BC
N=	13 082	1008	1008	1008	1008	1009	1008	1008	1008	1008	4009
Past Year Alcohol & Cannabis use											
Cannabis	10.6	8.4	9.2	13.1	12.2	10.4	10.5	8.7	8.0	9.7	12.7
Alcohol	76.5	70.7*	71.3*	75.1	73.8	79.6	76.1	73.2	75.6	75.4	75.6
Past Year Illicit Drug Use											
Cocaine/Crack	1.2	s	s	s	s	1.3[Q]	1.5[Q]	s	1.0[Q]	s	1.2
Speed	0.4	s	s	s	s	s	s	s	s	s	s
Methamphetamine/ Crystal meth	0.1	s	s	s	s	s	s	s	s	s	s
Hallucinogens	0.7	s	s	1.0[Q]	s	s	s	s	s	s	1.3
Ecstasy	0.9	s	s	s	s	1.0[Q]	s	s	1.6[Q]	s	1.3
Salvia	0.2	s	s	s	s	s	s	s	s	s	s
Heroin	0.0	s	s	s	s	s	s	s	s	s	s
Lifetime Illicit Drug Use											
Cocaine/Crack	6.9	3.1*	3.9*	5.5	4.8	8.3	4.8	6.9	6.8	7.4	10.9*
Speed	3.7	0.6[Q]*	1.4[Q]*	3.1	3.1	6.9	2.0[Q]	1.3[Q]*	3.2	3.9	3.7
Methamphetamine/ Crystal meth	0.9	s	s	0.9	s	1.0	s	s	1.1	1.4	1.2
Hallucinogens	11.8	6.8*	8.1*	12.8	10.1	11.9	10.4	10.4	11.5	12.8	16.3*
Ecstasy	3.9	2.7[Q]	3.0[Q]	4.4	2.1[Q]	3.9	3.2	3.8	4.5	4.3	6.1*
Salvia	1.6	s	1.9[Q]	2.5	1.8	1.5	1.8	s	1.7	1.7	1.3

Notes:
N = Sample size
95% Confidence Interval

* Significant difference between province and national estimate
s Estimate suppressed due to high sampling variability
Q Estimate qualified due to high sampling variability; interpret with caution

Source: Adapted from: Health Canada, *Canadian Alcohol and Drug Use Monitoring Survey*. Found at: http://www.hc-sc.gc.ca/hc-ps/drugs-drogues/stat/_2009/summary-sommaire-eng.php

In its extreme, multiple drug use can include taking drugs with different or opposite physical effects in sequence on the same occasion. In such cases, the motive for use seems to be change, positive or otherwise, from one drug experience to another.

> *"I think I did every drug known to mankind, smoked crack, boozed, dropped acid, you name it."*
> Kid Rock

International Comparisons of Drug Use

The national surveys on drug use that Canada conducts provide useful information. It would be valuable if similar data were available from other countries so that comparisons would be possible. With the exception of the United States, this has not been

DRUGS AND CULTURE BOX 1.3

Canadian Perspectives on Drug Abuse

The survey data reported in this chapter provides an overall look at the prevalence of reported drug use in Canada. But what do Canadians think about drug use? How do they think they are affected by drug use? Here are a few of the major perspectives reported from the 2008 survey (N = 16 672 respondents):

- Canadians reported that they perceived the major reason they thought people use drugs is because of their availability (28.4 percent); this is followed by psychological distress (15.1 percent), family problems (14.6 percent), stress (10.9 percent), and poverty (9.0 percent).
- Canadians most frequently reported that anyone (52.3 percent) was most at-risk of using drugs, followed by youth (23.5 percent) and those with a history of drug abuse (7.0 percent).
- Approximately 2/3 (65 percent) of Canadians agreed that "total abstinence is the only effective means to overcome drug problems."
- Canadians preferred prevention and treatment (78.0 percent) to law enforcement and incarceration (18.7 percent) as a means of addressing drug issues.
- From a list of possible ways drug use can have an impact on society, majority of Canadians reported that drugs have a large impact on criminality (76.1 percent), family problems (73.1 percent), law enforcement costs (71.1 percent), and costs to welfare and health care systems (68.9 percent and 62.9 percent, respectively).

How do these perceptions of drug use hold up to your perspectives about Canada's drug issues? Can you think of ways in which Canada's government is trying to counteract these perceptions or improve program availability to reduce any negative impacts on drug use?

DRUGS AND CULTURE BOX 1.4

Looking at Subgroup Differences—Aboriginal Alcohol and Drug Abuse in Canada

You know from our discussion that the Canadian Alcohol and Drug Use Monitoring Survey data give us a description of drug use among people living in Canada. At the same time, national surveys do not actually tell us as much as they seem to. We must take into account the differences in use patterns according to characteristics—such as age, gender, and ethnicity—of the user and the user's environment—such as area of residence and local laws and policies regarding alcohol and drug use.

Demographic group differences in drug use reflect differences in complex historical or current factors common to certain groups of people or regions. Therefore, drug use differences could reflect biological, psychological, or social/environmental factors that distinguish one group from other groups or from the population as a whole. These factors are so complex that certain groups have been designated "special populations." In Canada, Aboriginal populations are designated such a case. It is emphasized that, to understand a particular group's drug use, we need to understand its unique history and current circumstances. Other groups that today are considered special populations by experts who study drug use include women (because traditionally women have received far less attention from alcohol and other drug researchers than have men) and the homeless. A recent review suggests that adults and adolescents who identify their sexual orientation as lesbian, gay, or bisexual should also be considered a special population regarding their alcohol and drug use (Marshal et al., 2008). The drug chapters in this text incorporate cultural and regional differences with features such as a historical account of the drug or drug class in question, and with attention to special cultural differences in use of the drug.

Given the importance of subgroup differences within a total survey sample, how might you adjust the sampling in a national survey to get a more accurate look at a subgroup that is of particular interest to you?

possible with the exception of alcohol use in some cases. In this regard, population surveys of both alcohol and other drug use that different countries, including Canada, have done have not been designed with consideration of how other countries have designed their surveys. As a result, comparisons of findings across countries have been difficult. However, it is fortunate that recent epidemiological data on lifetime drug use in specific countries in North America, South America, and Europe provide an opportunity for cross-national comparisons of general population use of alcohol and selected other drugs.

JB Russel/Sygma/Corbis

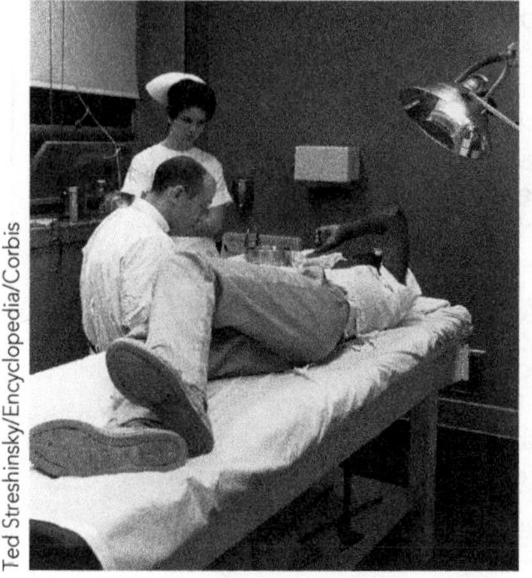

Ted Streshinsky/Encyclopedia/Corbis

Kenneth Summers/Shutterstock.com

The sometimes tragic consequences of drug use have drawn national attention and response.

The study we focus on here involved surveys similarly constructed and administered at seven sites to over 27 000 individuals aged between 14 and 54 years (Vega et al., 2002). The emphasis of this report was lifetime use of alcohol, defined as used at least 12 times, and lifetime use of other drugs, defined as used at least five times. Surveys were conducted in the following cities/countries: Fresno County, California, United States; Mexico City, Mexico; Ontario, Canada; the Netherlands; Sao Paulo, Brazil; and Munich, Germany.

The results showed interesting similarities and differences across the countries in alcohol and other drug use. It was true in all of the countries that lifetime use of alcohol or other drugs occurred at a higher rate for men than for women. Regarding alcohol use, the Netherlands was the highest, as about 94 percent of the men and 78 percent of the women reported lifetime use. Canada was second highest (84 percent of the men, 60 percent of the women), and the United States was third (80 percent of the men and 63 percent of the women). The lowest rates were reported in Mexico City, with 73 percent of the men but only 21 percent of the women reporting lifetime alcohol use.

CONTEMPORARY ISSUE BOX 1.5

Drugs, Criminal Activity, and Aggression

The association of alcohol, drugs, and crime is one we seem to see and hear about continually in the popular media. The problem of drugs, alcohol, and crime is an old, much-studied one. It should be clear that we are dealing with associations, or correlations, and not causes. For example, the pharmacological effects of cocaine are not known to *cause* a person to commit murder. Yet the high positive correlation between drugs and crime remains a fact. As drug use in a community increases, so does the occurrence of certain kinds of crimes, depending on the drug.

Much of the research on drugs and crime has concerned heroin. Most crimes committed by heroin addicts are either violations of the drug laws or ways to get money to buy more heroin. Therefore, the addict's most commonly committed crimes are burglary, larceny, assault, and other street crimes. These crimes are indeed serious and sometimes result in injury or death to the victims. The direct intent of the crime is not to harm the victim, however, but to get money. This same motive probably applies to much of the violence related to cocaine, and to conflicts over money among cocaine dealers and their customers.

Surprisingly, the use of some drugs has no relationship to criminal activity; there may even be a negative association between use of the drug and crime. Use of hallucinogens, for example, is not associated with crime, and marijuana seems to fall in the same category. The evidence is mixed for barbiturates and tranquilizers: Some studies show no relationship, but others suggest that the relationship between use and crime is the same for barbiturates and alcohol.

Alcohol intoxication has a high correlation with criminal activity. Because alcohol is legal and very available, little violence is connected with violating drug laws or stealing to obtain alcohol. Most of the crimes associated with alcohol intoxication are assaultive; that is, they are committed with the intent to harm the victim. Alcohol is correlated with other types of crime as well, such as aggravated assault, homicides, property offences, sexual offences, and cheque fraud.

So one point is clear: Some types of drug use are associated with criminal activity. But what is the explanation? Pharmacology figures complexly in the answer but seems to be only one of many factors. Others include the person's expectations about the drug's effects, the setting where the drug is being used, and personality characteristics of the user.

The drug–crime problem is a good example of how a society and its individual members are affected by drug use. It also illustrates that drug use and its effects on the user are influenced by many factors working together.

Other drugs showed not only some similarities across countries but also wide variability in lifetime use. Cannabis use was the second most prevalent behind alcohol for all countries. The level of cannabis use, however, varied considerably across countries. For example, the highest prevalence was in the United States, with 33 percent of the men and 24 percent of the women reporting lifetime use. Similarly, 29 percent of the male Canadians and 16 percent of the women in Canada reported cannabis use. These figures contrast with the lowest rates, recorded in Mexico: three percent of the men and 0.6 percent of the women. After cannabis, the rates of lifetime use of other drugs or drug classes (cocaine or other stimulants, opioids, hallucinogens, inhalants) were highly variable but generally at a low level, with the exception of cocaine or other stimulants in the United States. As you might guess, overall lifetime drug use, excluding alcohol and cannabis, was highest in the United States (19 percent) and lowest in Mexico (two percent).

Although the Vega et al. (2002) data on lifetime use of alcohol and other drugs are limited, they do provide a first look at how different countries, at least those in the western part of the world, compare. Cross-national data can be a valuable vehicle to understanding how cultural, legal, psychological, and biological factors affect alcohol and other drug use.

Entertainment Press/Shutterstock.com

Actress and recording artist Lindsay Lohan's life illustrates a main feature of drug addiction—the neglect of professional responsibilities and personal relationships for the sake of obtaining and using drugs.

Drug-Taking Behaviour: Summary

The discussion in this chapter shows that using a drug for a long time alters the patterns of use for that drug. Long-term use also relates to the DSM-IV criteria. Tolerance, withdrawal, and dependency may result not only in changes in drug use and preoccupation but also in the likelihood that the person's life and the lives of those around that person are affected by the drug in a snowballing effect, with one consequence building on another. The outcome can reflect some of the criteria included in the DSM-IV definition of substance disorder.

"If drinking is interfering with your work, you're probably a heavy drinker. If your work is interfering with your drinking, you're probably an alcoholic."

Anonymous

Of course, discussion of the effects of tolerance and dependence on motivations for drug use addresses only a small portion of the different reasons that people use drugs. In this regard, people give numerous reasons for "why" they use different drugs, and different drugs may be most strongly associated with different reasons. At the same time, multiple drugs may be used for the same reasons. The same drug may be used for different reasons in different times and places. This suggests that reasons for use are not limited to a drug's pharmacological effects but by a variety of other variables as well. For example, Boys, Marsden, & Strang (2001) conducted an interview study of 364 men and women ages 16 to 22 in the United Kingdom who had used two or more substances in the last 90 days. The study showed that use of substances such as alcohol, marijuana, cocaine, ecstasy, and LSD was associated with multiple "purposes" or functions, which referred to what the participants expected to gain by using the drugs. Each substance was associated with eight to nine different functions (such as feeling better when depressed, getting intoxicated, enhancing sex, helping to relax, helping to sleep, and enhancing another activity such as listening to music), and there was considerable overlap in the functions cited for each drug, despite their considerable differences in pharmacology. The upshot of findings such as these is that they highlight the complexity in motivations for drug use among humans.

SUMMARY

- Psychopharmacology is the scientific study of the effects of drugs on behaviour. Psychologists recognize that understanding how drugs affect human behaviour requires knowledge about biological, personal, social, and environmental factors.
- The general difference between *drug use* and *drug abuse* is the negative consequences associated with abuse.
- Drugs are commonly classified in different ways; six of the major classifications are reviewed in this chapter.
- The formal definition of substance disorders in North America is given in the fourth edition of the American Psychiatric Association's *Diagnostic and Statistical Manual.*
- The DSM-IV definition of substance dependence includes drug tolerance and withdrawal, which may powerfully affect drug-use patterns.
- There are two types of drug dependence: physical and psychological.
- Drug tolerance includes dispositional, functional, and behavioural aspects that influence a person's drug-taking behaviours.
- The experience that humans have from taking drugs is influenced by three sets of factors: pharmacological factors, characteristics of the drug user, and the setting in which the drug is used.
- Addiction is defined as an overwhelming involvement with using a drug, in which the person feels a need to have it, develops a tolerance to it, and has a strong tendency to resume use of it after stopping for a period.
- The CADUMS national and provincial survey of alcohol and drug use provides prevalence and patterns of alcohol and drug use in Canada.
- Some individuals use more than one drug regularly and may use different drugs together on the same occasion. This is called polydrug use.

Key Terms

addiction **p. 10**
addictive personality **p. 8**
craving **p. 4**
cross-tolerance **p. 6**
dependence **p. 4**
drug **p. 2**
drug abuse **p. 2**
drug dosage **p. 7**
drug effects **p. 3**
drug expectancy **p. 9**
initial sensitivity **p. 7**
pharmacology **p. 2**
placebo **p. 9**
polydrug use **p. 14**
prevalence **p. 11**
psychoactive **p. 4**
psychological set **p. 9**
psychopharmacology **p. 2**
route of drug administration **p. 7**
sensation seeking **p. 8**
syndrome **p. 6**
tolerance **p. 5**
withdrawal **p. 6**

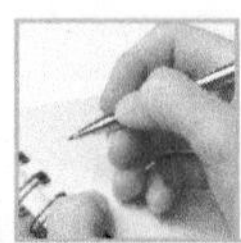

Essays/Thought Questions

1. This chapter argues that drug use has positive as well as negative consequences for humans. Considering the advantages and disadvantages of using different drugs, would you allow the use of a drug that currently is illegal for the most part, such as cocaine, marijuana, or heroin? Why or why not?
2. What are some of the advantages and disadvantages of having a formal, standard way to define a construct like "substance-use disorder," such as DSM-IV does? Should cultural differences in substance use and definitions of *abuse* matter in defining substance-use disorder? Why or why not? If you believe that cultural factors should be incorporated in definitions of substance-use disorder, how would you do it?

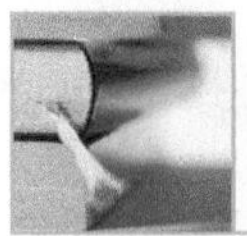

Suggested Readings

Kapoun, J. (1998). Teaching undergrads web evaluation: A guide for library instruction. *College and Research Library News, 59*, 522–523.

Nakken, C. (1996). *The Addictive Personality*. New York: Hazelden Publ.

Weil, A., & Rosen, W. (1983). *From chocolate to morphine*. Boston: Houghton Mifflin Co.

CHAPTER 2

History of Drug Use: Yesterday and Today

Did You Know

- The Opium Wars between China and Great Britain in the mid-1800s occurred in large part because Britain was unwilling to curtail its trade of opium into China.
- Many of the drugs that are now illegal in Canada were widely used in the 1800s and early 1900s to treat a broad spectrum of maladies.
- Heroin was first introduced as a treatment for morphine addiction.
- The Opium Act of 1908 was the first federal act to control the sale, trade, or distribution of drugs in Canada.
- The Single Convention on Narcotic Drugs of 1961 is an international treaty, signed by nine countries, to prohibit production and supply of specific drugs except under licence for specific purposes, such as medical treatment and research.
- The first alcohol prohibition in Canada was in Prince Edward Island in 1901.
- Canada's current legislation is the Controlled Drugs and Substances Act (1997), which lists specific types of controlled drugs and substances as well as states the offence committed and punishment resulting from violations.

Drugs have been used for a variety of reasons in different cultures: for religious purposes, for recreation, for altering states of consciousness, and for obtaining relief from pain or distress. This chapter provides you with a general historical overview of drug use and provides a background for considering the patterns of today's drug use for understanding our current drug laws.

cannabis sativa
The Indian hemp plant popularly known as marijuana; its resin, flowering tops, leaves, and stem contain the plant's psychoactive substances.

hashish
A drug produced from the resin that covers the flowers of the cannabis hemp plant. The resin generally contains a greater concentration of the drug's psychoactive properties.

opium poppy
A plant cultivated for centuries—primarily in Eurasia—for opium, a narcotic that acts as a central nervous system depressant.

Historical Overview

Drug Use in Early History

The use of drugs dates back thousands of years. First accounts of psychoactive substance use date back to the beginnings of recorded history and revolve around the use of alcohol and plants with psychoactive properties. Historical and primitive societies, such as the shamans, used plant-based medicines as part of their religious practices and rites of passage for connecting with the spirits and healing their followers of ailments and melancholy. Shamanism is still practised today in many cultures around the world where the use of hallucinogenic-producing plants play a large role in creating a spiritual and healing euphoria among followers. (See Table 2.1 for a summary of historical uses of drugs.)

TABLE 2.1 Historical Uses of Drugs in Early Times

Type	Historical Timeline	Group	Purpose of Use
Mushrooms (Amanita muscaria)	Middle Ages	Viking Warriors	To increase energy during battles; Vikings earned the name Berserkers because of the bad behaviour that occurred during battle
Belladonna, mandrake (plants); toad secretions	Medieval	'witches'; used brooms to stir their 'brews' when making potions	To induce hallucinations and the sensation of flying
Peyote cactus	1800s	Aztec and Mescalero Apache Indians (Mexico)	For religious purposes to initiate rite of passage; peyote buttons are still used today in the Native American church
Beer, huckleberry wine	6400 BCE (and throughout early history)	Egyptians	For recreational, social purposes such as relaxation and euphoria
Cannabis sativa	2700 BCE	China	Brewed as tea for medicinal purposes such as the treatment of gout, hysteria, and other common ailments
Coca leaves	2500 BCE	Central and South America	To produce altered states of consciousness
Hashish, among others	Stone Ages	South America; Asia	In religious ceremonies, to produce altered states of consciousness; and in preparation for battles
Opium poppy	5000 BCE	Asia Minor	To produce euphoria; known as the 'joy plant'

Sources: Blum, K. (1984). *Handbook of abusable drugs.* New York: Gardner Press; O'Brien, R., & Cohen, S. (1984). *The encyclopedia of drug abuse.* New York: Facts on File; Grilly, D. M. (2002). *Drugs and human behavior.* Boston: Allyn & Bacon.

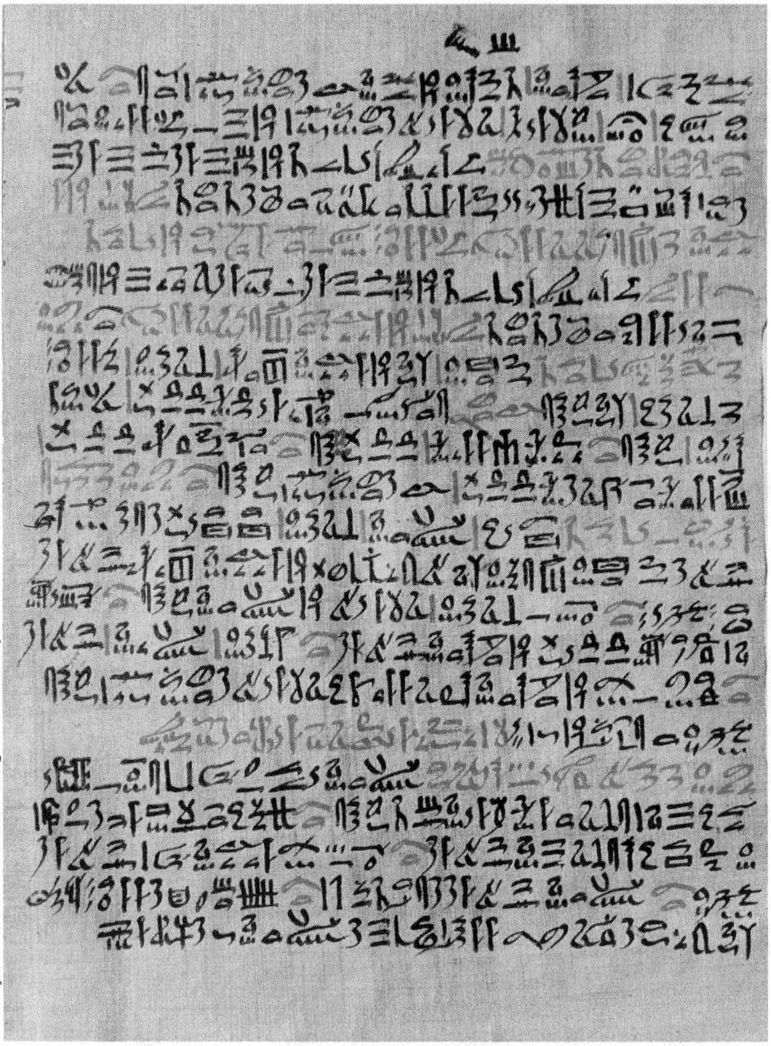

The Ebers Papyrus is an ancient Egyptian scroll discovered by a British Egyptologist in 1872. The document lists over 800 preparations for curing common ailments and diseases.

These religious healing practices became more formalized throughout early history when centralized religion began to dominate Egyptian societies. One of the earliest documentation of the use of drugs, dated back to 1500 BCE, was the Ebers Papyrus, an Egyptian scroll that contains more than 800 prescriptions for curing common ailments, such as bee stings, constipation, crying infants, toothaches, arthritis, and diseases such as heart disease and cancer. The 'potions' documented in the scroll consisted of the use of castor oil and the 'berry of the poppy' (opium) and other preparations, such as lizard blood, animal dung, and the teeth of swine (Bryan, 1930).

Throughout history, contact between distant cultures has often been forced by trade agreements or by wars or other hostilities. For example, the Crusades and the expeditions of Marco Polo exposed Europeans to the drugs, particularly opium and hashish, which were popular in Asian cultures. Other contacts were opened later through the travels of European explorers (particularly from England, France, Portugal, and Spain) to North America. The predominant psychoactive substances brought to Europe were cocaine (from South America), various hallucinogens (from Central America), and tobacco (from North America). And according to O'Brien and Cohen (1984), the exchange was not one-sided. The trees that produced the caffeine-containing coffee bean were native to Ethiopia. The coffee beverage derived from this bean was brought to Europe in the 1600s, and European sea-goers were responsible for the eventual spread of coffee bean cultivation to South America, which is now the current world-leading supplier of coffee. In addition, Europe introduced distilled alcoholic beverages to North and South America and cannabis to Chile in 1545 (O'Brien & Cohen, 1984).

There were relatively few restrictions on drug availability or drug use prior to the beginning of the 20th century. Occasional efforts were made to decrease or eliminate certain substances, but these efforts tended to be short-lived or ineffective. For example, initial introductions of tobacco, coffee, and tea to Europe all met some resistance.

Credit: Columbus at Hispaniola, from 'The Narrative and Critical History of America', edited by Justin Winsor, London, 1886 (engraving) (later colouration), Bry, Theodore de (1528-98) (after) / Private Collection / The Bridgeman Art Library

Rodrigo de Jerez, a colleague of Columbus and the first European thought to smoke tobacco, was jailed in Spain because the authorities felt the devil had overtaken him (Whitaker, 1987).

Medical Science and Drug Use

By the end of the 19th century, a parallel between the development and use of psychoactive substances in medicinal forms (discussed in more detail in Chapter 5) and the nonmedicinal use or misuse of these drugs became strong. Medical science only gradually became the well-respected institution that we know today. Even in the 20th century, folk cures, potions, and **patent medicines** were freely available and widely used.

patent medicines
Drugs or combination of drugs that were sold, most often in the 19th century, as medicines that would cure a host of illnesses and diseases.

Perhaps the best examples of this are the opiates opium and morphine that, throughout most of the 1800s, were used to treat a variety of ailments, including rheumatism, pain, fever, delirium tremens, and colds. The opiates were also used as an anesthetic for some surgeries and for setting broken bones. Unfortunately, such

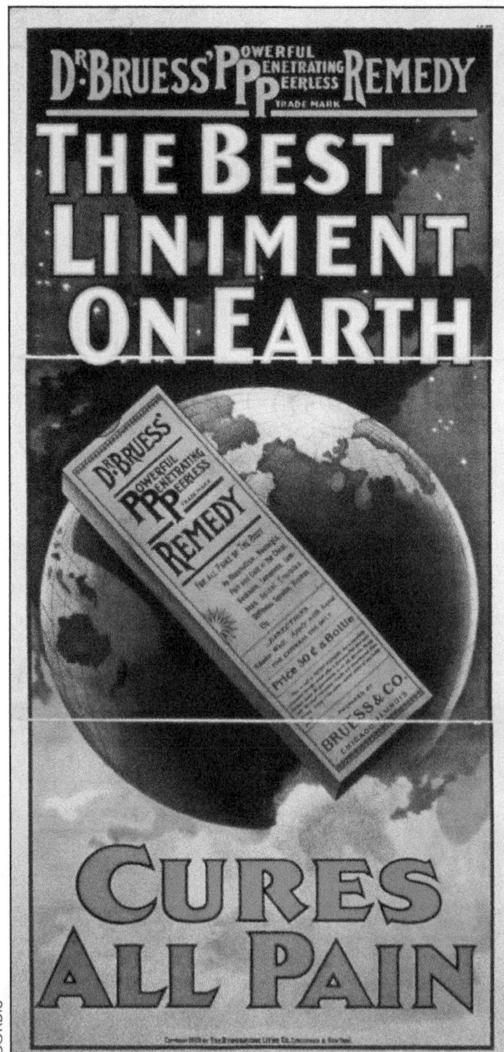

Patent medicines, such as Dr. Bruess' Remedy, were widely marketed in the 1800s as cures for a wide variety of ailments and illnesses.

widespread use contributed to a considerable number of people becoming physically addicted to these substances. Not until the 1870s did a clearer picture of the addictive properties of these drugs emerge.

By the 1890s, well-respected medical practitioners began to call attention to the social problems resulting in the uncontrolled access to psychoactive drugs. This marked the era of patent medicines (those containing opium, morphine, and cocaine), which were marketed through peddlers, general stores and advertisements promoting relief from any common ailment ranging from a cure for toothaches to ridding one of cancer. Opium, for example, was sold legally and at low prices; some opium poppies were grown in Canada and the United States. Morphine was commonly used, especially during and after the Civil War. Some examples include Godfrey's Cordial, Swaim's Panacea, Ayer's Sarsaparilla, and Mrs. Wilson's Soothing Syrup. Opium was frequently taken in liquid form in mixtures such as laudanum (which contained one grain of opium to 25 drops of alcohol), and one of its common uses was in calming and quieting crying babies!

Numerous other examples can be cited. Chloroform and ether were developed as anesthetics, but each also went through a period in the 1850s when its nonmedicinal use was quite popular. At one time, cocaine was used to treat complaints such as depressed mood and pain. In fact, one of its uses was as a treatment for opiate addiction. In the latter half of the 19th century, physicians recognized an array of uses for cannabis, including treatment of insomnia and nervousness, although its prescribed use was not nearly as extensive as with the opiates. The 20th century witnessed the development of the synthetic stimulant amphetamines, some of which initially were available without prescription.

We could provide additional examples, but the important point is that medicinal uses of psychoactive substances (whether folk medicine or more contemporary medicine), medical science, and nonmedical drug use and abuse will always be closely intertwined. In the past, folk or cultural use of a substance often became incorporated into the practice of medicine. More common today is the incorporation of a substance developed for the practice of medicine into the array of drugs that can be used in nonmedicinal ways. In any event, keeping the medical and nonmedical uses of drugs separate is impossible.

Moving Toward Modern Drug Uses

The use of psychoactive substances throughout history mirrors several movements in society with respect to the changes to both modern medicine and societal views about drug addiction. As we have discussed, most narcotic use throughout the 19th century was legal and recommended by physicians for relief of troubling symptoms. Table 2.2 describes several of the major trends in drug use reflected in the changing nature of the practice of modern medicine, changes in society, and societal views on drug use and addiction. You will encounter more details and information regarding each of these trends as you read through later chapters in this textbook.

TABLE 2.2 Drug Uses in Modern History

Drug Use in the 1930s

- Amphetamines were widely used to treat depression.
- Amphetamines were also used by World War II soldiers to enhance alertness.
- The use of marijuana was fairly constant in the 1930s through the 1950s, but was generally limited to urban areas and to the rural areas in which the marijuana was grown and harvested.

Drug Use in the 1950s

- The field of psychiatry advanced therapeutic drugs, such as tranquillizers for treatment of schizophrenia and other psychological disorders. One example is chlorpromazine, which was used to reduce hallucinations, agitation, and disordered thought among psychiatric patients.
- Smoking was considered sexy and romantic, as depicted in Hollywood movies and magazines.
- Social drinking at cocktail parties also was popularized among the middle-class.
- LSD was used as an adjunct to psychotherapy.
- The development of antibiotic drugs, such as penicillin to prevent bacteria-borne diseases, occurred after World War II.

Drug Use in the 1960s

- Dr. Timothy Leary expanded the use of LSD by promoting its mind-altering properties that heightened creativity. During this time, many prominent writers, politicians, and artists used LSD to enhance their creativity in their work.

Drug Use in the 1970s

- Introduction of neuroscience in North America began the new era of understanding the relationship between brain functioning and human behaviour.
- Heroin abuse across North America was profound as the media portrayals of fashion and glamour included 'heroin chic' look.

Drug Use in the 1980s

- Social and political reactions to drug addiction began to change from earlier decades; the view turned from a focus on the 'hippies' to the 'yuppies,' or young, white collared professionals who were no longer associated with the 'love drugs' of the 1960s or the heroin users of the 1970s.
- Cocaine became the drug of choice, with its appeal as glamour and a symbol of material success (because it was very expensive).
- This shift in perception led to the drug consequences we know about today and many cocaine overdoses were foreshadowed by a cheaper, smokable form of cocaine, called crack, moving into 'normal' neighbourhoods in North America.

Drug Use in the 1990s

- "Designer drugs" or club drugs gained considerable popularity in the context of the 'rave' culture. Drugs such as MDMA (ecstasy), GHB, LSD, and ketamine are among the most popular.

Drug Use in the 2000s

- A dramatic increase was seen in the amount of prescription drug abuse (e.g., Percocet and Oxycontin) among young adults.
- Social trends towards the use of recreational and medical marijuana increased and legalization and/or decriminalization are continually debated in Canada.

Image Courtesy of The Advertising Archives

The 'heroin chic' look of the 1970s portrayed skinny, pale-looking models who emitted sex appeal.

Development of Drug Laws

Legislation is the main way society establishes formal guidelines for drug use. Furthermore, such legislation essentially reflects a society's beliefs about drugs. Laws generally establish restrictions or prohibit the manufacture, importation, sale, or possession of the substance under evaluation. It is noteworthy that actual drug use in Canada, the United States, and in other countries as well, is not a crime under federal law, nor is it a crime to be a drug addict or an alcoholic.

Drug laws for the most part have had limited effectiveness in reducing overall illicit drug availability and use (Australian Drug Law Reform Foundation, 1996; Jung, 2001; Nadelmann, 1989). In fact, the more restrictive the laws, the less effective they have tended to be in the long run (Brecher, 1972, 1986). The only time these laws seem to be more effective is when drug use or abuse is particularly unpopular (Brecher, 1986; Hofmann, 1975). However, the duration of these periods and the time between them are variable. Nevertheless, legislation remains society's central means for addressing its concerns about drugs.

Describing the history of drug laws in Canada will provide an example of one society's response to drug use and abuse. Interestingly, the implementation of drug laws in Canada (and the United States) did not really begin until the turn of the 20th century. Various efforts were mounted to regulate opiates in the second half of the 19th century, but these were largely half-hearted and ineffective. That is not to say that sanctions on drug abuse did not exist, but rather there were no legal penalties to speak of.

In 1908 both federal and provincial regulations were established regarding the use of drugs in Canada, specifically opium. These regulations stemmed from the apparent dangers that threatened society through public fear of Chinese minorities and also political and monetary gains by the government. The history of opium and what is historically called, *The Opium Wars*, will be discussed in Chapter 9. In this chapter, we will recount the events that led to the 1908 Opium Act in Canada.

The Opium Act of 1908

In the early 1850s, Chinese labourers immigrated into British Columbia to work on the Canadian Pacific Railway (CPR), which connects the Atlantic and Pacific Coasts of North America. These immigrants worked for lower wages than their Canadian counterparts and typically lived in rural communities where the smoking of opium and opium dens were common. This led to negative perceptions from both the public and government that contributed to the creation of policy in Canada. There was much disdain among Chinese labourers who were looked at as 'economic threats' to Canadian employment. The decline in both the railroad and mining industries resulted in fewer jobs overall, as Canadian labourers could not compete with the wages of lower paid Chinese workers in these sectors. Chinese workers became targets of resentment and became known as 'dope peddling villains' in the manufacturing industry. The government's concern about opium was motivated by money. They received revenue on the taxation of opium factories in the Chinese communities, which resulted in the implementation of a $500 licensing charge on these factories in 1871. By 1875, opium-smoking became a profitable enterprise. Several factories in Vancouver, Victoria, and New Westminister manufactured opium, sold it to the local opium dens, and trafficked opium to the United States.

Following a major riot during a labour demonstration in 1907 that resulted in property damage among the Chinese communities, investigations led to the passing of the Opium Act of 1908. See Figure 2.1.

Mackenzie King, Deputy Minister of Labour, had four main concerns after investigating the 1907 riot: 1) opium smoking was becoming more popular among white people, and King was shocked by the opium trade in British Columbia; 2) the Chinese opium-traders were making large profits; 3) the opium trade was in violation of pharmacy legislation in British Columbia; and 4) Canada needed to set an example for an international campaign against opium.

FIGURE 2.1 History of Canada's drug laws

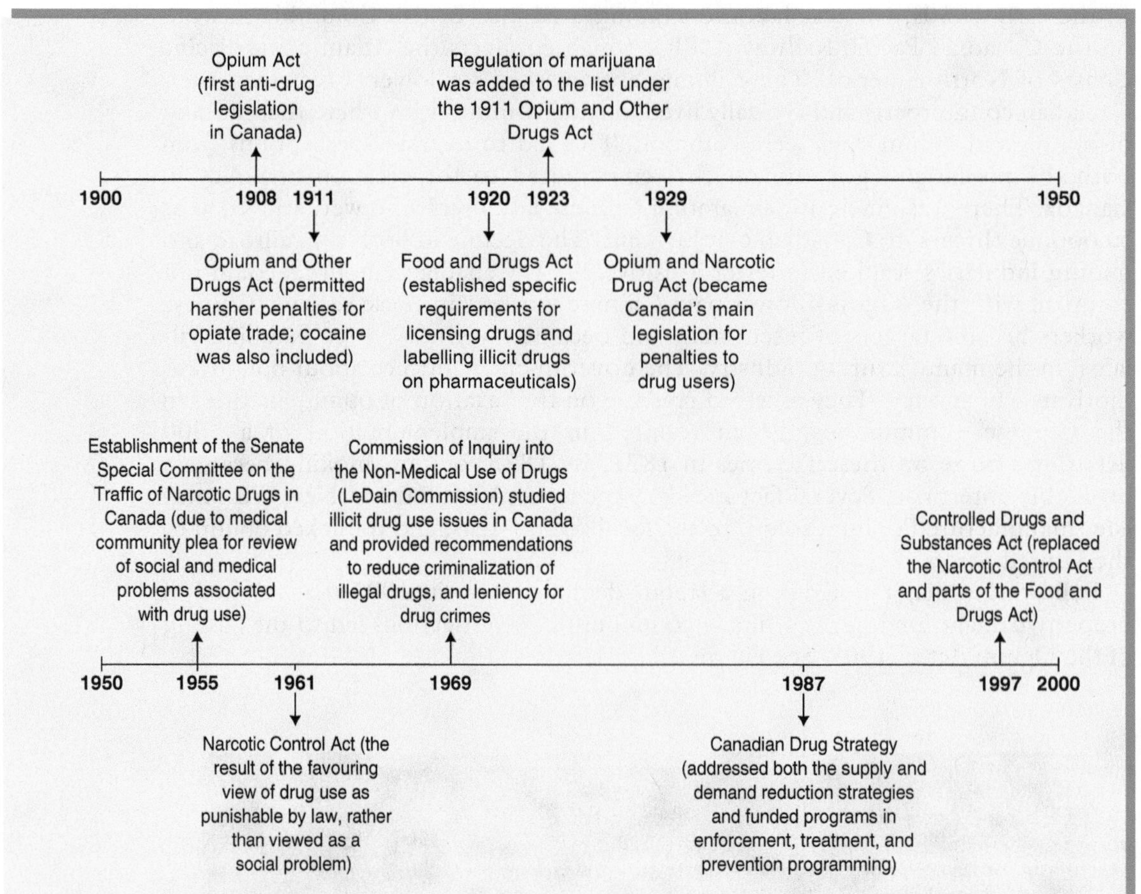

The Opium Act of 1908 was the first prohibitionist drug policy in Canada. This act made it an indictable offence to import, manufacture, possess, or sell opium for non-medical purposes (Soloman & Green, 1988). This led to black markets for opium drug trading. In 1911 the Opium and Other Drugs Act was enacted to permit harsher penalties to stop the opium as well as other drugs by law enforcement. This act remained the primary legislation and it was rarely challenged prior to the late 1950s.

Narcotic Control Act of 1961

It wasn't until the late 1950s that the idea of treating drug users became important as views within the medical field began to shift their attitudes about drug addiction towards addiction being like a disease. This prompted a Senate Special Committee to be formed in 1955, which was to enquire and report upon the trafficking of **narcotic** drugs in Canada. The Committee's conclusions and recommendations pointed out that the solution of the drug addiction problem required elimination of addicts, the suppression of narcotic traffic, and the prevention of an increase of the addict population (Hossick, 1956).

> **narcotic**
> A central nervous system depressant that contains sedative and pain-relieving compounds.

Subsequently, the enactment of the Narcotic Control Act was passed in 1961, which coincided with the international drug prohibition and regulation called the *Single Convention on Narcotic Drugs* of 1961. This convention played an important role in the creation of the modern international narcotic drug control system.

DRUGS AND CULTURE BOX 2.1

Emily Murphy

CP PHOTO/Files-Calgary Herald

Emily Murphy

Emily Murphy was the first woman magistrate in Canada and the British Empire. Most known for her contributions to the advocacy of the rights of women, she also was regarded as a significant contributor to societal views of drug abuse. The perspective contained in her book, *The Black Candle* (1922), is considered the most consequential in the history of drug abuse because it played a role in creating a widespread "war on drugs mentality" leading to legislation that "defined addiction as a law enforcement problem" (Tooley, 1999).

The Black Candle depicts an alarming picture of drug abuse in Canada during the 1920s. Her observations as a judge noted a disproportionate number of Chinese people represented in the courtroom, which led her to investigate the relationships between Chinese immigration and drug abuse. She blamed immigration laws as a factor in the drug abuse problem in Vancouver and looked at Chinese drug users as 'drug peddling villians' (and white drug users as victims).

Despite its racial controversy and criticism, Emily Murphy's *The Black Candle,* written to protect white women from immigrant men, shaped people's opinions about drug use and shaped social policies toward the restriction and prohibition of drugs, including opiates and marijuana.

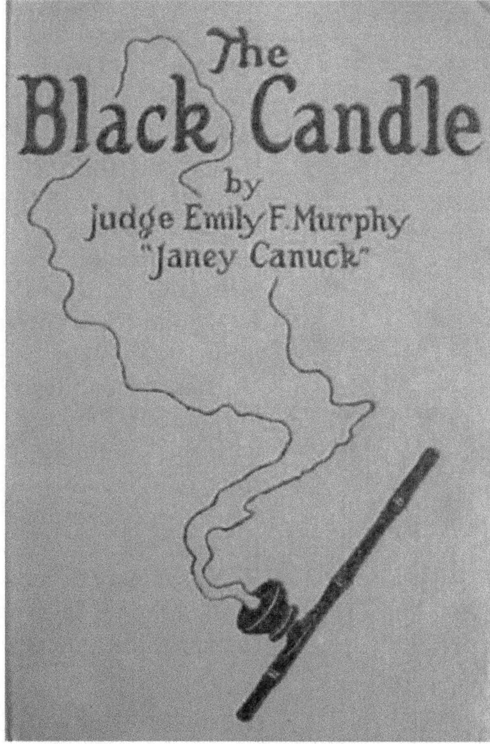

How might social policies today influence our ideas about drug use and addictions? Do you think that policies today still reflect Emily Murphy's early ideas about drug use?

Source: Haans, D. (1994) Why is there a war on drugs?

Beginning in 1948, nine multilateral treaties were signed during this period into a single international enactment, and Canada played a significant role in the negotiations and drafting that led to its adoption.

The Narcotic Control Act contained a series of schedules prepared by the World Health Organization containing the list of drugs subject to rigorous control for the purpose of preventing them from being used for other than medical or scientific purposes. Harsher penalties for trafficking of narcotics, possession for the purpose of trafficking, or importing/exporting drugs (i.e., longer prison sentencing) were passed.

prohibition
The legislative forbidding of the sale, distribution, or possession of a substance, as in the alcohol Prohibition era in North America during the 1920s–1930s.

Alcohol Prohibition

Prohibition in North America was brought about by temperance organizations across the world who viewed drinking as a harmful substance in society, ruining individuals, families, and communities. The enactment of the Canada Temperance Act in 1878 allowed all counties and municipalities to decide by majority vote whether they would forbid the sale of alcohol, extending the 1864 Dunkin Act passed in Upper Canada, one decade earlier. Following his election in 1896, and despite the majority of provinces in support of prohibition (all except Quebec), Prime Minister Wilfrid Laurier did not introduce a federal bill to forbid alcohol sale, so Canadian prohibition resulted in bills enacted by the provinces. Prince Edward Island was the first to enact prohibition in 1901, and other provinces followed suit (Ontario in 1916) by the end of World War I. In the United States, Congress passed the 18th Amendment to their Constitution. The legislation was a victory for the organizations that viewed alcohol as evil and destructive, notably the Anti-Saloon League and the Women's Christian Temperance Union. The amendment was not vague about its intent. It prohibited the production, sale, transportation, and importing of alcohol in any part of the United States. Other parts of the world also enacted prohibition laws during this time. Finland was under prohibition (called *kieltolaki*) from 1919–1932; Iceland prohibited the sale of alcohol from 1915–1922; and Russia prohibited the sale of alcoholic beverages (except in restaurants) from 1914–1925.

speakeasies
A slang expression used to describe saloons operating without a licence; popularly used during Prohibition.

These prohibition laws did not end the problem of alcohol. **Speakeasies** and local saloons became known as the epicentres for alcohol consumption and, along with this gambling, prostitution and organized crime were associated with these spots. During this time, illegal sale of alcohol continued to flourish. Organized crime became more organized (bootlegging) and more profitable as a result of Prohibition.

As you may be aware, and as is discussed further in Chapter 6, Prohibition was an experiment in drug control that did not succeed. For Canada, the realization that prohibition laws were unenforceable led to repeals of the laws. In 1920,

Archives of Ontario, F 1194 S 15000.

The temperance movement reached its height in Canada in the 1920s, when outside imports were cut off by provincial referendums. Bootleggers commonly poured smuggled alcohol for sale into flasks from large barrels that were illegally imported.

provinces in Canada, such as Quebec and British Columbia voted "wet" and, by the following year, some alcoholic beverages were legally sold in government stores. Manitoba enacted a system of government sale and control in 1923, followed by Alberta and Saskatchewan in 1924, Newfoundland in 1925, Ontario and New Brunswick in 1927, and Nova Scotia in 1930. Prince Edward Island finally gave up "the noble experiment" in 1948 (*The Canadian Encyclopedia*, 2011). In the United States, the 18th Amendment was repealed in 1933 by the 21st Amendment.

Post-Prohibition Legislation

Following the repeal of legislations, each province was given control over and regulation of alcohol. Beer sales were the first to be regulated. Laws became more relaxed in both Canada and the United States. Consumption rates were relatively stable during the 1950s, which led to lowering the drinking age to 18 or 19 across all provinces. However, concerns over increased deaths of young adults in the 1970s and 1980s created public concern. Prevalence and patterns of alcohol use in Canada will be discussed further in Chapter 6.

The Le Dain Commission (1969)

Throughout the late 1950s and early 1960s attitudes towards drug use as a social problem continued to shadow regulations of drug penalties. However, with the end of World War II and the introduction of the international human rights movement, as well as the democratization of access to universities and the development of new disciplines in the social sciences such as criminology, psychology, sociology, and political science, scientific progress and research into drug addiction were factors in the creation of new pressure groups consisting of more articulate individuals who disputed the use of criminal law as the solution to responding to drug problems (The National Legislative Context, n.d.).

In 1969, the Le Dain Commission of Inquiry into the Non-Medical Use of Drugs discovered that hundreds of thousands of Canadians were convicted of illicit drug possession with lifetime barriers to personal freedoms and that sweeping police powers were used largely against youth (Riley, 1998). The most significant recommendations from the Commission included the gradual withdrawal of criminalization against drug users and less coercive alternatives to the use of criminal law, as well as greater leniency for possession of drugs. Despite these recommendations, Canada's drug policy remained unchanged.

Canada's Drug Strategy (1985)

It was in the 1980s that President Ronald Reagan declared the war on drugs and implemented the Anti-Drug Abuse Act (1986) in the United States. For Canada, this began a change in the development of government policy on drugs as sensationalized media reports during the 1980s and U.S.driven drug reforms began following the scare of illicit drug use. Prime Minister Brian Mulroney deviated from a prepared speech to announce that "drug abuse has become an epidemic that undermines our economic as well as our social fabric" (Erickson, 1992). A rise in the illicit use of heroin and cocaine was not the only problem. Media reports of the impurities of street drugs, and the increased use by young adults fuelled the re-look at the current regulations to control drugs. As a result, the government formed a committee to draft new legislation in an effort to more effectively control the use of illicit drugs. Almost 10 years later, in 1996, the Controlled Drugs and Substances Act (Bill C8) was voted into law.

Current Drug Laws

Controlled Drugs and Substances Act (CDSA) of 1997

The *Controlled Drugs and Substances Act* replaced the Narcotic Control Act of 1961 and provided new legislation regarding the use of illicit drugs. The CDSA prohibits the importation, exportation, production, sale, provision, and possession of a wide variety of controlled drugs and substances, except where permitted by legislation. A conviction for trafficking or for unlawful possession, export, import, trade, or production of a drug can result in imprisonment, a fine, or, in some cases, both. Controlled drugs and substances for medical treatment may be legally obtained only with a prescription from a licensed medical professional (including dental and veterinary practitioners).

The CDSA consists of drug schedules that detail the types of controlled drugs and substances included in each schedule as well as the offence and punishment under each of the schedules (see Table 2.3 below). The details of offences under the CDSA

TABLE 2.3 Controlled Drugs and Substances Act: Schedules, Offences, and Punishment*

Schedule	Description	Offences & Punishment			
		Possession and Seeking to Obtain	Trafficking	Production	Importing and/or Exporting
I	Opium, heroin, morphine, coca leaves, cocaine, methadols, moramides, and fentanyl	Indictable offence: jail (max. 7 yrs) Summary conviction: 1st offence—fine (max. $1000) or 6 months jail, or both Subsequent offence—fine (max. $2000) or 1 yr jail, or both	Indictable offence: jail (max. life)	Indictable offence: jail (max. life)	Indictable offence: jail (max. life)
II	All forms of cannabis, cannabis resin. Specifically excludes non-viable seed and a stalk that has been stripped of leaves and branches.	Indictable offence: jail (max. 5 yrs less 1 day) Summary conviction: 1st offence—fine (max. $1000) or 6 months jail, or both Subsequent offence—fine (max. $2000) or 1 yr jail, or both	Indictable offence: jail (max. life)	Indictable offence (not cannabis): jail (max. life) Cannabis—max. 7 yrs	Indictable offence: jail (max. life)

III	Stimulants and hallucinogens listed in the Food and Drugs Act, including amphetamine, Quaaludes, psilocybin, LSD, DMT, MDA	Indictable offence: jail (max. 3 yrs) Summary conviction: 1st offence—fine (max. $1000) or 6 months jail, or both Subsequent offence—fine (max. $2000) or 1 yr jail, or both	Indictable offence: jail (max. 10 yrs) Summary conviction—jail (max. 18 months)	Indictable offence: jail (max. 10 yrs) Summary conviction—jail (max. 18 months)	Indictable offence: jail (max. 10 yrs) Summary conviction—jail (max. 18 months)
IV	Some prescribed drugs, anabolic steroids, anorexiants, sedatives (barbiturates and benzodiazepines), khat	(excluding possession) Indictable offence: jail (max. 18 months)	Indictable offence: jail (max. 3 yrs) Summary conviction: jail (max. 1 yr)	Indictable offence: jail (max. 3 yrs) Summary conviction: jail (max. 1 yr)	Indictable offence: jail (max. 3 yrs) Summary conviction: jail (max. 18 months)
V	Ingredients that may appear in non-prescription drugs, including phenylpropanolamine and propylhexedrine				Indictable offence: jail (max. 3 yrs) Summary conviction: jail (max. 18 months)
VI	Certain precursors (substances commonly used to manu-facture other listed drugs) CLASS A: ephedrine, isosafrole, LSD, 1,4-butanediol, red & white phosphorus CLASS B: acetone, ethyl ether, sulphuric acid, toluene				Indictable offence: jail (max. 10 yrs) Summary conviction—jail (max. 18 months)
VII	3kg Hashish 3kg Cannabis				discretionary
VIII	1g Hashish 30g Cannabis				discretionary

Notes:

* Details provided above concerning the various substances described are intended solely to provide general guidance and should not be taken to be a complete statement or interpretation of the law.

Source: Department of Justice Canada. Controlled Drugs and Substances Act (S.C. 1996, c.19) Found at: http://laws-lois.justice.gc.ca/eng/acts/C-38.8/index.html

are quite complicated to state in this textbook; however, some examples can be found in Table 2.3. One important thing to note is that offences and their subsequent punishment are governed under the law according to the seriousness of the offence committed. Therefore, not all offences under the CDSA result in a criminal record upon conviction.

An offence which is considered minor in the *Criminal Code of Canada*, called a **summary conviction**, does not normally result in a criminal record. For example, the possession of 30g or less of cannabis would be considered a summary conviction only. However, possession of more than 30g of cannabis for the purposes of trafficking is an example of an **indictable offence**, which will result in a criminal record (and imprisonment) upon conviction.

summary conviction
A minor offence under the Criminal Code of Canada, punishable under the CDSA, which does not result in a criminal record.

indictable offence
A more serious offence under the Criminal Code of Canada, punishable under the CDSA, which will result in a criminal record.

CONTEMPORARY ISSUE BOX 2.2

The Rise of "Club Drugs"

Throughout the 1990s and into the 2000s, the popularity of a group of substances collectively referred to as "club drugs" has been sustained. This term describes drugs being used by young adults at all-night dance parties such as "raves" and "trances" and at dance clubs and bars. All indications are that club drugs can cause serious health problems and even death in some cases. Some of these drugs are stimulants, some are depressants, and some are hallucinogens. When used in combination with alcohol, these drugs can be even more dangerous. Because some club drugs are colourless, tasteless, and odourless, individuals who want to intoxicate or sedate others (often to commit sexual assaults) can unobtrusively add them to beverages. Following is some information on the most popular club drugs, and more details on these substances are provided in later chapters of this text:

- *Methylenedioxymethamphetamine (MDMA)* (street names: Ecstasy, XTC, X, Adam, clarity, lover's speed). MDMA is chemically similar to the stimulant amphetamine and the hallucinogen mescaline. MDMA can produce both stimulant and psychedelic effects and can be extremely dangerous when taken in large doses.
- *Gamma hydroxybutyrate (GHB)* (street names: grievous bodily harm, G, liquid Ecstasy, Georgia homeboy). GHB can be produced in clear liquid, white powder, tablet, and capsule forms, and it is often used in combination with alcohol, making it even more dangerous. GHB has been increasingly involved in poisonings, overdoses, rapes, and fatalities. GHB is often manufactured in homes with recipes and ingredients found and purchased on the Internet. It is usually abused either for its intoxicating, sedative, or euphoriant properties or for its growth hormone-releasing effects, which can build muscle. When taken in smaller doses, GHB can relieve anxiety and produce relaxation; however, as the dose increases, the sedative effects may result in sleep and eventual coma or death.
- *Ketamine* (street names: special K, K, vitamin K, cat valiums). Ketamine is an injectable anesthetic that has been approved for both human and animal use in medical settings since 1970. Ketamine is produced in liquid form or as a white powder that is often snorted or smoked with marijuana or tobacco products. Taken in larger doses, ketamine can cause delirium, amnesia, impaired motor function, high blood pressure, depression, and potentially fatal respiratory problems. Low-dose intoxication from ketamine results in impaired attention, learning ability, and memory.
- *Rohypnol* (street names: roofies, rophies, roche, forget-me pill). Rohypnol (flunitrazepam) belongs to the class of drugs known as benzodiazepines. It is not approved for prescription use in Canada or the United States, although it is approved in Europe and is used in more than 60 countries as a treatment for insomnia, as a sedative, and as a pre-surgery anesthetic. Rohypnol is tasteless, odourless, and it dissolves easily in carbonated beverages. The drug can cause profound "anterograde amnesia"; that is, individuals may not remember events they experienced while under the effects of the drug.
- *Methamphetamine* (street names: speed, ice, chalk, meth, crystal, crank, fire, glass). Methamphetamine is a toxic, addictive stimulant that affects many areas of the central nervous system. The drug is often made in clandestine laboratories from relatively inexpensive over-the-counter ingredients. Available in many forms, methamphetamine can be smoked, snorted, injected, or orally ingested. Its use is associated with serious health consequences including memory loss, aggression, violence, psychotic behaviour, and potential cardiac and neurological damage.
- *Lysergic acid diethylamide (LSD)* (street names: acid, boomers, purple haze, yellow sunshines). LSD is a hallucinogen that induces distortions in sensory perceptions. The effects of LSD are unpredictable, depending on the amount taken; on the surroundings in which the drug is used; and on the user's personality, mood, and expectations. Two long-term disorders sometimes associated with LSD are persistent psychosis and hallucinogen persisting perception disorder (which used to be called "flashbacks").

Source: Adapted from *Community Alert Bulletin on Club Drugs* (National Institute on Drug Abuse [NIDA], 2004). Updated 2009

CONTEMPORARY ISSUE BOX 2.3

The War on Drugs in the United States

Prohibition in the United States was one of the most restricted and major attempts made during this period to investigate and punish violators of the 18th Amendment.

One of the foremost efforts of recent presidential administrations in the United States has been the "war on drugs," which was implemented in the 1980s and has continued unabated since. Hallmark features of this "war" are efforts to catch drug smugglers and sellers (in the United States and overseas) and the implementation of a "zero-tolerance" approach to drug users, including casual users of drugs. The U.S. government has been spending approximately a billion dollars a year on antidrug operations overseas alone, most of it used to catch drug smugglers.

All of these efforts appear to have had no significant impact on drug use. Most experts conclude that efforts to intercept drugs have been a failure. Hundreds of millions of dollars have been spent on these efforts, yet the flow of drugs into the United States has not been significantly altered. So what is the best strategy for combating the drug problem? Some organizations, such as the Physician Leadership on National Drug Policy, have been pushing for a greater focus on reducing the demand for drugs through prevention efforts and treatment (including the use of treatment services as an alternative to incarceration). This emphasis on demand reduction appears to reflect the attitudes of most individuals as well. An ABC News poll found that almost 70 percent of Americans favoured treatment over jail for first- and second-time drug offenders.

It is unlikely that the war on drugs will cease anytime soon. Instead, changes in the "battle plan" will reflect shifts in focus, such as paying more attention to policing drug supply routes than to drug demand, or vice versa. Overall efforts continue to be coordinated by the head of the White House Office of National Drug Control Policy, better known as the "drug czar." The most recently appointed "drug czar," Gil Kerlikowske, appointed in 2009 by President Barack Obama, has professed a desire to abolish the use of the "war on drugs" phraseology and to shift greater emphasis on treatment relative to imprisonment.

It is noteworthy that the two drugs most associated with deaths in the U.S.—tobacco and alcohol—are not a focus of attention in any of these efforts. Is the same true for Canada? What is the focus of Canada's "war on drugs"?

Medical Marijuana Access Regulations

Despite the fact that the Food and Drug Regulations for marketed drugs in Canada has not approved cannabis as a therapeutic drug, the Marihuana Medical Access Regulations provide patients access to medical marijuana with the referral from their physician. Currently, Canada is the first country to provide a mechanism for medically regulated marijuana access to patients suffering from debilitating illnesses.

In 2001, Health Canada implemented the Marihuana Medical Access Regulations (MMAR), which articulates the process for access to marijuana for medical purposes. The regulations include three main components:

1. Authorization to possess dried marijuana;
2. Licences to produce marijuana, which include Personal-Use Production Licences and Designated Person Production Licences; and
3. Access to supply of marijuana seeds or dried marijuana.

The MMAR details two categories of people who can apply to possess marijuana for medical purposes. These categories are discussed in Chapter 9. Each category refers to specific inclusions for the possession and/or manufacture of marijuana accordingly.

Possession, Cultivation, and Distribution of Medical Marijuana

Prairie Plant Systems Inc. (PPS) was contracted by Health Canada in 2000 to cultivate and produce a standardized supply of marijuana. PPS specializes in the growing, harvesting, and processing of plants for pharmaceutical products and research.

It is estimated that most individuals use an average daily amount of one gram to three grams of dried marijuana for medicinal purposes (taken orally, inhaled, or both). This amounts to approximately three to six joints. An authorized patient can order marijuana from Health Canada and can access a standardized supply produced under contract by PPS. Cultivation of marijuana by the authorized patient or by a designated person is permitted under the regulations, upon approval of an application for Personal-Use Production Licence or Designated Person Production Licence respectfully. The number of marijuana plants they can cultivate is based on the daily amount identified in the application.

Currently, 4884 persons hold an Authorization to Possess dried marijuana under the Marihuana Medical Access Regulations, and 3576 persons are allowed to cultivate/produce marijuana for medicinal purposes (2822 hold Personal-Use Licences, 754 hold Designated Person Licences). Chapter 9 contains a table that shows the number of physicians, by province, who have provided support for authorization to possess medicinal marijuana under the MMAR.

SUMMARY

- Drugs have been used for a variety of reasons in different cultures for thousands of years; the earliest drug use involved ingestion of alcohol and of plants with psychoactive properties.
- Prior to the 20th century, few restrictions were placed on drug availability or drug use.
- During the 19th century, drugs such as opium, morphine, marijuana, heroin, and cocaine could be obtained easily without prescription.
- Different drugs have enjoyed periods of popularity in Canada and North America. Cocaine was widely used in medicines and tonics during the late 1800s and early 1900s. Cocaine use again became popular in the 1980s, and its popularity continues today. Amphetamines were used relatively widely during the 1930s, minor tranquilizers and inhalants during the 1950s, and LSD during the 1960s. Heroin has been showing signs of increased use in recent years. A current trend is the emergence of a group of substances collectively known as "club drugs."
- A parallel exists between the development and use of psychoactive substances in medicinal forms and the nonmedicinal use or abuse of these drugs.
- The main mechanism through which society establishes formal guidelines regarding drugs and drug use is legislation. However, the history of drug laws in Canada does not really begin until the turn of the 20th century.
- The first major federal legislation regarding drugs was the 1908 Opium Act, which made it an indictable offence to import, manufacture, offer to sell or traffic opium for nonmedicinal purposes. Other major legislation of note include the Narcotic Control Act of 1961, which regulated the legal supply of certain drugs, and alcohol Prohibition in North America in the 1920s and 1930s.
- Drug classifications for law enforcement today are based on the 1997 Controlled Drugs and Substances Act, which classifies drugs according to their legitimate medical uses and their potential for abuse and dependence.
- Canada's Marihuana Medical Access Regulations provide a mechanism for patients to access marijuana for medical purposes. It is the only country that currently has such regulations.

Key Terms

cannabis sativa p. 23
hashish p. 23
indictable offence p. 35
narcotic p. 30
opium poppy p. 23
patent medicines p. 25
prohibition p. 31
speakeasies p. 32
summary conviction p. 35

Essays/Thought Questions

1. What efforts might be taken to reduce or eliminate the availability and use of "club drugs"?
2. What are the potential benefits of reducing the availability of illegal drugs versus reducing the demand for such substances?
3. Should efforts be supported to decriminalize or even legalize the use of certain drugs, such as marijuana?

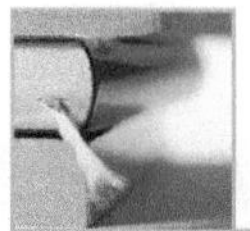

Suggested Readings

Burnham, J.C. (1993). *Bad habits: Drinking, smoking, taking drugs, gambling, sexual misbehavior, and swearing in American history*. New York: New York University Press.

McKenna, T. (1992). *Food of the gods: The search for the original tree of knowledge*. New York: Bantam Books.

Rudgley, R. (1993). *Essential substances: A cultural history of intoxicants in society*. New York: Kodansha International.

CHAPTER 3

Drugs and the Nervous System

Did You Know

- Your nervous system is divided into the central nervous system (brain and spinal cord) and the peripheral nervous system (neural tissue outside the brain and spinal cord).
- Drugs increase or decrease the natural functions that occur in the brain or body; that is, drugs affect the central and peripheral nervous systems.
- Your brain weighs only about three pounds, but it controls all of our psychological experiences.
- Your brain contains more than 100 billion neurons.
- These neurons have a unique ability to "talk" with each other—this is called neural communication.
- Neural communication requires chemical messengers, called neurotransmitters. Examples of neurotransmitters are dopamine, serotonin, and acetylcholine.
- Neurotransmitters play a role in many disorders such as depression, Alzheimer's disease, and Parkinson's disease.
- You have most of your neurons at birth. But you do continue to make some new neurons even through adulthood—this is called neurogenesis.
- While most drugs (opiates, alcohol, nicotine, and cocaine) suppress neurogenesis, cannabis may actually promote neurogenesis.

Every feeling or emotion you have—in fact, all psychological experience—is based on brain activity. The fact that this physical entity, the brain, is the basis of conscious experience is the key to understanding how the chemical agents we call drugs alter psychological processes.

One feature all psychoactive drugs have in common is that they produce their effects by acting in some way on nervous system tissue; this chapter is concerned with these physiological actions of drugs. Most of these actions occur at the level of the brain. As recent discoveries in neuroscience have led to a greater understanding of how the brain works, parallel advances have taken place in our understanding of drug actions. These developments have led to some radically new ways of thinking about drug effects and drug problems such as addiction. Before we discuss how drugs act on the brain, however, we must first cover some of the fundamentals of just how the brain works.

The basic building blocks of the nervous system are cells called neurons.

The Neuron

The basic building blocks of the nervous system are cells called **neurons**. Neurons are similar to other cells in the human body, such as blood cells or muscle cells, but they have the unique feature of being able to communicate with one another. The structural properties of neurons provide us with some clues to the nature of the neural transmission process.

Notice that the neuron depicted in Figure 3.1 has a cell body similar to those of any other cell. The cell body includes a nucleus that contains the genetic material for the neuron and other processes that control the metabolic activities of the cell. Extending from the cell body of the neuron are a number of small spine- or branch-like structures called **dendrites** and one long cylindrical structure called the **axon**. These structures are unique to the neuron and are responsible for some of its remarkable properties.

Axons vary in length but are usually much longer than shown in the illustration—sometimes thousands of times longer than the diameter of the cell body. The axon depicted in Figure 3.1 is enclosed within a sheath of a white, fatty substance called **myelin** (not all axons are covered by myelin sheaths; "unmyelinated" axons are gray). Myelin provides insulation for the axon, similar to insulation for a wire. The comparison is fitting because the principal function of the axon is to conduct electrical current. The axon transmits information by conducting an electrical signal from one end of the neuron to the other. Generally, information is gathered by dendrites and the cell body and transmitted along the axon in the form of an electrical signal called the **action potential**.

The action potential does not work in precisely the way that electricity travels along a wire. Rather it is produced by the flow of charged particles called ions through channels in the membrane that covers the axon. When the neuron is at rest, the concentration of positively charged sodium ions is greater outside the axon membrane, whereas negatively charged protein and chloride ions are concentrated

neurons
Individual nerve cells that are basic building blocks of the nervous system.

dendrites
Spiny, branch-like structures that extend from the cell body of a neuron and typically contain numerous receptor sites, thus making them important in neural transmission.

axon
A long cylindrical extension of the cell body of the neuron that conducts an electrical charge from the cell body to the axon terminals.

myelin
A fatty white substance that covers the axons of some neurons.

action potential
The electrical impulse along the axon that occurs when a neuron fires.

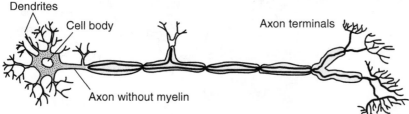

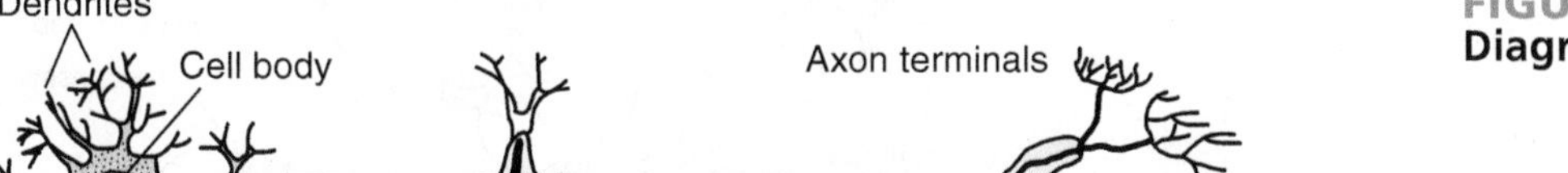

FIGURE 3.1
Diagram of a neuron

How does one neuron communicate with another without direct contact between them?

within the axon. When the neuron is stimulated, certain ion channels open, permitting positive ions into the axon, and some depolarization of the axon will occur. If the level of stimulation becomes high enough, a threshold of excitation is reached, and a massive depolarization of the axon membrane occurs as positively charged sodium ions rush into the axon. This rapid depolarization that produces a change of about 110 millivolts is also termed the *action potential*. The action potential travels rapidly along the axon like a wave and is said to be "all or none," in that the axon is either "firing" with the full voltage charge or at rest. Once the neuron has fired, sodium ions are pumped out of the axon, channels close, and the neuron returns to its resting potential.

axon terminals (or terminal buttons) Enlarged button-like structures at the ends of axon branches.

synapse The junction between neurons.

neurotransmitters Chemical substances stored in the axon terminals that are released into the synapse when the neuron fires. Neurotransmitters then influence activity in postsynaptic neurons.

Neural Transmission

The branches at the end of the axon shown in Figure 3.1 terminate in small button-like structures known as **axon terminals** or **terminal buttons**. These axon terminals hold the key to an important puzzle: how the electrical message actually gets from one neuron to another. When advances in microscopy made possible the viewing of neurons as they are seen here, a surprising finding was that most axon terminals of one neuron do not come into direct contact with the dendrites of the neighbouring neuron as had been supposed; instead, the junction between two neurons, the **synapse**, is generally separated by a gap called the synaptic cleft (see Figure 3.2). The question is: How does one neuron communicate with another without direct contact between them? It is now known that, when an action potential reaches the axon terminal, chemical substances stored in the terminal button are released into the synapse, and these chemical substances, called **neurotransmitters**, actually trigger activity in the adjacent neuron.

FIGURE 3.2
Diagram of a synapse
This diagram of a synapse shows an enlarged axon terminal with vesicles containing neurotransmitter molecules.

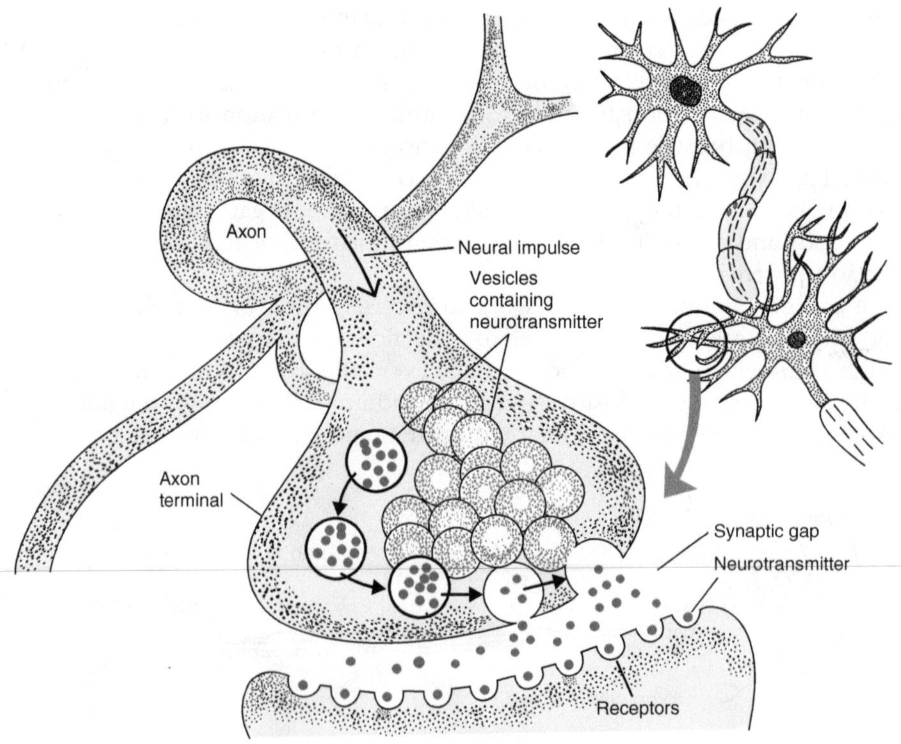

Thus, neural transmission may be thought of as an electrochemical event—electrical along the axon and chemical at the synapse. This is of some importance for our purposes; it suggests that drugs may interact with the nervous system at the synapse because that is where chemical transmission takes place. In fact, we now know that most psychoactive drugs produce their important effects by action at the synapse (see Valenstein, 2005, for an account of the discovery of neurotransmitters and synaptic transmission). Therefore, more detailed analysis of the chemical processes that occur at the synapse is required.

A lock–key analogy is useful for depicting the neural transmission process. Scattered along the dendrites and cell body are special structures known as **receptor sites**, or receptors. These structures may be viewed as locks that must be opened before the neuron fires. To fire, the receptors must be "unlocked," which is accomplished by the neurotransmitter substances released at the terminal button. The neurotransmitter molecules may be thought of as keys. The idea is illustrated in Figure 3.2. Receptor sites are depicted as circular holes in the dendrite and neurotransmitters as circles being released from the axon terminal. The notion is simple: The key must fit the lock to trigger an event such as neural firing.

receptor sites
Specialized structures located on dendrites and cell bodies for neurons that are activated by neurotransmitters.

In fact, neurotransmitter molecules and receptors have chemical structures that are considerably more complex than is illustrated, and the lock–key analogy does not completely explain the process. Transmitters and their receptors are said to have an affinity for one another; that is, the transmitter is attracted to the receptor site, and when a transmitter key occupies a receptor lock, they briefly become attached in a process called binding. When a neurotransmitter molecule binds to a receptor, changes occur in the neuron that may make the neuron more or less likely to fire. There are many different types of neurotransmitter keys and many corresponding receptor site locks. We now understand that the brain is chemically coded with different pathways that respond to different neurotransmitter chemicals.

Drugs and Neural Transmission

Several ways that drugs can interfere with synaptic transmission may have already occurred to you. For example, suppose the chemical structure of some drug is similar to the structure of a naturally occurring (endogenous) neurotransmitter. If the similarity is close enough, the drug molecules might bind to the receptor sites, thus duping the receptor into reacting as if the natural transmitter is present and stimulating the neuron. Just such a process, called *mimicry*, actually does occur with some drugs. For example, morphine and heroin are now thought to act by mimicking natural neurotransmitters called endorphins.

Mimicry is an obvious mechanism of drug action, but drugs can influence neural transmission in numerous other ways as well. A sampling of these mechanisms is listed in Table 3.1. Neurotransmitters must be manufactured from simpler building blocks, or precursor molecules. Transmitters are usually manufactured in a cell body or axon terminal, but if the substance is manufactured in the cell body, it must still be transported to the terminal before it is functional. Some drugs interfere with transmitter production or transport. Neurotransmitter molecules are stored in small packages called **vesicles** located in the terminal buttons. Some drugs affect the ability of the vesicles to store neurotransmitter substances. For example, the drug reserpine, once used to treat high blood pressure, causes certain vesicles to become leaky and then the transmitters involved are not effectively released into

vesicles
Tiny sacs in axon terminals that store neurotransmitters.

TABLE 3.1 Neurochemical Mechanisms of Drug Action

Drug effects can be produced by altering the following neurochemical systems:

1. ***Neurotransmitter synthesis.*** A drug may increase or decrease the synthesis of neurotransmitters.
2. ***Neurotransmitter transport.*** A drug may interfere with the transport of neurotransmitter molecules to the axon terminals.
3. ***Neurotransmitter storage.*** A drug may interfere with the storage of neurotransmitters in the vesicles of the axon terminal.
4. ***Neurotransmitter release.*** A drug may cause the axon terminals to release neurotransmitter molecules into the synapse prematurely.
5. ***Neurotransmitter degradation.*** A drug may influence the breakdown of neurotransmitters by enzymes.
6. ***Neurotransmitter reuptake.*** A drug may block the reuptake of neurotransmitters into the axon terminals.
7. ***Receptor activation.*** A drug may activate a receptor site by mimicking a neurotransmitter.
8. ***Receptor blocking.*** A drug may cause a receptor to become inactive by blocking it.

A drug can alter neural transmission by affecting enzyme activity.

enzyme breakdown
One process by which neurotransmitters are inactivated. Chemicals called enzymes interact with the transmitter molecule and change its structure so that it no longer is capable of occupying receptor sites.

reuptake
One process by which neurotransmitters are inactivated. Neurotransmitter molecules are taken back up into the axon terminal that released them.

acetylcholine
A neurotransmitter linked with cognitive processes and memory that is found both in the brain and in the parasympathetic branch of the autonomic nervous system.

the synapse. Alternatively, other drugs can enhance the release of neurotransmitter substances into the synapse; this is one of the ways stimulants such as amphetamines are thought to act.

Another important rule of neural transmission is that neurotransmitters, once released, must be deactivated to terminate cell activity. Neurotransmitters are deactivated in two ways: **enzyme breakdown** and **reuptake**. Certain chemicals called enzymes act both to build the complex molecules of neurotransmitters and to break down neurotransmitters to inactive form. These processes are complex and reveal one reason that identifying and isolating the functions of neurotransmitters in the brain are difficult. The brain contains many different chemicals, and they are constantly changing form. Consider the processes involved in the production and destruction of **acetylcholine**, one of the better-known neurotransmitters. The precursor molecule choline is acted on by an enzyme (choline acetyltransferase) to make acetylcholine. Acetylcholine itself is broken down by a different enzyme—acetylcholinesterase—to yield two metabolites: choline and acetate. (Enzymes are named by the stem of the chemical that they influence and always have an "-ase" ending.) A drug can alter neural transmission by affecting enzyme activity. For example, some antidepressant drugs alter brain levels of the neurotransmitters norepinephrine, dopamine, and serotonin by inhibiting the activity of monoamine oxidase, the enzyme that breaks down these compounds.

A second mechanism for removing neurotransmitters from the synapse is called reuptake. Neurotransmitters are taken back up into the terminal button after they have been released—hence the term *reuptake*. This is an economical mechanism of deactivating transmitters because the neurotransmitter molecule is preserved intact and can be used again without the expense of energy involved in the manufacture of new transmitters. Some drugs (notably cocaine) exert some of their action by blocking the reuptake process.

TABLE 3.2 Major Neurotransmitters with Representative Agonists and Antagonists

Neurotransmitter	Agonist	Antagonist
Acetylcholine	Nicotine	Atropine
Dopamine/norepinephrine	Cocaine/amphetamines	Chlorpromazine
Serotonin	LSD	Chlorpromazine
Endorphins	Morphine	Naloxone
GABA	Barbiturates	Bicuculline
Glutamate	Aspartic acid	Ketamine

As noted, an important site of drug action is directly at the receptor. Some drugs directly affect the receptor by mimicking the activity of natural neurotransmitters—similar to a duplicate key that fits into and opens a lock. Other drugs seem to act as if they fit into the lock but then they jam the lock and prevent the neuron from firing. Such a drug is called a *blocking agent.* In general, any chemical—natural or otherwise—that fits a receptor lock and activates it is said to be an **agonist** of that receptor. Any compound that occupies a receptor and does not activate it, but rather prevents other compounds from activating the receptor, is said to be an **antagonist**. In Table 3.2 we provide examples of neurotransmitters and their agonists and their antagonist. For example, naloxone is an antagonist of the receptors on which opiate drugs (such as heroin) work. If naloxone is promptly administered to a patient who has just taken a potentially lethal dose of heroin, the patient will survive and will rapidly be brought to a state in which it appears as if the heroin had never been taken. In fact, all effects of heroin and other opiates are blocked completely or reversed by naloxone. Thus, naloxone is called an opiate antagonist. The terms *agonist* and *antagonist* may also be used more generally to refer to drugs that enhance (agonist) or inhibit (antagonist) the activity of a particular neurotransmitter system.

agonist
A substance that occupies a neural receptor and causes some change in the conductance of the neuron.

antagonist
A substance that occupies a neural receptor and blocks normal synaptic transmission.

Chronic use of some drugs can result in a long-term reduction of the amount of neurotransmitter produced and released in affected neurons.

Up to now, we have considered only the acute effects of drugs on neural transmission, that is, effects that occur during a single use of the drug. When drugs are used more regularly, long-lasting changes in neurotransmission can occur that are important in the development of drug tolerance and dependence. For example, chronic use of some drugs can result in a long-term reduction of the amount of neurotransmitter produced and released in affected neurons. Alternatively, the number of available receptor sites can be reduced. Such changes result in the affected pathway becoming less sensitive to the drug and thus illustrate neural mechanisms of tolerance development. Depending upon the functions of the affected pathway, these changes may alter responsiveness to nondrug environmental stimuli as well. If the user stops taking the drug, the loss of stimulation in these pathways may result in withdrawal symptoms (see Nestler, 2009).

We have seen a number of ways that drugs can act to influence neural transmission (see Iversen et al., 2009, for a more detailed review). A point to remember, however, is that the effects of drugs always involve naturally occurring processes. That is, drugs increase or decrease the natural functions that occur in the brain or body. To understand how this occurs we must first examine the different neurotransmitters and the roles they play in our brain and body. In later chapters we will discuss how these neurotransmitters are affected by different drugs.

One gram of botulinum toxin (about the weight of a dollar bill) is enough to fatally poison more than three million people.
(Meyer & Quenzer, 2005)

Major Neurotransmitter Systems

Acetylcholine

One of the first neurotransmitters to be discovered was acetylcholine, probably because it is found in the more easily studied neurons located outside the brain. Acetylcholine resides in the axon terminals of neurons that activate the skeletal muscles. At sites where nerves meet muscles, there is a space similar to the synapse called the **neuromuscular junction**. When the neurons that synapse with muscle fibres fire, they release acetylcholine into the neuromuscular junction, and the muscle contracts. Some muscle disorders are related to problems with this process. For example, myasthenia gravis, a disease characterized by severe muscle weakness and fatigue, is caused by a blockage of acetylcholine at the neuromuscular junction. A related similar process is the basis for one of the deadliest toxins known: botulinum. One gram of botulinum toxin (about the weight of a dollar bill) is enough to fatally poison more than three million people (Meyer & Quenzer, 2005). Botulinum toxin is produced by a bacterium that grows in oxygen-free environments such as improperly prepared canned goods and, as you might well imagine, is a major concern with respect to biological warfare and terrorism. The basis for botulinum toxicity is that it blocks the release of acetylcholine at the neuromuscular junction, resulting in muscle paralysis and, in sufficient doses, death by asphyxiation. Interestingly, a carefully prepared form of botulinum toxin is now being marketed and used cosmetically under the brand name Botox. When Botox is injected into one of the facial muscles, it causes that muscle to become partially paralyzed; this can produce a temporary smoothing of certain types of facial wrinkles and lines. However, University of Calgary researcher Rafael Fortuna and colleagues (Fortuna, Vaz, Yousseff, Longino, & Herzog, 2011) report that Botox does not stay isolated to the injection area, but rather can travel to other muscles. In their study, rabbits injected with Botox experienced weakness and atrophy in muscles other than the ones that received the Botox injection. This study raises questions about the potential short and long-term effects of botulism use on neural communication.

neuromuscular junction Junction between neuron and muscle fibres where release of acetylcholine by neurons causes muscles to contract.

Alzheimer's disease The most common type of dementia leading to the progressive loss of thinking and memory functions and affecting primarily individuals over the age of 65.

Blue Skies, 1995 (oil on canvas), Utermohlen, William (1933-2007) / Private Collection / The Bridgeman Art Library

Artwork drawn prior to the onset of Alzheimer's Disease.

As a point of terminology, if the name of a neurotransmitter is to be used as an adjective, simply take the stem of the name (e.g., *choline*) and add the suffix "-ergic." Thus, neurons that contain acetylcholine are *cholinergic* neurons, and drugs that block acetylcholine, such as atropine, are *anticholinergic* drugs. Nicotine is an example of a cholinergic drug because it is an agonist at acetylcholine receptors.

Acetylcholine is also important in the brain, but like most neurotransmitters, its function in the brain is not thoroughly understood. Acetylcholine is thought to be important in sensory processing, attention, and memory. Researchers, such as Dr. Jane Rylett, Co-director of Molecular Brain Research at the University of Western Ontario, study the role of acetylcholine in neurological disorders, such as Alzheimer's disease. **Alzheimer's disease** is the most common type of dementia, affecting one in 11 Canadians over the age of 65. This progressive disease leads to the loss of thinking and memory functions (Alzheimer's Society, 2010). There is substantial evidence that Alzheimer's disease is related to the loss of neural function in some of the brain's cholinergic pathways. As such, researchers are particularly interested in determining what might be going wrong in these pathways so that they can develop ways of correcting or preventing the problem. Currently in Canada, there are three drugs that have been approved to treat the symptoms of Alzheimer's disease: Aricept, Exelon, and Reminyl (Alzheimer's Society, 2010). These drugs reduce the symptoms of Alzheimer's disease by elevating levels of acetylcholine in the brain through inhibition of the enzyme acetylcholinesterase. There are many other drugs that inhibit acetylcholinesterase including some pesticides and nerve agents. In addition, some drugs mimic acetlycholine such as nicotine and muscarine (found in some mushrooms).

Artwork drawn after the onset of Alzheimer's Disease.

Self Portrait (Green), 1997 (oil on canvas), Utermohlen, William (1933-2007) / Private Collection / The Bridgeman Art Library

The problem of Alzheimer's disease underscores an important point: When neurotransmitter systems malfunction, disease states are a likely consequence, and drugs that target the affected system may provide effective treatments. On the flip side, drugs may likewise harm the balance and health of neurotransmitter systems.

Monoamines

Three important neurotransmitters—**norepinephrine** (noradrenaline), **dopamine**, and **serotonin**—are collectively known as the **monoamines** because the chemical structure of each contains a single amine group. Like acetylcholine, norepinephrine was discovered early because it is found outside the brain. It serves as a key chemical to mediate the physical changes that accompany emotional arousal. Norepinephrine is also found in the brain as a neurotransmitter, where it seems to be important in the regulation of hunger, alertness, and arousal. Serotonin is found throughout the brain and has been shown to be important in the regulation of sleep. In fact, new research reports that the majority of infants who die from Sudden Infant Death Syndrome (SIDS) have a deficiency in serotonin levels (Duncan et al., 2010). Dopamine is a key neurotransmitter in the pathways that regulate coordinated motor movements. This discovery led to the hypothesis that dopamine insufficiency may be the basis of **Parkinson's disease**, a disorder characterized by progressive loss of fine motor movements, muscle rigidity, and tremor. Parkinson's disease afflicts more than 100 000 Canadians (Parkinson Society Canada, 2011).

The dopamine deficiency hypothesis of Parkinson's disease led to new treatment approaches involving the administration of **L-dopa**, a precursor of dopamine. L-dopa was administered to patients in hopes of correcting the dopamine deficiency and proved to be dramatically effective in relieving the symptoms of this disease. Dopamine itself is not effective because it does not enter the brain from the bloodstream. The brain is protected from toxic compounds that might enter the bloodstream by a

norepinephrine
A neurotransmitter in the brain that is involved in activity of the sympathetic branch of the autonomic nervous system.

dopamine
A neurotransmitter in the brain that is involved with movement and reward.

serotonin
A neurotransmitter in the brain that is involved with sleep and mood.

monoamines
A class of chemicals characterized by a single amine group; includes the neurotransmitters norepinephrine, dopamine, and serotonin.

Parkinson's disease
A progressive disease causing the deterioration of motor control.

L-dopa
A chemical precursor of dopamine used in the treatment of Parkinson's disease.

blood–brain barrier The system that "filters" the blood before it can enter the brain.

blood–brain barrier that screens many chemicals, including dopamine. But L-dopa does penetrate the barrier, and once it reaches the brain it is converted to dopamine (Deutsch & Roth, 2009). Using L-dopa in the treatment of Parkinson's disease is a dramatic example of the value of new knowledge about neurotransmitters for the treatment of disease. Although L-dopa does not cure the disease process (dopaminergic neurons continue to be lost and eventually even L-dopa cannot correct the loss), it has brought years of productive living to many whose lives would otherwise have been prematurely ended by Parkinson's disease.

Monoamines, particularly dopamine and serotonin, appear to be important as the biochemical basis of another important mental illness.

In addition to these functions, the monoamine neurotransmitters norepinephrine, dopamine, and serotonin have been closely linked to mood states and emotional disorders. In fact, drugs that influence the monoamine systems have revolutionized modern psychiatry. For example, considerable evidence shows that severe clinical depression has a biological basis. Current theories propose that clinical depression is associated with dysregulation of monoamines, particularly norepinephrine and serotonin. This monoamine theory of depression originated with the finding that certain drugs that depleted monoamines seemed to produce depression. Reserpine, once used to treat high blood pressure, makes monoaminergic vesicles leaky (as we noted earlier) and the transmitters are then destroyed by enzymes, resulting in a depletion of norepinephrine, serotonin, and dopamine. This process often causes depression in people whose mood states were normal before treatment (as you may have guessed, it also produces Parkinson's symptoms due to dopamine depletion, and this side effect led to the use of L-dopa previously mentioned). Evidence of abnormal monoamine activity in clients who suffer from depression has been reported; for example, numerous studies have linked deficient serotonin activity to suicidal behaviour (Arango & Mann, 2009). Finally, the drugs that are useful in the treatment of depression (e.g., Prozac) generally influence either norepinephrine or serotonin transmission or both, which further supports this monoamine-dysregulation hypothesis. Increased knowledge of neurochemical processes linked to depression is suggesting

Boxing legend Muhammad Ali pretends to punch actor Michael J. Fox. Both suffer from Parkinson's disease.

new and promising approaches to the understanding and treatment of depressive disorders (Berman et al., 2009; see Contemporary Issue Box 3.1).

Monoamines, particularly dopamine and serotonin, appear to be important as the biochemical basis of another important mental illness: schizophrenia. Schizophrenia involves a major loss of contact with reality, characterized by false beliefs or delusions, hallucinations, social withdrawal, and distortions of emotionality. Strong evidence ties these symptoms to high levels of monoamine activity. First, all the drugs that are effective in the treatment of schizophrenia also block monoamine transmission. In fact, it has long been known that a close correlation exists between the clinical potency of the various drugs used and their ability to block dopamine receptors (Snyder, Burt, & Creese, 1976). Another interesting piece of evidence is that stimulant drugs such as cocaine and amphetamines increase monoamine activity in the brain. Although low or moderate doses of these stimulants enhance mood, overdoses often lead to paranoid delusions and a loss of reality contact that strongly resembles some symptoms of schizophrenia. When the drug wears off and monoamine activity returns to normal, these symptoms generally dissipate—a finding that further supports the link between abnormal monoamine activity and schizophrenia (see Sawa & Snyder, 2002). Although complex disorders such as schizophrenia and depression cannot be understood completely without considering a host of psychological and social factors, the biological approaches just noted have certainly improved our understanding and treatment of them. We consider the use of drugs to treat these and other disorders in more detail in Chapter 12.

CONTEMPORARY ISSUE BOX 3.1

The Aging Brain: Adult Neurogenesis and Depression

Until the 1990s, it was almost universally accepted that the birth of new neurons—neurogenesis—ended very early in development. Young adults were considered to possess all the neurons they would ever have. It was believed that cells lost due to stroke, injury, or drug abuse could never be replaced. Although research as far back as 1965 challenged this belief, it was not until in the 1990s that a series of novel research findings clearly demonstrated that adults of many species, actually "grew" new neurons. For example, in 1992, Canadian researchers Sam Weiss and Brent Reynolds isolated neural stem cells in the brains of mice. The presence of stem cells in the brain was a novel and exciting finding because stem cells can differentiate into neurons. Additional research during this time showed neurogenesis in birds and these findings were later confirmed in adult humans. On-going research suggests that neurogenesis may occur in the hippocampus and certain other brain areas throughout adulthood. We still know very little about the functions and purpose of adult neurogenesis but the possibilities for the treatment of neurological disease are enormous if the process can be harnessed.

The role of neurogenesis in mental health has become a major research emphasis. One of the most exciting early developments in this research is the possible linkage between neurogenesis and depression. A number of studies have shown that various types of stress can suppress production of new neurons (Duman, 2009). Stress is also linked to depression, and there is evidence of reduced hippocampus size in depressed patients, which may indicate less neurogenesis (Jacobs, 2004). We noted earlier that antidepressant medication generally elevates levels of the neurotransmitter serotonin, and several studies now indicate that elevated serotonin levels increase neurogenesis. Importantly, it requires several weeks for new neurons to become integrated into functional neural pathways, and this corresponds well with the time course of antidepressant action. These drugs generally increase serotonin levels fairly rapidly, but it takes several weeks for the depression to lift, which suggests that it may be the increased birth of new neurons, rather than the elevation of serotonin itself, that is responsible for antidepressant action.

An additional area of research examines the role of recreational drugs in neurogenesis. While most drugs, such as opiates, alcohol, nicotine, and cocaine suppress neurogenesis, Canadian researcher Wen Jiang and colleagues (Jiang et al., 2005) report that cannabis promotes neurogenesis in the hippocampus of adult rats and produces antidepressant effects. Collectively, research into the role of neurogenesis in depression could lead to new and more effective treatments for this serious disorder (see Duman, 2009, for a review).

endorphins
Neurotransmitters in the brain that are mimicked by opiate drugs.

GABA
Short for gamma-aminobutyric acid; the most abundant inhibitory neurotransmitter in the brain.

glutamate
An excitatory amino acid neurotransmitter.

anandamide
A lipid neurotransmitter mimicked by marijuana.

Endorphins

During the late 1970s, compounds were discovered in mammalian brain tissue that were functionally similar to opiate drugs such as morphine and heroin. Unlike acetylcholine and the monoamines, these compounds were large molecules in the peptide family. Because they appeared to be, in effect, a naturally occurring morphine, they were named **endorphins**—a contraction of *endogenous morphine.* We now understand that the effects of opiate drugs are mediated through endorphinergic activity. The natural functions of the endorphins themselves are still far from clear but they certainly modulate pain relief. The endorphins are explained in more detail in Chapter 11.

Amino Acid Neurotransmitters

Two additional neurotransmitters are the amino acids gamma-aminobutyric acid, commonly referred to as **GABA**, and **glutamate**. GABA is among the most abundant of the known neurotransmitters in brain tissue, and it is the most significant inhibitory transmitter of the brain. That is, GABA opens negatively charged chloride ion channels that do not cause the neuron to fire but rather hyperpolarize the membrane and impede neural firing. If a neuron has a GABAergic receptor site that is activated, a larger quantity of the excitatory transmitter is required for the neuron to fire. A number of drugs act on the GABA system, including the classic depressant drugs: barbiturates, tranquilizers such as Valium (diazepam) and Xanax (alprazolam), and alcohol (see Figure 3.3). Glutamate is among the most abundant of the excitatory neurotransmitters and is known to be important in learning and memory processes. Canadian researchers have been exploring the role of glutamate in heart function (Gill, Veinot, Kavanagh, & Pulido, 2007), pain production (Castrillon et al., 2008), and spinal cord white matter (Ouardouz, Malek, Coderre, & Stys, 2006). Such research confirms the pervasive nature of glutamate in our bodies. Some hallucinogenic drugs (PCP and ketamine) act on glutamate receptors in some parts of the brain (see Chapter 10).

FIGURE 3.3 The roles of GABA and glutamate

You can remember the roles of glutamate and GABA by thinking of them as different lights on a traffic light. Glutamate, an excitatory neurotransmitter, acts like a "green" light by sending the message forward to another neuron. GABA is an inhibitory neurotransmitter, and acts like a "red" light because it stops the message.

Other Transmitters

The development of more sophisticated research techniques has led to the recognition that many more neurotransmitters await discovery. A thorough discussion of recent advances in neuropharmacology is beyond the scope of this text, but some developments have already had a substantial impact on our understanding of psychoactive drug actions. Indeed, many neurotransmitters have been discovered beyond those previously mentioned. We have much to learn about the brain's chemical code. Often the discovery of a new neurotransmitter increases our understanding of drug action. For example, one of the most recently discovered neurotransmitters is a lipid called **anandamide**. It is of considerable interest because the active chemical in marijuana appears to act by mimicking anandamide.

The Nervous System

We have been focusing on a microscopic view of the nervous system as we considered how drugs might act at the level of the single neuron. We now turn to the larger picture and consider a macroscopic view of the nervous system. The structure of the nervous system is outlined in Figure 3.4. The major distinction is between

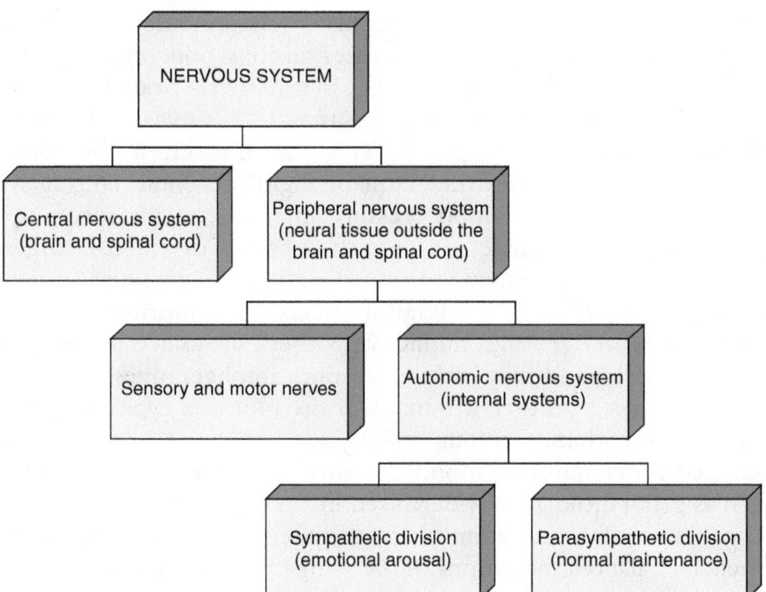

FIGURE 3.4
Organizational structure of the nervous system

central nervous system (CNS)
The brain and the spinal cord.

peripheral nervous system (PNS)
Sensory nerves, motor nerves, and the automatic nervous system.

the **central nervous system (CNS)** and the **peripheral nervous system (PNS)** (Figure 3.5). The CNS includes the brain and spinal cord. All nervous tissue outside (or peripheral to) the CNS is part of the PNS. The PNS includes nerves (nerves are simply bundles of axons) that send input from the senses to the brain (sensory nerves) and nerves that send output from the brain to muscles (motor nerves).

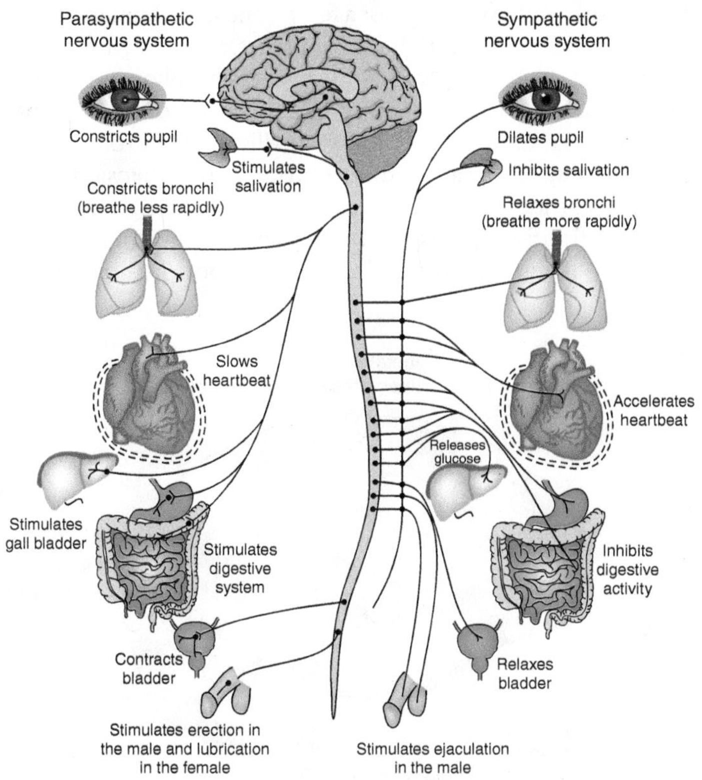

FIGURE 3.5
The parasympathetic and sympathetic nervous systems

Source: S. Rathus, S. Maheu, & S. Veenvliet. *PSYCH, 1e.* © 2012 Nelson Education Ltd. Reproduced by permission. www.cengage.com/permissions

autonomic nervous system (ANS)
Part of the PNS; it has two branches, the sympathetic and the parasympathetic.

sympathetic branch
Branch of the ANS that is activated during emotional arousal and is responsible for such physiological changes as increased heart and respiratory rate, increased blood pressure, and pupil dilation.

sympathomimetic
Drugs such as cocaine and amphetamines that produce the physiological effects of sympathetic activity.

beta-blockers
Drugs that block beta-adrenergic receptors of the sympathetic system and thus act to relieve high blood pressure.

parasympathetic branch
Branch of the ANS that is responsible for lowering heart rate and blood pressure.

The PNS also includes an important regulatory system known as the **autonomic nervous system (ANS)**. The ANS regulates various nonconscious or automatic functions and is divided into two parts. The **sympathetic branch** of the autonomic nervous system is activated during emotional arousal by a release of epinephrine and norepinephrine from the adrenal glands. This branch is responsible for the physiological changes that characterize the "fight-or-flight" reaction. During sympathetic arousal, heart rate increases, blood pressure increases, respiratory rate increases, sweating increases, pupils dilate, the mouth becomes dry, and changes occur in blood flow as blood is shunted away from the internal organs and to the brain and large muscle groups. These physiological effects are important to keep in mind because some psychoactive drugs mimic sympathetic arousal. Such drugs are said to be **sympathomimetic**, and they include cocaine, amphetamines, and some hallucinogens such as LSD. Another group of drugs blocks a type of norepinephrine receptor in the sympathetic nervous system called "beta-noradrenergic" receptors. These beta receptors regulate blood pressure, and the so-called **beta-blockers** (drugs such as propranolol) are widely used in the treatment of hypertension.

The other branch of the autonomic nervous system is the **parasympathetic branch**, which in general balances the actions of the sympathetic branch by exerting opposite effects. Parasympathetic activity reduces heart rate, blood pressure, and so on. In contrast to sympathetic neurons, parasympathetic synapses are primarily cholinergic.

The Brain

The complexity of billions of neurons and more billions of synapses is absolutely staggering and almost beyond comprehension.

The key organ of the nervous system is the brain (see Figure 3.6). Covered with tough membranes called the *meninges*, the brain floats within the skull in a liquid known as cerebrospinal fluid. Although weighing just a few pounds, the human brain is an extremely complex structure. We have just examined the processes involved when a single neuron fires. Now consider that the human brain contains literally billions and billions of neurons. Many of the brain's neurons synapse with several thousand other neurons because of an elaborate branching of axons. The complexity of billions of neurons and more billions of synapses is absolutely staggering and almost beyond comprehension. Despite the enormity of the task, great strides have been made in understanding how this most complex of organs works. One fruitful approach is to consider the different parts of the brain separately in an attempt to determine their individual functions (Figure 3.6).

FIGURE 3.6
Functions of the brain

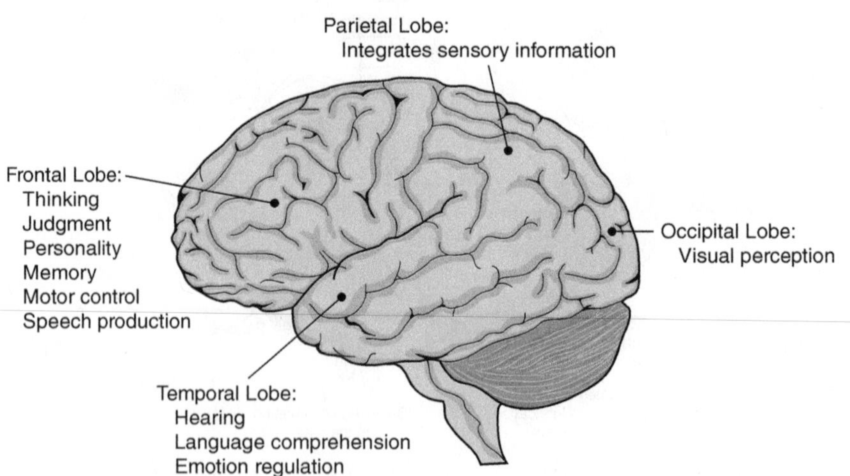

The major divisions of the human brain are the **hindbrain**, **midbrain**, and **forebrain**. If a voyage through the brain began at the spinal cord and moved up, the first part of the brain encountered would be the hindbrain.

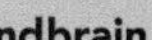

hindbrain
The lower part of the brain, including the medulla, pons, and cerebellum.

midbrain
Part of the brain that includes the inferior and superior colliculi and the substantia nigra.

forebrain
The largest part of the human brain; includes the cerebral cortex, thalamus, hypothalamus, and limbic system.

The Hindbrain

The hindbrain consists of three main components: the **medulla oblongata**, the **cerebellum**, and the **pons**. The medulla is located just above (and is really a slight enlargement of) the spinal cord. A highly significant structure for the regulation of basic life functions, the medulla controls breathing, heart rate, vomiting, swallowing, blood pressure, and digestive processes. Normal functioning of the medulla is critical, and when drugs begin to affect the medulla, the person is often in danger due to respiratory or cardiovascular failure. When toxic chemicals reach high levels in this area, the vomit centre is often triggered to purge the body, which may be why drinking large quantities of alcohol often causes nausea and vomiting. Farther up the hindbrain is an enlarged section called the pons. In addition to providing the pathways for input up and output down from the spinal cord, the pons plays a role in the control of sleep and wakefulness. Running along the pons and through the medulla is a pathway known as the **reticular activating system**, which is critical for alertness and arousal. Drugs that lower arousal and induce sleep (such as barbiturates and tranquilizers) are thought to act in this region of the brain.

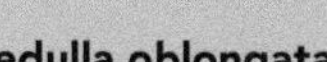

medulla oblongata
The lowest hindbrain structure of the brain; important in the regulation of breathing, heart rate, and other basic life functions.

cerebellum
Hindbrain structure important in motor control and coordination.

pons
Hindbrain structure important in the control of sleep and wakefulness.

reticular activating system
Pathway running through the medulla and pons that regulates alertness and arousal.

The cerebellum, the last major organ of the hindbrain, is a highly complex structure containing several billion neurons itself. The cerebellum is critical for motor control. Activities of the cerebellum are largely unconscious but do involve balance, coordinated movement of all kinds, and speech. The loss of motor control and balance produced by drugs such as alcohol may be caused by their action on the cerebellum.

The Midbrain

The midbrain consists of a number of structures, including the **inferior colliculi**, the **superior colliculi**, and the **substantia nigra**. The inferior colliculi form part of the auditory system. The superior colliculi function in localization of visual stimuli. These structures are specifically involved with localization of stimuli and mediation of reflexes. The actual recognition and interpretation of visual and auditory stimuli take place elsewhere in the brain (see the section on the cerebral cortex).

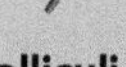

inferior colliculi
Midbrain structures that control sound localization.

superior colliculi
Midbrain structures that control visual localization.

substantia nigra
Literally "black substance," this basal ganglia structure is darkly pigmented; produces dopamine. Damage to this area produces Parkinson's disease.

Parkinson's disease involves damage to the substantia nigra and the nigrostriatal motor pathway. Specifically, Parkinson's disease develops when nerve cells in this brain region begin to degenerate. The substantia nigra produces dopamine, which is transported through this motor pathway, and as the substantia nigra deteriorates, less and less dopamine is available for neurotransmission. Parkinson's symptoms do not appear until about 80 percent of the substantia nigra is destroyed. Although the causes of Parkinson's disease are not completely understood, some toxins, including some "designer drugs," appear to be capable of killing neurons in the substantia nigra and triggering the disorder.

The Forebrain

The Thalamus and Hypothalamus

The most important brain regions from the perspective of interpreting complex human behaviour are in the forebrain, particularly the cortex, but also including the

thalamus
Forebrain structure that organizes sensory input.

hypothalamus
Forebrain structure that regulates eating, drinking, and other basic biological drives.

thalamus and **hypothalamus**. The thalamus is often referred to as a relay station because it receives incoming sensory stimuli and then "relays" that information to relevant centres throughout the brain. The hypothalamus is a critical structure in the motivation of behaviour. It contains areas that appear to be involved in the regulation of eating and drinking, and the control of body temperature, aggression, and sexual behaviour. Worth noting is that information about the particular function of a given brain region has not been easily determined and remains somewhat controversial. Historically, the methods for analyzing brain structures were primarily lesions and stimulation. Lesioning a structure involves performing surgery on an animal subject and causing localized damage to the structure in question. When the animal has recovered from surgery, changes in behaviour are then attributed to the damaged structure. For example, lesions in one part of the hypothalamus result in greatly reduced food intake, whereas if another part is damaged, overeating and obesity occur. Thus, the hypothalamus contains at least two sites that appear to be important in the regulation of food intake. One area seems to inhibit eating (because its loss results in overeating) and the other seems to excite hunger (because its loss results in less eating). The effects of electrical stimulation of a brain region generally are the opposite of the effects of lesioning or removing that region.

A note of caution accompanies these findings. When cells in the brain are lesioned or stimulated the effects extend beyond those specific cells, and indeed entire pathways may become damaged or stimulated. Thus, rather than speaking of the hunger or satiety *centres*, a more appropriate term is hunger or satiety *pathways*. However, even this may be an oversimplification because some researchers have noted that the role of these pathways may not be as specific to hunger as we first thought. That is, these pathways could affect motor movements, the sensation of taste, or more general motivational variables, and much current research is devoted to these effects. However, there is general agreement that the hypothalamus is an important structure in the regulation of hunger, thirst, and other basic biological motives (Carlson, 2008).

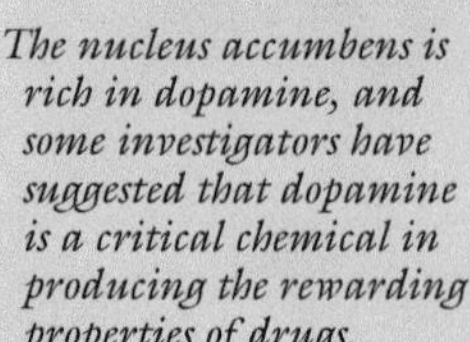

The nucleus accumbens is rich in dopamine, and some investigators have suggested that dopamine is a critical chemical in producing the rewarding properties of drugs.

The Neural Basis of Reward

Despite the difficulties of such research, electrical stimulation of brain regions led to one of the most significant discoveries in the quest to understand the relationship of brain, behaviour, and drugs. During the 1950s, the psychologist James Olds was trying to map the effects of stimulation on the rat brain by implanting electrodes into various regions. The rat seemed to enjoy the electrical stimulation in some areas of the brain. Here is how Olds describes his serendipitous discovery:

> I applied a brief train of 60-cycle sine wave electrical current whenever the animal entered one corner of the enclosure. The animal did not stay away from the corner, but rather came back quickly after a brief sortie which followed the first stimulation and came back even more quickly after a briefer sortie which followed the second stimulation. By the time the third electrical stimulus had been applied the animal seemed indubitably to be "coming back for more". (Carlson, 2001, p. 457)

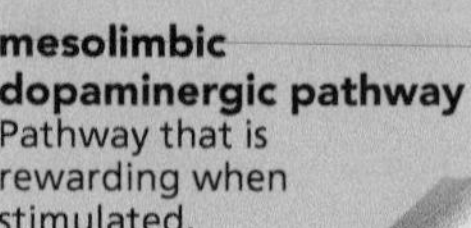

mesolimbic dopaminergic pathway
Pathway that is rewarding when stimulated.

Following up on this finding, Olds and Milner (1954) discovered that when electrodes are implanted in some brain areas, particularly in a region called the **mesolimbic dopaminergic pathway**, rats could actually be trained to press a lever to electrically stimulate themselves. The mesolimbic dopaminergic pathway includes a small subcortical area called the nucleus accumbens and travels through the ventral tegmental area all the way to the frontal cortex. When rats have been trained to self-stimulate this area, they often respond with great vigour (more than 1000 responses per hour), and the potency of the reinforcement related to this

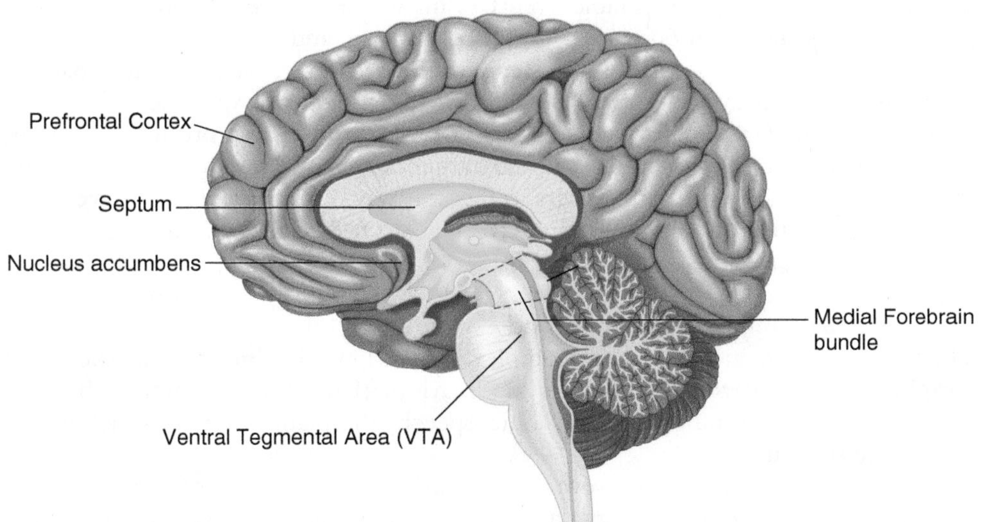

FIGURE 3.7 The reward circuit

From KALAT. *Biological Psychology, 10E*. © 2009 Wadsworth, a part of Cengage Learning, Inc. Reproduced by permission. www.cengage.com/permissions

centre led Olds and others to refer to it as the "pleasure centre." The notion is that the region may represent the final common pathway for pleasurable stimulation and reward (see Figure 3.7 above). It has been argued, too, that this brain region is of significance in understanding the rewarding properties of drugs. The nucleus accumbens is rich in dopamine, and some investigators have suggested that dopamine is a critical chemical in producing the rewarding properties of drugs (Koob & Le Moal, 2006; Nestler, 2009). Indeed, some have viewed this region of the brain as critical to drug addiction: "There is now a wealth of evidence that [the mesolimbic dopaminergic pathway] is a crucial substrate for the acute rewarding effects of virtually all drugs of abuse and for the derangements in reward mechanisms that contribute to drug addiction" (Nestler, 2009, p. 777). As Dackis and Gold (1985) once put it, addicts can be seen as individuals who have "tampered chemically with endogenous systems of reward and lost control of this shortcut to pleasure" (p. 476). Figure 3.8 illustrates the way drugs can affect the brain.

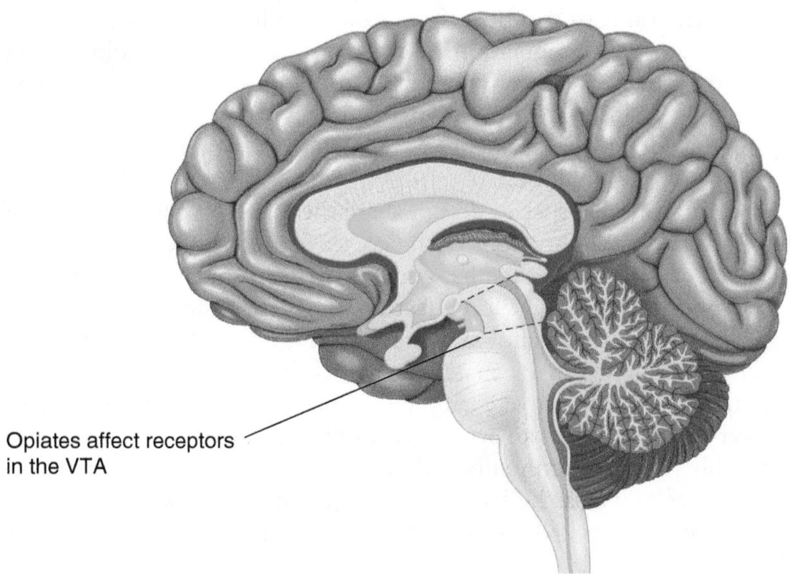

FIGURE 3.8 How drugs affect the brain

From KALAT. *Biological Psychology, 10E*. © 2009 Wadsworth, a part of Cengage Learning, Inc. Reproduced by permission. www.cengage.com/permissions

It is true that many pleasurable events result in the release of dopamine in this pathway—good-tasting food (especially chocolate), sex, and indeed many drugs such as cocaine, heroin, and nicotine (Goldstein, 2001). However, the idea that dopamine release in this pathway always translates into the psychological experience of pleasure appears to be an oversimplification. For example, events that are surprising or arousing but not especially pleasurable (like an electrical shock) seem to release dopamine in the nucleus accumbens, so perhaps activity in this pathway reflects events that have motivational significance or are "attention-getters" (Baron & Galizio, 2005; Berridge & Robinson, 1998; Martin-Soelch et al., 2001).

limbic system
Forebrain structures including the amygdala and hippocampus.

basal ganglia
Forebrain structures important for motor control, including the caudate nucleus, the putamen, and the globus pallidus.

cortex
The outermost and largest part of the human brain.

hippocampus
A structure of the limbic system thought to be important in the formation of memories.

The Limbic System, Basal Ganglia, and Cerebral Cortex

The forebrain also includes three complex systems: the **limbic system**, the **basal ganglia**, and the **cortex**. The aspects of behaviour that are most uniquely human, such as complex reasoning, memory, logic, speech, and planning, are largely derived from these structures.

The limbic system includes several structures in the interior of the forebrain. One limbic structure, the amygdala, seems to be important in mediating certain types of aggression, fear, and other emotional experiences. Another important limbic structure is the **hippocampus**, which appears to be critical in memory storage. People with damage to the hippocampus can remember things that occurred in their lives prior to the damage but, for the most part, are unable to store new memories. In other words, their long-term memories are intact, but they have difficulty in forming new permanent memories. The basal ganglia include the caudate nucleus, the putamen, and the globus pallidus. These structures are critical for motor movements.

One feature that distinguishes the human brain from those of most other animals is the greatly enlarged cerebral cortex. Indeed, many of the complex psychological functions that are characteristically human are thought to involve the cortex. Figure 3.6 shows the lobes of the cerebral cortex. The occipital lobe is at the back of the brain and is often referred to as the visual projection area. Stimulation of the eye is eventually perceived as a visual stimulus when the signal reaches the occipital cortex. The temporal lobe is similarly specialized for auditory stimulation and also appears to be important in language. Damage to the left temporal lobe results in severe impairment of language abilities (at least for most right-handed individuals). Right temporal lobe damage often results in dysregulation of emotions. This relationship between right and left temporal lobe mediation of language and emotions is reversed in some cases (e.g., left-handed individuals). The frontal lobe is important in the initiation of movement and is involved with emotionality, intelligence, and personality. Tactile stimuli are registered in the parietal lobe.

Some researchers have suggested that frontal lobe abnormalities may be caused by exposure to some drugs of abuse such as cocaine.

Because most nonhuman species do not share the enlarged cortex of humans, using animal models to study the functions of the cortex is more difficult. Much of what we know about the cerebral cortex then has come from unfortunate accidents and diseases such as strokes and tumours, which in effect produce lesions in the patient's brain that may result in some loss of psychological function. Upon autopsy, the nature of the psychological impairment can be matched to the site of the damage. For example, consider the tragic but instructive example of Phineas Gage. Gage was a 25-year-old railroad worker in 1848, when an accidental explosion drove an iron rod through his head. Remarkably, Gage not only survived but after a recovery period was able to walk, talk, and remember as well as he had before the accident. It was clear, however, that Gage's personality had changed. His friends said that he was no longer himself. Before the accident, he was regarded as a mild-mannered, well-adjusted, friendly man, but his brain damage left him impulsive, ill-tempered, and unreliable. He was apparently unable to execute or stick to even the simplest plans. His skull was preserved, and nearly a century and a half later, a reconstruction of the trajectory of the rod showed that the likely area of damage was the frontal lobe, which is now recognized to be important in the ability to plan, to control impulses, and generally to consider the long-term consequences of behaviour (Damasio, 1994). Some researchers have suggested that frontal lobe abnormalities may be caused by exposure to some drugs of abuse such as cocaine (e.g., Kalivas & Volkow, 2005).

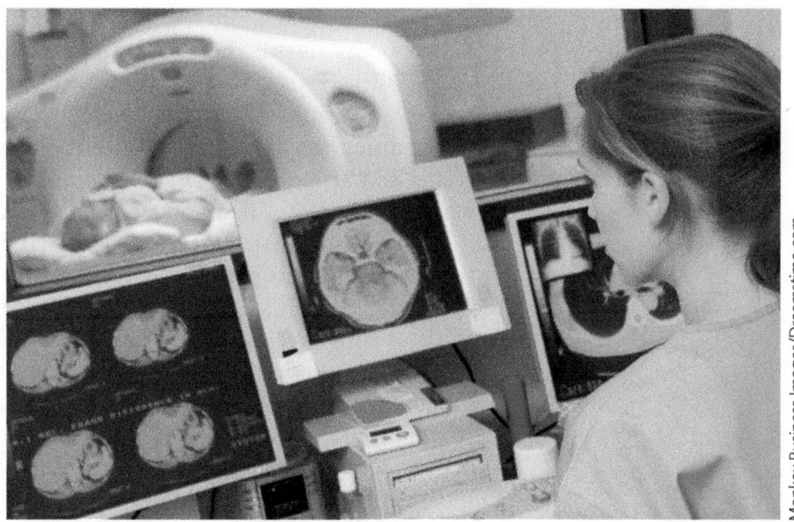

Monkey Business Images/Dreamstime.com

A technician monitors a patient during a CAT scan.

Imaging the Human Brain

Although much of what we know about the brain comes from a combination of research with animals and autopsy data from humans, new imaging technologies in recent years have opened new windows on the human brain. These technologies are teaching us much about the functional neuroanatomy of the normal brain. They also provide us with more sophisticated answers to questions that come up whenever chronic effects of drugs are discussed: the issue of drug-induced brain damage. We discuss this problem throughout the text as we consider individual drugs, but now, after this lengthy discussion of the brain, a few general comments are warranted. Detecting brain damage caused by drugs is often very difficult. Rarely do psychoactive drugs produce such dramatic long-term effects as those seen with Phineas Gage, for example, so we must rely on specialized methods to determine whether damage has occurred. Various neuropsychological tests are available that can be used to detect impairment in memory, perceptual motor skills, language, and other functions that may be influenced by chronic drug use. More direct analysis of brain tissue may be accomplished through **electroencephalography (EEG)**. This technique involves measuring the brain's electrical activity through the scalp. These brain waves change in predictable ways with sleep or various kinds of arousal, and abnormalities in EEG patterns can reveal gross brain damage.

electroencephalography (EEG)
Technique used to measure electrical activity in the brain.

computerized axial tomography (CT)
Technique that produces a three-dimensional X-ray image of the brain.

A more recently developed and more sensitive measure of brain impairment is **computerized axial tomography**, better known as the CT or CAT scan. The CT scan involves passing X-rays through the head in a circular pattern to get a three-dimensional image of the brain. The focus can be changed to different depths of the brain to detect internal tumours, enlarged spaces or ventricles, and other internal abnormalities.

CT scans provide a picture of the brain but reveal nothing about its functioning. However, a technique called the PET scan may greatly increase our ability to detect brain activity. **Positron emission transaxial tomography (PET)** involves injecting

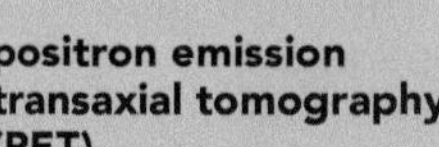

positron emission transaxial tomography (PET)
Technique used to measure activity in selected brain regions.

weak radioisotopes into the brain. Radioactive glucose or oxygen or even radioactive neurochemicals are then measured by sensitive detectors that can determine where the isotopes are absorbed, their rate of absorption, and so on. Then changes in activity in various brain regions can be assessed, including changes induced by drugs. Techniques like the PET scan and the closely related SPECT (single photon emission computed tomography) scan promise to greatly increase our ability to determine where in the brain damaging drugs produce their effects.

magnetic resonance imaging (MRI) Technique that creates a high-resolution, three-dimensional image of the brain.

Another sophisticated and sensitive technique used to image the brain is **magnetic resonance imaging (MRI)**. With this technique, a strong magnetic field is passed through a person's head. Radio waves are then generated, which cause the molecules of the brain to emit energy of different frequencies, depending on their properties. This technique creates a localized and detailed brain image and eventually may greatly improve our ability to detect and understand brain dysfunction (Uttal, 2001). A modification of MRI technology called functional MRI (fMRI) has been developed; fMRI permits very rapid imaging and enables us to measure oxygen levels in blood vessels of the brain. Oxygen levels are correlated with the metabolism of a particular brain region and are taken as an index of brain activity in that region. Thus, fMRI images obtained while a subject is engaged in some psychological activity (e.g., doing mental arithmetic) can be used to make inferences about the brain regions that were most active during the activity. These various imaging techniques are increasingly being used to learn about the neural mechanisms of drug action and dependence (see Contemporary Issue Box 3.2) and to evaluate changes in the brain after long-term exposure to drugs.

CONTEMPORARY ISSUE BOX 3.2

Drug Craving and the Brain

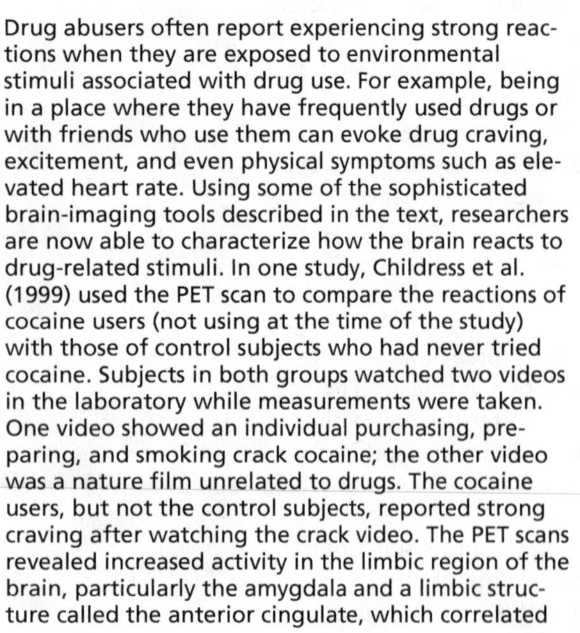

Drug abusers often report experiencing strong reactions when they are exposed to environmental stimuli associated with drug use. For example, being in a place where they have frequently used drugs or with friends who use them can evoke drug craving, excitement, and even physical symptoms such as elevated heart rate. Using some of the sophisticated brain-imaging tools described in the text, researchers are now able to characterize how the brain reacts to drug-related stimuli. In one study, Childress et al. (1999) used the PET scan to compare the reactions of cocaine users (not using at the time of the study) with those of control subjects who had never tried cocaine. Subjects in both groups watched two videos in the laboratory while measurements were taken. One video showed an individual purchasing, preparing, and smoking crack cocaine; the other video was a nature film unrelated to drugs. The cocaine users, but not the control subjects, reported strong craving after watching the crack video. The PET scans revealed increased activity in the limbic region of the brain, particularly the amygdala and a limbic structure called the anterior cingulate, which correlated with cocaine craving. That is, the cocaine users exhibited limbic activity while watching the crack video but not the nature video.

The nonusers did not show limbic activation during either video. Subsequent studies have replicated these findings with fMRI technology (Wexler et al., 2001) and shown similar patterns of brain activity when alcoholics and cigarette smokers experience craving as well (Lim et al., 2005; Myrick et al., 2004). Brain-imaging techniques have the potential to identify the brain regions involved with the psychological experiences, such as craving, that are thought to be important aspects of drug dependence. These techniques may also be useful in examining ways to minimize or eliminate the cravings for drugs and thereby prevent drug dependence. For example, Canadian researchers from the University of British Columbia have found a way for the brain to "forget" previous drug experience and craving (NeuroScience Canada, 2005). In the future we could use brain-imaging techniques to examine how the brain functions when drug cravings are blocked.

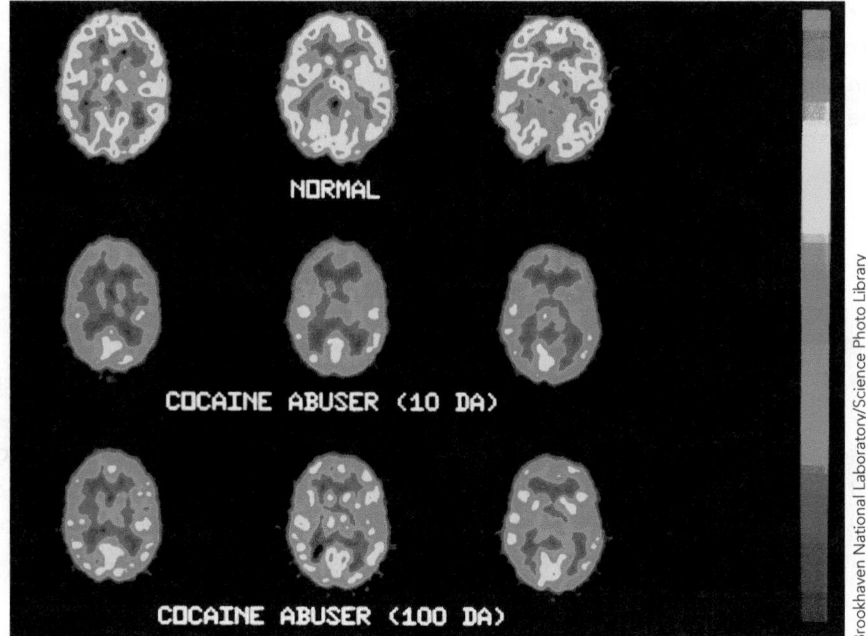

Cocaine use. Positron emission tomography (PET) scans that have been colour-coded to show brain metabolism and the effects of cocaine use. Each brain scan is axial (horizontal) with the front of the brain at top. Three scans at different levels were obtained through a normal, cocaine-free brain (top), the brain of a cocaine user ten days after the last cocaine dose (middle) and 100 days after the last dose (bottom). Metabolism ranges from low (dark to light blue) to high (yellow to red). The long-term recovery period is demonstrated, as well as the poorer recovery of the front of the brain. Results presented by Nora Volkow.

SUMMARY

- All psychoactive drugs produce their effects by action on the nervous system—primarily by altering normal brain function.
- The brain is composed of specialized cells called neurons. Neurons transmit information by conducting electrical currents along their axons and releasing chemical substances called neurotransmitters into the synapse. Most drugs act by altering this chemical phase of neural transmission.
- Neurotransmitters work through a lock–key mechanism. The transmitter substance is like a key, and specialized areas on the neuron, called receptor sites, are like locks. Neurotransmitter chemicals must occupy the receptor sites for the neuron to fire.
- Drugs alter neural transmission in several ways. For example, a drug may mimic a natural or endogenous neurotransmitter by activating receptor sites. Alternatively, a drug may block a receptor site. Drugs can also affect the deactivation or release of neurotransmitters.
- Dozens of different chemicals have been proposed to act as neurotransmitters in the human brain; several are known to be related to drug effects. These include acetylcholine, anandamide, dopamine, endorphins, GABA, glutamate, norepinephrine, and serotonin.
- The nervous system is divided into two main sections. The central nervous system includes the brain and spinal cord. The peripheral nervous system includes the sensory nerves, motor nerves, and the autonomic nervous system.
- The autonomic nervous system is divided into two branches. The sympathetic branch produces the physiological effects that accompany emotional arousal, and the parasympathetic branch controls the body when at rest.
- For convenience of description, the brain is divided into three divisions: the hindbrain, the midbrain, and the forebrain.

- The evolutionarily primitive hindbrain includes the medulla, the pons, and the cerebellum.
- The midbrain includes the superior and inferior colliculi and the substantia nigra.
- The forebrain includes the cerebral cortex, the thalamus, the hypothalamus, the basal ganglia, and the limbic system.

Key Terms

acetylcholine p. 44
action potential p. 41
agonist p. 45
Alzheimer's disease p. 46
anandamide p. 50
antagonist p. 45
autonomic nervous system (ANS) p. 52
axon p. 41
axon terminals (or terminal buttons) p. 42
basal ganglia p. 56
beta-blockers p. 52
blood–brain barrier p. 48
central nervous system (CNS) p. 51
cerebellum p. 53
computerized axial tomography (CT) p. 57
cortex p. 56
dendrites p. 41
dopamine p. 47
electroencephalography (EEG) p. 57
endorphins p. 50
enzyme breakdown p. 44
forebrain p. 53
GABA p. 50
glutamate p. 50
hindbrain p. 53
hippocampus p. 56
hypothalamus p. 54
inferior colliculi p. 53
L-dopa p. 47
limbic system p. 56
magnetic resonance imaging (MRI) p. 58
medulla oblongata p. 53
mesolimbic dopaminergic pathway p. 54
midbrain p. 53
monoamines p. 47
myelin p. 41
neuromuscular junction p. 46
neurons p. 41
neurotransmitters p. 42
norepinephrine p. 47
parasympathetic branch p. 52
Parkinson's disease p. 47
peripheral nervous system (PNS) p. 51
pons p. 53
positron emission transaxial tomography (PET) p. 57
receptor sites p. 43
reticular activating system p. 53
reuptake p. 44
serotonin p. 47
substantia nigra p. 53
superior colliculi p. 53
sympathetic branch p. 52
sympathomimetic p. 52
synapse p. 42
thalamus p. 54
vesicles p. 43

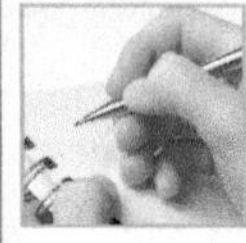

Essays/Thought Questions

1. Drugs produce psychological effects by altering the chemical activity of neurons. What implications does this mechanism have for the traditional distinction between mind and body?
2. Should addiction be viewed as a brain disease? Consider the implications of drug actions on the mesolimbic dopaminergic pathway.

Suggested Readings

Iversen, L.L., Iversen, S.D., Bloom, F.E., and Roth, R.H. (2009). *Introduction to neuropsychopharmacology*. New York: Oxford University Press.

Charney, D.S., & Nestler, E.J. (Eds.) (2008). *Neurobiology of mental illness* (3rd ed.). New York: Oxford University Press.

CHAPTER 4

Pharmacology

Did You Know

?

- The safest way to take a drug is orally, but that is the slowest way of getting the drug into the blood.
- All psychoactive drugs reach the brain tissue through the bloodstream.
- The body tries to protect the brain from toxic substances.
- The Canadian Human Rights Commission's Policy on Alcohol and Drug Testing provides specific guidelines for occupational alcohol and drug testing.
- Over 300 000 people in Canada are infected with a blood-borne disease (such as Hep-C or HIV). Approximately 70 percent of those infected are stated to be from a result of intravenous drug use.
- Alcohol is more lethal (toxic) than many other commonly abused drugs.
- When more than one drug is taken at a time, the effects of one can enhance or diminish the effects of the other(s).

The aim of this chapter is to cover the basic principles and methods of pharmacology that apply to the description and evaluation of all drugs. We will elaborate on an idea we first mentioned in Chapter 1—the drug experience, or a person's perception of the effects of a drug. A series of interrelated factors contributes to a given drug effect. The importance of any one factor or set of factors for a given drug-taking occasion depends on the importance of the other factors. This idea sounds complicated, and it is even more complicated to analyze in practice. To evaluate the importance or contribution of any one factor to a drug effect or experience, researchers must comprehend, or at least somehow control, the effects of other relevant factors.

feedback
In this context, in a series of events, what happens in a later event alters events that preceded it.

absorbed
When drugs have entered the bloodstream.

metabolism
The process by which the body breaks down matter into more simple components and waste.

distribution
The transport of drugs by the blood to their site(s) of action in the body.

To simplify, we will explain the path of the drug experience from beginning to end as if it were a logical and linear route. That analogy is flawed, however, because not only are the contributory factors of a drug effect interdependent, but **feedback** relationships may also occur among those factors. For example, a large quantity of some drug may be taken and **absorbed** into the blood. Then the drug is carried to its site of action (distributed). In some cases, a large quantity of a drug may cause the body to slow absorption or quicken **metabolism** of the drug to defend itself against a toxic drug effect. In this event, the **distribution** of the drug is information that the body "feeds back" to its regulators of absorption and metabolism to, in effect, reduce the drug quantity.

Table 4.1 lists the path of the drug experience. For each of the "steps" in the table, there may be two or more factors to consider. By the end of this chapter, you will begin to understand the great complexity of what humans experience when they take drugs.

pharmacokinetics
The branch of pharmacology that concerns the absorption, distribution, biotransformation, and excretion of drugs.

When considering pharmacology, there are two important factors: pharmacokinetics and pharmacodynamics. **Pharmacokinetics** concerns "the absorption, distribution, biotransformation, and excretion of drugs" (Benet, Mitchell, & Sheiner, 1990a, p. 1). Drug absorption and distribution are essential for determining how much drug reaches its sites of action and therefore its effects. Absorption and distribution are key factors in the drug experience (see Step 4 in Table 4.1).

Once in the body, drugs do not stay forever. The basics of how the body eliminates drugs and how that is studied are also covered in this chapter. Knowing about drug excretion or elimination is required for learning the effect a drug will have after it enters the body.

pharmacodynamics
The branch of pharmacology that concerns the biochemical and physiological effects of drugs and their mechanisms of action.

Pharmacodynamics is the study of the "biochemical and physiological effects of drugs and their mechanisms of action" (Benet et al., 1990a, p. 1). The neural mechanisms of drugs were discussed in Chapter 3. In this chapter, we introduce some of the language that pharmacologists use to describe drug effects and some ways that have been developed to depict them. Pharmacodynamics is relevant to the drug experience because this branch of pharmacology concerns the biological bases of observed drug effects.

TABLE 4.1 "Steps" in the Drug Experience

1. A drug of a specified chemical structure is present.
2. A certain quantity of this drug is measured.
3. This quantity of the drug is administered in one of a number of possible ways.
4. The drug is absorbed into the blood and distributed to site(s) of action.
5. Some pharmacological effect is produced.
6. In humans, a drug's pharmacological effects may be modified depending on characteristics of the person, such as genetic constitution, gender, age, personality, and drug tolerance.
7. The setting or context of drug use may also modify a drug's pharmacological effects.

Pharmacokinetics

We begin our overview of pharmacokinetics by describing how to specify and measure a given amount of a drug and how the drug gets into the body. The combination of drug and body chemistry determines the drug experience.

Drug Dose

You know from Chapter 1 that the effect of a drug depends most fundamentally on how much of the drug is taken (see Steps 1 and 2 in Table 4.1). A science about drugs relies on a standard way to determine drug quantities. How do pharmacologists compute drug dose? How is that quantity communicated? A drug's dose is computed according to a person's body weight. This is because heavier people have a greater volume of body fluid than lighter people do. Therefore, a given amount of a drug is less concentrated in the body of a heavier person and, similarly, at the site of drug action than it is in the body of a lighter person (White, 1991). As you will see later in this chapter, in general, the greater the drug concentration at a site, the greater the drug effect. Therefore, the amount of a drug that is administered has to be adjusted according to body weight to assure that the drug is given in equivalent strength (dose) to people who have different weights.

The first step is to determine the desired dose, expressed in milligrams of the drug per kilogram (mg/kg) of body weight. The next step is to weigh the person and record the weight in kilograms. With these two quantities, the amount of drug required for the desired dose is easily determined. For example, if the desired dose is 0.08 mg/kg and the person weighs 80 kg, the necessary amount is $0.08 \times 80 = 6.4$ mg of the drug (Leavitt, 1982).

Routes of Administration

In pharmacology, the "route of drug administration" may refer to either the site where a drug is taken or how a drug is taken.* The route of drug administration can strongly influence the effects that a drug has (see Step 3 in Table 4.1). No matter the route of administration, all psychoactive drugs reach the brain tissue through the bloodstream. In this section, we discuss eight administration routes. The three most common routes are oral, by injection, and by inhalation. Three other important routes are intranasal (sniffing), sublingual (under the tongue), and transdermal (through the skin).

ouh_desire/Shutterstock

Oral administration is regarded as the most common route of administration. It is usually the safest, most convenient, and most economical way to take a drug.

Oral

Oral administration (by mouth), or swallowing, is the route with which you probably are most familiar. Drugs taken orally are usually in the form of pills, capsules, powders, or liquids. Examples are the variety of headache medicines, cough syrups, and cold remedies available at any drugstore. Such accessible medications are

* Our discussion of routes of drug administration draws heavily from Benet, Mitchell, and Sheiner (1990a, 1990b); Brands et al. (1998); Jacobs and Fehr (1987); and Julien, Advokat, and Comaty (2008).

virtually always prepared for oral administration because it usually is the safest, most convenient, and most economical way to administer a drug.

When drugs are swallowed, they pass through the stomach and are absorbed primarily through the small intestine. This travel course affects both how fast a drug can register its effect physically and how much effect is registered. A major factor in determining the effect is how much food is in the digestive tract when the drug is taken. The presence of food delays the stomach from emptying and may dilute the concentration of a drug. The result: delayed absorption and a decrease in the maximum drug level achieved. People may notice this result when they compare drinking alcohol after eating a full meal to drinking on an empty stomach. Another point about oral administration is that food may encapsulate the drug so that it is passed out of the body in the feces. Finally, oral administration, even without the complications of food in the stomach, causes the drug to be absorbed into the blood more slowly than with other routes.

So, the relative safety and convenience of oral administration of drugs must be balanced against considerations of time to absorption and the maximum drug effect that can be reached with a particular drug dose. With some drugs, such as heroin, the stomach acids used in digestion actually break down the drug to some degree before it is absorbed into the blood. Once in the blood, the chemically altered drug is passed through the liver before it reaches the brain. Because the liver is the major site of the metabolization of most drugs, only a fraction of the drug dose actually reaches the brain. The outcome is a diminished drug effect. This is why heroin is much more effective when injected than when swallowed!

dissolved
When a drug changes from solid to liquid by mixing it with a liquid.

suspended
When a drug's particles are dispersed in solution but not dissolved in it.

Injection

There are three common routes of drug administration by injection. When drugs are taken using a needle and syringe, they are delivered directly to the bloodstream. Most commonly they are **dissolved** or **suspended** in some solution before injection. The three routes for administration by injection are intravenous, subcutaneous, and intramuscular.

Intravenous *Intravenous* means "into the veins," and therefore the effects can be immediate. A common street term for the route is "mainlining." The drug is injected in solution directly into the veins. As a result, intravenous administration is valuable in emergency medical situations, and doses can be precisely adjusted according to the person's response. In addition, irritating drugs can be taken intravenously because blood vessel walls are relatively insensitive and the drug is further diluted by blood.

Intravenous drug injection is associated with rapid drug effects, making it the preferred route of some drug abusers. Intravenous injection of drugs is considered dangerous because large quantities can reach the site(s) of action so quickly. The intravenous route is the one most highly associated with complications because large quantities of the drug quickly reach the site of action and it is possible to deliver extremely high concentrations of drugs this way.

Those who regularly take drugs like heroin or cocaine intravenously expect immediate and powerful drug effects. However, the risks of taking a drug intravenously, coupled with the

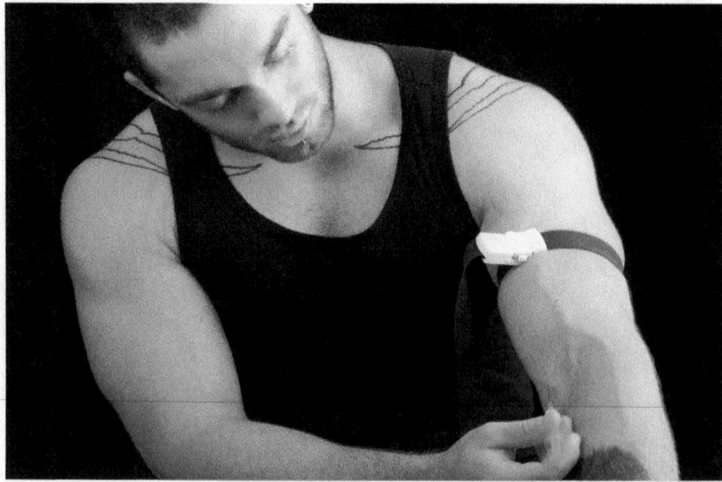

Intravenous drug injection is associated with rapid drug effects, making it the preferred route of some drug abusers. Intravenous injection of drugs is considered dangerous because large quantities can reach the site(s) of action so quickly.

assault that such drug taking has on the body, can be dangerous. Drug-induced deaths, intentional or not, are an ever-present danger among addicts and other nonmedical drug users who take their drugs intravenously.

Subcutaneous This route involves injecting the drug under the layers of the skin. It is the easiest of the injection routes to use because the target site of the needle is just below the skin surface. Many beginning drug abusers take their drugs subcutaneously. This route may also be preferred medically for drugs that are not irritating to body tissue because of the route's relatively slow (but faster than oral) and constant absorption rate. In fact, the solution in which the drug is administered may be selected to adjust the drug's absorption rate. A drug should not be taken subcutaneously when the drug irritates body tissue and when large volumes of solution must be taken to introduce enough of the drug to achieve the desired effect.

Intramuscular The name of this route means "within the muscle." Intramuscular injection requires a deeper penetration than the subcutaneous method but is associated with a faster absorption rate when the drug is prepared in a water solution and there is a good rate of blood flow at the site of administration. Absorption rates may differ depending on the rate of blood flow to the muscle group into which the drug is injected. In practice, the most common muscle sites are the deltoid, thigh, and buttocks. The absorption rate can also be modulated by the solution that the drug is prepared in for administration. One disadvantage is that intramuscular injection can result in localized pain (at the site of injection).

The critical point to consider when drugs are taken by injection is the concern about contracting AIDS, hepatitis, and tetanus (see Drugs and Culture Box 4.1).

DRUGS AND CULTURE BOX 4.1

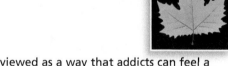

Needle Sharing and Blood-Borne Diseases

Intravenous (IV) drug use remains a risk factor for blood-borne diseases (BBDs). The reason the risk for BBDs is high among IV drug users is that they often share needles while taking drugs. The risk for contracting a BBD increases when one or more of the needle sharers are HIV- or Hepititis C-positive and the needle is not sterilized before being passed from person to person.

In Canada, approximately 250 000 people are infected with Hep-C and 65 000 with HIV. Surveillance reports estimate that 60 percent of Hep-C and 17 percent of HIV carriers were infected when injecting drugs (Public Health Agency of Canada, 2006). IV drug users may share needles for several reasons. It may be a simple matter of syringe availability. If few needles are around, then sharing becomes more likely. In this regard, the addicts' first priority is to get the drug into their body. A more entrenched and difficult-to-modify reason for needle sharing is that it may be part of local drug-taking social norms. Needle sharing is often part of socialization into the drug-taking subculture and has been viewed as a way that addicts can feel a sense of group belonging and friendship.

Canada's most common approach to combat the problem of HIV and Hep-C risk and needle sharing is needle exchange programs. In these programs addicts trade their used syringes for clean ones and they are educated on clean needle practices. Reviews of needle-exchange programs in Canada, the United States, and Europe show that addicts in these programs do less needle sharing and more often clean their syringes with bleach. In addition, needle exchange programs have not increased IV drug use where they have been implemented (Center for AIDS Prevention Studies, 1998; Rich et al., 2004).

Despite research evidence that needle exchange programs can make inroads into the risk of HIV, Hep-C, or IV drug use problems, such programs still are controversial in some parts of Canada. The controversy is rooted in the fear that free exchange of syringes without a physician's prescription will increase the spread of IV drug use. What would you consider the pros and cons of needle exchange programs in your city?

J&A Photography, 2009/Shutterstock.com

Probably the best-known way of inhaling a drug is taking nicotine by smoking cigarettes.

When any of the three injecting routes are used, the body's natural protections against microorganisms, such as skin and mucous membranes, are bypassed because delivery is directly into the bloodstream. Therefore, dirty needles or nonsterile solutions may carry illness-inducing microorganisms that the body cannot "screen out." This is why, for instance, street drug abusers who share their needles are at high risk for contracting AIDS or other blood-borne diseases.

Inhalation

Some drugs may be inhaled (such as smoking) and then absorbed through the lung's membranes. For such drugs, inhalation results in a fast and effective absorption. A drug has to be in one of a few states to be inhaled. Drugs that can be changed into gaseous states may be inhaled ("huffing"). For example, the vapours of substances such as gasoline and paint thinners may be inhaled. As we noted, inhaling a drug results in rapid and effective absorption. Blood leaving the lungs moves directly to the brain in only five to eight seconds. By contrast, blood from veins in the arm moves to the heart before it is pumped to the lungs before the brain.

Intranasal

In this route, a drug in powdered form is taken through the nose. The drug is then absorbed through the mucous membranes of the nose and the sinus cavities. Other terms for intranasal administration that you may have heard are *snorting* and *sniffing*. Examples of drugs commonly absorbed this way are cocaine, heroin, and powdered tobacco snuff. When a drug is fat soluble, sniffing is a rapid and effective way to absorb it. If a sniffed drug is irritating and disrupts blood flow, however, it can cause damage. An example that has been cited often is the damage that cocaine sniffing causes to the nasal septum and lining of the nose.

Sublingual

With this route, a drug tablet is placed under the tongue and dissolves in saliva. The drug is absorbed through the mouth's mucous membranes. Nitroglycerin, which is taken for treatment of angina pectoris (heart pain), is usually taken sublingually. Nicotine may be taken in the form of chewing tobacco or "dipping" snuff by the sublingual route.

The sublingual route results in faster and more efficient drug absorption than oral administration. It also is preferred to oral administration for drugs that irritate the stomach and cause vomiting. Almost any drug with the right chemical properties may be taken in pill form sublingually. However, this route is used less frequently than might be expected because of the unpleasant taste of many of the drugs that may be taken sublingually.

Transdermal

Some drugs may be taken transdermally, or "through the skin" (Wester & Maibach, 1983). The transdermal route actually is not an effective one for many drugs because the skin acts as a barrier to some chemicals and thus is relatively nonpermeable. For those drugs that more readily penetrate intact skin, absorption is better because the drug is applied to a wider area.

Drugs that penetrate the skin are absorbed better at sites that have a higher rate of cutaneous blood flow. In addition, a drug dose may be modified by mixing it with other substances, such as an oily preparation, to improve penetration at the site of administration.

Routes of drug administration should be thought of as ways to get drugs into the body, and they can have a considerable influence on the drug experience. Determining the preferred route depends on the drug administered, the goals of administration, and the advantages and disadvantages of using a particular route with a particular drug under particular circumstances.

Table 4.2 is a summary of general considerations in using the eight routes of drug administration that we have discussed. Table 4.3 is a summary of the routes typically used with drugs taken for medical and nonmedical reasons.

TABLE 4.2 General Considerations for the Eight Major Routes of Drug Administration

Route	Considerations
Oral	• Among the safest, most convenient, and most economical routes of administration. • Food in the stomach retards absorption or may diminish the amount of drug absorbed. • Stomach acids may break down some drugs, resulting in reduced drug effect.
Subcutaneous	• Easiest of the three injection routes to use. • Associated with absorption rates faster than oral administration but slower than intramuscular and intravenous routes. • Preferred for medical use of drugs that are not irritating to body tissue because of its relatively slow but constant absorption rate with sustained drug effects. • Should not be used when a drug irritates body tissue or when large volumes of solution must be used for taking the drug.
Intramuscular	• Requires deeper penetration of injection than subcutaneous but results in a faster absorption rate with proper preparation of solution and an injection site with good blood flow. • May be painful at the injection site. • Use by untrained people is associated with a high risk of infection from irritating drugs and tissue damage.
Intravenous	• Considered one of the fastest absorption rates. • Valuable for emergency medical needs because the resulting drug effects can be immediate. • Doses can be adjusted precisely according to the person's response because of immediacy of drug effects. • Better than subcutaneous or intramuscular routes for irritating drugs because blood vessel walls are relatively insensitive and the blood further dilutes the drug. • Danger in the potential for a large quantity of a drug to reach its site of action. • Repeated use requires maintenance of a healthy vein. • Drug dose must be administered gradually and the person's response monitored carefully to prevent serious complications.

(continued)

Inhalation	• When feasible, absorption is effective and the most rapid for some drugs. • Only a small amount of drug can be absorbed in any one administration.
Intranasal	• For a fat-soluble drug, absorption is rapid and effective. • Can cause damage when the drug is irritating or disrupts blood flow.
Sublingual	• May be used for many drugs in pill form. • Results in faster and more efficient absorption than oral administration. • Preferable to oral administration for drugs that irritate the stomach and cause vomiting. • Not used as often as it might be because of the unpleasant taste of many drugs.
Transdermal	• An alternative to the oral route when a drug may cause unwanted gastrointestinal effects. • Not used for many drugs because the skin is a relatively impenetrable barrier to many chemicals. • Resulting absorption is enhanced at sites that have greater cutaneous blood flow, and mixing a drug with another substance may improve penetration of the skin.

TABLE 4.3 Drugs Used for Medical and Nonmedical Reasons and Their Routes of Administration

Drug	Route
Alcohol	Oral
Amphetamines	Oral; intravenous (preferred by the chronic high-dose abuser); sniffed by occasional or new users
Barbiturates	Oral; rectal (through the mucous membrane of the rectum); subcutaneous; intramuscular; intravenous
Benzodiazepines	Most commonly oral; some intravenous or intramuscular
Caffeine	Most commonly oral; medically, occasionally by injection for mild stimulant properties; intravenous injection by abusers
Cannabis	Almost all routes; most commonly smoking (inhalation); injection not efficient because THC is not water-soluble
Cocaine	Cocaine hydrochloride is taken through nasal or other mucous membranes, such as those of the mouth, vagina, and rectum; also intravenous. Cocaine freebase (crack) is volatile and therefore most often vaporized in a freebase pipe and inhaled into the lungs
Heroin	Most commonly is dissolved in water and injected subcutaneously, intramuscularly, or intravenously; may be inhaled by smoking or sniffed
Nicotine	Inhaled by smoking (cigarettes); nicotine in cigar or pipe smoke mainly absorbed across membranes of the mouth and upper respiratory tract; may be absorbed through membranes of the mouth (chewing tobacco) and nose (snuff) and through the skin
LSD (lysergic acid diethylamide-25)	Oral; inhalation; the three injection routes; through the skin
MDA (methylenedioxy-amphetamine)	Most commonly oral
PCP (phencyclidine)	Oral; sniffed; inhalation by smoking (sprinkled on marijuana, parsley, tobacco, or other substance that can be smoked); intravenous injection

Drug Absorption

Absorption (of a drug into the bloodstream) may also be defined as the rate and extent to which a drug leaves its site of administration. This plays a major role in the drug experience. Absorption and the factors that affect it are extremely important because they influence **bioavailability**. Bioavailability is the portion of the original drug dose that reaches its site of action or that reaches a fluid in the body that gives the drug access to its site of action (Benet et al., 1990b). As such, the bioavailability of a drug tells us about its effects.

bioavailability
The portion of the original drug dose that reaches its site of action or that reaches a fluid in the body that gives it access to its site of action.

Differences among the routes in absorption rates are related to the factors that influence absorption in general. We cite a few major examples in the list below (Benet et al., 1990b; White, 1991).

- For all routes besides intravenous, the drug must pass through at least one body membrane before it can reach the circulatory system. Because membranes consist largely of lipids (fats), drugs that are more soluble in lipids are much more readily absorbed. Alcohol is an example of a drug that dissolves in lipids.
- Another factor is the form in which the drug is administered. Drugs taken in water solution are absorbed more rapidly than are drugs taken in suspension, in oily solution, or in solid form because they are dissolved more readily at the site of absorption. When a drug is taken in solid form, as aspirin is, for example, its solubility depends on conditions at the site of absorption. For instance, aspirin is fairly insoluble in the acidic environment of the stomach, and this places a limit on its absorbability. This point relates to the importance of the environment in the gastrointestinal system and its influence on the absorption of drugs that are taken orally, as we have discussed. Circulation at the site of absorption also influences it, as more blood flow speeds absorption.
- Finally, the size of the absorbing surface makes a difference. Drugs are absorbed more rapidly from larger surface areas.

Because each of these and other factors may singly or in combination affect absorption, you can see why it is so difficult to specify a drug effect for a person under specific conditions at a given time. Intravenous injection is typically the most efficient way to get a drug to its sites of action because it bypasses many factors that may slow absorption. It puts the drug in direct contact with the blood, which is the vehicle of drug distribution.

Drug Distribution

The biochemical properties of both the body and the drug have a lot to do with a drug's distribution to its sites of action. Because the blood transports a drug, it follows that regions of the body that receive the most blood get the most drug. Indeed the heart, brain, kidney, liver, and other systems that receive a lot of blood get major portions of the drug shortly after absorption. Other parts of the body that receive less blood flow, such as muscle, viscera, and fat, may take considerably longer to receive the drug. Besides blood flow, the **diffusibility** of membranes and tissues affects distribution—the more diffusible tissues receive the drug more rapidly.

diffusibility
The rate at which a substance enters the system or interacts with another substance.

Drug properties may influence distribution considerably. One such property is fat **solubility**. Drugs that are more soluble in lipids penetrate body membranes and therefore reach sites of action more easily than do less lipid-soluble drugs. The fat solubility of a drug also plays a role in how much of it can reach the brain.

solubility
The ease with which a compound can be dissolved or entered into a solution.

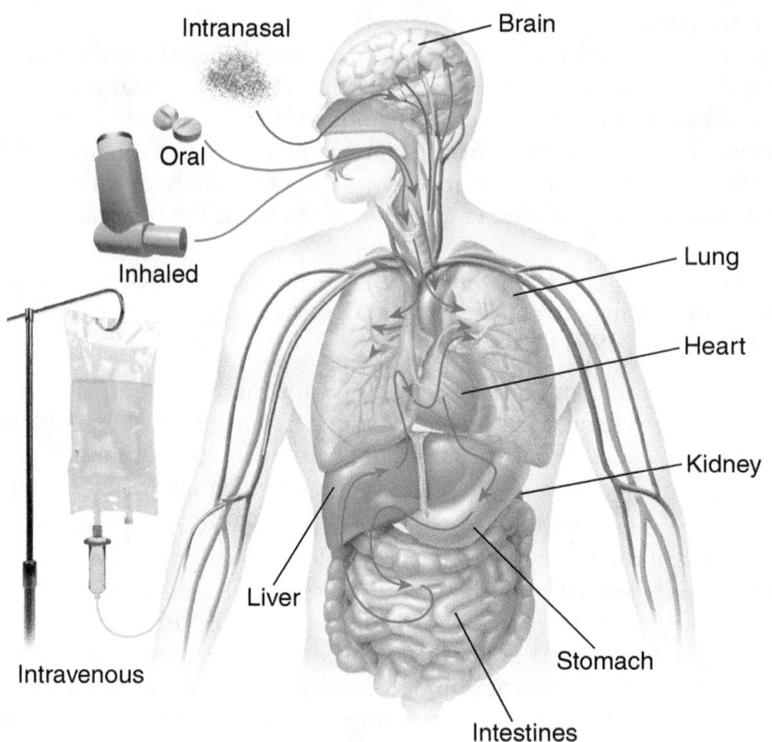

How drugs circulate through the body.

Although the blood flow to the brain makes it a natural repository for drugs (and other chemicals) that enter the body, substances must cross the blood–brain barrier before they can reach the brain. As noted in Chapter 3, the blood–brain barrier filters out toxins from the blood before they reach the brain. Pores of the capillary walls in the brain are small and close together, so they restrict the passage of substances through them. In addition, a thick wall of glial cells encloses the capillaries to form another line of defence. A drug that is highly fat-soluble, like the benzodiazepine diazepam (Valium), can easily pass through the capillary and glial cell membranes, but passage of less fat-soluble drugs is impeded (Johanson, 1992).

Another feature of a drug's chemistry that affects its distribution is whether it selectively binds to elements of the body. Some drugs, such as the barbiturates, may bind chemically to certain proteins in the plasma. The more "tightly" bound a drug is, the slower its distribution will be to sites of action (Benet et al., 1990b; Leavitt, 1982; White, 1991). Similarly, some drugs have an affinity for fatty tissue in the body. In this case, the drug may be released, but it can take a relatively long time. With such longer-term unbinding, the drug may remain in the blood for some time, yet the drug's release from fat tissues is slow enough that the psychoactive effects are negligible (White, 1991). A notorious example of a drug that has an affinity for fat is marijuana. Its distribution is uneven throughout the body because of selective binding, and the effects achieved by taking the drug are attenuated. Part of the dose does not immediately reach its sites of action.

In summary, the processes of drug absorption and distribution illustrate that a drug is a chemical that, when introduced into the body, disrupts its steady biochemical state. Absorption and distribution are the complex fundamentals of bioavailability. Bioavailability tells us most about drug effects. To understand the effects of a drug over time, it is essential to track its excretion or elimination from the body.

Drug Elimination

Drugs may be excreted from the body directly or first metabolized into water-soluble by-products that are less likely to be reabsorbed. The metabolic by-products are then excreted. Enzymes in the liver play the major part in drug metabolism. These enzymes also are present in other organs such as the kidneys and gastrointestinal (GI) tract. As a result, a drug administered orally is subject to a "first-pass effect," which means that enzymes in the GI tract break down a drug to some degree. Therefore, less drug than was administered is eventually distributed to its sites of action.

The kidney is by far the most important organ for excretion of both drugs and their metabolites, but excretion may occur in other ways as well. For example, drugs that are taken orally may be excreted directly in the feces. Drug metabolites may be excreted in liver bile. Drugs are excreted in mother's milk, which is not critical so much because of the proportion of drug that leaves the body this way but because of the dangers posed to the nursing infant. Drugs also may be excreted through the lungs, which is why you can smell alcohol on a person's breath after he or she drinks it. Finally, drugs may be excreted in perspiration.

Pharmacologists have discovered that the rate of elimination of drugs from the body obeys two general laws: zero-order kinetics and first-order kinetics (Clark, Brater, & Johnson, 1988). Zero-order kinetics means that the rate at which a drug is metabolized is independent of its concentration in the blood; a well-known example is alcohol (Julien, 1996). First-order kinetics means that the amount of drug that is metabolized in a unit of time depends on how much drug is in the blood. Most drugs obey the law of first-order kinetics. Knowledge of these laws is a great help to people who do research on drugs and to physicians when they prescribe medications.

Elimination half-life is the time that must pass for the amount of drug in the body to be cut by half. The rate of elimination can be important for the development of drug-testing procedures. Some drugs have a half-life of only a few hours (such as cocaine) while others have much longer half-lives (such as marijuana or prescription drugs).

elimination half-life
The amount of time that must pass for the amount of drug in the body to be reduced by half (50 percent).

Drug Testing

Discussing drug-elimination processes raises the topic of procedures that are used in drug testing. *Drug testing* is a term applied to various methods of determining drug use, most commonly by analyzing urine or blood samples. In recent years, drug testing by analysis of sweat, saliva, and hair samples has also been applied with increasing frequency as the technology for such application improves (Dolan, Rouen, & Kimber, 2004). Analysis of urine samples (urinalysis) remains the most commonly used method, in part because its technology is the best developed among the main methods, and its cost is relatively low. In addition, urinalysis is a sensitive method if samples are not adulterated, because a drug's metabolites may be detected in urine. If a drug is detected in the blood directly, it is an indication of recent use (Miller, 1991).

TABLE 4.4 Common Drugs of Abuse and Their Ranges of Elimination and Detection Times

Drug	Range of Elimination Times	Range of Detection Times (Days)
Alcohol	Hours	Up to 1
Cocaine	Hours to days	1–2
Marijuana	Weeks to months	2–8 (acute) 14–42 (chronic)
Benzodiazepines	Weeks	3–7
Opiates	Days to weeks	2–4
Barbiturates Amphetamines	Weeks Days to weeks	1–14 5–7 (or longer)

Note: Shorter time in the elimination range refers to the drug itself and longer time to the drug's metabolites.

Source: A. Verstraete. (2004). "Detection time of drugs of abuse in blood, urine, and oral fluids." *Therapeutic Drug Monitoring.* Vol. 26 (2), Pg. 200-205.

The validity of drug testing depends on factors such as the dose last taken of the drug, the testing method used, and the laboratory quality control procedures used in testing. The detectability of drug use is determined by the drug's clearance rates from the body and the clearance rates of the drug's metabolites. Table 4.4 above is a list of common drugs of abuse, their range of elimination times, and their range of detectability in days

DRUGS AND CULTURE BOX 4.2

Drug Testing in Canada

In Canada, drug testing is primarily used to reduce industrial or environmental accidents in the workplace. It is estimated that 10 percent of Canadian worksites (18 percent of BC worksites) have implemented drug testing programs (Macdonald, Csiernik, Durand, et al., 2006). The Canadian Human Rights Commission's Policy on Alcohol and Drug Testing (2002) provides their position on drug testing and related to guidelines for such testing in the workplace. The highlights of their position are outlined below.

The following types of testing are included for occupational purposes:

- Random alcohol testing of employees in safety-sensitive positions (i.e., those positions resulting in direct and significant risk of injury to employee, others, or environment)
- Drug or alcohol testing for "reasonable cause" or "post accident"
- Periodic or random testing following disclosure of a current drug or alcohol dependency or abuse
- Mandatory disclosure of present or past drug or alcohol dependency or abuse

The following types of testing *are not accepted* for occupational purposes:

- Pre-employment drug or alcohol testing
- Random drug testing
- Random alcohol testing of employees in non-safety-sensitive positions

Drug testing procedures remain controversial given the complications of the accuracy of drug testing procedures. Canada continues to research drug testing processes and improve the technology of drug testing by using biological samples. Urinalysis remains the most common biological test for detecting recent drug use; however, other technology, such as hair samples, needs further testing.

Do you think that drug testing should be conducted in the workplace? What might be some advantages and disadvantages of drug testing?

by testing of urine samples. The range of elimination times pertains to elimination of the drug itself (shorter time) and to elimination of the drug's metabolites (longer time) from the body. Alcohol has no range because its metabolites are used too efficiently in the body to be measured reliably (Miller, 1991).

Detection times are substantially longer if the drug's metabolites can be measured by the testing method. Note that the detection time ranges are generally much shorter than the elimination time ranges of drugs and their metabolites. This is because the testing method is not sensitive enough to pick up the metabolite(s) at some point. Where that point is depends on the metabolite and the testing method. Therefore, a positive drug test does not necessarily provide precise information about when the drug actually was used. The exception, as we noted, is that if the drug is detected in blood we then know that use was recent. Drug testing is a major social concern in the Canada and the United States because of the consequences to individuals in the workplace and other environments of confirmed illicit drug use.

Summary of Pharmacokinetics

Figure 4.1 summarizes the four steps of the drug experience and pharmacokinetics. A given quantity of a drug (dose) may be administered by one of several methods (routes of administration). The drug then leaves its site of administration (absorption) to be distributed to the sites of drug action. The route of administration and

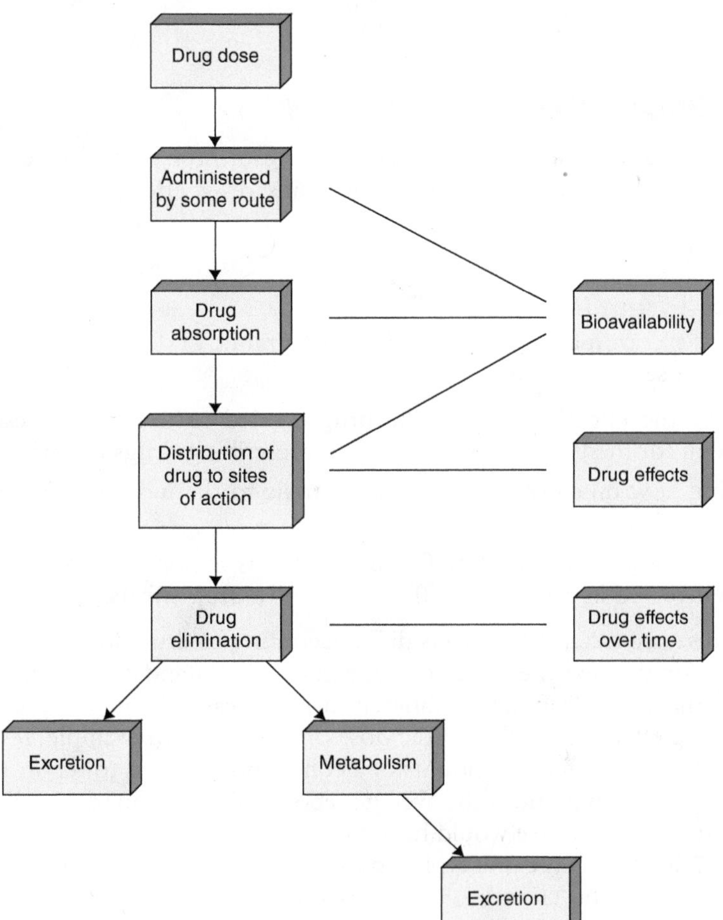

FIGURE 4.1
A summary of the first four steps of the drug experience and pharmacokinetics

biochemical factors influence the speed and amount of drug absorption. Biochemical factors also affect the amount of drug that is distributed. The latter refers to bioavailability, which determines what portion of the original dose reaches sites of drug action. Bioavailability is the pharmacological basis of the drug experience. Once they reach their sites of action, drugs are eliminated from the body either by direct excretion or by metabolism into by-products that are excreted. The course of elimination of a drug is one influence of a drug effect over time.

It is important to point out that a drug's exit from the body may not be the end of the drug experience. In later chapters on specific drugs, you will see that elimination of a drug from the body often is associated with physical and psychological changes that are the opposite of those that were caused by the drug. For example, the feelings of euphoria and tranquility that heroin causes switch to irritability and intense, extremely unpleasant physiological changes when the drug leaves the addict's body. The euphoria and high energy that cocaine and amphetamines typically induce turn to lethargy and depression as the drugs end their course of action. Such opposite (sometimes called "drug rebound") effects are important because of their influence on drug use patterns. The rebound effect of depression that follows cocaine use is sometimes so unpleasant, for example, that users feel a strong need to take more cocaine to stop the bad feelings. Avoiding the effects of heroin abstinence is a powerful force in addicts' continued use of the drug. When coming down from a dose of alcohol, people often feel sleepy and somewhat depressive, so they may start drinking again to try to recapture the more euphoric mood associated with just starting to drink.

Pharmacodynamics

Pharmacokinetics provided a basic understanding of how drugs move through the body. Pharmacodynamics describes and explains drug effects by focusing on the mechanisms of action.

The Dose–Effect (Response) Curve

Knowing the size or magnitude of an effect for a range of drug doses is important to understand for several reasons.

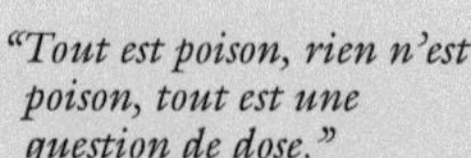

"Tout est poison, rien n'est poison, tout est une question de dose."

("Everything is poisonous, nothing is poisonous, it is all a matter of dose.")

Claude Bernard, experimental pathologist

1. Knowing the effective dose of the drug needed to obtain the desired goal is important for medical professionals when prescribing drugs to their patients.
2. Knowing how much of a drug (dose) is toxic to the individual is important for ensuring safety.
3. Knowing the margin of safety for drug doses is important given the numerous factors involved in producing different effective drug effects.

Earlier we discussed that drug effects differ according to drug doses. The dose–effect curve (commonly called the dose–response curve) is a standard way of representing drug effects that result from taking different drug doses. This curve is a representation of specific drug effects according to the dose of the drug. For example, several groups of people may drink different amounts of alcohol and be asked to report their degree of relaxation at a given point. If the average reports of relaxation (drug effect) for each group were then plotted, we would have a dose–effect curve.

Figure 4.2 is an example of a typical dose–effect curve, which is represented as an S-shape (sigmoid). The "Effect size," (on the vertical axis) represents the change in the drug effect we are interested in studying. Examples might include memory task performance, ratings of mood, or some measure of physiological arousal such as heart rate. The horizontal axis represents the range of doses under investigation, from smaller to larger doses. Typically, a minimum of three doses is studied to record changes in the drug effects.

Figure 4.2 shows how the effects of this hypothetical drug are not constant across different doses. The higher the drug dose, as shown, the larger the effect. However, a limit exists; the graph plateaus for the highest doses. The peak of the dose–effect curve (where the effect plateaus) is called a **drug's efficacy**. This means that increasing the dose beyond a given level does not increase the drug's effects. The peak dose—at the drug's efficacy point—is called a **drug's potency**. This is considered the minimum effective dose of a drug. One illustration of this is the effect of alcohol on reaction time. For the "average" drinker (see Chapter 6), having two 12-ounce beers in an hour has little effect on reaction time. After about four beers, however, reaction time is significantly increased (the person's response is slower). After five beers, reaction time is slowed even further. A person who drinks about nine beers in an hour might find it hard to stay conscious, so measuring any further deterioration in reaction time with additional drinking would yield little new information. At that point, if the person is having a hard time maintaining consciousness, then the possibility of—and the utility of—measuring further slowing of reaction time with a higher dose of alcohol would hover around zero. The plateau of the dose–effect curve in this instance would be reached at the alcohol dose equivalent of about nine beers. The example of alcohol and reaction time shows that the question is not what effects drug X has but rather what the effect of drug X is at a specified dose. Other drugs may have effects that go in one direction (i.e., heart rate)—say, increase as the dose goes up—but then the effect changes direction (decreases) as the dose continues to go up.

drug efficacy
The most intense, or peak, level of a drug effect.

drug potency
The minimum effective dose of a drug.

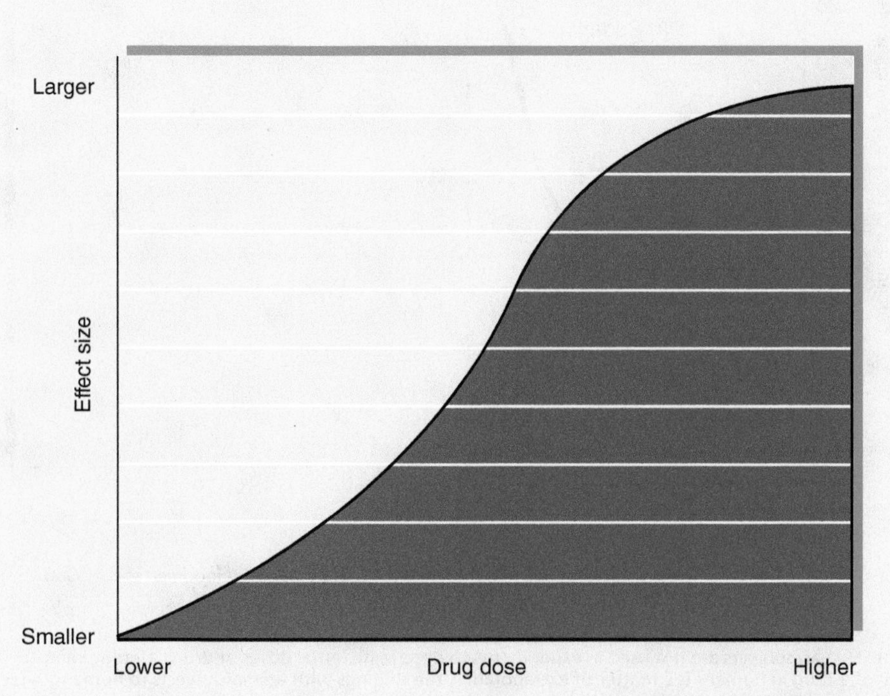

FIGURE 4.2
A typical dose–effect curve

Source: Adapted from *The Pharmacological Basis of Therapeutics, 7/e,* by Louis S. Goodman and A. G. Gilman. © 1985 McGraw-Hill.

Effective and Lethal Doses

Considering the variability in individuals' reactions to a given dose of a drug, testing only one person does not accurately show a drug's effect at a given dose. When discussing the toxicity profiles of drugs it is important to understand the differences in drug effects based on a proportion (or group) of individuals. Therefore, an effect is viewed in relative terms, or in the proportions of groups of people who show an effect at a specified dose.

effective dose
The dose at which a given percentage of individuals show a particular effect of a drug.

Figure 4.3 shows the dose–effect curves for two effects of a hypothetical drug.

The **effective dose** (ED) is the dose at which a given percentage of individuals show a particular effect of a drug. Figure 4.3 shows the ED for two percent, 50 percent, and 95 percent of the people showing the effect. ED 50 is a standard term that pharmacologists use, which represents 50 percent of the people who receive that amount of the drug will experience the effect studied (in Figure 4.3, sedation).

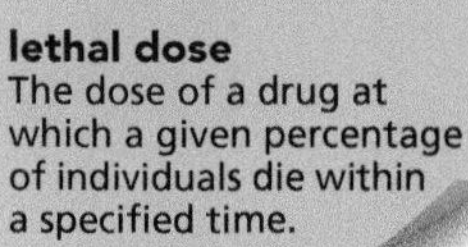

lethal dose
The dose of a drug at which a given percentage of individuals die within a specified time.

The **lethal dose** (LD) of a drug represents a given percentage of mortality of animals showing the effect within a specified time.* Similar to effective dose, LD 50 represents the dose at which 50 percent of the animals administered a given dose of a drug died within a stated time. The LD 50 of our hypothetical drug is illustrated on the curve on the right in Figure 4.3.

FIGURE 4.3 The dose–effect curves for two effects of a hypothetical drug (sedation and death)

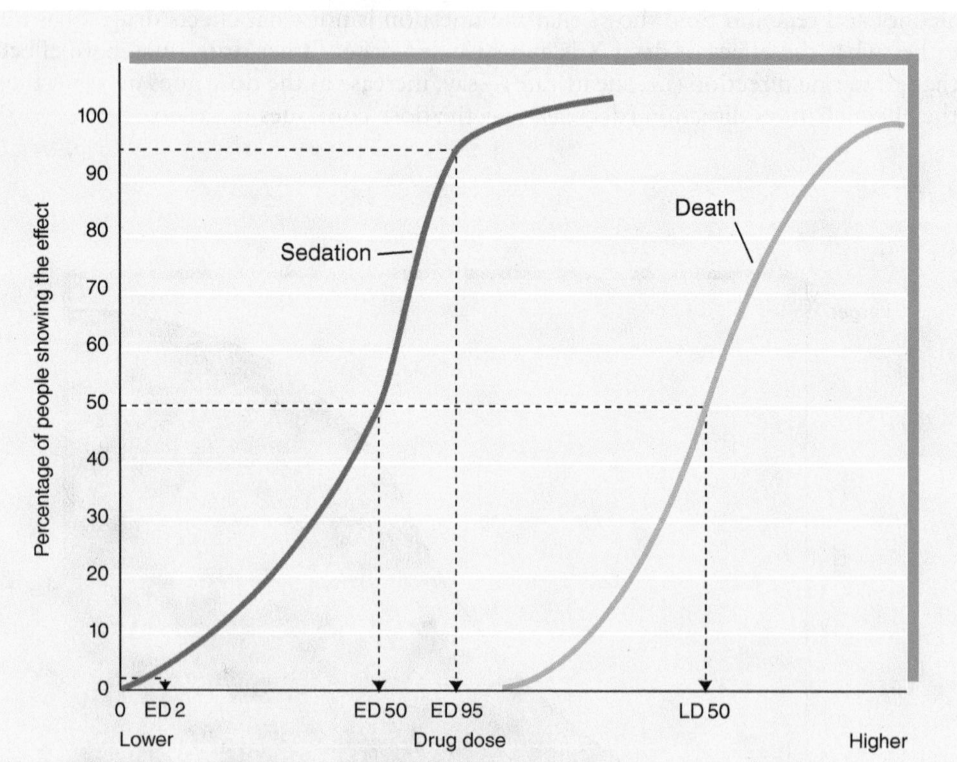

Source: Adapted from *The Pharmacological Basis of Therapeutics, 7/e*, by Louis S. Goodman and A. G. Gilman. © 1985 McGraw-Hill.

* Note: Human subjects are not used in experiments to determine lethal doses of drugs. Determining the LD 50 of a drug in humans is a matter of extrapolating the findings with animal subjects to humans; typically mice are used to study lethal doses.

A drug's ED and LD are of more than casual interest. Of particular importance is the difference between a drug's ED and LD. The difference is represented as a ratio. When the difference is small, much more danger of accidental overdose exists for a person who is using drugs for nonmedical reasons. Autopsy reports from fatal overdose provide important information about mortality and drug consumption (albeit, this is complex given the difficulties in determining accurate time of death and quantity of drug consumed) (Gable, 2006). For some drugs, such as caffeine, the ED–LD difference is large; however, other drugs pose more of a problem. Accidental deaths due to heart damage from a dose of cocaine have been described in the popular media, especially during the late 1980s when cocaine abuse and overdose among celebrity rock stars was readily reported. Alcohol is another example. A 160-pound man with average tolerance to alcohol typically would report feeling relaxed after drinking about two drinks in an hour on an empty stomach. However, that person would reach LD 50 for alcohol if he drank about a fifth (25.3 ounces) of whiskey in an hour. Such drinking occurs more often than you might think and has been responsible for serious injuries and deaths in fraternity hazings (initiation rites). Furthermore, when some drugs are combined, such as alcohol and the barbiturates, the resulting ED and LD are pushed even closer and the danger is greater. Figure 4.4 ranks common psychoactive drugs by their ratio of lethal dose to effective dose. The lower the ratio of fatal dose to effective dose, the more lethal the drug effects are, potentially resulting in an acute fatal reaction. We discuss the effects of combining drugs in the next section of this chapter.

A final point: The ED–LD difference is also important when a physician or nurse practitioner administers a drug for medical reasons. In medicine, the goal is to find a drug that can be given in a dose that is therapeutic (that is, effective) for all patients, has no side effects, and is not lethal. Accordingly, the **therapeutic index** has been derived: the ratio LD 50/ED 50 for a given drug. The higher a drug's

therapeutic index
A measure of a drug's safety in medical care; it is computed as a ratio: LD 50/ED 50.

FIGURE 4.4 Common psychoactive drugs ranked by their ratios of lethal dose to effective dose.

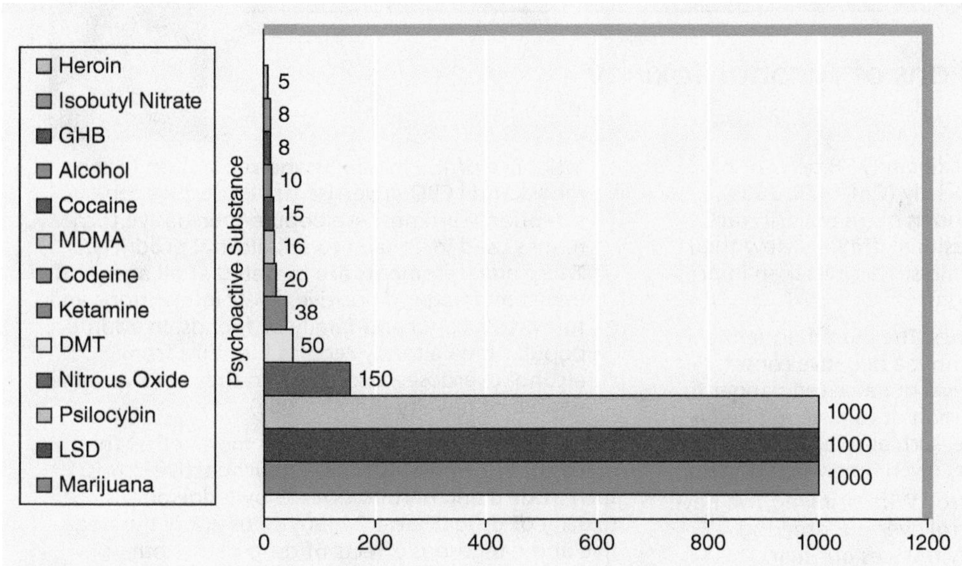

By this measure, many illicit drugs are considerably safer than alcohol.

Source: R. Gable. "The Toxicity of Recreational Drugs," *American Scientist*. Pg. 206. Vol. 94, No. 3. 2006.

CONTEMPORARY ISSUE BOX 4.3

Pharmacokinetics, Pharmacodynamics, and Cultural Factors

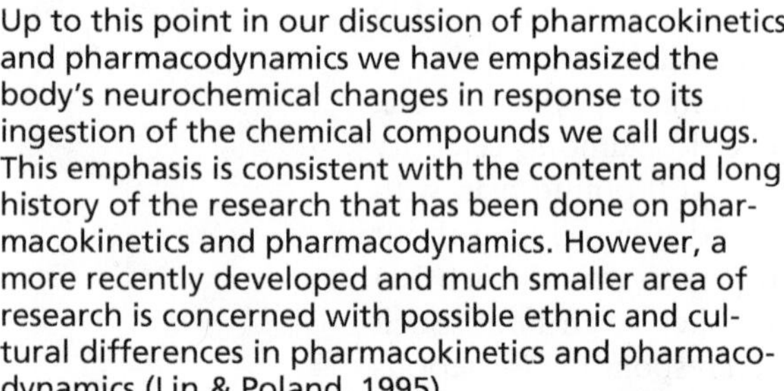

Up to this point in our discussion of pharmacokinetics and pharmacodynamics we have emphasized the body's neurochemical changes in response to its ingestion of the chemical compounds we call drugs. This emphasis is consistent with the content and long history of the research that has been done on pharmacokinetics and pharmacodynamics. However, a more recently developed and much smaller area of research is concerned with possible ethnic and cultural differences in pharmacokinetics and pharmacodynamics (Lin & Poland, 1995).

As reviewed in Lin and Poland (1995), studies have shown differences in drug metabolism among ethnic groups that seem to be due to environmental variables. Antipyrine, an analgesic drug, has a longer half-life among Sudanese living in their home villages compared to Sudanese living in Great Britain or to Caucasians living in Great Britain. Therefore, differences in the rate of the metabolism of a drug, a pharmacokinetic factor, seem to be based in environmental differences.

An example of ethnic differences in pharmacodynamics is response to propranolol, a beta-blocker drug used to control high blood pressure, or hypertension. Studies have shown that African Americans are least responsive (in regard to blood pressure and heart rate) to propranolol, Asians are most responsive, and Caucasians are midway between the two other groups.

The mechanisms underlying ethnic/cultural differences in pharmacokinetics and pharmacodynamics are not always clear and warrant considerably more study. Such group differences do remind us, however, that nonpharmacological factors may influence the drug experience at any point along the "steps" listed in Table 4.1.

margin of safety The difference between the maximum effective dose and the minimum lethal dose.

therapeutic index, the more useful the drug is in medical treatment. The lethal dose should be larger than the effective dose. In administering drugs, it is important to estimate the does that will produce a desired effect in most patients and the lowest dose producing a toxic reaction. The difference between these doses is called the **margin of safety**.

DRUGS AND CULTURE BOX 4.4

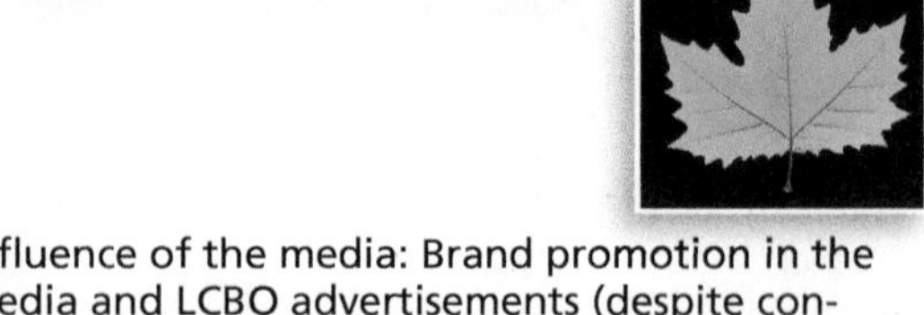

Mistaken Impressions of Alcohol Toxicity

Despite the fact that approximately 78 percent of Canadians drink alcohol socially (CADUMS, 2009), Figure 4.4 shows that alcohol is quite toxic. In fact, many people who are occasional drinkers view their own use of alcohol as harmless. This mistaken impression arises for several reasons:

- Lack of negative outcomes: The more frequently we experience an event without a negative consequence, the lower our level of perceived danger to ourselves. It is true that most of us have not had a major negative outcome, such as a car accident or alcohol poisoning, at any given time when drinking.
- Perceived sense of control: With drinking, we have a positive sense of control over our drinking events, which ultimately reduces our fear. This perceived control is stronger when we dilute our alcohol intake by mixing alcohol with another beverage (say, vodka and tonic water).
- Influence of the media: Brand promotion in the media and LCBO advertisements (despite consumption warnings) are popular persuasive techniques used in Canada to sell alcohol products. These advertisements are targeted at all ages and depict an image of positive, lively interactions and fun with alcohol and family or friends. In addition, popular media rarely reports fatalities from alcohol overdoses, except when they involve some degree of novelty (Gable, 2006).

Figure 4.4 shows that alcohol is more lethal than many other commonly abused psychoactive drugs, such as GHB and heroin. Does knowledge about the toxicity of drugs matter? Many of us know the negative and dangerous effects of drug abuse, but looking at toxicity can give us a different way to understand these effects. What does this say about alcohol toxicity?

Drug Interactions

So far we have simplified our discussion by considering only one drug at a time; however, the study of pharmacodynamics often involves the actions of two or more drugs. A person could take multiple drugs at the same time, or take one drug before another has totally cleared from the body. The extremes are seen in polydrug abuse, which we illustrated in Chapter 1.

Using more than one drug at a time increases the complexity of the drug experience because two or more drugs entering the body may **interact**. Two drugs have an interaction if the effect of one modifies or alters the effect of the other. Drug interactions may be analyzed qualitatively or quantitatively; the degree of effect, or quantitative study, is by far better understood in pharmacology. The quantitative study of drug interactions considers both enhancing and diminishing effects of combining drugs.

interact
When the effects of one drug are modified by the presence of another drug.

Enhancing Combinations

Drug **synergism or potentiation** is used to denote any enhancing drug interaction. When two drugs are synergistic, the effects of taking them together are greater than the effects of taking either drug alone. In practice, pharmacologists find it difficult to tell for sure whether synergistic effects are a simple result of adding the separate effects of the two drugs together or if somehow one of the drugs is "multiplying" the effects of the other.

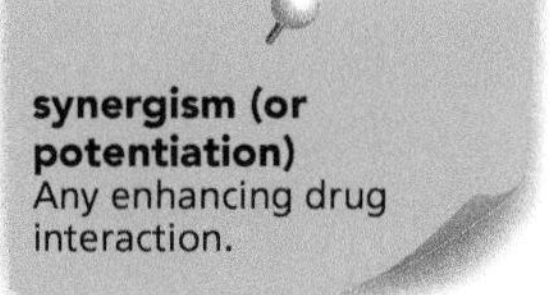

synergism (or potentiation)
Any enhancing drug interaction.

In quantitative studies of combining drugs, interactions are represented by changes in the dose–effect curve. Figure 4.5 represents a synergistic relationship between drug A and drug B. You can see that the solid line is like the typical dose–effect curve for a drug that we illustrated in Figure 4.2. The effect of synergy between the two drugs,

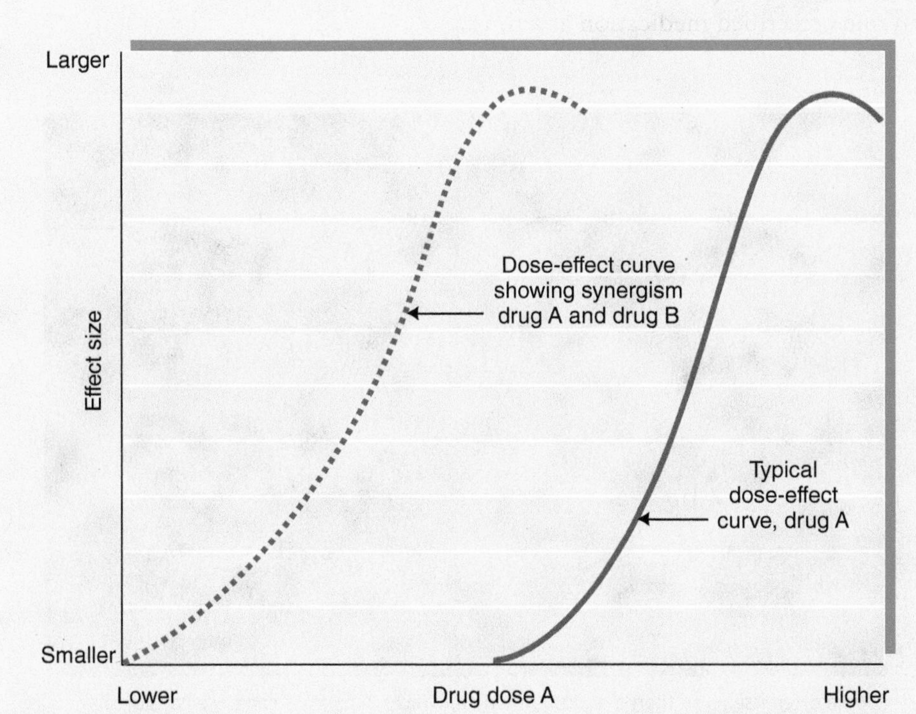

FIGURE 4.5
Representation by dose–effect curves of a synergistic relationship for drugs A and B

then, is to "shift" the dose–effect curve to the left, represented by the broken line in Figure 4.5. The broken line curve shows that larger effects of drug A are evident at lower doses of it when drug B is present.

Diminishing Combinations

antagonism
The diminished or reduced effect of a drug when another drug is present.

Drug **antagonism** is a term that refers to the diminished or reduced effect of a drug when another drug is present. As you might guess, drug antagonism is represented by a shift to the right of a drug's dose–effect curve. For example, the amphetamines, which are CNS stimulant drugs, antagonize alcohol's CNS depressant effects. However, the amphetamines do not reduce alcohol's impairment of motor skills, like driving (Blum, 1984).

The Importance of Interactions between Drugs

An awareness of interactions between drugs is important for several reasons. In medical practice, knowledge of drug interactions is vital because drugs are often used in combinations for more effective treatment of an illness. Therefore, drug interactions may be used to improve medical care. On the other hand, interactions could be a problem, for example, for a physician. Difficulties may occur if the physician is not aware of all the drugs a patient may be using at a given time. For example, the effects of one drug could cancel the therapeutic effects of another. Furthermore, prescribed medication could have detrimental or even lethal effects in the presence of other drugs. Fortunately, pharmacies now commonly have computerized profiles of the medications that a patient has been prescribed. Such information allows pharmacists to inform customers how newly prescribed medications interact with other medications they may be taking and what precautions they should follow to avoid harmful combined drug effects. This backup to physician advice is available to all patients but is probably of most help in treating the elderly, who often take more than one prescribed medication at a time.

People often use more than one drug at a time, which sometimes can pose considerable risks to safety.

Drug interactions also may cause problems with different nonprescribed drugs or combinations of prescribed and nonprescribed drugs. The most common examples are mixing drugs that depress the central nervous system. For example, as we said earlier, alcohol and the barbiturates may be lethal in enhancing the sedative effects of each. This drug combination has caused many intentional and accidental deaths.

Drug interactions also are important for their influences on the reasons for and patterns of human drug use, so they are of central concern in this text. Individuals may intentionally combine drugs that have the same or similar action to achieve a "super" high or effect. Or individuals may use drugs that have opposite effects in a deliberate effort for one drug to modify the other. An example heard commonly in treatment settings is using alcohol's depressant effects to modify the overstimulation sometimes induced by cocaine. Drinkers sometimes consume large amounts of black coffee (containing caffeine) in hopes of antagonizing alcohol's CNS depressant effects. In truth, however, caffeine seems to do little to counter alcohol's effects on the CNS. These two examples illustrate the drug user's attempt to modify the intensity (quantitative) of drug effects. However, drugs also may be combined to achieve **qualitative** interaction effects that could not be achieved by any of the drugs separately. Users might take a depressant drug, such as one of the benzodiazepines, along with LSD to have a tranquil state while they experience the perceptual alterations that result from LSD (Jacobs & Fehr, 1987).

qualitative
The kind, as opposed to the quantity, of effect.

SUMMARY

- The basic principles of pharmacology emerge in discussions of what contributes to the drug experience.
- To the pharmacologist, principles of pharmacokinetics and pharmacodynamics are most relevant to the drug experience.
- Drug dose is computed according to the recipient's body weight. A standard way of expressing dose is in milligrams of drug per kilogram of body weight (mg/kg).
- Eight routes of drug administration were discussed in detail: oral, subcutaneous, intramuscular, intravenous, inhalation, intranasal, sublingual, and transdermal. A route of administration is selected according to the drug taken and the goals and circumstances of administration.
- The route of drug administration affects the drug experience primarily through the rate of drug absorption and the amount of drug absorbed.
- Once they enter the body, drugs are absorbed into the blood and distributed to their site(s) of action. The body also works to metabolize and excrete drugs that enter it.
- Drug elimination may occur either by direct excretion of the drug from the body or by metabolism of the drugs and excretion of its by-products.
- Drug absorption, distribution, and elimination are affected by different biochemical factors and accentuate the complexity of the drug experience.
- Pharmacodynamics most directly concerns actions of the drug on the body and thus drug effects. This chapter covered fundamental terms that pharmacologists use to describe drug effects and ways to depict them graphically.
- Pharmacologists use the dose–effect curve as a standard way to represent graphically the size of an effect in relation to the dose of a drug taken. The typical dose–effect curve has an S shape, but variations depend on the effects studied.
- A drug's effective dose and lethal dose are important measures of a drug's action and potential for therapeutic uses. Pharmacodynamics often involves the consideration of more than one drug in the body at the same time. Multiple drugs interact to contribute to the drug experience. Interactions may be enhancing or diminishing.

- Drugs that enhance the effects of each other are called synergistic. Antagonism between drugs creates diminished drug effects.
- Enhanced and diminished drug effects refer to the quantitative (degree of effect) study of drug interactions. Qualitative study of drug interactions also is possible.
- It is essential to be aware of drug interactions in both medical and nonmedical drug use.

Key Terms

absorbed **p. 62**
antagonism **p. 80**
bioavailability **p. 69**
diffusibility **p. 69**
dissolved **p. 64**
distribution **p. 62**
drug efficacy **p. 75**
drug potency **p. 75**
effective dose **p. 76**
elimination half-life **p. 71**
feedback **p. 62**
interact **p. 79**
lethal dose **p. 76**
margin of safety **p. 78**
metabolism **p. 62**
pharmacodynamics **p. 62**
pharmacokinetics **p. 62**
qualitative **p. 81**
solubility **p. 69**
suspended **p. 64**
synergism (potentiation) **p. 78**
therapeutic index **p. 77**

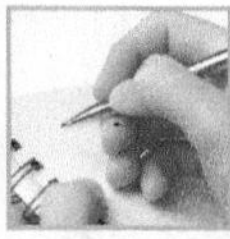

Essays/Thought Questions

1. Sketch a map marking the steps of the drug experience, from the point of a drug's entry into the body to an individual's perception of that drug's effects.
2. What factors might be considered in determining the "safety threshold" of a drug's therapeutic index?

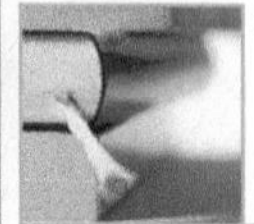

Suggested Readings

Center for AIDS Prevention Studies. (1998). *Does needle exchange work?* Chicago: American Medical Association.

CHAPTER 5

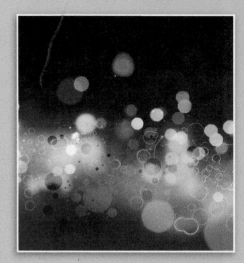

Cocaine, Amphetamines, and Related Stimulants

Did You Know

?

- Cocaine and other stimulants are Schedule I drugs listed in Canada's Controlled Drugs and Substances Act.
- Stimulants have been consistently shown to impair one's ability to learn highly complex tasks, despite the ability to speed up performance.
- Stimulant drugs are often used to treat children who have attention deficit/hyperactivity disorder.
- Amphetamine effects are very similar to cocaine effects.
- "Crank" is a popular street name for methamphetamine.
- Overdoses of cocaine and amphetamine may produce a psychotic state.
- "Cocaine blues" is the term used to describe the feeling of depression and lack of joy during cocaine withdrawal.
- In Canada, 10–12 percent of school-aged children are prescribed Ritalin for the treatment of ADHD, which is only one-half of the amount prescribed in the United States.

Many drugs used for recreational as well as medical purposes are referred to as stimulants because they heighten mood, increase alertness, and decrease fatigue. Controlled stimulants such as cocaine, amphetamines, methylphenidate (Ritalin), and related compounds are discussed in this chapter, and over-the-counter stimulants such as nicotine and caffeine are dealt with in Chapters 7 and 8, respectively. We first consider the history of stimulant use and discuss some of the effects of cocaine and the amphetamines (ATSs) as we review their history. Then we look at a more detailed pharmacology of these stimulants.

The Coca Leaf

The earliest uses of cocaine have been traced to the Andean regions of Bolivia, Ecuador, northern Argentina, and Peru, where a low shrub called the coca bush or coca tree (*Erythroxylum coca*) grows. From the leaves of this plant comes the powerful stimulant cocaine. For centuries, the native inhabitants of this region of South America, including the Incas and their descendants, have engaged in the practice of chewing the coca leaf. The coca leaf had important religious significance to the Inca people (i.e., called 'Mama coca' for its view as possessing a goddess-like essence) but was used for medicinal and work-related purposes as well. When the Spanish *conquistadores* encountered the Incas during the 16th century, they were at first disturbed by the religious use of coca, which was, of course, inconsistent with Catholicism. After conquering the Incas, the Spanish permitted and actually encouraged the use of coca because they believed it helped the Incas to work harder and longer. The Spanish ultimately came to control Inca access to the coca leaf by using it as a form of payment and levying taxes to be paid in coca leaves. The Spanish considered chewing coca a vice and neither used coca themselves nor encouraged other Europeans to use it (Kennedy, 1985; Streatfeild, 2001).

Thus, until the 1800s, the coca plant was relatively unknown in Europe. When European naturalists began to explore Peru and experiment with coca, the rise of

Pilar Olivares/Reuters/Landov

Andean women harvest coca in Peru. Today natives still chew the leaves and hold a ball of coca leaf in their mouth. The addition of powdered lime increases absorption of cocaine from the leaf.

scientific interest in coca became noticed. This scientific interest led to the increased availability of the coca leaf in laboratories, and in the 1850s the European chemist Albert Niemann was able to isolate the far more potent active agent in the leaf, which they called cocaine. The extraction of cocaine from the leaf led to a new era in the history of stimulant drug use.

Freud Museum, London

Fleischl-Marxow suffered from chronic pain and had become a morphine addict. Freud prescribed cocaine, and Fleischl-Marxow began to consume larger and larger doses of it. Although doing quite well at abstaining from morphine, Fleischl-Marxow eventually was consuming one gram of cocaine daily. Not only had he become the first European cocaine addict, but he also began to show bizarre symptoms that we now recognize as characteristics of cocaine overdose.

Early Use of Cocaine

The next chapter in the history of cocaine is fascinating because it broadened the early use of cocaine for recreational (social), medical, and psychological purposes in the late 19th century. Though he is now best known for his contributions to psychoanalysis, Sigmund Freud was first recognized for his writings on cocaine. Freud obtained a sample of cocaine in 1884 and, after taking it a few times, felt he had come across a miracle drug. In his first major publication, "On Coca," he advocated cocaine as a local anesthetic and as a treatment for depression, indigestion, asthma, various neuroses, syphilis, morphine addiction, and alcoholism. Freud also thought cocaine was an aphrodisiac (Byck, 1974). Freud's influence prompted a major period of cocaine abuse. Ironically, an indication of what was to come was observed in one of Freud's friends, Ernst von Fleischl-Marxow.

During this time, cocaine was prescribed by physicians as a topical medication and application for eye surgery and dental work. It also was readily available in patent medicines. The

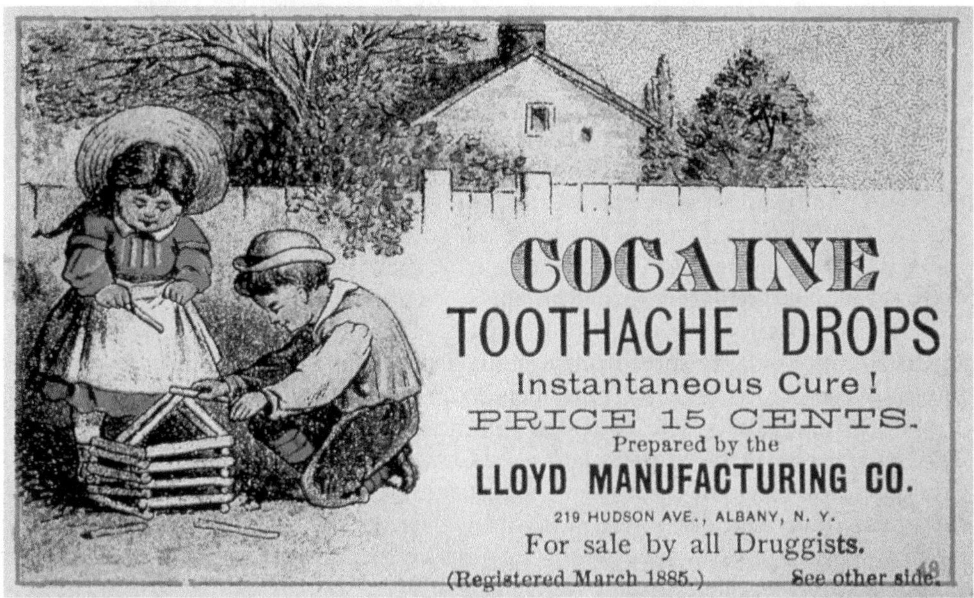
COCAINE
TOOTHACHE DROPS
Instantaneous Cure!
PRICE 15 CENTS.
Prepared by the
LLOYD MANUFACTURING CO.
219 HUDSON AVE., ALBANY, N. Y.
For sale by all Druggists.
(Registered March 1885.)
See other side.

Bettman/Corbis

Cocaine was a popular ingredient in many remedies and tonics of the late 19th century, as shown in this advertisement for toothache drops.

TABLE 5.1 Early References to Cocaine in Popular Literature in Late 19th Century

Literature Title	Author	Cocaine Reference
Sherlock Holmes	Sir Arthur Conan Doyle	Depicted Sherlock Holmes as using cocaine to give him energy and aid his powers of deductive reasoning.
Dr. Jekyll and Mr. Hyde	Robert Louis Stevenson	Wrote the story while taking cocaine treatments for tuberculosis.

Image Courtesy of The Advertising Archives

Front cover of *'The Strange Case of Dr. Jekyll and Mr. Hyde'* by Robert Louis Stevenson (1850-94) c.1910 (litho), Sullivan, Edmund Joseph (1869-1933) / Private Collection / Archives Charmet / The Bridgeman Art Library

French chemist, Angelo Mariani, used an extract from coca leaves in various patented products used to cure common ailments. His most famous marketing of cocaine was sold as a popular wine, Mariani's Coca Wine. This tonic was enjoyed by popes and heads of state for over 40 years. Dr. John Stith Pemberton invented Coca-Cola. This non-alcoholic beverage was advertised as containing the "tonic and nerve stimulant properties of the coca plant"—back when it *was* the real thing! (The extract was later replaced with 'caffeine' in 1903 after increasing discoveries of cocaine's hazards.)

Cocaine's popularity spread throughout Europe and North America through its public praise for its effects. This included references in popular literature (see Table 5.1) and others who provided testimonials to the value of cocaine include Thomas Edison, Jules Verne, Emile Zola, Henrik Ibsen, Czar Nicholas of Russia, and President Ulysses Grant (Grinspoon & Bakalar, 1976). By the end of the 19th century, many users had discovered firsthand the hazards of cocaine, and with cocaine psychosis, overdose death, and severe dependence becoming major problems, popular sentiment turned against cocaine (Spillane, 2000).

Beliefs and attitudes about cocaine continued to change. In addition to dramatic accounts of addiction to cocaine, reports of violent acts committed under the influence of the drug led to a dramatic swing of public opinion, culminating in the control of cocaine under the 1911 Opium and Other Drugs Act in Canada, and the 1914 Harrison Narcotics Act in the United States. Although these Acts were primarily designed to control opiates such as morphine and heroin, cocaine's inclusion as a dangerous drug was no accident.

Cocaine Use and Canada

Following cocaine's early uses in the late 19th century and with the creation of drug policy cocaine use declined for the period of 1920–1960s. The implementation of the Opium and Other Drugs Act in Canada acted as the first dry prohibition with other drugs (such as cannabis and alcohol). The Act changed in 1929 to be called the Opium and Narcotic Drug Act, which became the instrument of drug policy for the next 40 years. In the early 1970s, cocaine began to re-emerge to the public but it was fairly difficult to obtain and was quite expensive. It became glamourized as the drug of movie stars and pro athletes (who were among the few who could afford to buy it), and thus acquired a reputation as the "champagne" of the stimulants. Most users during this period experimented with low doses taken intranasally and thus rarely encountered the problems associated with intravenous use. This sparked public interest in cocaine and accounted for its popularity as a 'club drug' in the late 1970s and 1980s.

In Canada, large quantities of illicit cocaine were exported by South American cartels through the United States borders reportedly by motorcycle gangs. By the 1980s the cocaine trade became the top organized crime in Canada (Ontario Addiction Helpline, 2011). Today, cocaine is a Schedule I drug under the Controlled Drugs and Substances Act. In 2009 cocaine was made the subject of increased criminal sanctions in Canada for serious drug crimes (Narconon, 1999–2011).

Types of Cocaine and Routes of Administration

Part of the reason that cocaine use increased between the 1980s–1990s was the increased availability of cheaper cocaine. This has led to changing patterns of use, as more people were able to regularly use the drug in high doses. Another critical factor was the practice of smoking cocaine, or crack. Although **freebasing** cocaine seemed to emerge in the late 1970s, **crack** burst upon the national scene in 1986.

The form in which cocaine is administered is an important determinant of abuse liability (see Table 5.2). Street cocaine, which takes the form of a white powder, is produced by combining a paste made from coca leaves with a hydrochloric acid solution to form a salt—cocaine hydrochloride. Because it is a salt, street cocaine is water-soluble and can be injected or taken intranasally (sniffed or snorted). Intranasal cocaine can produce intense effects but because it causes constriction of blood vessels in the nose its absorption is slowed. Overdose deaths, psychosis, and dependence are

freebasing
The term used to describe the practice of smoking cocaine by heating it until it vapourizes.

crack
A freebase cocaine produced by mixing cocaine salt with baking soda and water. The solution is then heated, resulting in brittle sheets of cocaine that are "cracked" into small smokable chunks or "rocks."

TABLE 5.2 Types of Cocaine and Routes of Administration

Cocaine	Form	Method
Coca leaf	—	Oral
Coca paste (basuco)	Cocaine sulfate	Smokable
Street cocaine	Cocaine hydrochloride	Intranasal injection
Crack	Freebase cocaine	Smokable

all possible consequences of intranasal cocaine but are less common than with injected cocaine. Because sniffing was the major method of administration on the street until the late 1980s, the hazards of cocaine abuse were underestimated.

The practice of freebasing became a popular method of administration. When the vapourized cocaine is inhaled, it is absorbed rapidly and completely in lung tissue and produces an intensely pleasurable high of very short duration followed by a severe crash. However, cocaine is broken down at the high temperatures necessary to smoke it when it is in the salt form. To smoke cocaine, the hydrochloride salt must be separated from the cocaine base and this is where "freebase" and crack come in.

Freebase cocaine is made by mixing street cocaine with a highly flammable substance—ether. Many people have been badly burned by failing to handle the ether properly. Base cocaine can be produced more simply and safely by dissolving the cocaine salt in an alkaline solution (for example, baking soda). When the water in the solution is boiled off, what remains is a hard, rocklike substance called "crack" or "rock" cocaine. Crack has a low melting point and thus can be heated and the fumes inhaled while the potency of the cocaine is preserved. The name *crack* comes from the crackling sound made by the baking soda left in the compound when it is heated (Inciardi, 2002). Smoking crack results in rapid and concentrated delivery of cocaine to the brain, and the intense "rush" is so pleasurable that addicts actually prefer it to comparable doses of injected cocaine (Foltin & Fischman, 1993). The euphoria is short-lived, however, and within 10 to 20 minutes, users report a "crash" and begin to crave another hit.

Crack is cheaper and less dangerous to produce than other forms of freebase, so dealers became attracted to it. Also it is so potent that it can be sold in small chunks or rocks and so is relatively affordable. Because it produces such strong cravings and dependence, a large market for crack developed almost overnight. Although there is evidence of sporadic crack use in the 1970s, it came to the attention of the media in late 1985, and by early 1986, national media such as *Time*, *Newsweek*, and various television documentaries reported that crack use had emerged as a national crisis in the United States. In Canada, the first seizure of crack was made in Metropolitan Toronto in 1986 (Smart, 1988). Other seizures were reported but not to the degree reported in the United States. By the late 1980s, millions of Americans had tried crack and overdose deaths were increasing. Other cocaine overdose emergencies, such as paranoid reactions, also increased rapidly during this period. According to National Institute on Drug Abuse (NIDA) statistics, more than 80 000 cocaine-related emergency room visits occurred in 1990, up from 10 000 in 1985, and almost none in the early 1970s (NIDA, 1991).

Alessia Pierdomenico/Reuters/Corbis

Supermodel Kate Moss lost many of her high-profile contracts when a video showing her snorting cocaine was released in 2005.

Dependence on cocaine, once viewed as a minor problem in the United States, came to be seen as one of the nation's major health problems with the introduction of crack. In Canada, crack use is a relatively neglected public health problem in comparison to injection drug use (Haydon & Fisher, 2005). However, the risks and harms of crack smoking have underlined the need for targeted intervention. Surveys by the Centre for Addiction and Mental Health (2008) and CADUMS (2009) suggest that peak levels of use in the 1980s were much higher than the present levels. The most recent CADUMS data (2009) reported that three percent of individuals between the ages of 15–24 have used crack/cocaine during the past year. Contemporary use among adults is somewhat lower, with 0.9 percent of Canadians between the ages of 25 or older reporting use of some cocaine during the past year (CADUMS, 2009). These statistics are much lower than national surveys in the United States.

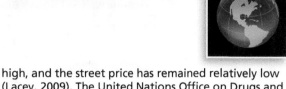

CONTEMPORARY ISSUES BOX 5.1

The Coca Leaf Today

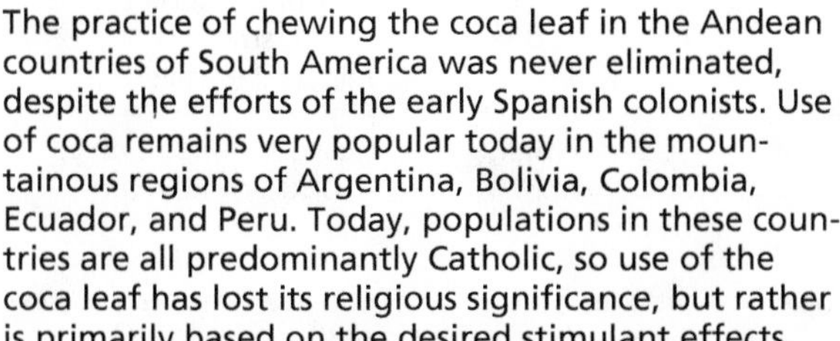

The practice of chewing the coca leaf in the Andean countries of South America was never eliminated, despite the efforts of the early Spanish colonists. Use of coca remains very popular today in the mountainous regions of Argentina, Bolivia, Colombia, Ecuador, and Peru. Today, populations in these countries are all predominantly Catholic, so use of the coca leaf has lost its religious significance, but rather is primarily based on the desired stimulant effects.

Chewing coca and drinking tea brewed from coca leaves are common daily activities in the region, and these practices are thought to stimulate alertness, reduce fatigue, and combat altitude sickness, among other health benefits. Despite pressure from the United States to eradicate coca production, limited cultivation of coca is legal in Bolivia, Colombia, and Peru, and coca leaves and coca teabags are sold legally at local markets throughout the region.

Opposition to the U.S. coca eradication policies has become a nationalistic issue in several Latin American countries. As an example, Evo Morales was elected president of Bolivia in 2006, in part because of his pledge to decriminalize coca production. President Morales spoke to delegates at the Vienna meeting of the United Nations Commission on Narcotic Drugs in March 2009, to demand that coca be removed from the United Nation's list of prohibited drugs. He is not arguing for the legalization of cocaine powder or crack, but rather argues that the small amounts of cocaine absorbed by chewing coca are not harmful, a position that has some scientific support (Grinspoon & Bakalar, 1976). He dramatized his speech by holding up a coca leaf and chewing it after his presentation.

The United States has spent billions of dollars since 2000 on a plan for drug eradication in Latin America, but availability of cocaine in the United States remains high, and the street price has remained relatively low (Lacey, 2009). The United Nations Office on Drugs and Crime *World Report 2009* estimates that the annual prevalence of cocaine use worldwide ranges from 15.6 to 20.8 million people in 2007. Canada's cocaine use statistics reveal that only approximately one percent of the population have used (or use) cocaine. What are some considerations regarding the annual prevalence of cocaine usage worldwide being so high?

Spencer Platt/Getty Images

Bolivian President Evo Morales held up a coca leaf at a United Nations conference to dramatize his defence of the traditional use of coca in South America.

Because the allure of crack is so great, dependence on the drug leads many people to tragic levels of desperation and self-destruction. The "crack house"—a place where crack is sold and smoked—has become the contemporary den of iniquity, and the media are filled with stories of degradation. When addicts run out of money, sexual activities become the medium of exchange, and then the transmission of HIV is an additional risk factor.

The Amphetamines (ATSs)

Use of cocaine in Canada and the United States declined during the years following the Opium and Other Drugs Act and Harrison Narcotics Act, respectively, but new stimulants soon entered the scene: the amphetamines (ATSs). ATSs are a class of drugs first synthesized in the late 19th century that include amphetamine, dextroamphetamine, and methamphetamine (see Table 5.3). Although amphetamines had been

TABLE 5.3 Amphetamine-Type Stimulants (ATSs)

Generic Names	Brand Names	Slang Terms	Form & Use
Amphetamine	Adderall, Benzedrine	bennies, white crosses	capsule or tablet, taken orally
Dextroamphetamine	Dexedrine, Biphetamine	black beauties, cadillacs, dexies	capsule or tablet, taken orally, smoked or injected intravenously
Methamphetamine	Desoxyn	speed, crank, ice, crystal, meth	powder, taken orally, snorted or injected
Methylphenidate	Ritalin, Concerta	vitamin R	capsule or tablet, taken orally
Methcathinone	—	cat	whitish powder mixed with commercial products, smoked in crack pipe, snorted or orally with liquid

available for research for many years, the first medical applications were developed in the 1920s and were patented in 1932. Amphetamines have been used as a treatment for cold and sinus symptoms (the original inhalers contained Benzedrine, an amphetamine), obesity, narcolepsy (a disease in which the patient uncontrollably falls asleep), and paradoxically, attention deficit/hyperactivity disorder. Amphetamines also have a high potential for abuse. Soldiers on both sides during World War II used these drugs for their stimulant properties. After the war, amphetamine abuse reached epidemic proportions in Japan, Sweden, and other parts of Europe, yet the drugs were not recognized as dangerous in Canada and the United States until the 1960s.

The use of injected amphetamine resulted in a pattern of abuse reminiscent of the cocaine problems seen at the turn of the century and again today. Users experience a brief but intense "flash" or "rush" immediately after the drug is injected. The strongly pleasurable feeling produced following amphetamine or cocaine injection is often described as orgasmic in nature, but because it lasts only a few minutes, users are soon craving a return to the heights of pleasure even though the level of the drug in the body remains high. A series of injections often follows; users become more and more stimulated but have difficulty obtaining a rush as pleasurable as the first. Because both cocaine and amphetamines suppress appetite and prevent sleep, people may go for days without sleep, eating very little and administering dose after dose.

In the 1960s, people who engaged in this pattern of use came to be called "speed freaks." When speed freaks burst onto the drug scene, it became clear that amphetamine shares virtually all the effects of cocaine. For example, when dose levels of amphetamine get large enough, users develop formication symptoms (called "speed bugs" or "crank bugs" by users) and paranoid delusions (called **stimulant psychosis**). By the late 1960s amphetamine overdose deaths had occurred, but they were relatively rare. Far more common was the development of a paranoid state that often led to acts of violence. In addition, after a long binge of amphetamine abuse, users may crash (sleep for an extended period) and then awaken deeply depressed. The depression could last for days and is now recognized as a common withdrawal symptom after heavy use of either amphetamine or cocaine. The depression often leads users back to drugs to try to get "up" again, and the cycle is repeated. Eventually, users' physical and mental health deteriorates badly unless

stimulant psychosis
Paranoid delusions and disorientation resembling the symptoms of paranoid schizophrenia, caused by prolonged use or overdose of cocaine and/or amphetamine.

they can break out of the cycle. As a result of the potential dangers and abuse of ATSs, there are limited medical uses in Canada. Today, ATSs are used in the treatment of narcolepsy, **attention-deficit hyperactivity disorder (ADHD),** and Parkinson's disease.

attention-deficit hyperactivity disorder (ADHD)
It is a behavioural disorder, more commonly diagnosed in children, characterized by an individual's inattention, disorganized thinking, and failure to complete tasks.

The Re-Emergence of Methamphetamines

Although restrictions on cocaine and amphetamines in Canada and the United States were in place, the dangers of illicit distribution of these stimulants grew during the 1980s. A more potent form of amphetamines began to appear on the street, called 'ice,' 'crystal,' 'crank,' or 'meth.' This led to the re-emergence of methamphetamines in the early 1990s. Illegal methamphetamine laboratories began to spring up with great frequency in the midwest United States and in western Canada in the late 1990s, and by 2005 production had spread to the eastern United States and metropolitan cities in Canada. Some describe methamphetamine use as reaching epidemic proportions across the United States (not Canada), but use today is relatively stable and still remains most concentrated in the west and midwestern regions of the country (Owen, 2007). Distribution of methamphetamine use is not well documented in Canada; however, recent focus on crystal meth abuse in British Columbia has alerted RCMP to take note of crystal meth's popularity as the drug of choice for youths (see Drugs and Culture Box 5.2).

The focus of the potential for harm from meth use became extended due to dangers related to meth production in small "kitchen" labs. It does not require much space or sophisticated equipment to produce meth, and a meth lab can be set up easily in a garage, shed, or trailer. As these "kitchen" meth labs proliferated around the country, new problems emerged. Many of the chemicals used to produce meth are highly flammable, and the process also requires that the ingredients be heated with a burner; therefore, a significant risk of explosion and fire is present. Several of the chemicals used to make meth are toxic, as are some of the by-products that can cause significant health hazards wherever they are dumped. As a result, meth labs represent a biohazard not only to those making the drug but to nearby residents as well (Halkitis, 2009).

DRUGS AND CULTURE BOX 5.2

Crystal Meth Across Canada

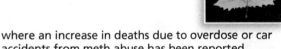

The CBC *Fifth Estate* documentary series in 2005, titled "Dark Crystal," reported on the rise of crystal meth across Canada in the last five years. The documentary noted the increase of clandestine methamphetamine laboratories seized in Canada, from four in 1998 to 37 in 2003. Because of the tighter controls in the United States on the sale and purchase of pseudoephedrine (active ingredient in crystal meth), illegitimate drug-making labs began to be set-up and an increase in meth use among Canadian youths (predominantly in Alberta and British Columbia) was evident.

Outlaw motorcycle gangs, Asian crime groups, and independent trafficking networks became heavily involved in the production and trafficking of methamphetamine. At the same time, the RCMP noticed that the use of amphetamines had spread to the mainstream rave and club scenes. The biggest problem with crystal meth is in British Columbia,

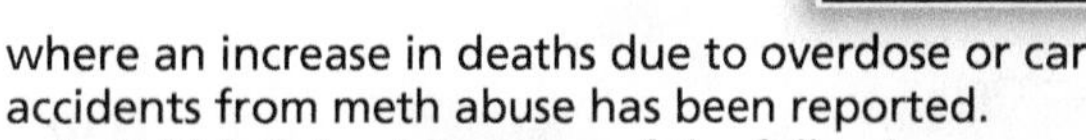

where an increase in deaths due to overdose or car accidents from meth abuse has been reported.

In British Columbia, some of the following problems related to the increase in meth use were reported:

- meth-related deaths have increased;
- there has been a rise in crimes, such as car theft, fraud, sexual assault, connected to meth abuse; and
- charges in possession, trafficking, importation, and production of synthetic drugs have risen significantly.

For more information on the "Dark Crystal" report, access the CBC *Fifth Estate* website, where you will find detailed stories about crystal meth problems.

Source: CBC. The Fifth Estate, "Dark Crystal," (2005) Report aired March 23, 2005.

CONTEMPORARY ISSUE BOX 5.3

Methamphetamine and Health

In addition to the hazards associated with meth production, heavy meth users risk a number of health problems. Exposure to very high doses poses a risk of seizures, convulsions, and cardiovascular collapse. Overdose can also produce the paranoid symptoms of stimulant psychosis often associated with violent behaviour. A study of young adults who were heavy meth users found that over one-third of the respondents reported committing acts of violence while under the influence of meth (Sommers, Baskin, & Baskin-Sommers, 2006). Chronic users face additional problems. Depression is a common feature of methamphetamine withdrawal syndrome. "Meth mouth," characterized by deterioration and loss of teeth, is also common among heavy users (Halkitis, 2009). Another issue has surfaced recently. Several studies in animals and humans suggest that methamphetamine may produce long-lasting damage to the brain. Using PET scan technology to study chronic methamphetamine users, two independent research teams have reported damage in the dopaminergic pathways. The brain damage may sometimes be associated with long-lasting motor and memory impairments. However, at least some studies have shown improvement in brain and cognitive function after extended periods of abstinence from meth, so these changes may not be permanent (Caligiuri & Buitenhuys, 2005; Iversen, 2008; Volkow et al., 2001; Yuan et al., 2006).

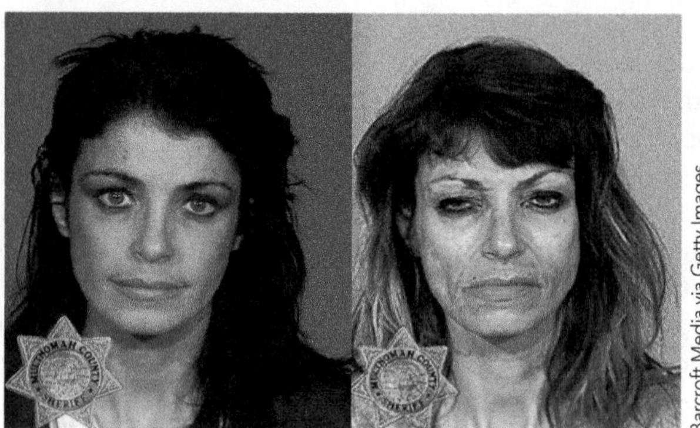

Barcroft Media via Getty Images

Continued use of Crystal Meth causes physical deterioration of the body. This 'face of meth' demonstrates the negative physical consequences of regular meth use. This 'face' image is also used in educational campaigns that target youth to deter them from using meth.

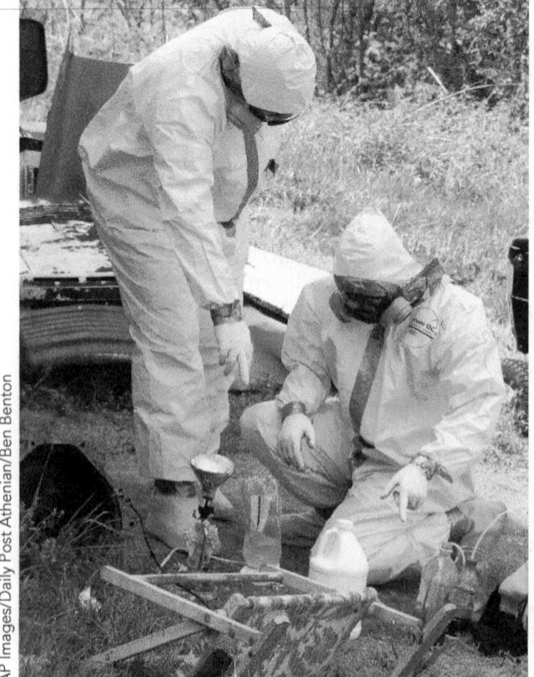

AP Images/Daily Post Athenian/Ben Benton

Law enforcement officers clean up hazardous waste from a small "kitchen" meth lab.

Meth users are also at risk for a number of health complications that we review in Contemporary Issue Box 5.3.

The emerging use of crystal meth in First Nations communities has also been observed. Some statistics reveal a higher crystal meth problem in areas of Canada where there are higher First Nations populations, such as Saskatchewan. For example, Yorkton, SK reports 33 percent user rate of crystal meth (First Nations Centre, 2006). However, it does not differentiate between First Nations and non-First Nations. The concern for First Nations meth abuse grows as these areas report higher meth user rates, especially in rural communities where First Nations populations live.

Most meth labs use pseudoephedrine (or ephedrine) as a key chemical component. Pseudoephedrine is used in a wide variety of over-the-counter cold formulations (see Chapter 13) and, until recently, was easily obtained. In an effort to shut down "kitchen" meth labs, the United States Combat Methamphetamine Epidemic Act went into effect in 2006. This Act now regulates sales of any products containing pseudoephedrine and ephedrine. Sales are restricted to pharmacies and, although no prescription is required, the drugs must be kept behind the counter and pharmacists are required to record each purchase and purchaser. The amount that any individual may purchase is restricted to relatively low levels.

THIS IS YOUR BRAIN ON STIMULANTS

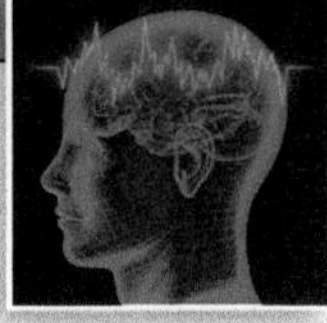

How Cocaine Produces Euphoria and Why People "Crash"

A. In the normal functioning of the nervous system, neurotransmitters are released into the synaptic cleft by vesicles in terminal buttons of sending neurons. Many are taken up by receptor sites in receiving neurons.

B. In the process called *reuptake*, sending neurons typically reabsorb excess molecules of neurotransmitters.

C. Molecules of cocaine bind to the sites on sending neurons that normally reuptake molecules of neurotransmitters. As a result, molecules of norepinephrine, dopamine, and seratonin remain longer in the synaptic cleft, increasing their typical mood-altering effects and providing a euphoric "rush." When the person stops using cocaine, the lessened absorption of neurotransmitters by receiving neurons causes the person's mood to "crash."

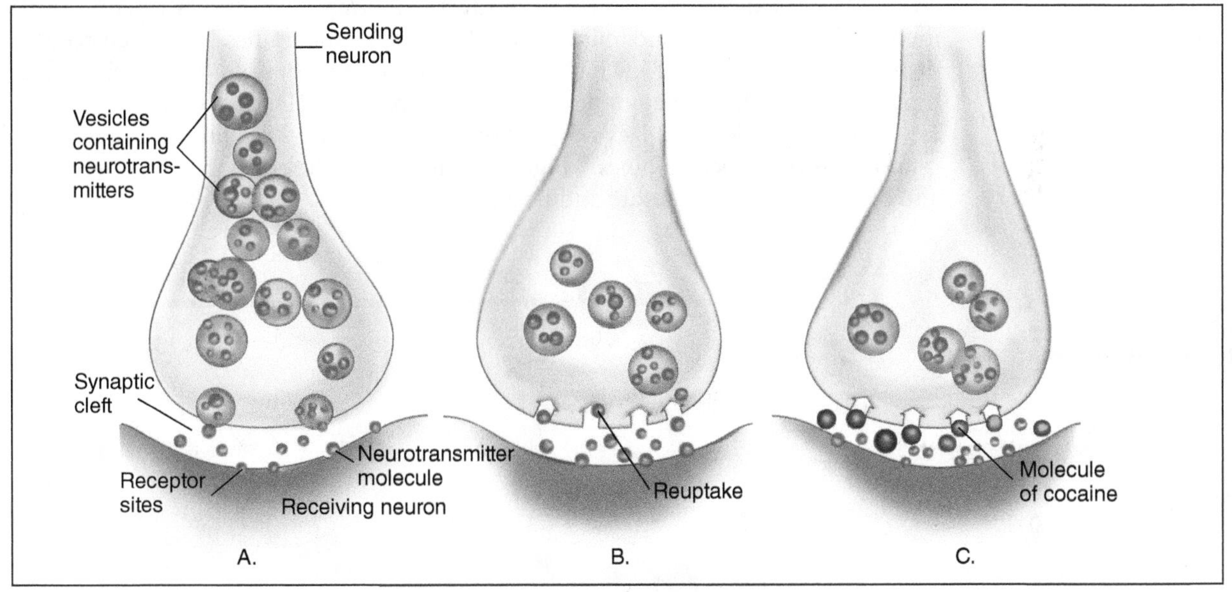

S. Rathus, S. Maheu, & S. Veenvliet. *PSYCH*, 1e. © 2012 Nelson Education Ltd. Reproduced by permission. www.cengage.com/permissions

Pharmacokinetics of Stimulants

As noted, stimulant drugs may be administered and absorbed in a variety of ways, and their intensity and duration of action vary accordingly. Cocaine, amphetamines, and **amphetamine-type stimulants (ATSs)** are readily absorbed after oral administration, but the onset of drug action is slower and the peak effect somewhat less than with other methods. Both cocaine and ATSs are commonly administered intranasally, and the absorption properties are similar to those associated with oral administration (Iversen et al., 2009). In contrast to oral or intranasal routes, which require 10–15 minutes for drug action to begin, intravenous injection of stimulants results in intense effects within 30 seconds. When crack cocaine and crystal methamphetamine are smoked in the form of crack or freebase, the onset of action is even faster (Jones, 1987a).

amphetamine-type stimulants (ATSs)
Refer to a group of drugs which commonly include amphetamine, methamphetamine and methcathinone. There are others, such as MDMA or "Ecstasy"—an amphetamine-type derivative with hallucinogenic properties.

In general, the effects of stimulant drugs are quite similar. One important difference between cocaine and ATSs is their duration of action. Cocaine is metabolized rapidly, with most of its effects dissipating 20–80 minutes after administration (Newton et al., 2005). Cocaine or its metabolites (chemicals produced when the drug is broken down in the body) are detectible in human urine for two to three days after administration (Hawks & Chiang, 1986). Amphetamines are much longer acting, with effects that persist from four to 12 hours (Newton et al., 2005), and they or their metabolites are also detectible in urine for two to three days (Hawks & Chiang, 1986).

Mechanisms of Action

As noted in Chapter 3, stimulant drugs such as cocaine and ATSs are thought to affect the brain primarily through complex actions on monoamine neurotransmitters: dopamine, norepinephrine, and serotonin. For example, both cocaine and the amphetamines block reuptake of dopamine, norepinephrine, and serotonin. In addition, ATSs and methylphenidate also increase the release of dopamine and norepinephrine (Iversen et al., 2009). Thus, the initial effect of stimulants is to produce a storm of activity in neural pathways that are sensitive to the monoamine transmitters. Because of this increased activity, however, and particularly because reuptake is blocked so that enzymes break down the neurotransmitters, the long-term effects of stimulant use involve depletion of monoamines. Low levels of monoamines are linked to clinical depression (see Chapter 3), which is the basis for one theory of why the aftereffects of heavy cocaine and amphetamine use involve depression (Dackis & Gold, 1985). The feeling of depression and lack of joy is so common during cocaine withdrawal that it is known as the "cocaine blues." Figure 5.1 illustrates the relationship between mood and cocaine use for moderate and heavy use.

FIGURE 5.1 Relationship between cocaine dose and mood

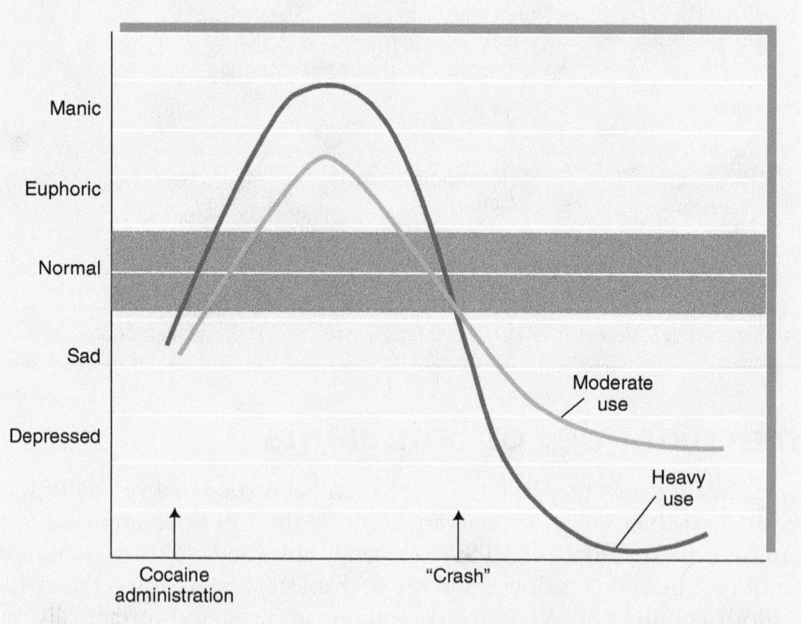

The peak at the left shows the mood elevation that occurs upon cocaine administration; the valley at right depicts the consequent depression. The depression of mood is greater with heavy use. Note that these general observations seem to hold for the dose in a single session and longer-term use. However, the depressive abstinence syndrome is thought to be stronger and last longer in those who have been abusing the drug for an extended period. The function for amphetamines is of similar shape, but is more extended because of their longer duration of action. Of considerable concern is that some alterations in the monoamine systems after chronic stimulant use may be long-term or even permanent (Koob & Le Moal, 2006).

Acute Effects at Low and Moderate Doses

Physiological Effects

Stimulant drugs produce physiological effects that are observable outside the brain. We discuss the effects of cocaine and amphetamines together because, for all practical purposes, their measurable effects are identical. Although users often claim to notice subjective differences between stimulants, even experienced stimulant users under controlled laboratory conditions cannot discriminate among the effects of cocaine, amphetamines, and methylphenidate except for the different durations of action (Fischman, 1984; Sevak et al., 2009).

Stimulants are classic examples of **sympathomimetic drugs**; that is, they act to stimulate or mimic activity in the sympathetic branch of the autonomic nervous system. Thus, many of their physiological effects are the same as those seen during emotional arousal: heart rate is up, blood pressure is up, respiratory rate is up, and sweating increases. Meanwhile, blood flow decreases to the internal organs and extremities but increases to the large muscle groups and the brain. Finally, body temperature is elevated and pupils are dilated.

sympathomimetic drugs
Drugs that stimulate or mimic actions in the sympathetic branch of the autonomic nervous system.

Cocaine and amphetamines also produce appetite-suppressant or **anorectic effects**. People simply do not feel hunger after taking these drugs. It is the anorectic effects that were sought when amphetamines were prescribed as diet pills. Although patients definitely ate less and lost weight on diet pills, they had to take larger doses to maintain the weight loss, and patients typically regained the weight when they went off the drugs. Thus, the benefits of diet pills were outweighed by the risk of

anorectic effects
Causing one to lose appetite; suppression of eating.

FIGURE 5.2 The effects of cocaine on the body

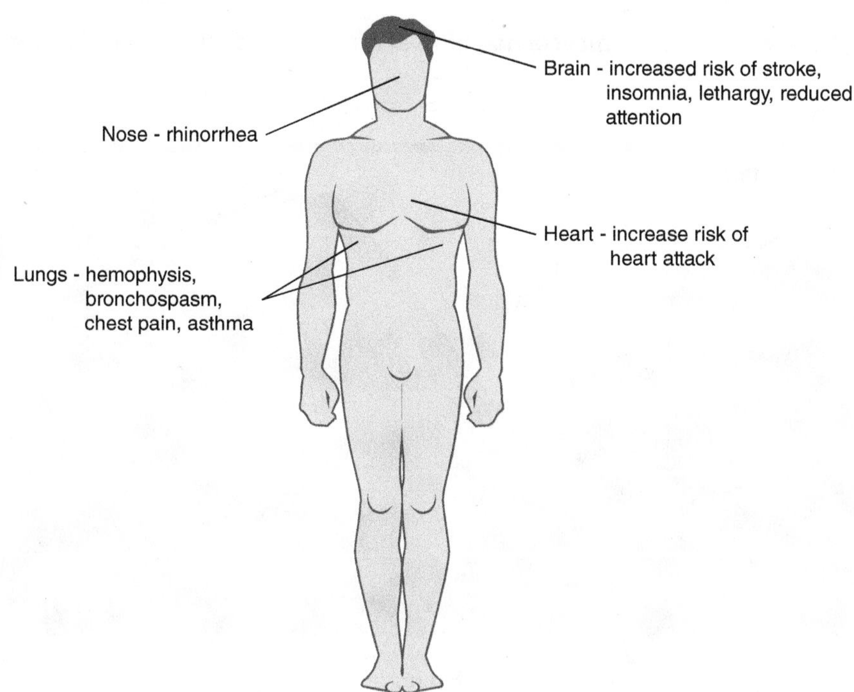

The effects of cocaine on the body are shown in this illustration to demonstrate the hazards and risks to health when using cocaine.

Source: Zubada/Shutterstock

dependence and other side effects. This approach to the treatment of obesity is now considered questionable at best.

Behavioural Effects

Moderate doses of cocaine and amphetamines produce a sense of elation and mood elevation (Hart et al., 2008; Iversen, 2008). Individuals show increased talkativeness and sociability (Higgins & Stitzer, 1988). Alertness and arousal are increased, and marked insomnia often develops. These drugs also enhance performance on a wide variety of tasks involving physical endurance, such as running and swimming, and they increase physical strength. In a review of the literature on amphetamines and sports, Laties and Weiss (1981) concluded that amphetamines offer a small but significant edge to athletes. Consider the effects, shown in Figure 5.3, of methamphetamine on performance on a stationary bicycle. Note that a control injection does little to reverse the effects of fatigue on rate of cycling, but a methamphetamine (Methadrine) injection administered at the three-hour point produces a large improvement that is sustained for several hours. Although the data on cocaine are scantier, it appears to have the same effects but is limited by its short duration of action (Grinspoon & Bakalar, 1976).

state-dependent learning
When learning under the influence of a drug is best recalled when one is in the same "state."

Because stimulants increase resistance to fatigue and boredom, they have often been used as a study aid, as in the amphetamine-induced "all-nighter." Several problems result from this type of stimulant use. One is that information learned under the influence of a drug is best recalled when the individual is in that same drug-induced state. This phenomenon is called **state-dependent learning**, and it is true of a number of drugs other than stimulants (Poling & Cross, 1993). State-dependent

FIGURE 5.3 Performance on a bicycle machine after control and methamphetamine injections

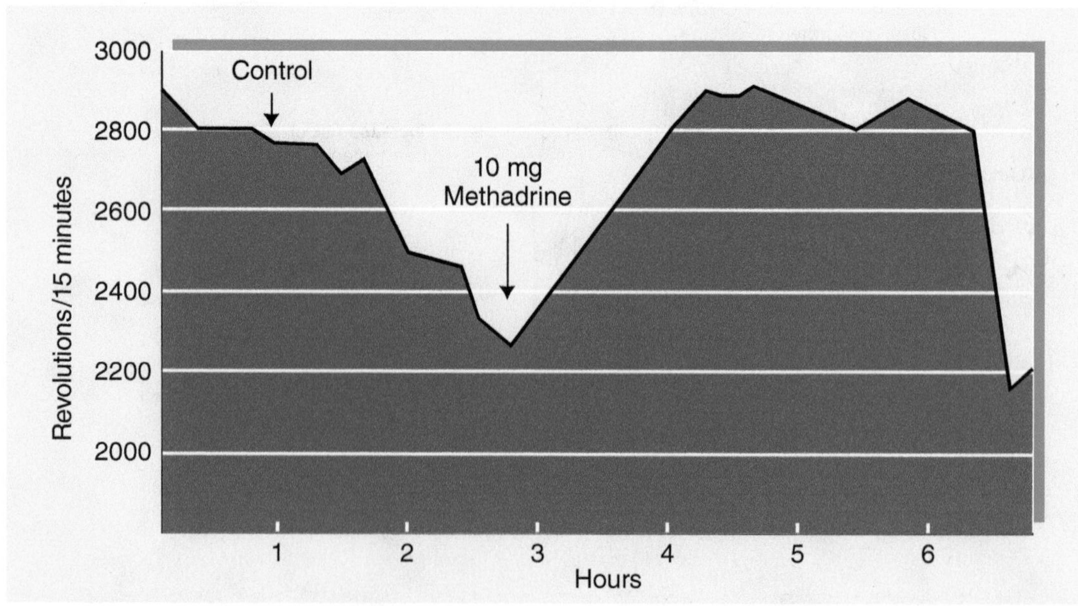

Source: Adapted from "The Amphetamine Margin in Sports," by G. Laties and B. Weiss, in *Federation Proceedings*, 40(12). 1981. Reprinted with permission.

learning suggests that people will have problems learning information when under the influence of a drug because the ability to retrieve the information will not be as good when sober. This debunks the 'myth' of pulling a stimulant-induced all-nighter success.

Stimulants can enhance some types of cognitive performance. They have consistently been shown to speed up performance on a variety of moderately complex cognitive tasks (such as responding to multiple choice questions), but often with the cost of increased errors (Iversen, 2008). However, stimulants may impair one's ability to learn highly complex tasks (Fischman, 1984). Considerable anecdotal evidence suggests that stimulants may impair performance in complex reasoning.

Another popular notion about cocaine and the amphetamines deals with their ability to enhance sexual prowess. The story with this one is complex. Although this has not been well studied, surveys suggest that although some report enhanced sexual feelings and performance with stimulants, most people do not. Men may experience increased sexual desire under stimulant drugs, but these drugs can also interfere with erectile function and often cause impotence (Iversen, 2008). However, in recent years, a trend has emerged in the gay community to combine methamphetamine with drugs designed to treat erectile dysfunction (e.g., Viagra). This drug combination apparently allows users to maintain an erection while under the influence of methamphetamine and has been associated with high frequencies of risky sexual behaviour and an increased probability of testing HIV positive among homosexual men (Halkitis et al., 2009).

Acute Effects at High Doses

As we noted earlier, when people take high doses of stimulant drugs, a characteristic psychotic state emerges. Such psychotic reactions are currently a serious problem with high-dose uses of methamphetamine or crack cocaine. Paranoid delusions are the most common symptom of stimulant psychosis, but a second symptom commonly noted is compulsive stereotyped behaviour like rocking, hair pulling, chain smoking, or "fiddling with things." Other symptoms may include hallucinations and, as noted earlier, formication. Interestingly, stimulant psychosis may be successfully treated with chlorpromazine (Thorazine) or other drugs used in the treatment of schizophrenia (Davis & Schlemmer, 1980).

A risk of overdose death also accompanies high doses of cocaine or amphetamines. Specifying the dose that places users at risk is difficult. With cocaine in particular, when we speak of low to moderate doses, we refer to 15 to 60 milligrams (a typical "line" contains 10 to 20 mg). But cocaine overdose deaths have been reported in individuals who were given as little as 20 milligrams as a local anesthetic, apparently because they suffered from a rare deficiency in the enzyme that breaks down cocaine in the blood and liver (Weiss & Mirin, 1987). Such cases are certainly exceptional, and generally much higher doses are taken before either stimulant psychosis or death results. When very high doses of stimulant drugs are taken, several complications may produce a medical emergency or overdose death. These include convulsions or seizures that may result in respiratory collapse, myocardial infarction (heart attack) due to coronary artery spasm, and stroke (Sorer, 1992). To further complicate matters, users often combine cocaine with other drugs to produce complex and often unpredictable drug interactions (see Contemporary Issue Box 5.4).

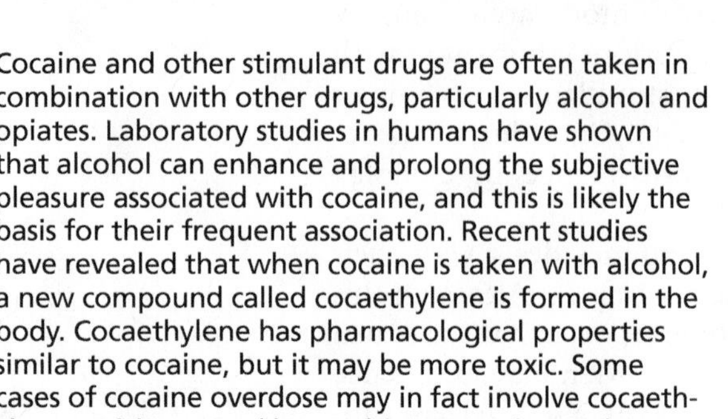

CONTEMPORARY ISSUE BOX 5.4

Mixing Cocaine with Other Drugs

Cocaine and other stimulant drugs are often taken in combination with other drugs, particularly alcohol and opiates. Laboratory studies in humans have shown that alcohol can enhance and prolong the subjective pleasure associated with cocaine, and this is likely the basis for their frequent association. Recent studies have revealed that when cocaine is taken with alcohol, a new compound called cocaethylene is formed in the body. Cocaethylene has pharmacological properties similar to cocaine, but it may be more toxic. Some cases of cocaine overdose may in fact involve cocaethylene toxicity caused by combining cocaine and alcohol (Raven et al., 2000; Rush, Roll, & Higgins, 1998). The combination of cocaine (or amphetamine) and heroin (or other opiate) is called a "speedball" and is particularly popular among heroin addicts. Morphine and cocaine combinations have been studied in the laboratory and, as with alcohol, morphine appeared to enhance the pleasurable effects of cocaine but also increased the cardiovascular effects. Combinations of cocaine and heroin have sometimes been blamed for drug overdose deaths (as in the deaths of comedian John Belushi and actor River Phoenix), and the synergistic effects on blood pressure and heart rate may be a factor (Foltin & Fischman, 1992; Rush et al., 1998) leading to respiratory failure. There are only a few scientific studies into the effects of combining psychoactive drugs. This is likely related to the numerous factors contributing to drug effects for individuals in general. Different people will respond differently to different drugs and drug combinations. Health Canada has recently launched its advertising campaign that includes children calling out the word 'juicy', which is the street name for mixing cocaine and marijuana. Consider the effects of mixing these drugs and the desired effects.

Effects of Chronic Use

Tolerance

When stimulants are taken regularly over a long period (chronic use), several additional problems and issues arise. Users may develop a tolerance for the drug, and this turns out to be fairly complex in the case of the stimulants. First, acute tolerance develops for cocaine; that is, the effects obtained from the first administration of the drug are not produced by a second administration shortly afterward, unless a higher dose is used.

Acute tolerance to the subjective effects of cocaine has been demonstrated in humans in laboratory settings (Ward et al., 1997). This acute tolerance dissipates rapidly too, usually within 24 hours. But studies of the development of long-term protracted tolerance to cocaine and amphetamines have not yielded consistent findings. Ward et al. (1997) found both acute and chronic tolerance to the heart rate increases produced by cocaine in the laboratory. That is, tolerance to the heart rate-increasing effects developed within a single session, and the tolerance persisted and developed further across sessions. However, only acute tolerance was found with the effects of cocaine on blood pressure and subjects' self-reports of stimulation and feeling high. On a given day, the effects of the first cocaine injection were not matched by subsequent injections, but strong effects could still be obtained the next day (Ward et al., 1997).

Comer et al. (2001) studied the effects of chronic methamphetamine use in a 15-day residential study with seven volunteers. The participants lived in the dormitory-style laboratory during the experiment and were given questionnaires several times each day about their subjective state as well as computer-based cognitive and performance tasks. On days 4 through 6 and 10 through 12, they were administered methamphetamine tablets, and on all other days, they received identical placebo tablets. Participants reported feeling a "good drug effect" and "high" on the first day of each methamphetamine run (days 4 and 10), but they did not report these positive effects on the second and third methamphetamine days (days 5 and 6, and days 11 and 12). Instead, on the third methamphetamine days (days 6 and 12), participants reported unpleasant effects such as dizziness and flu-like symptoms. Their food intake declined, and their sleep patterns were also disrupted across each of the methamphetamine exposure periods. In sum, Comer et al. (2001) found that tolerance developed to positive subjective effects of methamphetamine use. The increase in negative effects with repeated administration was attributed in part to the accumulation of sleep loss and reduction of caloric intake. Although there is evidence of tolerance to both cocaine and the amphetamines, some studies have shown the development of what might be termed **reverse tolerance or sensitization** following repeated administration. In these cases, a given dose of cocaine produces a larger effect after one or more repetitions (e.g., Kollins & Rush, 2002). In any case, the occurrence of reverse or regular tolerance may depend on complex aspects of the situation and response being studied (Hughes, Pitts, & Branch, 1996; Reed et al., 2009).

reverse tolerance or sensitization
It is the reversal of the side effects from a drug, such as a user of an ATS becomes more aware of the effects of the drug the longer the usage.

Dependence

For many years, drug dependence was defined by physical withdrawal symptoms like those produced after heroin withdrawal (see Chapter 11). As a result, the severity of cocaine and amphetamine dependence was underestimated because users do not show dramatic signs of physical illness upon withdrawing from these drugs. The broader definition of drug dependence provided by DSM-IV (see Chapter 1) has helped to change perceptions about dependence on stimulants. Although the withdrawal syndrome associated with cocaine or amphetamines does not involve life-threatening physical symptoms, it is real and compelling. The primary symptoms are depression, anxiety, changes in appetite, sleeping disturbances, and craving for the drug (Schuckit, 2000). The temptation to resume use of the drug is described by many as overpowering. Some individuals go through distinct phases of withdrawal, but variability is considerable. The "crash" occurs first and involves several days of intense craving and exhaustion alternating with agitation and depression. Particularly in methamphetamine withdrawal, users may show greatly increased sleep time and food intake during this phase (McGregor et al., 2005). For several weeks, addicts continue to feel intense cravings, moderate to severe depression, and an inability to experience normal pleasure (*anhedonia*). Although improvement gradually occurs, addicts may continue to experience intermittent cravings for months or even years. This phase has been called the *extinction phase* because the cravings seem to be caused by exposure to particular cues in the environment that were associated with cocaine use in the past and continue to "trigger" craving until eventually, perhaps via classical conditioning, the craving response is extinguished to these cues (Halkitis, 2009).

Media reports about the dependency potential to babies born under the influence of cocaine has led to the overstated occurrence of 'crack babies' and the associated negative effects related to dependency. Although reports of the acute negative effects of 'crack babies' has some merit, the long-term effects are less known. See Drugs and Culture Box 5.5 for recent research on these effects.

DRUGS AND CULTURE BOX 5.5

Cocaine Babies: Legacy of the Crack Era?

Taking drugs during pregnancy creates additional risks. Women who use cocaine during pregnancy have higher rates of spontaneous abortion, fetal death, and premature labour and birth. Infants born of cocaine-using mothers had lower birth weights and lengths and were more likely to die during infancy. There has been widespread publicity and concern that children exposed to cocaine in utero would show permanent neurological damage with attendant learning disabilities.

Many reports have indicated a higher percentage of abnormal arousal patterns and other neurological problems in "crack babies." However, these effects may be relatively short-lived. Some studies have reported long-term learning and behaviour problems in children exposed to cocaine in utero, but the studies often lack an appropriate comparison or control group. Remember that "crack babies" are likely to suffer from maternal neglect and an impoverished family and social environment as well. It is difficult to separate the effects of prenatal cocaine exposure from the other problems that the child faces after birth. In studies that have controlled for such factors, "crack babies" generally do not appear to perform worse than the comparison group. Neither group does very well on intellectual tasks, however, with IQ scores well below the national average. Perhaps for children growing up under deprived environmental circumstances, adding cocaine exposure makes little long-term difference. If there is any good news here, it is that the difficulties may not involve permanent neurological damage induced by cocaine. Although well intentioned, labelling children as "crack babies" may stigmatize them and create a self-fulfilling prophecy (see Schama, Howell, & Byrd, 1998; Zuckerman, Frank, & Mayes, 2002, for reviews).

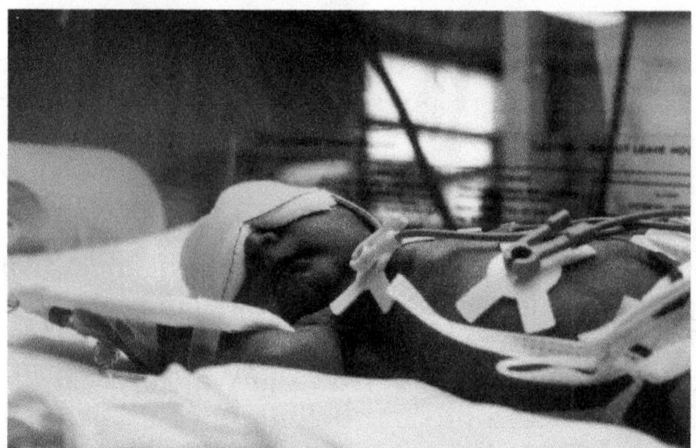

John Chiasson/Getty Images News/Getty Images

Mothers who use cocaine during pregnancy have a higher rate of spontaneous abortion, fetal death, and premature labour. 'Crack babies' are often born addicted to cocaine.

Stimulant Drugs and ADHD

The use of stimulant drugs and attention-deficit/hyperactivity disorder (ADHD) has been a big source of contention for parents, physicians, teachers, and policy. When attention issues are serious enough to interfere with a child's ability to perform in school, the dilemma begins regarding intervention strategies and diagnosis of the behavioural disorder, ADHD. Children with ADHD are not necessarily hyperactive, and many suffer primarily from symptoms of inattention. ADHD often leads to impaired academic performance; misbehaviour at school; and conflict with peers, siblings, and parents. Although some children outgrow ADHD during puberty, more often these problems persist into adulthood.

In 1937, a physician named Charles Bradley discovered what appeared to be an extraordinary paradox: hyperactive children were calmed by a dose of the stimulant drug amphetamine. Since then, many millions of children with ADHD have been treated with stimulant drugs, and methylphenidate (e.g., Concerta and Ritalin) and amphetamines (Adderall*) are now the most widely prescribed treatments for ADHD. The effects of

*Note: In 2005 Health Canada suspended the market authorization of Adderall due to safety information related to death from its use (Consumer Affairs, 2011).

methylphenidate are by and large the same as those of amphetamines reviewed previously in this chapter. Whether stimulants are overprescribed in North America today has become controversial in part because of the enormous increase in prescriptions for Ritalin and other stimulants. Since 1990, use of these stimulants increased by nearly 500 percent, and it is estimated that over two million school-aged children in the United States take Ritalin or some other prescription stimulant drug. Prescription drug sales for ADHD exceeded three billion dollars in 2004 (Cox et al., 2008; Kollins, 2005; Tyre, 2005). In Canada, 10–12 percent of school-aged children (mostly boys) take Ritalin for treatment of ADHD. However, Canada and Britain use about half of what the United States uses and no other country comes close to the American prescription rate (CMAJ, 2001).

We look at the diagnosis of psychological disorders in Chapter 12, but the ADHD controversy is certainly a thorny one. What seems clear is that although many of the symptoms of ADHD (inattention, fidgeting, and restlessness) are indeed common to virtually all children (and adults) these problems are far more severe and debilitating for some children.

One thing is certain. Stimulant drugs *do* improve performance in children with ADHD. Numerous studies have evaluated the effects of Ritalin and other stimulants on children's performance, and it is well documented that these drugs improve attention, time on task, and other measures of classroom performance, while decreasing disruptive behaviour (see Brown et al., 2005, for a review). A recent study showed that children who received medication for ADHD scored higher on standardized tests for mathematics and reading achievement than unmedicated peers with ADHD (Scheffler et al., 2009). There are problems as well, however. Some children experience physical side effects such as insomnia, loss of appetite, and weight loss. Growth delays may occur but are usually managed by giving the child a "drug holiday," often during the summer months, and although some "catching up" may then occur, there is evidence of continued mild growth suppression (Lerner & Wigal, 2008). There are concerns about psychological effects as well. Some have argued that Ritalin is a gateway drug to other stimulants or to other drug-abuse problems, but the literature on this indicates otherwise. Children diagnosed with ADHD are more likely to develop substance-abuse problems as adults, but several studies suggest that boys with untreated ADHD are more likely to develop drug and alcohol problems than are boys with ADHD who were treated with stimulants (see Wilens et al., 2003, for a review).

The short duration of action of Ritalin can also lead to problems. Because the beneficial effects of the drug wear off in about four hours, children often experience a mid-day loss of functioning and have to be given another dose. This entails a visit to the school nurse or other school staff and can lead to compliance problems. An extended-release methylphenidate preparation (Concerta) with a 12-hour duration of action is now widely used to solve this problem.

Although ADHD used to be thought of as a disorder that children "outgrew," the symptoms may persist into adulthood for many individuals. Another source of controversy is that prescription stimulants are increasingly being diverted (illegally sold or traded). In fact, Ritalin (vitamin R) has come to be one of the popular "club" or "dance" drugs because, like amphetamines, it makes users feel energetic and enhances mood (Hall et al., 2005).

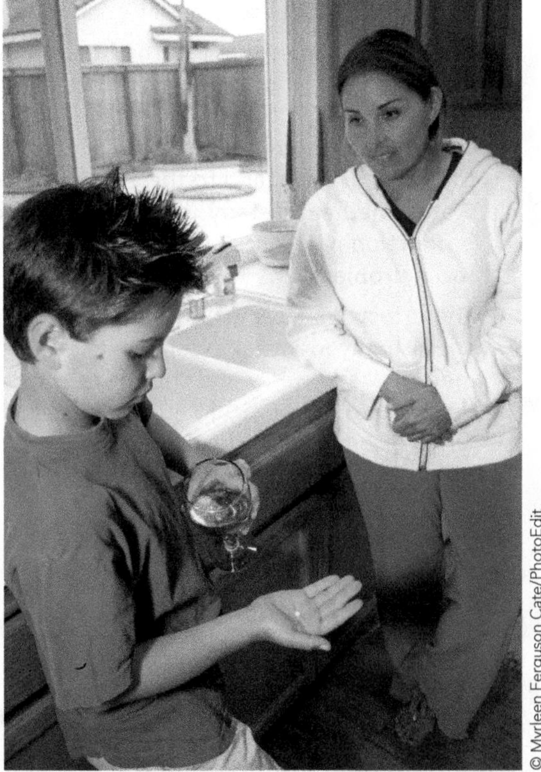

In Canada, 10–12 percent of school-aged children are prescribed Ritalin for the treatment of ADHD.

In summary, Ritalin's advocates view it as a nearly miraculous treatment for ADHD, whereas its detractors argue that it is a greatly overprescribed drug with substantial abuse potential. This controversy cannot be resolved here and is expected to be a major research focus in the next decade. Hopeful developments include the introduction of drugs such as atomoxetine (Strattera) with different mechanisms of action that appear to be effective treatments of ADHD, but that may present fewer problems to users (Prasad et al., 2009).

SUMMARY

- Cocaine comes from the leaves of the coca bush, and the practice of chewing coca leaves by South American Indians goes back many centuries. The Spanish introduced cocaine to Europe, and when the process necessary to separate cocaine from the leaf was developed in the 19th century, a major epidemic of cocaine abuse swept the world.
- Cocaine became one of the most frequently abused drugs in the 1980s and 1990s with the introduction of an inexpensive smokable form—crack.
- Amphetamines are synthetic stimulant drugs discovered in the 1920s. They became major drugs of abuse as well, but their popularity waned in the 1970s and 1980s as cocaine returned to favour.
- Methamphetamine has returned to popularity in recent years, moving from western Canada (primarily British Columbia) and the United States to the major metropolitan areas of Toronto, Montreal, Halifax, and to the eastern United States. Methamphetamine abuse and illegal production have once again become significant social problems.
- The effects of cocaine and the amphetamines are virtually identical except that cocaine is metabolized rapidly and thus has a short duration of action (20 to 80 minutes), whereas amphetamine effects are more prolonged (4 to 12 hours).
- Both cocaine and the amphetamines act through the monoamine neurotransmitter systems, particularly by enhancing dopamine activity. This action in the brain's reward pathways may account for the highly addictive nature of cocaine.
- Both cocaine and the amphetamines are sympathomimetic drugs that increase heart rate, blood pressure, and respiratory rate, and cause pupil dilation.
- Other effects of stimulants include anorectic effects, increased alertness and arousal, mood elevation, and at low doses, enhanced performance on a variety of tasks.
- High doses of cocaine or amphetamines may produce a paranoid state called stimulant psychosis, or death through overdose.
- Dependence may develop after chronic use of cocaine or amphetamines. The abstinence syndrome is characterized primarily by depression and craving with few measurable physiological effects. Thus, a drug that does not cause severe physical withdrawal symptoms can still be highly addictive.
- Ritalin (methylphenidate) and other stimulants are widely used to treat attention deficit/hyperactivity disorder (ADHD) in Canada and the United States.

Key Terms

amphetamine-type stimulants (ATSs) **p. 93**

anorectic effects **p. 95**

attention-deficit hyperactivity disorder (ADHD) **p. 91**

crack **p. 87**

freebasing **p. 87**

reverse tolerance **p. 99**

state-dependent learning **p. 96**

stimulant psychosis **p. 90**

sympathomimetic drugs **p. 95**

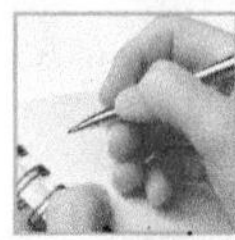

Essays/Thought Questions

1. Consider the different effects and risks associated with the various forms of cocaine (chewing the coca leaf, snorting cocaine, injecting cocaine, and smoking crack). Should different laws and penalties be applied to the different forms?
2. Should drugs be prescribed to children who have ADHD? What about adults?

Suggested Readings

Halkitis, P. N. (2009). *Methamphetamine addiction: Biological foundations, psychological factors, and social consequences.* Washington: American Psychological Association Press.

Iversen, L. (2008). *Speed, ecstasy, Ritalin: The science of amphetamines*. Oxford: Oxford University Press.

CHAPTER 6

Alcohol

Did You Know

?

- Humans have consumed alcohol since between 6000 BCE and 5000 BCE.
- The highest rates of heavy drinking, and thus the greatest vulnerability to drinking problems, are in men between the ages of 18 and 25.
- A lethal dose of alcohol is not as difficult to achieve as you might think according to its toxicity.
- The cognitive deficits that seem to occur in some people as a result of years of heavy drinking are reversible.
- Ten to 20 percent of alcoholics eventually develop cirrhosis of the liver.
- Moderate drinking (one to three drinks a day) is associated with reduced risk of heart disease.

In the preceding chapter, we said alcohol, nicotine, and caffeine are the most popular psychoactive drugs. Of the three, alcohol has by far been known, manufactured, and used the longest. Most important, this drug has had profound influences on the societies around the world in which it is used. "Alcohol" actually refers to several substances—for example, isopropyl alcohol (rubbing alcohol), methyl alcohol (wood alcohol), and ethanol. Ethanol is the alcohol we drink, and the word *alcohol* in this text means ethanol unless otherwise specified.

In this chapter, we give you an overview of the many facets of alcohol use and abuse. We begin with information on the major alcoholic beverages, how they are manufactured, and some history of the use of alcohol. We follow with a discussion of trends in alcohol consumption in Canada, including a discussion of heavy drinking. We also explore more detailed information about alcohol use and patterns of alcohol consumption. With this general background, we then examine the pharmacology of alcohol, including site of action, processing of the drug in the human body, and the development of tolerance and dependence. Then we examine the acute and chronic physiological, psychological, and social consequences of alcohol use in humans. The chapter ends with a discussion of the causes of alcohol dependence.

Alcoholic Beverages

Fermentation and Distillation

Alcohol virtually always is drunk in one of the three major classes of alcoholic beverages: beer, wine, and hard liquor (also called distilled spirits). For their manufacture, all these beverages depend on the process of fermentation, and on the further process of **distillation** for hard liquor. Fermentation begins when sugar is dissolved in water and exposed to air, which creates the perfect environment for living microorganisms called yeasts. In this environment, yeasts multiply rapidly by eating the sugar, which is then converted to ethanol and carbon dioxide by the yeasts' metabolic processes. The carbon dioxide bubbles to the top of the mixture, leaving ethanol. As the yeasts grow, so does the percentage of ethanol—as much as 10–15 percent. At this highest point, the yeasts cease their work. Therefore, fermented beverages do not have an alcohol content higher than 15 percent. Which kind of beverage results from fermentation depends on what sugar-containing substance is used. When grapes are used, the grape juice ferments to form wine; when grains are used, fermentation produces beer.

distillation
The process by which the heating of a fermented mixture increases its alcohol content.

Distillation was developed to increase the ethanol content of fermented beverages. Distillation first involves heating a fermented mixture. Because alcohol has a lower boiling point than water, the steam emitted through boiling has a higher alcohol content than does the original fermented mixture. The vapour then is condensed through cooling, and the resulting liquid has a higher alcohol content than the original fermented mixture. By repeating this cycle, it is possible to raise the alcohol content of a beverage to progressively higher levels.

Martin Benjamin/The Image Works

A variety of alcoholic beverages is available to interested consumers.

Expressing the Alcohol Content of a Beverage

In both Canada and the United States, alcohol percentage is denoted by volume. This calculation is straightforward: 16 ounces of a beverage that is 50 percent ethanol contains eight ounces of alcohol. (Another way of expressing alcohol content is by weight, which is done, for example, in Britain.)

proof
The proportion of alcohol in a beverage, by volume. Proof typically is used in reference to distilled spirits and equals twice the percentage of alcohol.

The alcohol content of a beverage is also designated by **proof**. Proof is used primarily for distilled spirits and is equal to twice the percentage of alcohol by volume. Accordingly, a beverage that is 43 percent alcohol by volume is 86 proof. This somewhat indirect way of expressing alcohol content comes from 17th-century England, where it was determined that a mixture that was 57 percent alcohol by volume, if poured over gunpowder, would cause its ignition in an open flame. The English still refer to their beverages as "over proof" (more than 0.57 percent alcohol by volume) or "under proof" (less than 0.57 percent alcohol by volume) (Becker, Roe, & Scott, 1975).

Table 6.1 is a summary of the major types of alcoholic beverages commercially available. Varying the substances that form the base of the beverage and varying the alcohol concentration produce different alcoholic beverages.

TABLE 6.1 Major Kinds of Alcoholic Beverages, How They Are Made, and Their Alcohol Content

Beverage	How It's Made	Percentage of Alcohol (by volume)
Beer (includes lager, carbohydrate ale, malt, stout)	Lager 3–6, extracted from barley malt (or rice or corn) by cooling with water. The product is boiled with hops, cooled, and fermented. Types of beer vary in malt, hops, and alcohol content	Fermentation of others 4–8
Wine		
Red (table wine)	Fermentation of red grapes in skins	
White (table wine)	Fermentation of skinless grapes	
Champagne	Same as white wine, with carbon dioxide	Average 12
Fortified (dessert) wines	Ordinary table wines with alcohol content raised	Up to 20
Distilled spirits		
Brandy	Distilled from any sugar-containing fruit. Brandy was probably first to be produced commercially.	About 40
Whiskeys	Grains brewed with water to form a beer of 5–10 percent alcohol. Beer is distilled and aged in new or used charred oak barrels for two to eight years before blending.	40–50
Bourbon	Corn with rye and malted barley	
Scotch	Malted barley and corn	
Rye whiskey	Rye and malted barley	
Other spirits		
Rum	Distilled from fermented molasses; aged about three years	40–75
Gin	Distilled from any fermentable carbohydrate (barley, potato, corn, wheat, rye); flavoured by a second distillation with juniper berries	35–50
Vodka	Distilled from potato or almost any other carbohydrate source; kept free of flavours	35–50

Source: Abstracted from C. E. Becker, R. L. Roe, and R. A. Scott (1974), *Alcohol as a Drug*, Krieger Publishing Co.

History of Alcohol Use

Humans have used alcohol for thousands of years. The first nondistilled alcoholic beverages were made inadvertently by natural fermentation. The first wines, which probably were drunk several thousand years ago, were likely made from fruit juice. The juices obtained from most types of fruit are contaminated with microbes, including yeasts, which constitute the flora on the fruit (Rose, 1977). Alcoholic fermentation results when the environmental temperature is right. Researchers believe the first beers were produced in Egypt as long ago as between 6000 BCE and 5000 BCE. Traditionally, it has been thought that the first beer production was similar to baking bread. An earthenware vessel filled with barley was placed in the ground until germination occurred. At that point, the barley was crushed, made into dough, and then baked until a crust formed. This cake of dehydrated dough was soaked in water until fermentation was complete. The resulting product of acid beer was called "boozah." However, a study of beer residue in Egyptian tombs dating to 2000 BCE provides strong evidence that the brewing process of the times was far more sophisticated. The study suggests that the process consisted of blending water and malt to yield a refined liquid (Williams, 1996). The earliest reference to distilled spirits appeared in China about 1000 BCE. Western Europe does not have any record of distilled spirit production and consumption until about 800 CE.

Since the beginning of its use, alcohol has been a double-edged sword to human societies. On the one hand, alcoholic beverages have played a role in important social occasions, such as births, religious ceremonies, marriages, and funerals. Such drinking was not viewed as harmful to individuals and as positive to societies. On the other hand, alcohol seemingly always has been consumed in excess by some, with consequent problems to individuals and to the society in which they lived. Such negative social consequences have led the clergy, prophets, physicians, and philosophers to repeatedly condemn alcohol (Keller, 1979).

The two faces of alcohol were seen clearly when distilled spirits came to western Europe. Many Europeans sang the praises of this drug. For example, a French professor in the 13th century dubbed alcohol *aqua vitae*, which means "water of life." The Danes expressed the same sentiment with their *akkevitt*; the Swedes, with *akvavit*. European societies also attributed many of their problems to alcoholic beverages, especially distilled spirits. For instance, the social problems in 18th-century England were represented in works of art such as William Hogarth's "Gin Lane."

Colonial America adopted alcoholic beverages and many drinking customs from western Europe. In Colonial America, the tavern was the centre of town politics, business, trade, and pleasure. These Americans drank beer, wine, cider, and distilled spirits in considerable quantities. The practice of drinking was pervasive: Colonial American drinking showed no distinction among time, place, or person. The attitudes toward alcohol consumption were positive, and alcohol was viewed as meeting an array of physical, psychological, and social needs. With such supporting attitudes and customs, America became known as a country of drunkards. In 1790, adult citizens of the young country annually drank six gallons of pure alcohol per capita, and by 1830, per capita alcohol consumption had risen to seven gallons. That amounts to almost five alcoholic beverage drinks a day for each adult! With this consumption, the ills of heavy drinking became more evident, especially in a society that was moving increasingly toward urbanization and industrialization. Some people began to speak out against the ravages of alcohol, again mostly in reference to distilled spirits. The most influential among these critics, and a pillar of the temperance movement that was to gain strength in the 19th century, was the physician Benjamin Rush. Dr. Rush's 1785 treatise, "Inquiring into the Effects of Distilled Spirits on the Human Body and Mind," delineated the effects of distilled spirits on humans. It also was the basis of the idea that alcoholism is a disease.

The Trustees of the British Museum/Art Resource, NY.

Eighteenth-century Colonial Americans tended to attribute many of their social problems to alcoholic beverages, particularly distilled spirits. In 1737, Benjamin Franklin published a "Drinkers Dictionary," which included more than 235 terms to describe the drunkard. Included among these were "Loaded his cart," "Cock ey'd," "Moon-ey'd," "Tipsy," and "He carries too much sail" (Mendelson & Mello, 1985).

In the 19th century, America expanded westward, and with that came the saloon. The word *saloon* comes from the French word *salon*, which refers to a public meeting place and entertainment hall. The saloon did serve a social function for the frontier people, but it quickly moved away from a centre of civilized interchange to a reflection of the rural community of the American West (Mendelson & Mello, 1985). The first saloons were not exactly pictures of fine carpentry; as little as a tent and a few barrels might make up the bar (Mendelson & Mello, 1985). This decor was in tune with the typical clientele, which was made up of aggressive men who were inclined to exploit other men, women, and nature. These explorers, soldiers, Native Americans, trappers, settlers, and cowboys had few of the attachments to family or community that might have helped to limit excessive drinking. Instead, their drinking in the saloon was characterized by downing large quantities of whiskey for the purpose of engaging in violent behaviour (Keller, 1979). The whiskey was plentiful and usually wretched (common names for it included "extract of scorpions" and "San Juan paralyzer").

The behaviour associated with the saloon led to a rebirth of the temperance movement, which had been quieted somewhat by the American Civil War. The saloon was the focal scapegoat of the temperance movement and was blamed for social ills such as thievery, gambling, prostitution, and political corruption. The temperance movement also changed its stand from support of moderate use of nondistilled beverages to total abstinence from alcohol. The captains of industry of the late 19th and early 20th centuries, such as John D. Rockefeller, Andrew Carnegie, and Henry Ford, supported the temperance movement. They believed that sober employees would be better employees. These industrial giants also gave money to back their moral support.

The public remains ambivalent about alcohol. This is reflected in the saying, "everybody enjoys a drink, but nobody enjoys a drunk." Since the 1980s, the general trend in Canada and the United States has been toward limiting alcohol's use through changes in social attitudes and tighter governmental controls. Drinking remains a major part of many social rituals, however, and many people hail the benefits of moderate alcohol consumption. The negative consequences of excessive alcohol use are probably more apparent than ever because of activists with access to sophisticated communications techniques, yet they and government regulations are far from successful in stopping or limiting alcohol consumption. This seems to be especially true among people who have alcohol dependence.

NYPL/Science Source/Getty Images

Benjamin Rush was the first American to call chronic drunkenness a distinct disease. In his pamphlet *Inquiring into the Effects of Distilled Spirits on the Human Body and Mind* (1785) he proposed: 1) hard liquor is an addictive substance; 2) there exists a compulsion to drink that arises from a loss of control; 3) frequent drunkenness is a disease, and; 4) total abstinence is the only way to cure a drunkard (Katcher, 1993).

Consumption of Alcohol and Heavy Drinking in Canada

Several trends in alcohol use were discussed in Chapter 1. Here we discuss the prevalence of specific alcoholic beverages and the prevalence and correlates of heavy drinking.

Prevalence of Alcohol Use in Canada

The Canadian Alcohol and Drug Use Monitoring Survey (2009) reports the prevalence and patterns of use across Canada. As tabled in Chapter 1, 76.1 percent of Canadians reported drinking in the past 12 months. These reports are used to estimate the number of people that consume alcohol generally and are used to report consumption rates within each province. The "quantity of alcohol" part of the computation is based on beverage sales figures federally and provincially. In 2009, beer and liquor stores in Canada sold $19.4 billion worth of alcoholic beverages. The quantities of different types of beverages (beer, wine, hard liquor) are translated to amounts (in gallons) of pure alcohol according to standard alcohol equivalence formulas. Therefore, this equates to 226.4 million litres of absolute alcohol.

General trends in consumption of all alcoholic beverages show that beer is the drink of choice, both in volume and dollar value. In 2009 Canadians purchased

TABLE 6.2 Market Share of Alcoholic Beverages, 1997 and 2007

	1997 (% of market share)	2007 (% of market share)
Beer	52	47
Wine	21	28
Liquor (distilled spirits)	27	25

Source: Table 4-1 Sales of alcoholic beverages per capita, 15 years and over-Value. Statistics Canada, *The Control and Sale of Alcoholic Beverages in Canada*, 63-202-XWE2007000, March 2007.

2.3 billion litres of beer (Statistics Canada, 2009). Table 6.2 above reflects the market share for beer, wine, and liquor. Canadians consume approximately:

- 1.5 litres of wine per year;
- 2 litres of liquor per year; and
- 4 litres of beer per year; for a total of 7.5 litres of pure alcohol per person per year (Statistics Canada, 2009).

The proportion of alcohol consumption is related to the value of sales of alcoholic beverages per capita. The value of sales of alcoholic beverages in Canada in 2007 is $667.3 per capita. Figure 6.1 shows the per capita distribution of sales by province. Territories in the north have the highest per capita sales; Manitoba and Saskatchewan have the lowest.

Generally speaking the rates of consumption in each province range near the national average of 76.5 percent although several provinces are statistically significantly lower than the average (see Chapter 1, Table 1.5).

Essential to any discussion of alcohol is the rate of "heavy" drinking. Of course, what is "heavy" is open to wide interpretation and is highly dependent on the setting where the drinking occurs. From a public health point of view, however, what is called "heavy" is drinking that is associated with negative consequences: accidents, job and family problems, and symptoms of dependence on alcohol (such as an inability to cut down on drinking and memory loss associated with drinking). What seems to be important is the volume consumed on one drinking occasion, even if these occasions do not occur with great frequency (Midanik & Room, 1992).

FIGURE 6.1 Value of sales of alcoholic beverages per capita, 2007

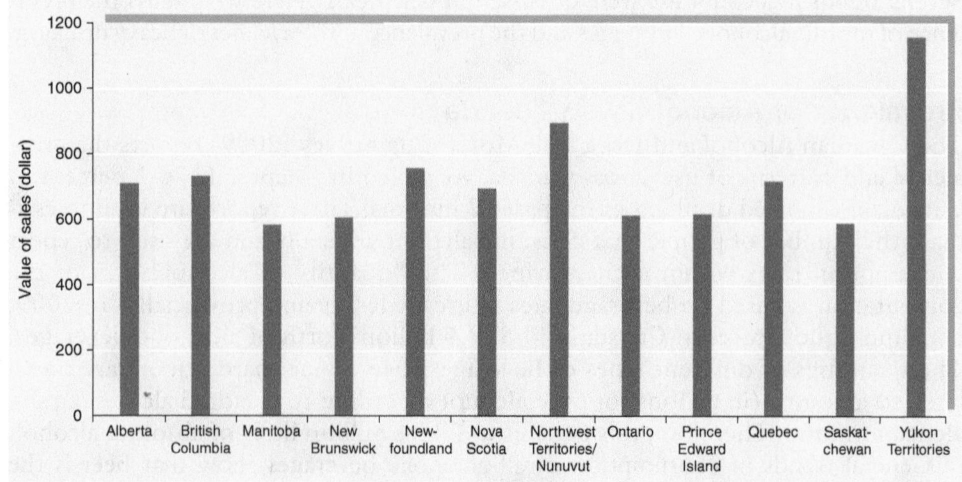

Source: Table 4-1 Sales of alcoholic beverages per capita, 15 years and over - Value. Statistics Canada, *The Control and Sale of Alcoholic Beverages in Canada*, 63-202-XWE2007000, March 2007.

According to CADUMS (2009) five percent of Canadians labelled themselves as heavy frequent drinkers (consuming five drinks or more per drinking occasion, once or more per week per year). Four percent of Canadians reported heavy infrequent (less frequent than once per week per year) drinking. Men reported more prevalence of drinking (8.2 percent) than women (2.3 percent) and heavy drinking among youth (ages 15–24 years) is three times higher than the rate for adults 25 years or older. Equally interesting consumption reports include the following statistics*:

- 67 percent of Canadians label themselves as light drinkers (consuming less than five drinks per occasion)
- 36 percent label themselves as light infrequent drinkers (less than once per week)
- 31 percent drink frequently (more than once per week)
- 12 percent label themselves as abstainers (never used alcohol in their life)
- 12 percent label themselves as past drinkers

Consumption of Alcohol and Heavy Drinking among College and University Students

Alcohol consumption among college and university students has been discussed for a long time and regularly receives attention from the media, educators, and national politicians. Indeed, drinking has been such a large part of life at most colleges and universities that many believe there is a campus "culture of alcohol" (National Institute on Alcohol Abuse and Alcoholism [NIAAA], 2002; 2008). That is, on many campuses, a tradition of customs and beliefs regarding alcohol permeates campus social life, and each generation of students passes it on to the next.

Heavy drinking and 'binge drinking' among undergraduates attracts national attention because it is associated with accidental death, injury, assault, unwanted and unprotected sex, drunk driving, vandalism, suicide, and academic problems (Neal & Fromme, 2007).

The typical college or university student is in the young adult age range (18–24 years). National surveys of both Canadian and U.S. colleges and universities have been conducted for at least a decade. These surveys have found generally that majority of college and university women and men who respond to college and university questionnaires report that they drank alcohol in the last year. For many of the students, "binge drinking"—consuming at least five (for men) or four (for women) drinks on at least one occasion—tends to be the most common consumption pattern throughout their college or university experience.

The most recent research on college and university drinking conducted by the Harvard School of Public Health and the Centre for Addiction and Mental Health compared the drinking habits of students in the United States and Canada (Meichun, 2002). The findings from this research comparison demonstrate that more Canadian students drink alcohol than American; however, American college students tend to drink more heavily (41 percent versus 35 percent, respectively). Several other findings are noted in the Drugs and Culture Box 6.2.

Various other studies in the U.S. have found that students who drink the least attend religious schools, commuter schools, and historically black colleges and universities. The students who drink the most are first-year students, whites, members of fraternities and sororities, and athletes (NIAAA, 2002).

Research on college and university students' drinking patterns have led to an increase on alcohol prevention efforts. Most of these prevention programs target beliefs about

* Statistics Canada, *The Control and Sale of Alcoholic Beverages in Canada,* 2007 Statistics Canada, Catalogue no. 63-202-X.

CONTEMPORARY ISSUE BOX 6.1

Patterns of Alcohol Use: Cultural and Social Factors

It is important to note that drinking patterns and practices among countries differ. These differences are often noted on the basis of history, ethnic, and social factors that underlie various countries views of alcohol. Have a look at how culture has shaped drinking patterns and practices in other countries.

Irish Culture

- The Irish culture is associated with heavy drinking of liquor, often attributed to early invasions by Vikings (known for heavy drinking practices) during the development of national identity.
- Irish families forbid children and young adults to drink; but it is expected that adult men drink excessively.
- Hard liquor is more commonly promoted than beer in pubs, restaurants, and bars.
- Drinking is encouraged outside of the family system.
- Irish people consume approximately 131 litres of beer per capita.

Italian Culture

- The Italian culture is associated with celebratory drinking during holidays, family gatherings, etc.
- Children are offered glasses of wine from an early age as participants in celebrations.
- Disapproval of intoxication within the family setting is set as an important consideration.
- Italy is second to France in wine consumption per capita.

French Culture

- The French culture is associated with drinking wine, usually consumed at dinner.
- Wine is associated with virility (masculine, manly, strong).
- The French drink more alcohol per capita than any other country.

Czechoslovakian Culture

- The Czechoslovakian culture is known as the world's leading beer drinkers (averaging 157 litres per capita).
- Beer is represented in all social and cultural events.

Interestingly, Canada ranks 19th in per capita beer consumption.

DRUGS AND CULTURE BOX 6.2

Highlights from the First National Comparison of Alcohol Use among U.S. and Canadian College Students

Based on the 1999 College Alcohol Study and the 1998 Canadian Campus Survey, the responses of 12 344 American and 6729 Canadian students under the age of 25 were compared to discover similarities and difference in prevalence and consumption use among college students in North America.

Several key findings are noted in the table below:

Prevalence	Canada	United States
Lifetime use of alcohol	92%	86%
Past year use of alcohol	87%	81%
Heavy alcohol use in the past year	35%	41%
Heavy alcohol use in the past week	42%	54%

It was also found that students living at home with their parents are less likely to be heavy drinkers than students who live on campus. Heavy alcohol use is more prevalent among underage students than legal-aged students. Despite the differences in the drinking age among Canada and the U.S., heavy alcohol use is more prevalent among students age 20 or younger.

Overall, the findings suggest that college and university drinking patterns are significantly influenced by the post-secondary environment. Differences between alcohol use in Canada and the U.S. are only slighted by the proportion of heavy usage among U.S. college students.

Think now about your own drinking practices: Would you report a similar pattern of alcohol use as reported here? If not, why do you think that is the case? How do you think living at home during the college or university years affects drinking behaviour?

Source: Adapted from: *College Alcohol Study*, Press Release; "Highlights from the First National Comparison of Alcohol Use among U.S. and Canadian College Students." Harvard School of Public Health (2005).

alcohol and try to increase students' awareness of the negative consequences of heavy drinking. In other words, prevention programs try to change the alcohol culture on campuses. Other possible ways to reduce heavy alcohol use involve environmental change. Examples are decreasing alcohol's availability to underage drinkers, raising alcohol prices and taxes, introducing responsible beverage service, limiting the number of places where alcohol can be purchased, and changing the hours of service and days of sale (NIAAA, 2008; Wechsler et al., 2002).

In conclusion, heavy drinking among college and university students has drawn attention not because it predicts that students will have alcohol problems after they leave college or university. Research has shown that significant percentages of people who do have alcohol problems as adults drank heavily in college and university, but most people who drink heavily in college and university do not have later alcohol problems. Rather, heavy drinking among college and university students gets attention because it is associated with serious consequences for students while they are students—that is, right now.

THIS IS YOUR BRAIN ON ALCOHOL

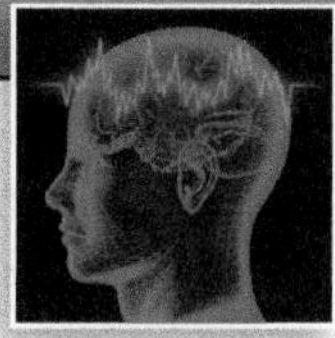

Alcohol is a drug that depresses the CNS; that is, it slows the brain down. It exerts its effects by dissolving in lipid membranes, which disturbs the normal chemical actions that occur there (Rall, 1990b). Actually pinpointing a site of action or a single mechanism of alcohol effects is difficult because alcohol affects cell membranes, all neurochemical systems, and all endocrine systems (Abel, 1985).

A. In the normal functioning of the nervous system, neurotransmitters are released into the synaptic cleft by vesicles in terminal buttons of sending neurons. Many are taken up by receptor sites in receiving neurons.

B. In the process called *reuptake*, sending neurons typically reabsorb excess molecules of neurotransmitters.

C. Alcohol alters the cell membranes' anatomy by entering their internal structure. The result is reduced efficiency of conduction of neural impulses along axons, which reduces the action potential that reaches the synapse. As a result, the transmission of impulses across the synapse by GABA neurotransmitters are inhibited. This slows down the central nervous system, and the resulting effects are slower reaction time among others. There is increasing evidence that alcohol enhances serotonin and dopamine activity (Julien, 2005) also.

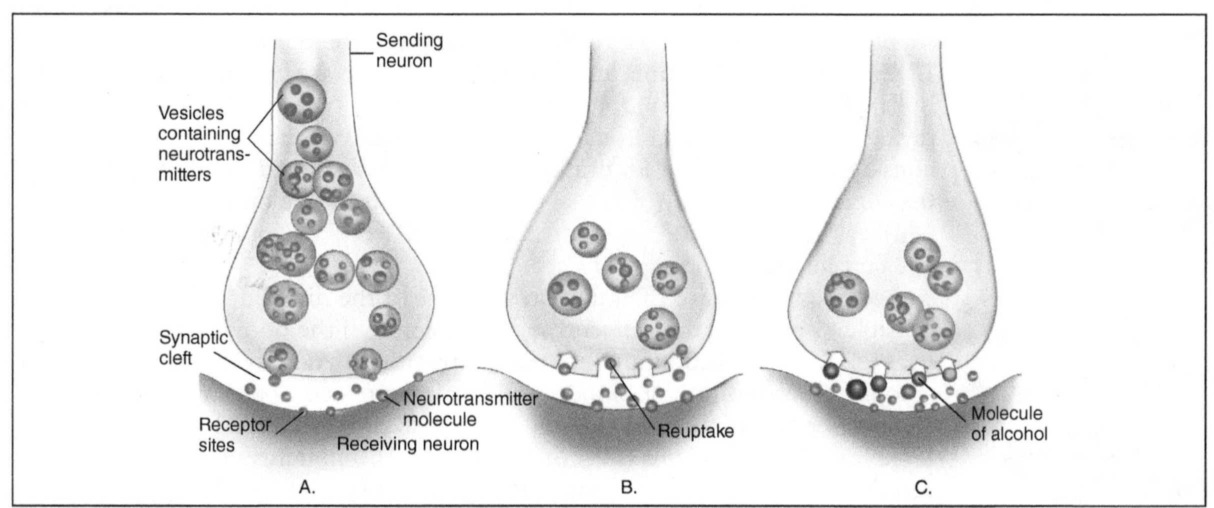

S. Rathus, S. Maheu, & S. Veenvliet. *PSYCH*, 1e. © 2012 Nelson Education Ltd. Reproduced by permission. www.cengage.com/permissions

Pharmacokinetics of Alcohol

Absorption

Most of the alcohol that is consumed must pass from the stomach to the small intestine for rapid absorption to occur. This is by far the most common way humans absorb alcohol. If alcohol is vaporized, however, it can be absorbed through the lungs and subcutaneous sites (Ritchie, 1985).

As you saw in Chapter 4, the rate at which a drug is absorbed varies widely among people, depending on individual differences in physiology and situational factors. Alcohol is no exception to this rule. The major factors influencing absorption are those that alter the rate of alcohol's passage from the stomach to the intestines. Drinkers can considerably slow absorption by eating while drinking because the presence of food in the stomach retards absorption. Milk is especially effective for slowing alcohol absorption. Another factor is the rate at which an alcoholic beverage is consumed; faster drinking means faster absorption. Drinks that have a higher concentration of alcohol, such as whiskey on the rocks, are absorbed more quickly than those with a lower concentration, such as a scotch and water. The food substances in beer slow its absorption. Carbonated beverages are absorbed more quickly than noncarbonated ones; this explains why people may feel a quick kick from a glass of champagne on an empty stomach, when they may not get the same effect from drinking a comparable amount of table wine. Given these factors, the time between stopping drinking and the peak concentration of alcohol in the blood may range from 30 to 90 minutes (Rall, 1990b).

Distribution

After absorption, the blood distributes alcohol to all of the body's tissues. Because alcohol is easily dissolved in water, the proportion of water in a tissue determines the concentration of alcohol in it. Blood is about 70 percent water and therefore gets a high concentration of alcohol. Muscle and bone contain smaller percentages of water and have correspondingly smaller percentages of alcohol.

standard drink
The alcohol equivalent in a drink of beer, wine, or distilled spirits. A standard drink equals 0.5 ounce of alcohol—about the alcohol content in 12 ounces of beer, four ounces of table wine, or one ounce of 90- to 100-proof whiskey.

Alcohol affects primarily the CNS, especially the brain. The concentration of alcohol in the brain approximates that in the blood because of the brain's large blood supply and because alcohol freely passes through the blood–brain barrier. Alcohol's LD 50 varies as a function of different factors. The average adult would reach alcohol's LD 50 after drinking about 25 standard drinks in an hour or so. Of course, saying this estimate is an average means that many people would die from drinking considerably fewer than 25 drinks in an hour. A **standard drink** may be defined as 0.5 ounces of alcohol, which is about the amount in one ounce of 90- to 100-proof whiskey, 12 ounces of four percent alcohol beer, or four ounces of table wine (12 percent alcohol).

blood alcohol concentration (BAC)
A measure of the concentration of alcohol in the blood expressed in grams per 100 mL.

Because we all have the same proportions of the different tissues and water, it is possible to estimate the concentration of alcohol in the body from its concentration in the blood. The **blood alcohol concentration (BAC)**, as the name implies, is the amount of alcohol in the bloodstream. It is expressed as a percentage of weight of alcohol per 100 units of blood volume (Sobell & Sobell, 1981). Typically, the ratio is expressed as milligrams (mg) of alcohol per 100 millilitres (mL) of blood. Therefore, one drop of alcohol (about 10 mg) in 1000 drops of blood (about 100 mL) gives a BAC of 0.01 percent (100 mL of blood weighs about 100 g). Alcohol's LD 50 is a BAC of between 0.45–0.50 percent, although there have been case reports of people surviving BACs up to a little more than 1.0 percent (Berild & Hasselbalch, 1981).

You can translate a BAC into an approximation of the number of drinks consumed over time. We emphasize *approximation* because a person's BAC depends in part on the different factors that influence absorption. Factors besides dose of alcohol determine the peak BAC that is reached. Here are some factors to consider:

- Total body mass is a major factor because alcohol is distributed in both muscle and fat. As a result, heavier people will have a lower BAC than lighter ones after drinking the same amount of alcohol.
- Another factor is how much of a person's body consists of fat and muscle. Alcohol is soluble in fat but is even more soluble in water. Everything being equal, a drink will result in a lower BAC for a leaner person than for a drinker who has a higher percentage of body fat. This is the reason a woman tends to reach higher BACs from drinking a given amount of alcohol than does a man of the same body weight. Women tend to have a higher percentage of body fat than men do. Also, one study suggests that women have less of the enzyme alcohol dehydrogenase in their stomachs, which prevents them from metabolizing as much alcohol in their stomachs. More alcohol enters a woman's bloodstream and eventually the brain and other organs (Frezza et al., 1990). This finding suggests that, for a man and a woman of equal weight, the same amount of alcohol affects the woman more (this is one reason "binge drinking" is defined as five drinks for men and as four drinks for women).
- Aspirin also may affect the amount of alcohol that is metabolized in the stomach. If a person who has recently eaten takes a moderate dose of aspirin as drinking begins, the resulting BAC will be higher than it would be if the aspirin were not taken (Roine et al., 1990). It seems that aspirin suppresses alcohol dehydrogenase in the stomach, so less alcohol is metabolized there. The "recently eaten" part of this finding is important because aspirin makes no difference when alcohol enters an empty stomach. In that circumstance, alcohol enters the intestines so rapidly that there is no time for aspirin's effect on alcohol dehydrogenase.
- Individual differences in the rate at which the body metabolizes alcohol are also variables that influence what peak BAC is reached.

For these and other reasons, the following formula for computing BAC gives only an approximation.

$$\text{Estimated BAC} = \text{NSD} \times (0.025\%) - \text{NHD} \times (0.015\%)$$

The formula above estimates the BAC that would result at a given time in a hypothetical 160-pound man who drank a given number of standard drinks. In the formula, BAC = blood alcohol content, NSD = number of standard drinks, and NHD = number of hours since drinking began. In the formula, NSD is multiplied by 0.025 percent because that is the midpoint of our estimated range of increase in BAC that results when the 160-pound drinker has a standard drink. NHD is multiplied by 0.015 percent because that is the BAC equivalent of the estimated hourly rate that the liver metabolizes alcohol (Rall, 1990b). The metabolic rate is independent of body weight, unlike the rise in BAC for a given amount of alcohol that is drunk.

Based on our approximation formula, a 160-pound man who drinks three 12-ounce regular beers in an hour will have a BAC of about 0.06 percent. That result would be adjusted up or down depending on the important factor of body weight; many

FIGURE 6.2
A conversion chart for approximating blood alcohol concentration as a function of number of drinks, time, and body weight

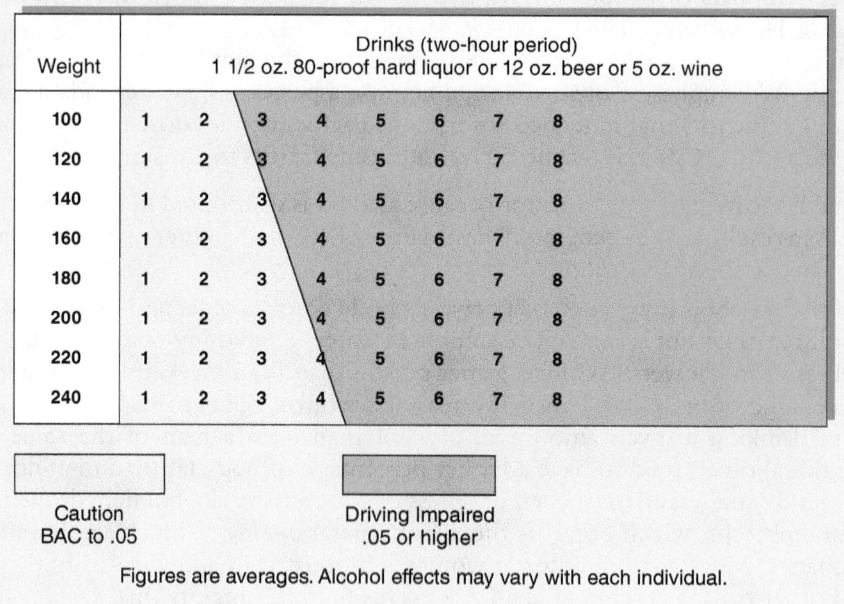

Weight	Drinks (two-hour period) 1 1/2 oz. 80-proof hard liquor or 12 oz. beer or 5 oz. wine							
100	1	2	3	4	5	6	7	8
120	1	2	3	4	5	6	7	8
140	1	2	3	4	5	6	7	8
160	1	2	3	4	5	6	7	8
180	1	2	3	4	5	6	7	8
200	1	2	3	4	5	6	7	8
220	1	2	3	4	5	6	7	8
240	1	2	3	4	5	6	7	8

Caution BAC to .05

Driving Impaired .05 or higher

Figures are averages. Alcohol effects may vary with each individual.

conversion charts like Figure 6.2 are available to make such corrections. The estimation formula reflects that the BAC essentially depends on the dose of alcohol that is consumed and the time that it takes to drink it. Figure 6.3 shows the BAC–time relationship. The figure illustrates that the BAC rises quickly and then more gradually returns to zero after drinking stops. Therefore, time is an important factor in determining BAC. Time enters the formula independent of the number of standard drinks because

FIGURE 6.3
Acute tolerance to alcohol's effects

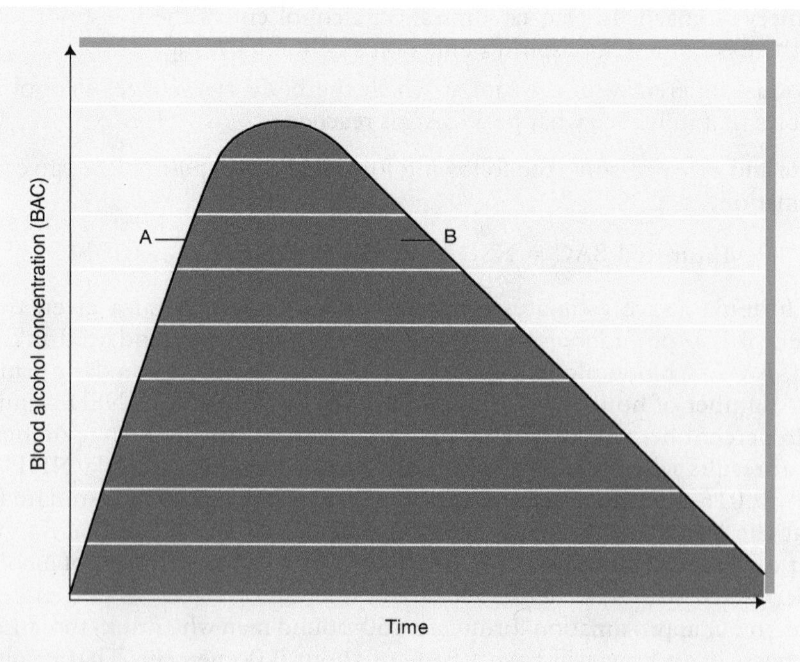

The effects of alcohol at time A are greater than the effects at time B.

DRUGS AND CULTURE BOX 6.3

BAC and DUIs in Canada

In Canada, driving under the influence of alcohol has been at the forefront of much of the discussion related to highway traffic fatalities since the 1980s. In 1982, 60 percent of traffic fatalities were alcohol related. This percentage has dropped significantly since then, as 40 percent of traffic fatalities in 2007 reported related to drinking and driving (Transport Canada, 2008). This accounted for an estimated 1054 fatalities and 60 000 injuries reported during this year.

In Canada, it is a criminal offence to drive with a blood alcohol concentration (BAC) of 0.08, or 80 milligrams of alcohol in 100 mL of blood. Drinking drivers at lower BAC are dealt with under provincial and territorial traffic acts. There are two sections under the Canadian Code for driving under the influence.

- Part (a) of Section 253(1) makes it illegal to operate aircraft or railway equipment, or have any kind of 'care or conrol' over a motor vehicle, vessel, aircraft, or train.
- Section 253(1) of the same code makes it illegal for an individual to operate any vehicle, vessel, aircraft, or train while his or her blood alcohol concentration (BAC) is above 0.08. Police are allowed, under Canadian law, to test the BAC of individuals that may be in violation of this section.

There are several levels of punishment for individuals who commit driving offences under the Canadian Code.

- 1st offence—the individual may have his or her licence suspended for 12 months and face a $1000 fine.
- 2nd offence—carries a 30-day jail sentence and a 24-month prohibition on his or her licence.

Photos.com

of the way the liver metabolizes alcohol—generally, at a constant amount over a given time, regardless of the amount that is drunk.

For medical or legal purposes, BAC is not estimated by formula but as precisely as possible by standardized procedures. Blood and urine samples are taken frequently for medical and medical/legal reasons to measure BAC. For example, blood samples often determine the BACs of drivers killed in motor vehicle accidents. BAC is commonly measured by breath sample because of the known ratio (1:2,100) between the amount of alcohol in the lungs and the amount in the blood. Gas chromatography (breath analysis) is used to obtain estimates of BAC as part of road tests in Canada, and are considered legally admissible evidence. Refer to the Drugs and Culture Box 6.3 to learn more about the use of breathalyzers and DUIs in Canada.

Metabolism and Excretion

More than 90 percent of the alcohol that is absorbed is metabolized by the body, mainly in the liver. (We saw earlier that the stomach also plays a part in metabolizing alcohol.) The small percentage of alcohol that is not metabolized is excreted in pure form through the kidneys and the lungs. When alcohol is metabolized in the liver, it is broken down to acetaldehyde by the enzyme alcohol dehydrogenase. Acetaldehyde eventually is

The Canadian Press/Darryl Dyck

Blood alcohol concentration can be measured by breath analysis, as shown here. These tests are accurate enough to be admissible in Canadian court, which is often the case for many DUI cases throughout Canada.

broken down to carbon dioxide and water. At this point, there is a release of energy, or calories (Julien, 1996). The carbon dioxide is excreted from the body through air exchange in the lungs, and the water is excreted in urine. Unlike other foods, such as proteins and carbohydrates, the rate that alcohol is metabolized is independent of the body's need for the calories it could provide or of the amount of alcohol consumed. The rate of alcohol oxidation is constant and averages about 0.35 ounce an hour.

Oxidation is the process by which the energy in foods is released in the form of heat. In this respect, alcohol liberates about 75 calories in each half ounce. Therefore, one standard drink of whiskey has about 75 calories because all the calories in distilled spirits are from alcohol content. However, beverages such as beer provide calories from foods such as proteins and carbohydrates as well as alcohol. A regular 12-ounce, four percent alcohol beer has about 150 calories, and a comparable amount of the commercial light beers has 95 to 135 calories. Light beers have fewer calories primarily because they contain less alcohol.

Alcohol is unaffected by attempts to hasten its removal from the body. Efforts such as vigorous exercise do nothing to speed up alcohol oxidation, except to the extent that exercise takes time and the individual does not drink while exercising. In fact, little can be done to hasten sobriety except to wait for the liver to do its work in its own constant time. Therefore, if you go to bed on Saturday at 2 A.M. with a BAC of 0.15 percent, you will still be legally drunk three hours later at 5 A.M. (your BAC will be 0.105 percent) and will not be alcohol-free until noon.

Tolerance and Dependence

Tolerance

Regular use of alcohol results in some dispositional tolerance (see Chapter 1 for a detailed discussion of tolerance). Therefore, a drinker must consume greater quantities of alcohol to maintain a certain BAC. Dispositional tolerance can be reversed with a period of abstinence from alcohol. Functional tolerance has a greater practical influence than does dispositional tolerance in altering how alcohol affects a person with repeated use. Tolerance to alcohol may be both acute and protracted. Because of acute tolerance, the effects of alcohol at a given BAC are greater when the BAC curve is rising than on the descending limb of the curve. For example, at a BAC of 0.10 percent as it is ascending, an individual may show considerably impaired performance on tasks related to driving. If the BAC peaks at, say, 0.15 percent and then hits 0.10 percent as it is falling, however, an individual's performance on those same driving-related tasks would be improved, although still probably far from its level with no alcohol in the blood. Of course, such improvement would make no difference to the police. A person with a BAC of 0.10 percent is legally drunk in every province and territory that has per se intoxication laws, regardless of what direction the BAC is heading when it is measured. Acute tolerance is illustrated in Figure 6.3.

As with dispositional tolerance, the development of protracted tolerance requires that the individual drink greater amounts of alcohol to achieve an effect once achieved with less alcohol. Because protracted functional tolerance far outpaces dispositional tolerance, the person becomes more susceptible to serious health and other consequences of heavy alcohol consumption. For example, a person may drink large quantities of alcohol to achieve a mood change that was once reached with much less alcohol. However, the BAC does not behave in the same way. Drinking large quantities of alcohol still results in a high BAC. With higher BACs, the body is more vulnerable to suffering alcohol's toxic effects, which we review shortly. Similarly, chronic heavy drinkers may not feel drunk or even impaired at BACs greater than 0.08 percent, but they still are defined legally as drunk. Such a designation leaves people liable to arrests for drunk driving and other alcohol-related charges.

As noted in Chapter 1, there is cross-tolerance between alcohol and other CNS depressant drugs. We also noted how cross-tolerance might cause difficulties for an anesthesiologist preparing a patient for surgery. Sometimes the problem is acute in the emergency room, where surgery must be performed immediately following a serious accident. You will see later how alcohol intoxication is associated with the occurrence of accidents, and as you might expect, the heaviest users (most tolerant) of alcohol are the people who are most likely to have the accidents (USDHHS, 1993).

Alcohol also shows cross-dependence with CNS depressant drugs. This means that taking one drug can suppress withdrawal symptoms of the other. For example, alcohol and the benzodiazepine drugs such as Valium and Librium show cross-dependence. This phenomenon has proved valuable in managing withdrawal from alcohol in individuals who are physically dependent on it.

Physical Dependence

With chronic heavy drinking, individuals can develop physical dependence on alcohol. Symptoms of physical dependence can be severe and may be classified into three phases, as outlined in Table 6.3. As you can see, a wide range of symptoms is associated

TABLE 6.3 Symptoms of Alcohol Withdrawal Syndrome

Phase	Onset	Symptoms
1	As soon as a few hours after drinking stopped	Tremulousness (shakes), profuse perspiration, weakness, alcohol and other drug seeking. Also may include agitation, headache, anorexia, nausea and vomiting, abdominal cramps, high heart rate, and exaggerated and rapid reflexes. Visual and auditory hallucinations may follow in increased intensity. Hallucinations may also occur when the individual is severely intoxicated (called acute alcoholic hallucinosis).
2	Within 24 hours of drinking cessation	Grand mal seizures, ranging from one seizure to continuous severe seizure activity with little or no interruption.
3	About 30 hours after drinking cessation. This is the most protracted phase, and may last 3 to 4 days; commonly called delirium tremens (DTs).	Severe agitation, often appearance of confusion and disorientation; almost continual activity; very high body temperature and abnormally rapid heart beat; terrifying hallucinations, may be visual, auditory, or tactile. The latter is most often felt as bugs or little animals crawling on the skin. Hallucinations are accompanied by delusions, with a high potential for violent behaviour without medical management. Deaths during DTs still occur due to high fever, cardiovascular collapse, or traumatic injury.
End of withdrawal course	About 5 to 7 days after drinking stopped	Exhaustion and severe dehydration.

Source: M. R. Jacobs and K. O'Brien Fehr (1987), *Drugs and Drug Abuse: A Reference Text (2nd ed.)*. Copyright © 1987 Addiction Research Foundation. Used with permission.

with time of onset after drinking cessation, although some symptoms overlap in the different phases. You should note that not all people who are physically dependent on alcohol experience all three phases of symptoms. For example, Phase 2 symptoms probably appear least frequently, and individuals may go directly from Phase 1 to Phase 3 symptoms. Another important point is that withdrawal symptoms may appear when the BAC is falling but still at a fairly high level, such as 0.15 percent. The BAC does not need to have fallen all the way to zero for withdrawal to begin.

intoxication
A transient state of physical and psychological disruption caused by the presence of a toxic substance, such as alcohol, in the CNS.

Acute Effects of Alcohol

In this section, we review both the acute and chronic effects of alcohol consumption.

One point about alcohol's acute effects is that alcohol generally acts on the body as a depressant, and its acute effects are proportional to the magnitude of the BAC. Simply put, as the BAC increases, acute effects increase in number and intensity. However, how humans experience some degree of **intoxication** and behave under different doses of alcohol may be modified by psychological and situational factors as well as alcohol dose and tolerance to this drug. For some behaviours, these non-drug factors may be even more powerful determinants of alcohol's acute effects than drug factors.

Physiological Effects

Alcohol taken at low doses has several physiological effects. Alcohol inhibits the secretion of the antidiuretic hormone, which causes increased urination. The effect happens when the BAC is rising but not when it is falling. Alcohol also reduces the amount of body fat that is oxidized. This acute effect of alcohol accumulates to result in long-term increased body fat and weight gain when alcohol is used in addition to normal food intake (Suter, Schutz, & Jequier, 1992). Alcohol's dilating effect on peripheral blood vessels causes some loss of body heat, however, and such action was thought to ultimately decrease protection against the cold. It turns out the problem is not a serious one, as experimental studies have shown that alcohol does not significantly tilt the balance of the body's temperature regulation in cold environments.

One acute alcohol effect is that it increases gastric secretion, which stimulates the appetite (this may be why bars and restaurants offer 'cocktail hour'). Unfortunately, alcohol at high doses harms the stomach mucosa and causes gastric distress. Nausea and vomiting may occur at BACs greater than 0.15 percent. Another physiological effect of alcohol when taken in high doses and when the BAC increases rapidly is a release of corticosteroids, part of the body's general reaction to stress. In this case, the stressor is a high dose of alcohol, which is toxic to the body.

REM sleep
Acronym for "rapid eye movements," which are associated with dream activity and are one stage in a cycle of sleep.

Another important acute effect of alcohol is disruption of sleep patterns. Even at lower doses, alcohol suppresses **REM sleep**, which is the stage of the sleep cycle when most dreaming occurs. When the dose is low, REM sleep is suppressed only in the first half of the night, but REM time rebounds and increases in the second half. At larger doses of alcohol, REM sleep is suppressed throughout the night.

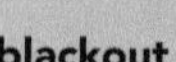

blackout
Failure to recall events that occurred while drinking even though there is no loss of consciousness.

Alcohol impairs short-term memory, and when high BACs are reached rapidly, a **blackout** may occur. Blackouts are an individual's amnesia about events when drinking, even though there was no loss of consciousness. For example, a person who had a lot to drink the night before may wake up and have absolutely no recollection of where he or she parked the car. Blackouts are thought to result from a failure in the transfer of information in **short-term memory** to **long-term memory**. People also have "grayouts," in which they can partially recall events that occurred in full consciousness during a drinking occasion. Grayouts probably reflect state-dependent learning. Blackouts and grayouts do not happen consistently in the same individuals with a given dose of alcohol, and the factors that specifically determine their occurrence have not been identified.

Ostill/Shutterstock.com

A headache is one symptom of a hangover, which is a common consequence of alcohol overindulgence.

Every drinker probably has had at least one somewhat-delayed consequence of an episode of overindulgence—the hangover. Hangovers may be thought of as a minor withdrawal syndrome because they are the body's readjustment to a nonalcohol state. Hangovers begin to appear about four to 12 hours after reaching the peak BAC and generally are not considered a pleasant alcohol effect. Symptoms may include headache, dizziness, nausea, vomiting, increased heart rate, fatigue, and thirst (Gauvin, Cheng, & Holloway, 1993). Furthermore, although the BAC is zero, hangovers are associated with a reduced ability to perform the complex skills required to drive a motor vehicle (Franck, 1983). Although people usually do not think of hangovers as a serious negative consequence of overindulging in drinking alcohol beyond not feeling well temporarily, the cumulative effect of hangovers for a society are considerable. For example, in England, hangovers cost the economy about two billion pounds a year, primarily because of people skipping work (Pittler, Verster, & Ernst, 2005).

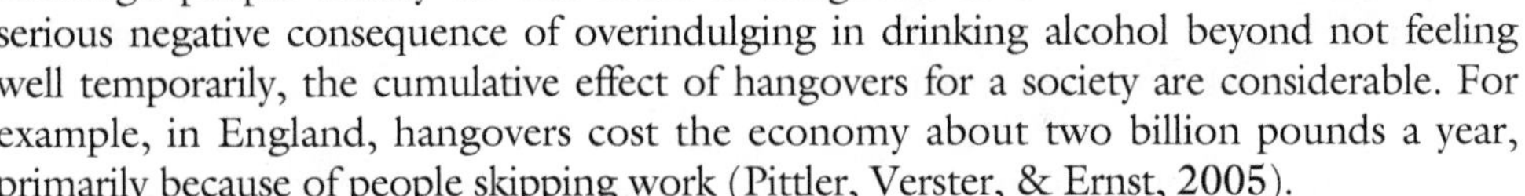

short-term memory
Memory for recent events, which is thought to differ from long-term memory in several important ways, specifically in duration and capacity for retaining information.

long-term memory
Memory for remote events. According to one theory of memory, information enters long-term memory through short-term memory.

In discussing alcohol's acute effects, we must reemphasize that it interacts synergistically with other CNS depressants. The point is worth repeating because of the dangerous effects of mixing alcohol and barbiturates—a common method of intended and unintended suicides. Alcohol and the benzodiazepines do not have the potential for suicide that alcohol and the barbiturates have, but they can cause serious decrements in the performance of skills essential to survival, such as driving a car or staying awake while driving a car. Similarly, marijuana and alcohol are frequently consumed on the same occasion, and there seem to be synergistic effects of these two drugs on skills related to driving (for example, Perez-Reyes et al., 1988). Antihistamines, which are available over the counter, also combine synergistically with alcohol. In addition, combining alcohol with other drugs may also have antagonistic effects. For example, alcohol decreases the effects of certain prescribed medications, such as antibiotics, anticonvulsants, anticoagulants, and **monoamine oxidase (MAO) inhibitors**.

monoamine oxidase (MAO) inhibitors
Drugs used to treat depressions that inhibit the activity of the enzyme monoamine oxidase, which degrades the neurotransmitters of norepinephrine and serotonin.

Alcohol causes slight respiratory depression at lower doses, but this effect does not reach dangerous levels in healthy people unless they consume very high doses. Higher doses also are associated with the induction of sleep, stupor, and in extremely high doses, coma. In the overdose range of consumption, cardiovascular depression can occur. Earlier, we noted that a dose of alcohol could be lethal (lethal dose 50, or "LD 50" BAC of 0.45–0.50 percent) due to dysfunction of the more primitive areas of the brain like the medulla that control breathing and heartbeat.

Sensorimotor Effects

At moderate (0.05 percent) to higher BACs, alcohol has several acute effects on the senses. Vision decreases in acuity, and taste and smell are not so sensitive. Pain sensitivity decreases when the BAC is in the 0.08–0.10 percent range. Simple reaction time begins to slow significantly at a BAC of 0.10 percent. An example of a simple reaction time task is to press a key as quickly as possible when a single light on a panel shines. In a complex reaction time task, research participants are asked to integrate two or more stimuli and then respond to them as quickly as possible. An example is to press a key when a white and a red light shine but not to press it when only the white light shines. Complex reaction time may be impaired in both speed and accuracy at BACs of 0.05 percent or even lower.

Alcohol strongly affects body sway, which is measured by asking people to stand steady with their eyes closed. The body's deviation from a "steady state" is then recorded. At a BAC of 0.06 percent, body sway is impaired by about 40 percent. At a high BAC, we see alcohol's effect on body sway manifested as staggering and, eventually, as an inability to walk independently at all. The sensitivity of body sway to alcohol is the reason for the "walk a straight line" test that police use to decide whether a suspect is drunk. Alcohol's influence on body sway is due to its effects on balance controls in the inner ear. This also is why the room may spin when partygoers lie down and close their eyes to sleep after a night of heavy drinking.

Alcohol impairs psychomotor skills. In tasks designed to measure these skills, participants are asked to make controlled muscular movements to adjust or position a machine or some mechanism on an experimental apparatus in response to changes in the speed or direction of a moving object (for example, see Levine, Kramer, & Levine, 1975, p. 288). A common example is the mechanical or computerized version of the pursuit rotor task, in which participants must keep a stylus on a target that moves circularly on an automated disk.

Psychomotor task performance on the average shows deterioration at BACs of about 0.03 percent and higher (Levine, Kramer, & Levine, 1975). These tasks commonly require relatively fine motor dexterity. At high BACs, 0.15 percent or more, there is clear abnormality in gross motor functions like standing and walking. At these levels, alcohol has impaired the brain centres responsible for

Fiorentini Massimo/Shutterstock.com

Motor vehicle accidents are the single most common nonnatural causes of death in Canada and the United States.

motor activity and balance to such a degree that the neural messages are not being sent to the muscles.

Sensorimotor skills constitute a major part of driving ability. During the early 1980s, public awareness of drinking and driving a motor vehicle increased enormously. Probably most influential in opening the public's eyes and ears about drunk driving were citizens' organizations such as Mothers Against Drunk Driving (MADD) and Students Against Drunk Driving (SADD). These movements contributed to and were strengthened by the more conservative attitudes toward alcohol and drug use that marked the 1980s in Canada and the United States. Part of this trend was increased enforcement of stricter legal penalties for driving under the influence (DUI) of alcohol (or other drugs).

The case for alcohol as a causal factor in traffic fatalities becomes even more solid with experimental data on how alcohol affects performance on tasks that require psychomotor skills and an integration of sensory information. An example, called a "divided-attention" task, is combining the pursuit rotor and complex reaction time tasks into one experimental task. Participants are required to keep the stylus on target (pursuit rotor) while they are simultaneously responding to the two light stimuli on a panel (complex reaction time). Driving a car requires the same motor control and sensory integration abilities that are necessary to perform such a divided-attention task. Alcohol impairs performance on divided-attention tasks at BACs of 0.05 percent or lower.

Psychological Effects

Alcohol combines with other factors to change emotion and mood. Different people report a range of psychological effects at a given BAC, and the same drinker may report different effects at a given BAC on different occasions. The influences of nondrug factors, particularly situational and cognitive variables (for example, expectancies and attitudes), are perhaps most powerful in this domain. The person's mood state before starting to drink also is an important factor.

"Always do sober what you said you'd do drunk. That will teach you to keep your mouth shut."

Ernest Hemingway

At lower BACs, drinkers report feeling elated and friendly when the BAC is rising, but when it is falling, common feelings are anger and fatigue. Other reports when the BAC is rising have been expansiveness, joviality, relaxation, and self-confidence. The importance of nondrug factors is accented in the finding that during the ascending phase of these same BACs, other subjects have reported feeling hostile, depressed, and withdrawn. When BACs go above 0.10 percent, drinkers commonly become more labile and may change abruptly from friendly to hostile. Often the level of tolerance for frustration is lowered.

Alcohol's effects on thinking and perception are less influenced by nondrug factors and are influenced more by BAC. Alcohol significantly impairs short-term memory at BACs higher than 0.05 percent. At a BAC of 0.05 percent, the ability to estimate time is impaired. Drinkers seem to overestimate the passage of time at a BAC of 0.05 percent; they might estimate a time passage of 8 minutes to be 12 minutes. The ability to estimate distance (depth perception) also is disrupted at lower BACs, as are attention and concentration. At higher BACs, these cognitive effects are intensified and are compounded by more disorganized thinking.

Alcohol and Behaviour

Among alcohol's effects, those involving interpersonal behaviour are of great social interest. The interpersonal behaviours of sex and aggression in combination with alcohol have garnered the greatest interest and concern.

Alcohol and Aggression

There are many studies that suggest that when people commit violent crimes, they tend to be under the influence of alcohol. Violent crimes include murder or attempted murder, manslaughter, rape or sexual assault, robbery, and others such as kidnapping, purse snatching, hit-and-run driving, and child abuse. These findings hold for western Europe and the U.S. (Collins, 1980). The co-occurrence of alcohol use and violent crime is especially prevalent among men 18 to 30 years old, who have a relatively high rate of both heavy drinking and criminal activity. Another problem of national concern is domestic violence (predominantly husbands abusing wives), and alcohol has been estimated to be involved (offender or victim) in 25–50 percent of spousal abuse incidents (Collins, 1980).

National statistics show associations between alcohol and violence toward others and also violence toward oneself. For example, suicide is one of the three leading causes of death (the other two are homicide and accidental death) among men 15 to 34 years old and one of the 10 leading causes of death among all people 34 to 54 years old. One study of the causes of violent death focused on 3400 individuals who had had their BACs tested at the time of their deaths. Among those people who died by suicide, 35 percent had been drinking alcohol when they took their lives (USDHHS, 1987a). The consistency of the co-occurrence of drinking and violent behaviour tempts us to conclude that alcohol causes such behaviour. Data such as government statistics are only descriptive and correlational, however, and cannot be the bases of valid causal statements about alcohol and aggression. Nevertheless, the adult drinking public believes that alcohol does indeed cause aggression. A consistent finding in many studies of beliefs about the effects of alcohol is that it increases power and aggression (Goldman, Darkes, & Del Boca, 1999).

Of course, aggressive behaviour is a highly significant social concern, and it is important to find the reasons for the association between drinking and violent behaviour. A traditional explanation is the **disinhibition theory**, which was first proposed in the early 20th century. This theory holds that alcohol releases behaviour normally inhibited by society, such as aggression and sex, as a result of its depressant action on the brain.

disinhibition theory
A theory that states that social inhibitions that act in opposition to the depressant action on the brain (in this case, through alcohol), causes a lack of anxiety or awareness towards inhibitive behaviour (i.e., aggression).

Essentially the theory suggests that whatever anxieties we have about the social consequences of behaviour such as aggression vanish as a result of alcohol's pharmacological action. Thus, people who have been drinking should be more aggressive than people who have not.

Controlled laboratory experiments involving human subjects do not support the disinhibition theory, however. Some epidemiological studies have shown a correlation between alcohol and aggression, but this was not a simple matter of alcohol's pharmacological action, as disinhibition theory predicts. Rather, alcohol combines with situational factors, such as social pressure and threat of retaliation (Adesso, 1985; Graham et al., 1998), as well as personal factors, such as how angry a person is characteristically (Parrot & Giancola, 2004). Furthermore, drinkers' expectancies about alcohol and aggression also seem to contribute to aggression, sometimes considerably more than actually drinking alcohol does (Bartholow & Heinz, 2006).

It seems, therefore, that alcohol does not simply cause aggression, despite the beliefs of some public officials and the general population. Instead, aggression is a complex social behaviour affected by the characteristics of the aggressor and situational factors, only one of which is alcohol consumption (Exum, 2006).

Alcohol and Sex

For the last 500 years, Shakespeare probably has been the author most frequently cited on the acute effects of alcohol on human sexual response. The specific reference is from *Macbeth*, act 2, scene 2: "It [alcohol] provokes and unprovokes; it provokes the desire, but it takes away the performance." It turns out that the results of experimental studies are in part consistent with Shakespeare's observations.

Alcohol and sexual response in men and women has been a favourite subject of writers for thousands of years. Much of the writing has been like Shakespeare's comments, based on informal personal observations. With regard to male sexual response, the folklore leads to dose-dependent conclusions. Alcohol has been thought to be an aphrodisiac in men at lower doses but an impediment to sexual performance at higher doses.

Efforts have been made to systematically study human sexual response to a dose of alcohol, but it has only been possible to do well-controlled research on this topic in the past 30 years or so. The significant breakthroughs have been the invention of the penile strain gauge to measure penile erectile response and the photoplethysmograph to measure vaginal blood volume and pressure. These advances paved the way for experimental study of human sexual response and alcohol.

Experimental studies of men have consistently shown that, at BACs of 0.05–0.10 percent, alcohol pharmacologically retards sexual arousal. When the BAC climbs to more than 0.10 percent erection and ejaculatory competence are inhibited or eliminated. These results have been found repeatedly in samples of college students who were not problem drinkers and in those with alcoholism. Alcohol does not stimulate men's libido, especially at moderate or higher BACs.

At lower BACs, alcohol effects are not so dominant. It appears that cognitive factors, such as expectancies about alcohol effects, may work to increase men's libido. Indeed, studies of alcohol expectancies suggest that the drinking public generally believes alcohol enhances sexual experience (Brown, Christiansen, & Goldman, 1987). Consistent with this finding, balanced placebo design studies (see Contemporary Issue Box 6.4) suggest that men's sexual arousal is increased when they believe they are drinking a dose of alcohol that brings them to a BAC less than 0.05 percent. Alcohol itself, however, has no effect on measured arousal at such BACs, which agrees with many other studies of the pharmacology of alcohol (Peugh & Belenko, 2001). Another characteristic of male drinkers that seems to affect their sexual arousal at BACs lower than 0.05 percent is personality. One study showed increased sexual response was especially evident in subjects who thought they were drinking alcohol and who scored high on a measure of guilt about sex (Lang et al., 1980).

A reasonable conclusion about the acute effects of alcohol on male sexual response is that, similar to aggression, the disinhibition theory falls far short of explaining the information that is available. Rather, social and psychological factors seem to be important determinants of sexual response in men at low BACs and often work to increase libido. However, the pharmacology of alcohol begins to dominate at BACs greater than 0.05 percent, which cause a decrease in arousal and sexual competence.

The folklore about the acute effects of alcohol on sexual behaviour in women is that it promotes promiscuity, a belief that even adolescents in high school in Canada and the United States report (Young, McCabe, & Boyd, 2007).

Previous nonexperimental studies, as well as studies of alcohol expectancies we cited earlier, suggest that alcohol increases sexual arousal in women and that women believe alcohol has that effect. The recent experimental evidence is that, as in men,

CONTEMPORARY ISSUE BOX 6.4

The Balanced Placebo Design

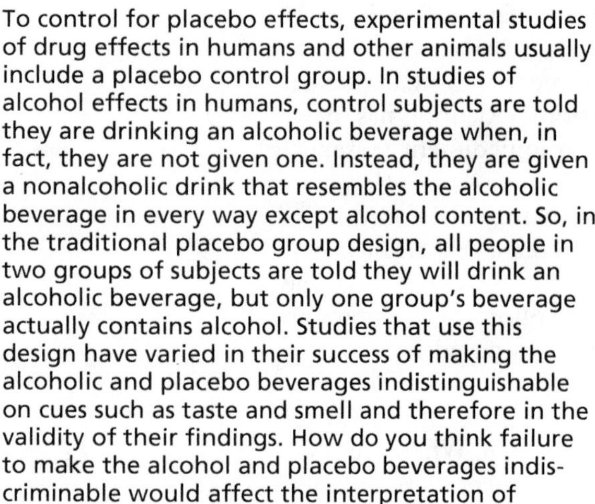

To control for placebo effects, experimental studies of drug effects in humans and other animals usually include a placebo control group. In studies of alcohol effects in humans, control subjects are told they are drinking an alcoholic beverage when, in fact, they are not given one. Instead, they are given a nonalcoholic drink that resembles the alcoholic beverage in every way except alcohol content. So, in the traditional placebo group design, all people in two groups of subjects are told they will drink an alcoholic beverage, but only one group's beverage actually contains alcohol. Studies that use this design have varied in their success of making the alcoholic and placebo beverages indistinguishable on cues such as taste and smell and therefore in the validity of their findings. How do you think failure to make the alcohol and placebo beverages indiscriminable would affect the interpretation of study results?

A significant advance in studying the effects of drugs on human behaviour was made over 40 years ago in what has been named the balanced placebo design (BPD), which is illustrated in Table 6.4. The design has helped to advance knowledge about alcohol's effects on aggression and sex, among other human behaviours.

In the BPD, two groups are added to the traditional two-group placebo group design. The participants in each of the two additional groups are told they will not receive a drug; then those in one group get the drug and those in the other group do not. Therefore, comparisons may be made with a group of subjects who believe they are not getting and do not get a drug (the sober control group). It also is possible to make comparisons with a group of subjects who believe they are not receiving a drug but really do get one. The design offers the advantage of separating a pure drug effect, an "expectancy" (about drug actions) effect, and their interaction. Under the best conditions of control, the traditional placebo design provides a comparison of drug plus expectancy and expectancy conditions, which permits conclusions about drug action. In investigations of the effects of lower doses of alcohol, the BPD seems much better suited than the traditional placebo design for studying the complexity of drugs and human behaviour.

TABLE 6.4 Balanced Placebo Design

		Beverage Received	
		Alcohol	**Placebo**
	Alcohol	Group 1	Group 2
Beverage Told	**Placebo**	Group 3	Group 4

(An outline of the balanced placebo design in studying alcohol effects. The traditional design includes groups 1 and 2 only.)

women's physiological sexual response decreases with increasing alcohol dose. Unlike men, however, women continue to perceive increased sexual arousal and sexual pleasure even as the physiological indexes of their response and arousal are declining. It also is important not to conclude that the disinhibition theory accounts for the data on alcohol effects in women. Despite their perceived increased sexual arousal when they drink, whether women act on such perception depends on characteristics in the drinking setting and what the drinker has learned is acceptable sexual behaviour in that setting. Therefore, again, a theory about the acute effects of alcohol on women's sexual behaviour should incorporate social and psychological factors as well as the pharmacology of alcohol.

Table 6.5 provides a summary of the acute effects of alcohol at different BACs. The table clearly shows how pervasive alcohol's effects are. It is essential to remember, however, that the effects listed for given BACs are what might be observed in "typical" drinkers. Alcohol's effects are variable among people and in the same person on different drinking occasions. And, as our discussion of alcohol and aggression and sex

Test

TABLE 6.5 Typical Acute Effects of Alcohol Associated with Different Ascending Blood Alcohol Concentrations (BACs)	
BAC (%)	**Effects**
0.01–0.02	Slight changes in feeling; sense of warmth and well-being
0.03–0.04	Feelings of relaxation, slight exhilaration, happiness; skin may flush; mild impairment in motor skills
0.05–0.06	Effects become more noticeable; more exaggerated changes in emotion, impaired judgment, and lowered inhibitions; coordination may be altered
0.08–0.09	Reaction time is increased, muscle coordination is impaired; sensory feelings of numbness in cheeks, lips, and extremities; further impairment in judgment
0.10	Deterioration in motor coordination and reaction time; person may stagger and slow speech
0.15	Major impairment in balance and movement; large increase in reaction time; large impairment in judgment and perception
0.20	Difficulty staying awake; substantial reduction of motor and sensory capabilities; slurred speech, double vision, difficulty standing or walking without assistance
0.30	Confusion and stupor; difficulty comprehending what is going on; possible loss of consciousness (passing out)
0.40	Typically unconsciousness; sweatiness and clamminess of the skin; alcohol has become an anesthetic
0.45–0.50	Circulatory and respiratory functions may become totally depressed; LD 50 in humans

most clearly illustrated, situational and psychological factors also influence what behaviours occur in people when they drink as well as the effects they perceive alcohol is having on them.

Effects of Chronic Heavy Drinking

Chronic heavy use of alcohol may have numerous physiological and psychological effects. All the effects involve increased dysfunction, and some may be fatal. Some chronic alcohol effects are caused directly by alcohol's toxicity to the body, such as damage to the liver. Other effects are indirectly related to long-term heavy drinking. For example, Wernicke's disease, which involves impaired cognitive functioning, is caused by nutritional deficiencies that tend to occur in people who are dependent on alcohol (Brands, Sproule, & Marshman, 1998).

Chronic heavy drinking is difficult to define precisely. Suffice it to say, many of alcohol's long-term effects take years to become evident, and heavy drinkers vary greatly in their susceptibility to alcohol-related impairments.

A standard for what is heavy, or at least "unsafe," drinking has been proposed. However, long-term drinking of a given quantity of alcohol affects different drinkers in different ways, in both number and severity of symptoms. Furthermore, the standard could vary according to what risk (for example, liver disease, pancreatitis, or

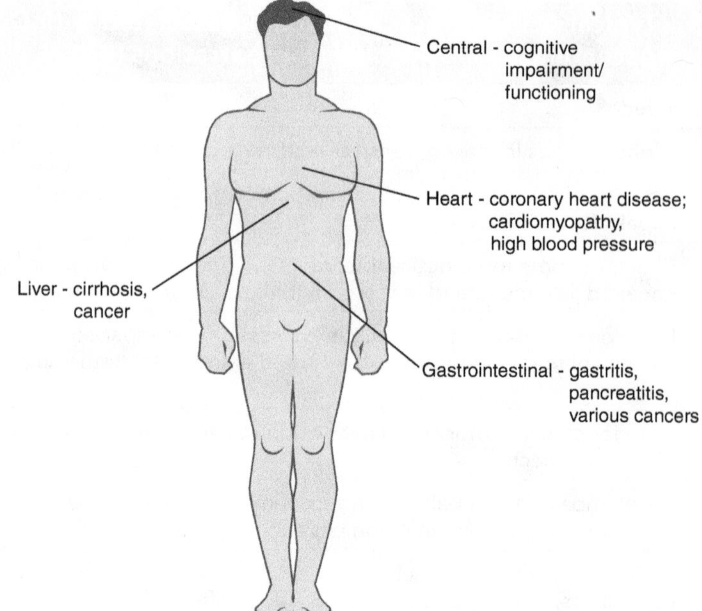

FIGURE 6.4
The effects of chronic heavy drinking on the body

Source: Zubada/Shutterstock

brain damage) we are concerned about (Bradley, Donovan, & Larson, 1993). Nevertheless, it is useful to have a guide to what is a "safe" level of alcohol consumption for the average drinker. One estimate is to set an upper limit of four drinks a day for men and three drinks a day for women, with a frequency of no more than four times a week for both genders (Dawson, 2000; Sanchez-Craig, Wilkinson, & Davila, 1995).

Figure 6.4 lists the major effects of chronic heavy drinking on body systems. Worldwide, the effects are devastating. For example, in 2004, a total of 6.3 percent of global deaths for men were attributable to alcohol (death by cancer, cardiovascular disease, liver cirrhosis, and injury), as were 1.1 percent of the deaths among women. The large discrepancy in rates between men and women characterized the data from all countries of the world. These rates varied wide, ranging across both sexes from 0.5 percent in the eastern Mediterranean countries, to 6.5 percent in the countries of Europe. The rate for the Americas was 5.6 percent, second to Europe (Rehm et al., 2009). It is important to note that the estimates that Rehm et al. provided consider or "partial out" the possible beneficial effects that moderate alcohol consumption has on disease and disability, which we discuss later in this chapter.

These global mortality data reflect what Figure 6.4 shows, that alcohol can be highly toxic to the human body and can cause extensive damage in a variety of ways. Two prominent body systems that alcohol harms are the brain and the liver. We will look at alcohol's chronic effects on these systems in more detail. Alcohol's chronic effects also extend to human reproductive functioning, which has to do with alcohol's altering effect on the functioning of the hypothalamic-pituitary-gonadal endocrine axis and with fetal alcohol syndrome (FAS).

Alcohol and Brain Functioning

The acute effects of alcohol on memory and other cognitive functioning are manifest at moderate BACs and are reversible. However, alcohol—if drunk long enough and heavily enough—affects these same functions in the long term in some people. Such chronic effects vary in severity, evidenced from mildly impaired performance on

neuropsychological tests, to severe, irreversible brain structural and functional damage shown as severe memory impairment in people who have Korsakoff's syndrome (Charness, 1993; Parsons, 1986).

neuropsychological tests
Formal ways of measuring behavioural functions that may be impaired by brain lesions.

The average alcohol-dependent individual who has been studied, when abstinent from alcohol or other psychoactive drugs, performs more poorly than nonalcoholic control groups on tests of abstracting, problem solving, memory, learning, and perceptual-motor speed. Reviews of research have shown consistently that such impairments are associated with alcohol dependence. Other characteristics of the drinkers also influence their vulnerability to alcohol's effects on brain function. A major one is the individual's drinking history. Although the evidence is mixed, in general, the longer a person drinks and the greater the quantity consumed, the greater the impairment in cognitive functioning (NIAAA, 2001).

Fortunately, with long-term abstinence from alcohol, most alcohol-related neuropsychological impairment once evidenced can be virtually reversed, with only mild deficits left compared with control subjects. This conclusion is based on studies that followed participants' test performance during periods of abstinence lasting from one month to five years (Fein et al., 2006; Sullivan, Rosenbloom, & Pfefferbaum, 2000).

The reversibility of cognitive deficits may be due to several factors, including increased cerebral blood flow, better nutrition, the reorganization of brain-cell networks, and some recovery of brain atrophy (Mello, 1987; Nace & Isbell, 1991; NIAAA, 2001; USDHHS, 1990). The more recent findings on changes in the brain and recovery of cognitive function are the result of technology that allows noninvasive study of brain structure and activity, such as computerized axial tomography (CT).

Wernicke-Korsakoff Syndrome

This severe CNS disorder results from the combination of extreme nutritional deficiency, specifically vitamin B_1 or thiamine, and chronic heavy drinking. Basically there are two diseases.

Wernicke's disease is characterized by confusion, loss of memory, staggering gait, and an inability to focus the eye (USDHHS, 1987a, 1990). In the absence of permanent brain damage, Wernicke's disease is reversible by giving the patient vitamin B_1.

Korsakoff's syndrome may have a nutritional component but is primarily due to alcohol. It is associated with damage to brain structure and most affects memory. The impairments in short-term memory and learning are serious. Because of these dysfunctions, there often is considerable confusion and **confabulation**. There also is a lesser degree of impairment in memory for events in longer-term memory.

confabulation
A fabrication of events, when asked questions concerning them, because of an inability to recall.

Alcohol and the Liver

As the major metabolic site of alcohol, the liver is highly vulnerable to alcohol's toxic effects. The damage that alcohol can cause to the liver occurs in three ways: fatty liver, alcohol hepatitis, and cirrhosis. Fatty liver is characterized by fat accumulating in the liver and is the earliest, most benign effect of alcohol on the liver. This condition is reversible with abstinence from alcohol, and there is no evidence that it is a precursor of cirrhosis. Alcohol hepatitis is more serious and involves the inflammation and death of liver cells. Often jaundice occurs because of the accumulation of bile. This condition is reversible with abstinence and medical treatment but can cause death if it is severe enough and not treated. Liver hepatitis can be caused by means other than heavy drinking. Evidence of such drinking must be obtained to diagnose alcohol hepatitis.

The most serious and life-threatening of alcohol's liver assaults is cirrhosis. Alcohol dependence is major cause of cirrhosis. It is twice as common in men as in women and

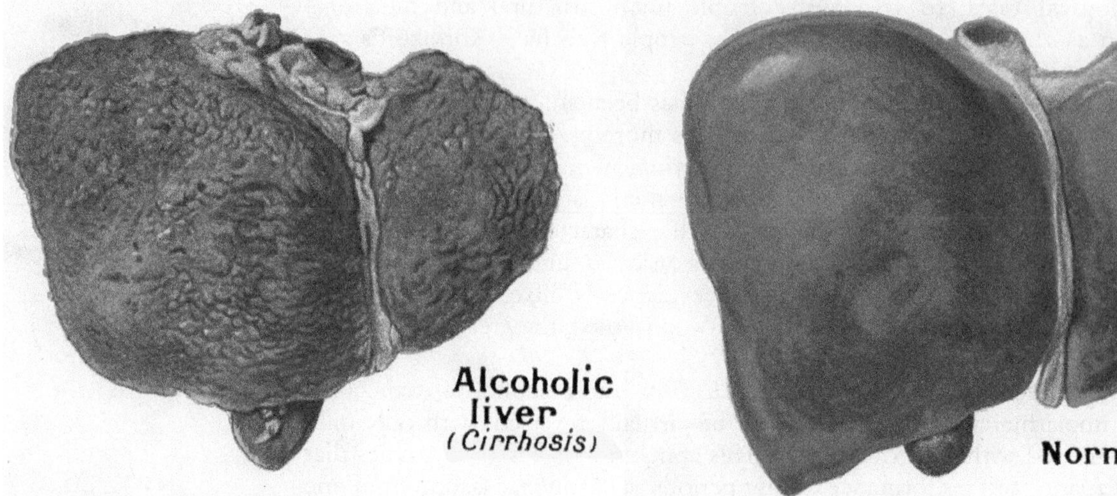

A cirrhotic liver (left) is compared with a healthy human liver (right).

30 times more common among heavy drinkers. In the U.S. it is the eighth leading cause of death by disease (National Institutes of Health, 2000). Drinking must be prodigious and long-term for someone to develop cirrhosis. For example, one survey showed that people with alcohol dependence who developed cirrhosis drank an average of 13 drinks a day for about 20 years! It did not matter what beverage form the alcohol was consumed in. It should be noted that a minority of people with alcohol dependence develop cirrhosis—between 10 percent and 20 percent. Individuals with alcohol dependence who are diagnosed with cirrhosis often have other liver diseases at the same time, such as alcohol hepatitis (NIAAA, 2000).

For those who do get cirrhosis, the condition is not reversible and only half are still alive five years after receiving the initial diagnosis. Cirrhosis is a chronic inflammatory disease of the liver involving cell death and the formation of scar tissue. Alcohol hepatitis may or may not precede it. Death results from cirrhosis because the liver fails to metabolize various toxins, such as ammonia, and these toxins accumulate in the body.

Fetal Alcohol Spectrum Disorder (FASD)

In this section, we discuss a chronic alcohol effect that does not focus on a specific body system or on the drinker. Rather, it focuses on the fetus and what alcohol consumption may do to it if its mother drinks during pregnancy. A characteristic set of symptoms that appear in some newborns of mothers who drink during pregnancy has become known as the fetal alcohol syndrome (FAS). FAS falls into the class of alcohol **teratogens**.

teratogens
Any chemical or environmental factor that negatively effects the development of an embryo or fetus during pregnancy.

FAS involves a range (or spectrum) of severity of syndromes that effect physical, social, and psychological deformities. Some physical deformities include small eyes and small eye openings, drooping eyelids, underdeveloped midface, skin folds across the inner corners of the eyes, underdevelopment of the depression above the upper lip, and a small head circumference. Furthermore, abnormal creases in the palm were reported, along with abnormalities in the joints. Some of the children observed have had cardiac defects, benign tumors consisting of dilated blood vessels, and minor ear abnormalities (Jones et al., 1973). Although estimates vary, FAS occurs in one to three of every 1000 live births (USDHHS, 1990). As you think about these statistics, remember that there is great individual variability in the effects on the fetus of prenatal exposure to alcohol. In this regard, the rate of occurrence of FAS is much lower than the rate of women who use alcohol while they are pregnant. Furthermore, rates of FAS vary with the population in question. For example, rates of FAS seem to be much higher among Aboriginals and African American mothers of low socioeconomic status than they are among white, middle-class mothers (USDHHS, 1993).

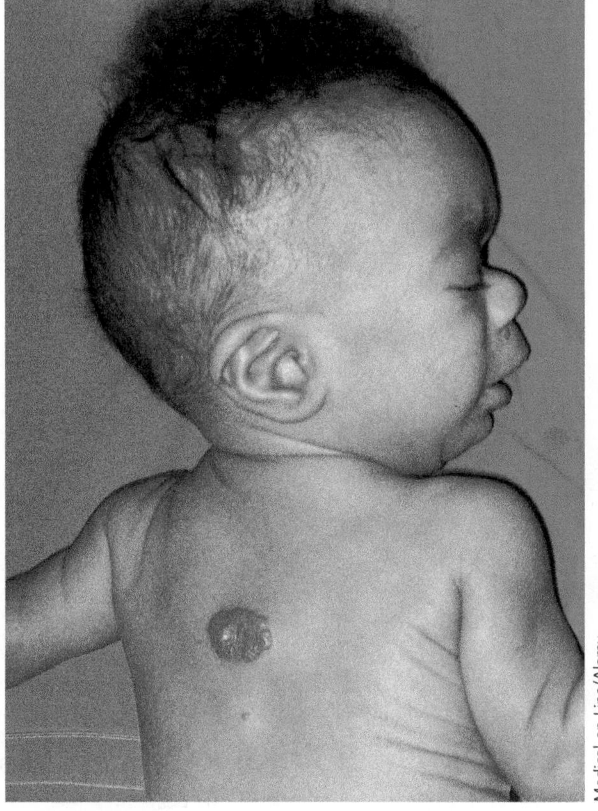

Medical-on-Line/Alamy

This child was diagnosed as being affected by fetal alcohol syndrome.

The variability in rates of FAS hints at the complexity in conducting studies of this serious public health problem. For one reason, it is extremely difficult to get accurate self-reports from pregnant women about their drinking; this seems to be particularly true for women who are heavier, with a drinking problem (Alvik, Haldorsen, & Lindermann, 2005). Because FAS can be detected only after a child is born, postpartum environmental and other factors cloud an interpretation of what part prenatal alcohol exposure played in the resulting FAS. It is sometimes even difficult to determine whether alcohol was the only prenatal substance that may have resulted in FAS. For example, other drug use during pregnancy is possible, and this would be most likely to occur among the heaviest drinkers (Erenhart, 1991). When other drugs are taken during pregnancy, they may harm the fetus in ways similar to alcohol.

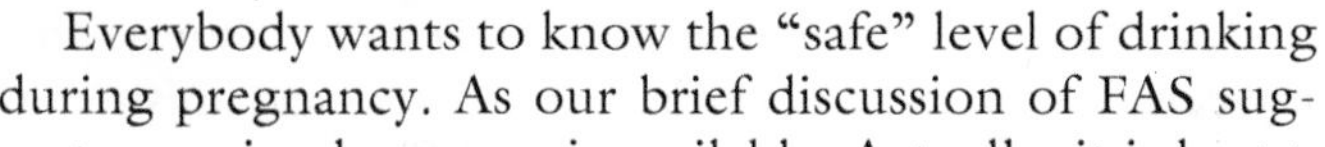

Everybody wants to know the "safe" level of drinking during pregnancy. As our brief discussion of FAS suggests, no simple answer is available. Actually, it is best to think of FAS as the most severe result of a continuum of effects of prenatal exposure to alcohol (Rasmussen, 2005). Subtle behavioural or cognitive effects may be observed on the other end of the continuum. Each abnormal outcome may have its own yardstick of amount of alcohol exposure and timing of exposure (Jacobson et al., 1993; USDHHS, 1990).

Moderate Drinking and Health

As we suppose you are convinced at this point, long-term heavy use of alcohol could seriously damage the body. However, what about long-term abstinence from alcohol and long-term lighter drinking? A number of studies have suggested that the moderate drinkers turn out to be the healthiest, followed by the abstainers, and dead last are the heavy drinkers. "Health" most often has been measured by risk of cardiovascular disease and mortality.

The surprise here, of course, is that drinking can be healthful, although the medical community has considered this possibility since the 19th century (Doll, 1998). The first question is: What is 'moderate'? Generally, moderation with alcohol has been defined as one to three drinks a day. How could such drinking possibly aid health? One hypothesis is that light alcohol consumption increases the production of high-density lipoproteins (HDLs), which take damaging cholesterol away from artery walls (Gaziano et al., 1993). Alcohol also appears to affect other biological indicators of risk of cardiovascular disease (Dejousse et al., 2009; Rimm, 2000).

Food Drink and Diet/Mark Sykes/Alamy

The discovery that moderate use of red wine is associated with a lower incidence of heart disease stimulated research on the effects of moderate alcohol use on health.

Most experts have concluded that moderate drinking is associated with lower risk of coronary disease (Lee et al., 2009; Marmot, 2001). Until recently, many people doubted this conclusion, however, because some studies failed to consider factors that correlate with drinking patterns and that also are associated with risk of cardiovascular disease. One of these factors is income; more of the abstainers than the moderate drinkers were defined as poor, and income is negatively related to health. There also has been a question of whether many "light/moderate daily drinkers" exist. Most light drinkers do not drink every day, and most people who drink every day do not drink lightly. Moreover, a review by Fillmore et al. (2006) suggests that the abstainers in these studies may have included many people who recently stopped drinking because they had become ill. On the other hand, recent better-designed correlational studies have shown an association between moderate alcohol use and cardiovascular health. Furthermore, experiments have demonstrated a reduction in biological indicators of risk of cardiovascular disease following administration of a moderate dose of alcohol (one to three drinks).

In conclusion, it seems that the connection between moderate drinking and cardiac health question still would benefit from additional research; for example, a large longitudinal study from Denmark suggests that the moderate drinking–heart health relationship is evident in men who have seven to 35 drinks a week, and it is evident in women who have as little as one drink a week (Tolstrup et al., 2006). This is the first study that suggests that whatever the relationship between alcohol use and cardiac health, its mechanism may be different for men and women and may be triggered by different amounts of alcohol between the sexes, with as little as a drink a week for women. However, the weight of the evidence is that moderate alcohol use in general is associated with cardiovascular health.

The Development of Alcohol Abuse and Dependence

The Canadian Alcohol and Drug Use Monitoring Survey data we covered in this chapter and in Chapter 1 showed that well over 75 percent of Canadians drink alcohol and that the minority of them drinks heavily. Some of those who drink heavily develop problems with alcohol to different degrees. When they do, the effects on themselves, their families, and their society are devastating. Accordingly, this question has preoccupied many for many years: How do alcohol abuse and dependence develop, or what is their etiology? In this last section, we briefly present approaches taken to address this question and describe the current thinking.

Traditional Approaches to Etiology

Until recently, researchers and clinicians alike usually sought a single-factor explanation of what causes alcohol problems. Theories frequently outpaced data available to evaluate them and can be classified as biological, psychological, or sociological.

Biological approaches have waxed and waned in popularity over the years. Such theories hold that a physiological or structural anomaly causes the individual to become alcohol dependent. Earlier single-factor biological approaches, which have not received experimental support, have included hypotheses that the source of the structural deficit is metabolic, glandular, due to body chemistry, or due to an allergic condition. The most prevalent position among Canadian medical and treatment providers is that alcohol dependence is a physical disease (see Contemporary Issue Box 6.5). Although the cause of the disease process is not specified, disease model adherents use the process of a physical disease, such as a fever, as an analogy to understand alcohol dependence. As a result, the disease model is classified as a biological model.

Biological explanations of alcohol problems have regained popularity among scientists because of findings that suggest there is a genetic predisposition at least to some "types" of alcohol dependence (Kendler et al., 1992; Schuckit, 1987). The evidence comes primarily from family, twin, and adoption studies. In summary, family studies show that sons and daughters of alcohol-dependent parents are four times more likely to develop the disorder themselves, relative to people whose parents are not dependent on alcohol. In addition, studies of twins show a greater likelihood of both members of

CONTEMPORARY ISSUE BOX 6.5

Is Alcohol Dependence a Disease?

Periodically, controversy flares over whether alcohol dependence is a disease. *Disease* may be defined broadly, but in the strict medical sense, it refers to a clearly identified physical process that is pathological. A critical feature of the definition is that once a disease is contracted, the afflicted individual has no control, or is not responsible, for the disease running its course. Typically when alcohol dependence is called a disease, the traditional medical model of disease is the referent.

Treatment providers and other citizens fought long and hard in the early 20th century to get alcohol dependence acknowledged as a disease in order to take "treatment" of alcohol dependence out of the legal system and into the medical profession. The campaign has been more than successful. In 1957, the American Medical Association formally recognized alcohol dependence as a disease and still does. Other professional organizations that followed include the Canadian Medical Association, American Academy of Pediatrics, and the Canadian Surgeon General. Public opinion polls consistently have shown that a large majority of Canadians and Americans say they believe that alcohol dependence is a disease. Moreover, advances in neuroscience research have bolstered this widespread support with more direct studies of drug action on the brain than were once possible (Peele, 1996).

The controversy is over whether the symptoms we call alcohol dependence are not more accurately thought of as a result of behaviour that is learned and voluntary rather than as a manifestation of some disease process. The question is based on research and clinical findings over the last 30 years that have sparked much discussion in scientific journals (see Chapter 15).

The question is not just an academic one. It has important implications for how alcohol-dependent people are provided with treatment, for one thing. Alcoholics Anonymous is among the popular treatment programs that supports that alcohol dependence is a disease. Other medical programs focusing on treatment throughout Canada are also well recognized through the Canadian Medical Association, such as outpatient treatment and rehabilitation centres.

Views of alcohol dependence also have legal ramifications. For example, in a 1988 Supreme Court case, two U.S. military veterans argued unsuccessfully that they should have an extension of the time to take advantage of their benefits because they were "afflicted" with alcoholism within the usual benefit period. The gist of their argument was that, because alcoholism is a disease, they should not be punished for having something they have no control over. The Department of Veterans Affairs instead asserted alcoholism is the result of "willful misconduct."

With this example, what might be some ramifications of adherence to a strict position that alcohol dependence is the result of a biological disease process?

identical twin pairs having alcohol dependence ("concordance") than of concordance in fraternal twins. This finding is significant because identical twins are genetic matches, whereas members of fraternal twin pairs have only 50 percent of their genes in common. Another finding pertains to adopted children of alcohol-dependent parents. These studies show that the development of alcohol problems in the offspring is far more influenced by having an alcoholic parent than by the adoptive home environment. This conclusion is especially strong for males. Based on this body of research, the argument for a biological predisposition to alcohol dependence has gained considerable strength. In this regard, genetic factors may account for up to a half of the variance in the etiology of alcohol dependence (Schuckit, Smith, & Kalmijn, 2004). Moreover, the mapping of the human genome has made the identification of specific gene candidates far more accessible that it was formerly (Johnson et al., 2006).

Psychological explanations of etiology have centred on identifying the "alcoholic personality," which means a psychological trait or set of traits that predispose someone to having alcohol dependence. Failure to find such a high-risk profile has not been due to lack of trying, as evidenced by the number of publications on the topic. However, recent research has revealed that the personality dimensions of neuroticism–emotionality, extraversion–sociability, and impulsivity–disinhibition predispose people to alcohol dependence (McCarthy, Kroll, & Smith, 2001).

Sociological models of etiology were proposed partly in response to the failure to discover the unique alcoholic personality. The models are supported by findings of cross-cultural differences in drinking patterns (the benchmark citation is MacAndrew & Edgerton, 1969) as well as demographic factors that you have seen are correlated with drinking patterns and problems. Studies that take them into account have shown consistently that sociological factors help to explain the development of alcohol dependence.

"Biopsychosocial" Approaches to Etiology

Although each type of single-factor explanation has merit, each alone ultimately fails to explain how alcohol abuse and dependence develop. For example, a minority of children of parents with alcoholism develop alcohol dependence themselves. What happens to the rest? A set of psychological characteristics may be associated with developing alcohol dependence, but those same characteristics could be correlated with other outcomes. Demographic factors are correlated with drinking problems, but the factors themselves are often associated with biological and psychological variables, too. It seems that single-factor researchers design their studies so that one type of factor—say, psychological—is emphasized and other types are underplayed or not represented at all. Indeed, the fact that there are seeds of support for each type of approach, but not strong support for any one alone, suggests that multiple types of factors influence the development of alcohol dependence. At least among scientists, the most current thinking is that alcohol, as well as drug dependence, is caused and maintained by a combination of biological, psychological, and sociological factors (see, for example, Galizio & Maisto, 1985). As we discuss further in Chapter 15 on treatment, the three types of factors together are called *biopsychosocial.*

What this means in practice is that scientists and practitioners alike cannot hope to understand alcohol dependence unless they consider together all the types of influencing variables. A good example is some of the exciting research done with sons of alcoholics who do not have alcohol dependence. One finding is from electrophysiological studies of the brain that show preadolescent sons of fathers with alcoholism may have a deficit that is expressed as a lesser ability to focus on stimuli in the environment (Porjesz & Begleiter, 1995). This difference from boys who do not have alcohol-dependent parents is presumably inherited and cannot be a consequence of the person's own drinking. In theory, such a deficit could increase the risk of developing alcohol dependence because of, say, a decreased ability to discriminate degree of intoxication when drinking moderately. Additionally, discrimination deficits could affect performance on various cognitive tasks and how individuals relate to other people (Schuckit, 1987). Whether risk actually is translated into alcohol dependence, however, depends in large part on how the environment (say, the family and school systems) "reacts" to any deficit in discrimination. Another example is a magnetic resonance imaging study of adolescents that Hill et al. (2009) reported. In this study, adolescents who were "high risk" for developing alcohol use disorders because of the multiple "layer" presence of that disorder in their family histories showed lower volume of brain orbital frontal cortex (OFC) matter than did adolescents who were "low risk" because they did not have a family history of alcohol use disorders. The OFC is an area of the brain that is associated with emotional processing and impulsivity. Furthermore, the differences in right-brain OFC matter seemed to be due to genetic variation between the high- and low-risk groups.

Saying that multiple factors combine to cause alcohol dependence is, after all, an extension of a theme we have followed since Chapter 1. Human experience and behaviour under the influence of drugs can be understood only by considering multiple types of factors in combination. The research suggests that the same thinking should be applied to understanding alcohol dependence.

SUMMARY

- Alcohol virtually always is drunk in the form of three major classes of alcoholic beverages: beer, wine, and hard liquor (also called distilled spirits).
- Alcoholic beverages are produced through fermentation and distillation.
- The alcohol content of a beverage is expressed by volume in Canada and the U.S.
- The proof of an alcoholic beverage refers to its percentage of alcohol content.
- People have used alcohol for thousands of years, but societies always have viewed alcoholic beverages as mixed blessings.
- In Canada, per capita alcohol consumption increased from the end of Prohibition into the 1940s. In 1980, a decline in consumption began attributed to educational campaigns on the impact of drinking and driving that were slightly reversed in 1990. This continued to the mid-late 1990s. Since then, there has been a slight decrease.
- Social and environmental factors, such as urban versus rural residence, gender, age, and racial/ethnic background, are associated with alcohol consumption rates. The same is true for the prevalence of heavy drinking.
- Alcohol is a drug that depresses the CNS. It exerts its effects by dissolving in lipid membranes.
- The GABA receptors are one locus that is a specific neural site of alcohol's action in the body. However, identifying a specific receptor mechanism is difficult, because alcohol's effects on the body are so diffuse.
- Alcohol passes through the stomach and is absorbed from the small intestine. The rate of alcohol absorption can vary widely according to an individual's physiological and situational factors.
- Following its absorption, alcohol is distributed to all of the body's tissues. Blood gets an especially high concentration of alcohol.
- Alcohol primarily affects the CNS, particularly the brain. The LD 50 for alcohol is a BAC of 0.45–0.50 percent.
- BAC is approximated by a simple equation that includes alcohol dose and time. Other factors that influence BAC are percentage of body fat, gender, and rate of alcohol metabolization.
- Breath analysis is a practical, precise way of measuring the BAC.
- The body metabolizes more than 90 percent of the alcohol it absorbs, primarily in the liver.
- The liver metabolizes alcohol at a constant rate of about 0.35 ounce of alcohol an hour, and little can be done to quicken the pace.

- Alcohol use leads to dispositional tolerance and, more important, to both acute and protracted functional tolerance.
- Chronic heavy use of alcohol can lead to physical dependence on it. Alcohol's acute action is evident in a wide variety of physiological, sensorimotor, and behavioural effects. In general, as the BAC increases, acute effects increase in number and intensity. However, both how we experience degree of intoxication and how we behave under different doses of alcohol are modified by psychological and situational factors as well as alcohol dose and tolerance to this drug.
- Sensorimotor skills, which alcohol impairs, are crucial in driving motor vehicles.
- Alcohol seems to be a major contributor to fatal and nonfatal automobile accidents. Gender and age combine with alcohol to influence risk of involvement in an automobile accident.
- Alcohol's effects on sex and aggression are major topics of social interest and concern. To understand alcohol's association with aggressive behaviour, it is necessary to take into account characteristics of the aggressor and situational factors, only one of which is alcohol.
- Alcohol's effects on sexual behaviour are similarly complex. It is necessary to know the physiological basis of alcohol's effect on sexual function, as well as situational and psychological factors, to explain its effects on sexual behaviour.
- A history of chronic heavy drinking is associated with damage to most of the body's organs and systems. Two of the most prominent ones are the liver and the brain.
- A chronic effect of alcohol use is impaired memory and other cognitive functions. Some of these effects are reversible with abstinence from alcohol. However, when the brain has structural damage, as in Korsakoff's syndrome, the effects are permanent.
- As the major metabolic site of alcohol the liver is vulnerable to the chronic effect of heavy alcohol use.
- Three liver disorders that are attributable to drinking are fatty liver, alcohol hepatitis, and cirrhosis. The first two disorders are reversible with abstinence; cirrhosis is not.
- A mother's drinking during pregnancy may result in fetal alcohol syndrome (FAS) in the newborn child. FAS consists of gross physical deformities that are identifiable at birth. FAS is associated with continued physical problems as well as below-average intellectual functioning later in childhood.
- The idea that moderate alcohol consumption is associated with lowered risk of cardiovascular disease and mortality has good research support, but this conclusion remains controversial.
- The development of alcohol dependence is an unsolved problem. It does seem that "single-cause" theories are inadequate to explain the etiology of alcohol dependence. Instead, it is necessary to incorporate biological, psychological, and sociological factors.

Key Terms

blackout **p. 120**
blood alcohol concentration (BAC) **p. 114**
confabulation **p. 129**
disinhibition theory **p. 124**
distillation **p. 105**
intoxication **p. 120**
long-term memory **p. 121**
monoamine oxidase (MAO) inhibitors **p. 121**
neuropsychological tests **p. 129**
proof **p. 106**
REM sleep **p. 120**
short-term memory **p. 121**
standard drink **p. 114**
teratogens **p. 130**

Essays/Thought Questions

1. What is your opinion of the efforts at college and university campuses to have an "alcohol-free" environment? How is this policy similar to or different from banning tobacco smoking in public places?
2. What would be the advantages and disadvantages of creating a definition of "legal intoxication" that considers an individual's protracted functional tolerance to alcohol?
3. Would requiring alcohol warning labels on alcoholic beverage containers be effective in moderating alcohol consumption? Why or why not?

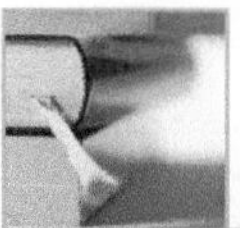

Suggested Readings

Heath, D.B. (2000). *Drinking occasions. Comparative perspectives on alcohol and culture*. New York: Brunner/Mazel.

National Institute on Alcohol Abuse and Alcoholism. (2002). *A call to action: Changing the culture of drinking at U.S. colleges*. Washington, DC: U.S. Department of Health and Human Services.

CHAPTER 7

Nicotine

Did You Know

?

- For over 360 years tobacco was viewed as a panacea.
- Archeological evidence dates tobacco use in Canada to the 8th century.
- Cigarette smoking is the most popular way to use tobacco. Currently, 21 percent of Canadian males and 14 percent of females report that they are smokers, smoking an average of 15 cigarettes a day.
- Nicotine stimulates the same receptors that are sensitive to acetylcholine. It is biphasic, which means that it is both a stimulant and a depressant.
- Nicotine's acute effects involve the central nervous system and the autonomic nervous system. It has stimulant effects at lower doses but more depressant effects at higher doses.
- You can become nicotine dependent.
- Major diseases linked to smoking are heart disease, chronic obstructive lung disease, and cancers of various types.
- The World Health Organization (WHO) estimated that, in the 20th century, 100 million people around the world died due to smoking; by the year 2100, the WHO projects one billion premature deaths due to smoking worldwide.
- In 2008, secondhand smoke killed over 1200 Canadians.

In this chapter and in Chapter 8, we review two more stimulant drugs: nicotine and caffeine. We cover these two drugs separately from other stimulant drugs because nicotine and caffeine are used so prominently in societies around the world. Use of other stimulant drugs has a small fraction of the prevalence that use of nicotine or caffeine does.

This chapter is a review of nicotine and begins with some background information about its source and the ways that nicotine is consumed, followed by a history of tobacco use. We then discuss the prevalence of nicotine use and the mechanisms of its pharmacological action. We also review the acute and chronic effects of nicotine. The chapter concludes with a description of professional services available to help individuals stop smoking.

Nicotine is found naturally in one source: the leafy green tobacco plant. The plant belongs to the genus *Nicotiana* and has 60 species. Only two of these can be used for smoking and other human consumption: *Nicotiana rustica* and *Nicotiana tabacum*. First Nations communities in Canada predominantly used *Nicotiana rustica* for pipe smoking, but it was *Nicotiana tabacum* that became the most popular form of tobacco throughout the world. By the 17th century *Nicotiana tabacum* could be found in nearly every part of the globe (Collishaw, 2009). Today, *Nicotiana tabacum* provides all of the tobaccos typically consumed in North America, including burley, oriental, and cigar tobaccos. Table 7.1 outlines the history of tobacco use and legislation in Canada.

Different types of tobacco result mostly from differences in cultivation and processing. In this regard, tobacco leaves are harvested when still green and then undergo curing and fermentation. The tobacco then is converted into commercial products—cigarettes, cigars, snuff, chewing tobacco, and pipe tobacco (Blum, 1984).

Tobacco has many constituents, but nicotine is singled out as having the broadest and most immediate pharmacological action. Nicotine is extremely toxic—about as toxic as cyanide (Rose, 1991)—and only 60 milligrams are needed to kill a human. When tobacco is burned, the smoke contains a small portion of nicotine, which the body metabolizes to a nontoxic substance.

Nicotine is extremely toxic—about as toxic as cyanide (Rose, 1991)—and only 60 milligrams are needed to kill a human.

The tobacco products meant for smoking—in the form of cigarettes, cigars, or pipes—are generally familiar. Not so familiar are the forms of smokeless tobacco, which include snuff and chewing tobacco (Gritz, Ksir, & McCarthy, 1985). Snuff is powdered tobacco that is mixed with salts, moisture, oils, flavourings, and other additives. It is marketed in two forms, dry and moist. Chewing tobacco is marketed in loose-leaf form, pressed as a rectangle called a plug, or in a twist or roll. As with snuff, aroma and flavouring agents are added to chewing tobacco. A quid (piece) of tobacco can be either chewed or held between the cheek and gum. "Dipping" is holding a pinch of moist snuff in the same place. In Europe, snuff is most commonly taken dry and intranasally.

Dusan Zidar, 2009/Shutterstock.com

These tobacco plants await conversion to commercial products such as cigarettes and chewing tobacco.

TABLE 7.1 A Timeline of Key Issues in Canadian Tobacco Use and Legislation

Date	Event
8th century	Earliest archeological evidence of tobacco use in Canada.
16th century	First Nations peoples use *Nicotiana rustica* for pipe smoking.
Late 1500s	Basque sailors trade tobacco to Newfoundland Beothuks in exchange for furs.
17th century	*Nicotiana tabacum* becomes the most popular form of tobacco worldwide.
Late 17th and early 18th centuries	Inuit are introduced to tobacco by Siberian natives, Russian fur-traders, English and American whalers, and Danish colonists from Greenland.
17th to the early 20th century	French-Canadian farmers grow *Nicotiana rustica* in their gardens for personal use. This allowed them to avoid stiff duties on tobacco and prohibitions on its use.
1870s	Tax is imposed on the tobacco leaf when it entered factories for processing.
1871	Census reports 1.2 million pounds of tobacco grown in Quebec. Most tobacco was homegrown for personal, not commercial use.
1905	The Department of Agriculture establishes a Tobacco Division to advise Ontario and Quebec how to cultivate tobacco for industrial buyers, such as the American Tobacco Company of Canada (ATCC).
1908	The Tobacco Restraint Act is passed, making it illegal to sell cigarettes to those under 16 years of age.
Early 20th century	The Women's Christian Temperance Union (WCTU), with branches in the United States and Canada, begin campaigning for governmental prohibition on cigarettes (a fairly new tobacco product at the time).
By the 20th century	Montreal is, and remains today, the centre of Canada's tobacco industry.
1912	The American Tobacco Company of Canada (ATCC) becomes Imperial Tobacco.
1916	Women in Canada win the right to vote. They enter the workplace in increasing numbers during the war and afterwards. It is now more socially acceptable for women to smoke.
1920s	Advertising for cigarettes targets this growing female market.
1920s–1950s	"Three Golden Decades for Cigarettes."
1947	Canadian Dr. Norman Delarue examines the link between cigarette smoking and increased rates of lung cancer. Although his study was not made public, his research was replicated with similar findings.
1950	Ernst Wynder and Evarts Graham (Delarue's supervisor) replicate Delarue's study with a larger sample size and publish the findings. Their research along with others during that time document the link between cigarette smoking and lung cancer.
1950s	The tobacco industry responds to fears about the dangers of cigarettes by putting filters on cigarettes.
1950s–1960s	The Canadian tobacco industry increases research examining the link between cigarettes and cancer. In 1956, they identify in Canadian tobacco benzopyrene, a known carcinogen, and in 1959 they discovered that perforating cigarette filters increased the nicotine–tar ratio. However, Imperial Tobacco does not tell consumers about these research findings.
1962	Canada's six tobacco companies enter into a secret agreement in not to make any public statements about tar and nicotine levels.
1963	The Canadian Tobacco Manufacturers Council is established by the Canadian tobacco industry. In 1964, the council voluntarily decides to restrict tobacco advertising.
1966	The greatest recorded use of cigarettes by Canadian adults: 4100 cigarettes annually per capita.

Late 1960s to 1980	Cigarette use reaches a plateau of 3700–3900 cigarettes per Canadian adult per year.
1981–1986	Canadian cigarette use decreases to 3000 cigarettes per adult per year. Increased tobacco taxes, improved advocacy for tobacco control, more publicity about tobacco, and protection from tobacco smoke are credited with this decline in Canadian cigarette use.
1987	The Canadian government proposes the *Tobacco Products Control Bill*, which would ban tobacco advertising, require health warnings on cigarette packages, and ban smoking in all government workplaces.
1988–1989	The Tobacco Sales to Young Persons Act (TSYPA) passes, replacing the 1908 Tobacco Restraint Act. It prohibits any person from selling or giving tobacco to those under the age of 18. It also requires tobacco vending machines to be removed from all public places except bars and taverns. The House of Commons passes *the Tobacco Products Control Act* and *the Non-Smokers' Health Act*. The Tobacco Products Control Act requires manufacturers to list the additives and amounts for each brand. The Non-Smoker's Health Act, a private member's bill proposed by Lynn McDonald (Bill C-204), regulates tobacco under the *Hazardous Products Act*.
1992	The Canadian government removes export taxes on cigarettes. This leads to a decrease in illegal cigarette smuggling and makes all cigarettes cheaper.
1993	The legal age to buy cigarettes is raised to 18.
1994	Legislation requires cigarette packages to carry warning messages.
1995	The Canadian Supreme Court rules that the *Tobacco Products Control Act* violates the *Charter of Rights and Freedoms*.
1997	The *Tobacco Product Control Act* and the *Tobacco Sales to Young Persons Act* are replaced by the *Tobacco Act*.
1999	New regulations come into effect requiring retail establishments that sell tobacco to post signs that read: "It is prohibited by federal law to provide tobacco products to persons under 18 years of age."
2000	A law passes that requires cigarette packages to carry one of 16 new health warnings that cover half of the cigarette pack and include graphic images. The new warning labels appeared on packages starting in January 2001.
2000s	The tobacco industry argues that the *Tobacco Act* violates the *Charter of Rights and Freedoms*. Courts rule that provinces may sue tobacco companies for tobacco-related health costs.
2006	Cigarette companies in Canada (Imperial Tobacco, Rothmans, Benson & Hedges, and JTI-Macdonald) voluntarily phase out the use of "light" and "mild" on their cigarette packaging.
2007	The Supreme Court of Canada rules unanimously to uphold the *Tobacco Act* in its entirety.
2008–present	Court cases involve individual provinces suing tobacco companies over smoking related health-care costs.
2008	Nova Scotia bans smoking in vehicles with anyone under 19 years of age.
2009	Ontario bans smoking in vehicles with anyone under 16 years of age.
2010	New Brunswick and Saskatchewan ban smoking in vehicles with anyone under 16 years of age.
2011	The Supreme Court of Canada rules that the federal government cannot be held liable in lawsuits directed at recovering smoking-related health costs from tobacco companies.

Source: Collishaw (2009), *History of Tobacco Control in Canada*; CBC News (2011), *A Legal History of Smoking in Canada.*

History of Tobacco Use*

In the late 15th century, Columbus and other explorers found First Nations in the New World smoking dried tobacco leaves. The pleasant effects of nicotine caught on like fire, and smoking quickly became popular among the Europeans. They brought home seeds of the tobacco plant and spread them to other parts of the world on their ventures. In these early years, the Spanish held a monopoly on the world tobacco market because *Nicotiana tabacum* is indigenous to South America. However, the English took a piece of the business when John Rolfe's *Nicotiana tabacum* crop flourished in the colony of Virginia.

By the middle of that century, tobacco use had spread throughout central Europe, and signs of the addictive nature of the drug were evident.

At first, only the wealthy could afford tobacco. For example, in England, tobacco was worth its weight in silver, and people paid that price. By the early 17th century, however, tobacco use had become widespread and even the poor could afford it. In 1614, London had about 7000 tobacco shops. By the middle of that century, tobacco use had spread throughout central Europe, and signs of the addictive nature of the drug were evident. For example, African natives would trade land, livestock, and slaves for tobacco. As with most of the world, Canada's history with tobacco dates back centuries (see Table 7.1).

Not everybody regarded tobacco so highly. In the middle 1600s, Popes Urban VIII and Innocent X issued papal bulls against tobacco use, but clergy and laymen alike continued to smoke. In 1633, in Constantinople, the Sultan Murad IV paid surprise visits to his men in combat during war. If the soldiers were caught smoking, the good sultan punished them by quartering, hanging, beheading, and worse. Yet the soldiers continued to smoke. The Russian czar in 1634 also prohibited smoking. He punished offending subjects by slitting their nostrils and by imposing other consequences that might discourage them from smoking. However, the Russians did not give up tobacco either.

Portuguese seamen gave tobacco to the Japanese in 1542. Like their Western counterparts, the Japanese quickly took to smoking—so quickly that the emperor had issued an edict against smoking by 1603. However, the Japanese did not stop. In 1639, smoking had become so established in Japan that a person was offered a smoke with a ceremonial cup of tea. "From these days until today... no country that has ever learned to use tobacco has given up the practice" (Brecher, 1972, p. 213). No substance has replaced tobacco in people's hearts, minds, and bodies. When tobacco smokers discovered the pleasures of smoking marijuana or opium, even these drugs did not displace tobacco; they were merely smoked in addition to it.

Tobacco as Panacea

From the time Columbus and his colleagues discovered tobacco use among the Native Americans until about 1860, the tobacco plant was accepted widely as having medical therapeutic value. Tobacco probably reached its peak of recognition as a medicinal herb at the beginning of the 17th century, even though King James I of England published his skepticisms about tobacco's curative powers at the same time. The king admonished that using tobacco for pleasure was morally wrong. To give you an idea of how its reputation exceeded its critics' influence, Table 7.2 lists some of the ways tobacco has been used medically. During the 360 years the table covers, some people believed it was literally possible to breathe life into another person as long as that breath carried tobacco smoke. Tobacco was esteemed at one time as a panacea weed.

*This section on the history of tobacco use is taken from Blum (1984), Brecher (1972), and Stewart (1967).

TABLE 7.2 Uses of Tobacco as Medical Treatment, 1492–1853

- Applied externally in various forms (such as ashes, hot leaves, balm, lotion, mush, oil, and many more) for pain due to internal or external disorders and for skin diseases or injuries of any kind
- Introduced into all openings of the head to treat diseases of the ears (such as smoke blown into), eyes (juice to cleanse), mouth (such as small ball chewed), and nose (such as snuff blown up nose of patient by physician)
- Introduced into the mouth to reach other organs, such as the lungs (such as smoke introduced directly by the physician), the stomach (such as through juice, boiled, or uncooked), and the teeth (such as use of ashes to clean)
- Introduced into the nostrils to reach lungs (such as inhaled odour of snuff powder)
- Introduced into the intestinal canal (such as smoke or tobacco enema)
- Introduced into the vagina by injection

Source: Adapted from Stewart (1967), Appendix 5.

From Panacea to Panned

The promotion of tobacco as a therapeutic agent took a serious blow in 1828, when two Frenchmen, W.H. Posselt and L.A. Reimann, isolated nicotine. The chemical was named after a man named Nicot, who was the French ambassador to Portugal and who conducted exacting experiments with tobacco as a medicinal herb. He published his purported successes worldwide. The isolation of nicotine was damaging to its medical reputation because the toxic and addictive properties of the compound began to be understood.

Prevalence of Tobacco Use

History shows that tobacco's popularity can resist even the most severe obstacles. In North America today, cigarette smoking is by far the most common way to use tobacco. Cigarette smoking is the most toxic way to smoke tobacco, followed in order by cigar and pipe smoking (Blum, 1984). Accordingly, we begin this discussion with the prevalence of cigarette smoking.

FIGURE 7.1 Overall manufacturer share of Canadian tobacco market, 2005–2006

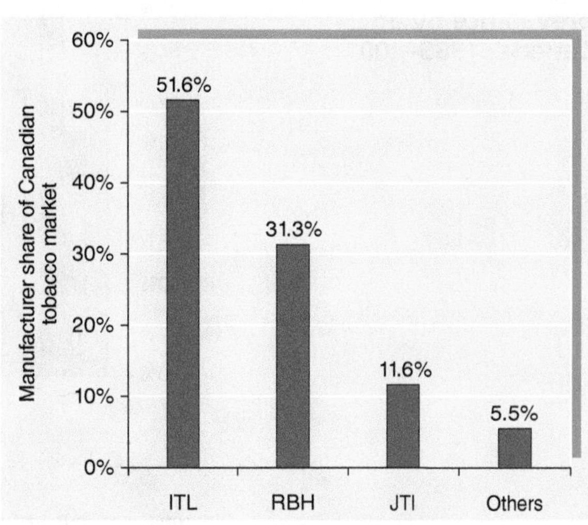

Source: Non-Smokers' Rights Association. *Backgrounder on the Canadian Tobacco Industry and Its Market.* Page 10.

Smoking in Canada

Canada has three major cigarette companies: Imperial Tobacco Canada Limited (ITL), Rothmans, Benson & Hedges Inc. (RBH), and JTI-Macdonald Corporation (JTI). Collectively, these companies manufacture the vast majority of tobacco in Canada (see Figure 7.1), and produce the top 10 cigarette brands (see Figure 7.2). Tobacco is big business, bringing in billions of dollars in sales each year. For example, in 2006, tobacco sales equivalent to 32.6 billion cigarettes generated federal and provincial taxes of $2.49 billion and $4.17 billion, respectively (not including revenue from GST and provincial sales tax) (Backgrounder, 2008).

Health Canada uses the Canadian Tobacco Use Monitoring Survey (CTUMS) to collect continual data on tobacco use by Canadians aged 15 and older. From 1999 to

FIGURE 7.2 **Top 10 premium cigarette brands in Canada that account for over 96 percent of domestic premium cigarette shipments by Canadian manufacturers in the 12 months ending March 31, 2006**

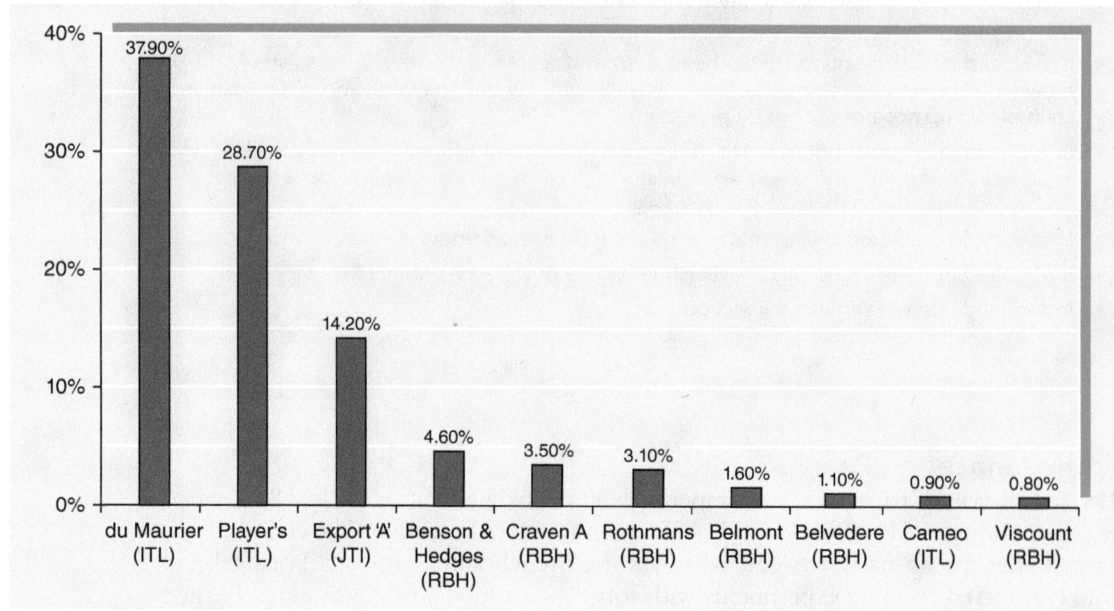

Source: Non-Smokers' Rights Association. *Backgrounder on the Canadian Tobacco Industry and Its Market*. Page 10.

The average Canadian smoker smokes 15 cigarettes a day.

2009 there has been a decrease in the overall percentage of Canadians who smoke, from 25 percent to 18 percent. Figures 7.3 and 7.4 illustrate the prevalence rates of smoking in Canada from 1985 to 2009. According to the CTUMS, 21 percent of Canadian males and 14 percent of females report that they are smokers. Fourteen percent of Canadian teenagers (aged 15–19) are smokers; this accounts for 298 000 Canadian teens. The average Canadian smoker smokes 15 cigarettes a day. Males smoke almost

FIGURE 7.3
Current smoking prevalence by age, Canada, 1985–2001

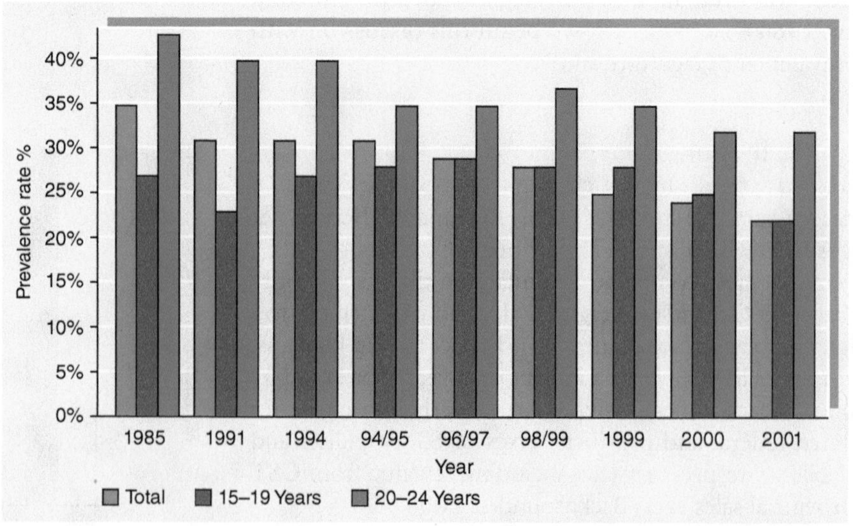

Source: *Canadian Tobacco Use Monitoring Survey 2009*. Statistics Canada and Health Canada, 2010. Minister of Public Works and Government Services Canada, 2012.

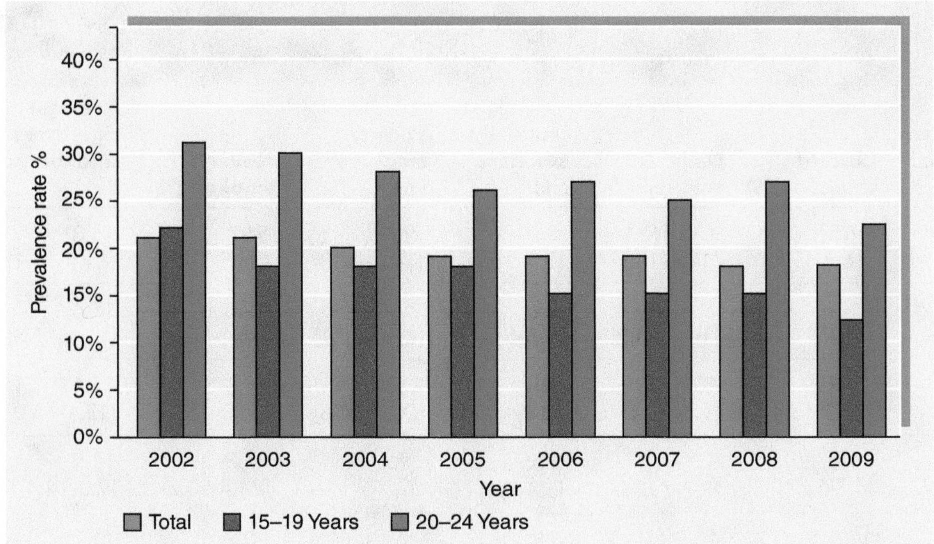

FIGURE 7.4
Current smoking prevalence by age, Canada, 2002–2009

Source: *Canadian Tobacco Use Monitoring Survey 2009*. Statistics Canada and Health Canada, 2010. Minister of Public Works and Government Services Canada, 2012.

17 cigarettes a day while women smoke 13 cigarettes a day. Table 7.3 shows the distribution of smoker types and the average number of cigarettes smoked per day in Canada.

The CTUMS, along with additional studies conducted in the U.S., illustrate some common trends in cigarette use in North America. These studies show that the percentage of men and women who smoke declined in the latter part of the 20th century. Coupled with the decline in smokers is a steady increase in the percentage of adults who identified themselves as former smokers (Hughes, 1993; Molarus et al., 2001; USDHHS, 1987b). That is, increasing numbers of people have said they quit smoking, and most of them did so on their own (Zusy, 1987). Self-quitters are thought to have been "lighter" smokers (smoking fewer than 25 cigarettes a day). Nevertheless, many current smokers say they want to quit but find it difficult to do so.

On the other hand, there is some alarm over the resurgence in popularity among college and university students and other young people of the "hookah" (or water pipe, among other names). The water pipe, which is a device to deliver nicotine by smoking, is so named because the smoke that is inhaled first passes through water (Maziak, 2008). The water pipe first appeared in Africa and Asia over four centuries ago, but has gained new popularity around the world since the 1990s. A main reason for the reemergence seems to be the perception among young people that the hookah is a harm-free, pleasant way to smoke tobacco. In Canada, almost seven percent of Canadian youth in grades 7–12 reported ever using waterpipes, and many of those thought that water pipe smoking was not as risky as cigarette smoking: 29 percent thought that smoking tobacco in a water pipe was less harmful than smoking cigarettes; 34 percent thought smoking a water pipe reduced the level of tar you inhale compared to smoking cigarettes; 24 percent thought that smoking tobacco in a water pipe reduced the risk to health compared to smoking cigarettes (Tobacco Research Unit, 2011).

In Canada, almost seven percent of Canadian youth in grades 7–12 reported ever using waterpipes, and many of those thought that water pipe smoking was not as risky as cigarette smoking.

Others feel this way also; according to a Tobacco Regulation Advisory Note published by the World Health Organization (WHO) in 2005, the Indian physician who invented the water pipe billed it as a safer way to smoke tobacco. In addition,

TABLE 7.3 Smoking Type and Average Number of Cigarettes Smoked Per Day, by Age Group and Sex

Sex	Age group (years)	Population estimate ('000)	Current smokers (%)	Daily smokers (%)	Nondaily smokers (%)	Former smokers (%)	Never smoked (%)	Average cigarettes smoked per day[1]
Total	All age groups	27 982	17.5↑ [16.0-19.0]	13.5↑ [12.1-14.9]	4.0 [3.3-4.8]	26.1 [24.4-27.8]	56.4 [54.5-58.2]	15.3 [14.4-16.1]
Male		13 811	21.4 [18.9-24.0]	16.5↓ [14.1-18.9]	4.9 [3.6-6.2]	29.6 [27.0-32.1]	49.0 [46.1-51.9]	16.6 [15.4-17.8]
Female		14 171	13.7 [12.1-15.4]	10.6 [9.1-12.1]	3.1 [2.3-4.0]	22.7 [20.6-24.8]	63.6 [61.3-65.9]	13.1 [12.1-14.0]
Both sexes	15-17	1380	11.0 [8.3-13.7]	5.8* [3.7-7.8]	5.3* [3.4-7.1]	#	87.3 [84.4-90.2]	11.9 [9.3-14.4]
	18-19	818	17.8 [14.3-21.2]	10.9 [8.0-13.9]	6.8 [4.6-9.0]	#	80.2 [76.6-83.8]	11.3 [9.7-13.0]
	15-19	2197	13.5↑ [11.4-15.6]	7.7 [6.0-9.3]	5.9 [4.4-7.3]	1.8* [1.1-2.5]	84.7 [82.4-86.9]	11.6 [10.2-13.0]
	20-22	1492	19.5↑ [16.1-23.0]	11.3 [8.7-13.9]	8.2 [5.6-10.8]	6.3 [4.3-8.2]	74.2 [70.3-78.1]	13.0 [11.1-14.8]
	23-24	802	20.5↑ [15.5-25.6]	15.8 [11.0-20.5]	4.8* [2.2-7.3]	10.6* [6.9-14.3]	68.9 [63.0-74.8]	12.2 [10.2-14.2]
	20-24	2295	19.9 [17.0-22.8]	12.9 [10.5-15.2]	7.0 [5.1-8.9]	7.8 [6.0-9.5]	72.3 [69.1-75.6]	12.6 [11.4-13.9]
	25-34	4696	22.6 [17.9-27.3]	17.4 [12.7-22.0]	5.3* [2.8-7.8]	17.7 [13.2-22.1]	59.7 [54.5-64.9]	15.7 [13.5-17.8]
	35-44	4760	20.3 [16.0-24.7]	15.3 [12.0-18.6]	5.0* [2.3-7.8]	15.4 [11.1-19.6]	64.3 [58.9-69.7]	14.2 [12.4-15.9]
	45-54	5354	19.1 [15.2-23.0]	15.7 [12.0-19.4]	3.4* [1.7-5.1]	32.1 [27.3-37.0]	48.7 [44.1-53.4]	15.5 [13.9-17.1]
	55+	8680	12.7 [10.2-15.1]	10.7 [8.5-13.0]	1.9* [1.0-2.9]	43.7 [40.4-47.1]	43.6 [40.3-46.9]	17.0 [14.9-19.2]
	25+	23 490	17.7 [15.9-19.4]	14.1 [12.5-15.7]	3.6 [2.7-4.5]	30.1 [28.1-32.2]	52.2 [50.0-54.4]	15.7 [14.7-16.7]
Male	15-17	711	11.3* [7.1-15.4]	5.8* [2.8-8.8]	5.5↓ [2.5-8.4]	#	86.7 [82.2-91.2]	12.3 [8.9-15.7]
	18-19	415	16.0 [11.6-20.4]	10.4* [6.5-14.2]	5.6* [3.2-8.0]	#	81.2 [76.6-85.8]	13.2 [10.6-15.9]
	15-19	1127	13.0 [9.9-16.1]	7.5↓ [5.2-9.8]	5.5*↑ [3.5-7.5]	2.3* [1.2-3.5]	84.7 [81.3-88.0]	12.8 [10.7-14.9]
	20-22	810	21.2 [16.3-26.1]	12.3 [8.4-16.2]	8.9* [5.6-12.2]	6.7* [4.0-9.4]	72.1 [66.5-77.7]	13.9 [10.9-16.8]

	23-24	361	25.6 [17.8-33.3]	18.6* [10.9-26.4]	#	10.5*↑ [5.3-15.7]	63.9 [55.0-72.9]	13.2 [10.2-16.3]
	20-24	1171	22.5↑ [18.3-26.8]	14.3 [10.7-17.8]	8.3 [5.6-11.0]	7.9 [5.3-10.4]	69.6 [64.9-74.3]	13.6 [11.5-15.7]
	25-34	2365	33.1 [24.7-41.5]	25.4* [17.0-33.8]	#	16.8* [10.1-23.6]	50.0 [41.2-58.9]	17.2 [14.5-19.9]
	35-44	2388	23.0 [16.2-29.9]	17.1 [11.8-22.4]	#	16.9* [10.6-23.2]	60.0 [51.9-68.2]	14.6 [11.8-17.3]
	45-54	2673	23.6 [17.4-29.8]	19.3 [13.3-25.4]	#	34.5↑ [27.3-41.7]	41.9 [34.8-49.0]	16.4 [14.4-18.4]
	55+	4088	14.3 [10.7-17.9]	12.2 [8.8-15.6]	#	54.8 [49.9-59.7]	30.9 [26.1-35.8]	19.1 [16.2-22.0]
	25+	11 514	22.1 [19.1-25.2]	17.6 [14.8-20.4]	4.5*↑ [3.0-6.1]	34.4 [31.4-37.4]	43.4 [40.0-46.8]	17.0 [15.6-18.3]
Female	15-17	669	10.8* [7.2-14.4]	5.7* [3.2-8.2]	5.1* [2.3-7.8]	#	87.9 [84.1-91.7]	11.5* [7.9-11.2]
	18-19	402	19.6 [14.2-25.0]	11.5*↑ [7.1-15.9]	8.1* [4.4-11.8]	#	79.2 [73.6-84.7]	9.5 [8.2-12.3]
	15-19	1071	14.1 [11.1-17.1]	7.9 [5.6-10.2]	6.2* [4.0-8.4]	#	84.6 [81.6-87.7]	10.4 [8.6-12.2]
	20-22	683	17.6 [12.9-22.2]	10.2* [6.8-13.5]	7.4* [3.7-11.1]	5.8* [2.8-8.7]	76.7 [71.4-81.9]	11.6 [9.9-13.3]
	23-24	441	16.4* [10.5-22.4]	13.4* [8.0-18.8]	#	10.6* [5.4-15.9]	72.9 [65.6-80.3]	11.0 [8.6-13.4]
	20-24	1124	17.1 [13.4-20.9]	11.4 [8.4-14.4]	5.7* [3.2-8.2]	7.7* [5.0-10.3]	75.2 [70.9-79.6]	11.3 [9.9-12.7]
	25-34	2331	12.0* [7.7-16.3]	9.2* [5.3-13.0]	#	18.6 [13.7-23.4]	69.5↓ [63.5-75.5]	11.4 [9.4-13.4]
	35-44	2372	17.6 [12.9-22.3]	13.5*↓ [9.8-17.2]	#	13.8* [8.1-19.5]	68.6 [61.5-75.7]	13.6 [12.0-15.3]
	45-54	2681	14.6 [10.3-19.0]	12.1 [8.2-15.9]	#	29.8 [23.5-36.1]	55.6 [49.2-62.0]	13.9 [11.5-16.2]
	55+	4591	11.2 [8.2-14.1]	9.3 [6.6-12.1]	#	33.9 [29.5-38.3]	54.9 [50.3-59.5]	14.2 [11.9-16.4]
	25+	11 977	13.4 [11.5-15.3]	10.7 [9.0-12.4]	2.6* [1.6-3.6]	26.0 [23.6-28.5]	60.6 [57.9-63.3]	13.4 [12.3-14.6]

Notes:

95% confidence intervals in brackets

[1] Daily smokers only.

The symbols ↑ and ↓ refer to the direction of rounding to integers.

* Moderate sampling variability, interpret with caution.

High sampling variability; although an estimate may be determined from the table, data should be suppressed.

Source: Tobacco Control Directorate, Supplementary Tables, CTUMS Wave 1, 2010. Table 1. Reproduced with the permission of the Minister of Public Works and Government Services, 2012.

a proliferation of websites promoting the water pipe and retailing it in ways that are highly appealing have fed what Maziak (2008, p. 1763) called a water pipe use "epidemic." Unfortunately, as with other alternatives to tobacco cigarettes that have been promoted as "safe," smoking from a water pipe is a threat to health; in this case, the smoke from a water pipe contains nicotine, tar, and carbon monoxide. We show later in this chapter how tar and carbon monoxide are especially toxic. Although few studies have addressed this question, the prevalence of use of the water pipe among college students in the United States in the past month has been estimated to be in the range of 15–20 percent (Eissenberg et al., 2008).

In addition to water pipes, the increase use of cigarillos has also created new concern about tobacco use. Nearly one-third of Canadian youth aged 15–19 years have tried little cigars with eight percent reporting that they have smoked them within the past 30 days. Almost half of young adults, aged 20–24, have tried little cigars, with nine percent reporting that they smoked them within the past 30 days (CTUMS, 2010). In July 2010 the "Cracking Down on Tobacco Marketing Aimed at Youth Act" (Bill C-32), came into effect. This act put an immediate end to all tobacco advertising in publications and to the use of flavourings in cigarillos and cigarettes aimed at young smokers. Further, cigarillos are to be sold in packages of at least 20 units so that they are not easily accessible and affordable to young smokers (Euromonitor, 2011).

Initiation of Smoking

It is important to know who initiates smoking and the number of people who do so because people tend to become dependent on nicotine quickly and before they are 20 years old. The 2008–2009 Youth Smoking Survey (YSS) reported that three percent of Canadian youth in grades 6–9 were smokers while 13 percent of youth in grades 10–12 were smokers (Health Canada, YSS, 2009). The average age at which youth first smoked a whole cigarette was 12 years for youth in grades 6–9 and 14 years for youth in grades 10–12. Daily smokers in grades 6–9 smoked 10.9 cigarettes on average per day, while daily smokers in grades 10–12 smoked 9.0 cigarettes on average per day. For grades 6–9, 22 percent of youth have tried cigarettes, with males at trying cigarettes more often than females (23 vs. 19 percent); while 48 percent of youth in grades 10–12 have tried smoking a cigarette, with no difference between males and females. But, more males (15 percent) in grades 10–12 reported being current smokers than females (11 percent). Statistics like these take on practical significance because, once nicotine dependence is initiated in adolescence, it tends to persist into the adult years (O'Loughlin et al., 2009).

> *Moreover, the younger the age at which a person starts to smoke, the harder it seems to be able to quit later.*
> Breslau & Peterson (1996)

Moreover, the younger the age at which a person starts to smoke, the harder it seems to be able to quit later (Breslau & Peterson, 1996). This tendency can be seen during the undergraduate college years. One study (Wetter et al., 2004) classified first-year college students as "nonsmokers," "occasional smokers," or "daily smokers." Four years later, these students were reassessed, and the findings showed that the majority of students who smoked as freshmen still smoked as seniors—this was true for 90 percent of the daily smokers and for 50 percent of the occasional smokers. Overall, it seems a lot easier to start smoking than it is to stop (Colder et al., 2001). However, most smokers regret starting to smoke. Canadian researcher Geoffrey Fong and his colleagues (2004) conducted a survey of over 8000 adult smokers in four countries: Canada, the United States, the United Kingdom, and Australia. They asked participants to rate how much they agreed with the following statement: "If you had to do it over again, you would not have started smoking." They found that across all countries about 90 percent of respondents replied that they either "agreed" or "highly agreed" with this statement.

As you might guess, because of the enormous public health consequences of smoking a lot of research has been devoted to explaining smoking initiation. Consistent with the approach to understanding human drug use that is taken in this text, the reasons for smoking initiation are a complex interplay of biological, psychological, and social/environmental factors. We will give you a few examples of findings that have led to this conclusion. From the biological side, recent animal research suggests a major reason why smoking tends to begin in adolescence is that teens' brains are more sensitive to the rewarding (reinforcing) effects of nicotine than are the brains of older individuals (Belluzzi et al., 2004). In this same vein, biopsychological research has used brain imaging (PET scans) to provide data suggesting that individuals who score higher on the personality characteristics of hostility and aggression are more stimulated by a dose of nicotine than are individuals who score lower on these characteristics. This finding suggests that certain people not only are more likely to begin smoking, but also are more likely to continue the behaviour than are other individuals (Fallon et al., 2004).

Psychological factors also may combine with environmental variables to affect smoking initiation. One study found that adolescents who score high on the characteristic of "novelty seeking" (they tend to be impulsive, to take risks, and to have a high need for stimulation) are more receptive to tobacco company advertisements than are people who score lower on novelty seeking (Andrain-McGovern et al., 2003).

In summary, biological, psychological, and social/environmental variables affect smoking initiation and its continuation. As we will discuss, the consequences are substantial.

THIS IS YOUR BRAIN ON NICOTINE

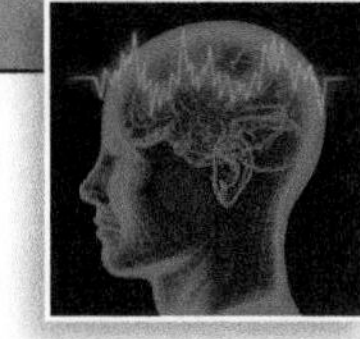

To understand the action of nicotine (see accompanying figure), it is essential to understand the neurotransmitter acetylcholine (ACH), which we reviewed in Chapter 3. Nicotine stimulates the same receptors that are sensitive to ACH and therefore is a cholinergic agonist drug (Julien, 2005). ACH stimulates both the autonomic and central nervous systems. Table 7.4 is a summary of the effects of ACH on biology and behaviour. Julien (2005) also noted that nicotine acts to raise dopamine levels in the mesocorticolimbic system (the reward circuit, see Chapter 3). Nicotine is called a biphasic drug because it stimulates ACH receptors at low doses but it retards neural transmission at higher doses (Taylor, 2001). This biphasic action, described in the accompanying figure, partly explains the complex effects that humans perceive when they ingest nicotine, which we discuss shortly. Nicotine also affects the

TABLE 7.4 Effects of Acetylcholine on Biology and Behaviour

Increases blood pressure
Increases heart rate
Stimulates release of adrenalin from adrenal glands
Increases tone and activity of the gastrointestinal tract
Facilitates release of dopamine and serotonin
Affects CNS functions of arousal, attention, learning, memory storage and retrieval, mood, and rapid eye movement (REM) during sleep

Source: Adapted from *A Primer of Drug Action*, by R.M. Julien, W.H. Freeman and Company, 2005.

(continued)

level of dopamine by decreasing monoamine-oxidase-A (MAO-A), the enzyme responsible for breaking down dopamine. This decrease in MAO-A allows dopamine to remain in the synatic cleft longer, leading to a temporary increase in dopamine levels of the cigarette smoker, or the "high" experienced from cigarette smoking. Figure 7.5 compares the levels of MAO-A for a nonsmoker and smoker.

- In the normal functioning of the nervous system, neurotransmitters are released into the synaptic cleft by vesicles in terminal buttons of sending neurons. Many are taken up by receptor sites in receiving neurons.
- In the process called *reuptake*, sending neurons typically reabsorb excess molecules of neurotransmitters.
- Nicotine mimics ACH and binds to acetylcholine receptors, known as "nicotinic" receptors. At low doses nicotine stimulates these nicotinic receptors, but at high doses it prevents the receptors from responding to neurotransmitters. Nicotinic receptors are found in the VTA and when stimulated cause an increase in the release of dopamine in the nucleus accumbens.

FIGURE 7.5 PET scan comparing MAO-A levels in the brain of a non-smoker and smoker

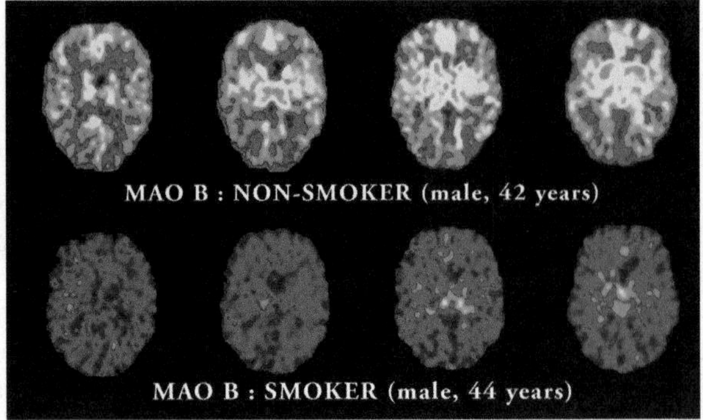

Pascal Goetgheluck/Science Photo Library

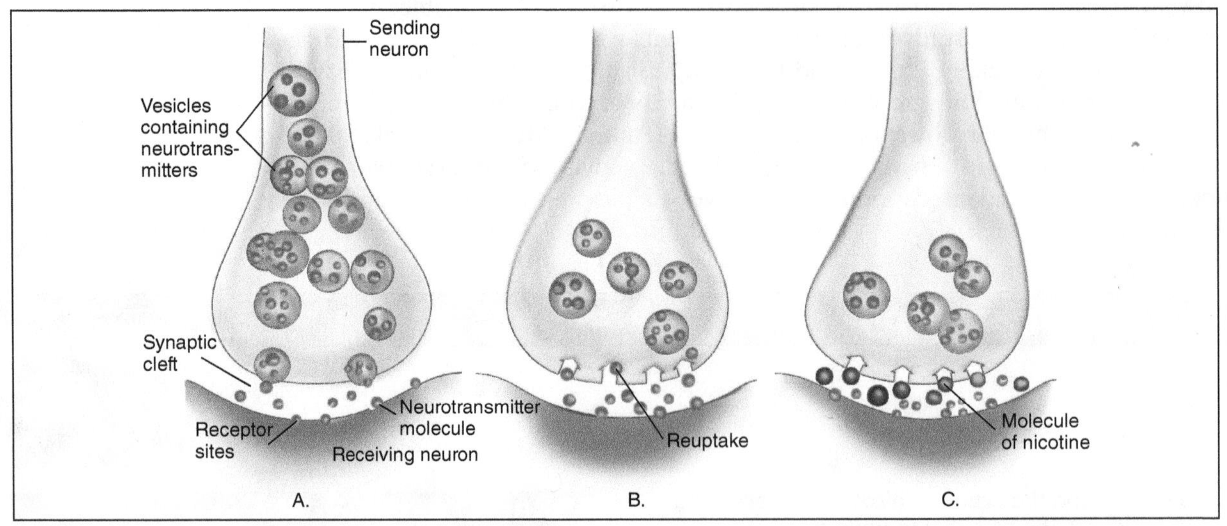

S. Rathus, S. Maheu, & S. Veenvliet. *PSYCH*, 1e. © 2012 Nelson Education Ltd. Reproduced by permission. www.cengage.com/permissions

Pharmacokinetics

Absorption

Nicotine can be absorbed through most of the body's membranes and can very quickly affect the nervous system (see Figure 7.6). The drug is rapidly absorbed through the oral, buccal (the cheeks or mouth cavity), and nasal mucosa; the gastrointestinal tract; and the lungs (O'Brien, 1995). Russell (1976) related a story to illustrate how readily nicotine can be absorbed: A florist was using a pesticide spray that contained nicotine and soaked the seat of his pants with it by accident. In only 15 minutes, the florist had **nicotine poisoning** and had to be hospitalized for four days. When he recovered and was dressing to return home, the florist put on the same pants, which still had some nicotine on them. He was readmitted to the hospital an hour later with nicotine poisoning.

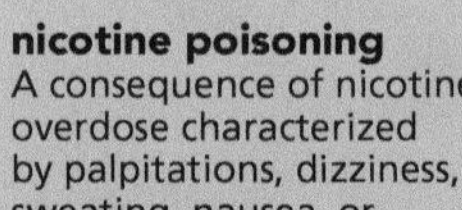

nicotine poisoning
A consequence of nicotine overdose characterized by palpitations, dizziness, sweating, nausea, or vomiting.

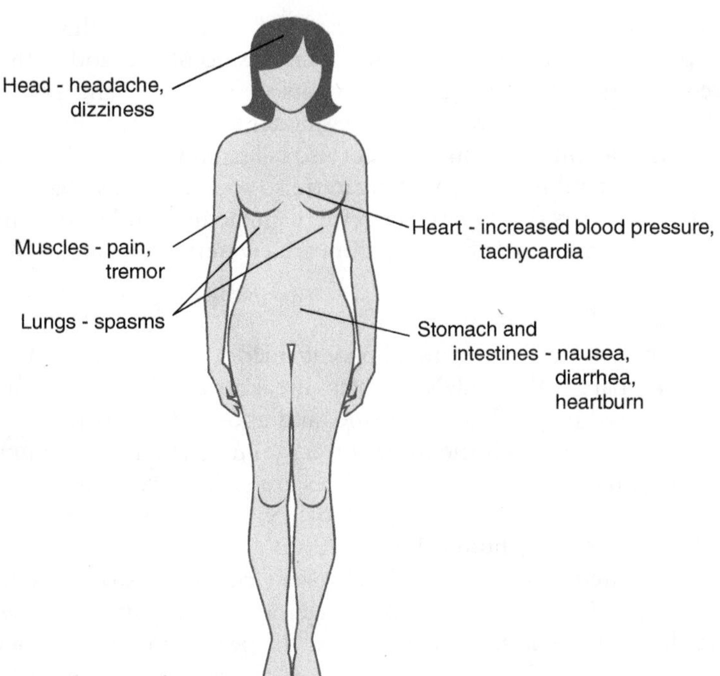

FIGURE 7.6
Effects of nicotine on the nervous system

Source: Zubada/Shutterstock

Nicotine absorption depends on both the site of absorption and how the nicotine is delivered. Nicotine is most readily absorbed from the lungs, which makes inhaling cigarette smoke an efficient way to get a dose of nicotine. Nicotine is not as readily absorbed through the oral, buccal, or nasal mucosa. The nicotine in cigar or pipe smoke, for example, is not as readily absorbed as the nicotine in cigarettes because people usually do not inhale smoke from cigars or pipes. As a result, the nicotine is absorbed through the mouth. When nicotine is taken by using snuff or by chewing tobacco, it is absorbed through the mucosa of the nose and the mouth, respectively.

How nicotine is delivered also affects its absorption. You will recognize some of the factors that affect absorption from reading Chapter 4. One factor is the acidity of the medium (for example, smoke) of delivery. The more alkaline (basic) the medium, the easier the absorption. Cigar or pipe smoke is more basic than cigarette smoke, which compensates to some extent for the difference between the mouth and lungs in ease of absorption. Length of contact of the nicotine-containing substance with the absorption site also is important. The longer the contact, the greater the amount of nicotine absorbed. For example, using snuff and chewing tobacco allows considerable time for nicotine absorption at the nose and mouth (Blum, 1984).

Distribution

After nicotine is absorbed, the blood distributes it to a number of sites of pharmacological action. When a cigarette is inhaled, nicotine reaches the brain from the lungs within seven seconds. By comparison, it takes 14 seconds for blood to flow from the arm to the brain, which is the typical route for intravenous injection. Therefore, in the delivery of nicotine, brain levels rise rapidly and then decline just as quickly as the drug is distributed to other parts of the body. The effects of nicotine can be observed rapidly because its distribution half-life is only 10 to 20 minutes (Heishman, Taylor, & Henningfield, 1994). A study using PET scan methods illustrates this phenomenon

When a cigarette is inhaled, nicotine reaches the brain from the lungs within seven seconds.

nicely. It showed that, with only one cigarette puff, almost one-third of the primary nicotine receptors (nicotinic ACH) of the brain are occupied, and with three puffs, almost three-quarters of the receptors are occupied. After smoking two and one-half cigarettes, the receptors are saturated and the smoker feels satiated (Brody et al., 2006). However, because nicotine levels in the brain also fall rapidly, we have a major biological reason why smokers tend to reach for a cigarette so soon after they have finished their last one. Average smokers of a typical cigarette manufactured in North America absorb between 0.1 and 0.4 milligram of nicotine for each cigarette they smoke (Julien, 2005).

Metabolism and Excretion

The major organ responsible for metabolizing nicotine is the liver. The lungs and kidneys also play a part in the body's chemical breakdown of nicotine (Taylor, 2001). Nicotine is eliminated primarily in the urine, and about 10–20 percent of nicotine is eliminated unchanged through the urinary tract (Blum, 1984). Less important vehicles of eliminating nicotine and its metabolites are saliva, sweat, and the milk of lactating women (Jones, 1987b; Russell, 1976). Nicotine's elimination half-life in a chronic smoker is about two hours (Julien, 2005).

One study compared blood nicotine levels over a course of two hours in 10 subjects administered comparable doses of nicotine in cigarettes, oral snuff, and chewing tobacco (Benowitz et al., 1988). The study showed that the peak nicotine blood levels reached through the three sources did not differ. However, the rise in nicotine level was steepest for smoking, with a quick and then a more gradual decline leveling off to about one-third the peak level. In contrast, with both snuff and chewing tobacco, the rise in blood level was slower, but higher levels of nicotine were maintained considerably longer. These findings follow from the quicker nicotine absorption time through inhalation but the increased nicotine exposure time in using chewing tobacco or snuff.

The course of nicotine blood levels by smoking gives additional insight into why smokers often smoke many cigarettes a day. They need to smoke often to maintain a nicotine blood level that is not below a threshold for the beginning of withdrawal symptoms. Figure 7.7 is a graph of the average level of nicotine in the blood of a

FIGURE 7.7
Blood nicotine levels in a typical cigarette smoker over a 24-hour period

Source: Adapted from Julien (2005) and Taylor (2001).

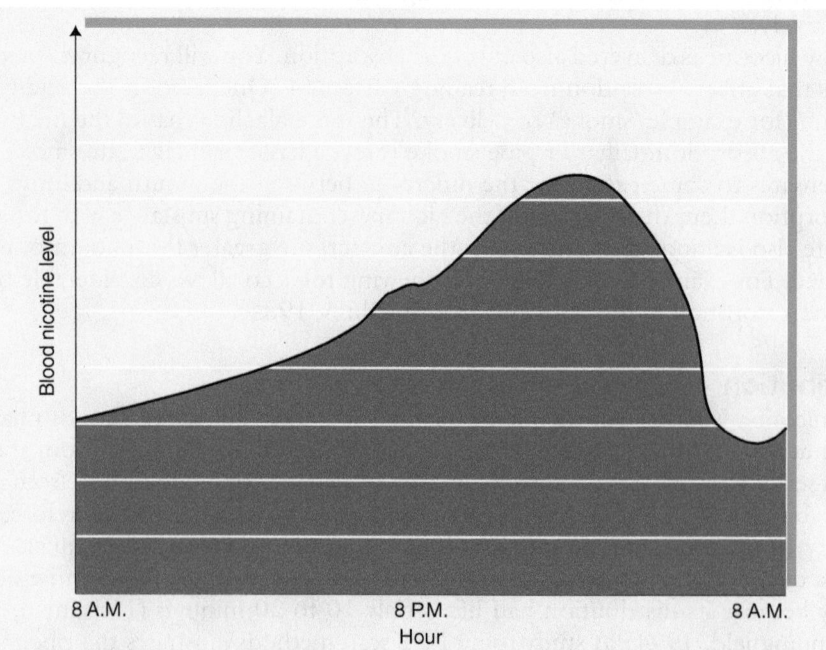

cigarette smoker over the course of a full day. The level of nicotine in the blood rises during the 16-hour part of the day when people are awake, with a peak around midnight. The level then declines during sleeping hours, but there is a positive level upon wakening in the morning.

Tolerance and Dependence

Tolerance

Tolerance to nicotine develops quickly. For example, a person's first attempts at smoking usually result in palpitations, dizziness, sweating, nausea, or vomiting (Russell, 1976). These are signs of acute nicotine poisoning. However, signs of tolerance to these autonomic effects of nicotine are evident even within the time of smoking the first cigarettes. Similarly, the effects of the nicotine in the initial puffs of the first cigarette of the day are greater than those in the last few puffs of that cigarette (Jones, 1987b). The rapid development of tolerance to nicotine also is apparent in the short time it takes some people to become seasoned smokers. The time from their unpleasant first cigarette to pleasurable smoking of a pack a day or more can be as short as several weeks. Besides tolerance to the effects of nicotine, dispositional tolerance develops. For instance, smokers metabolize the drug more quickly than nonsmokers do (Edwards, 1986).

Physical Dependence

There is no question that people can become physically dependent on nicotine. The major criterion for classification of a drug as one that induces physical dependence is what ensues when the drug is taken away for long enough that the amount of it in the blood drops considerably or is eliminated. When a consistent set of physical symptoms results, it is said that the drug induces physical dependence. The reverse side of this criterion of physical dependence is that readministration of the drug alleviates any withdrawal symptoms that are present. In 1988, the U.S. Office of the Surgeon General issued a full report with the conclusion that physical dependence on nicotine develops and that the drug is addicting. In 1989, the Royal Society of Canada came to the same conclusion.

Actually, studies have shown for some time that users of nicotine may become physically dependent on it. For example, Hughes, Grist, and Pechacek (1987) collected smokers' reports of the symptoms they experienced 24 hours after stopping smoking. The most common report (73 percent of the smokers) was a craving for tobacco, followed in order by irritability, anxiety, difficulty concentrating, restlessness, increased appetite, impatience, somatic complaints, and insomnia. A range of what are generally considered unpleasant symptoms results when dependent smokers stop smoking. As we noted earlier, once people begin smoking cigarettes, they have a high likelihood of becoming dependent on nicotine.

Acute Effects of Nicotine

You have seen that nicotine's effects are pervasive and complex. Table 7.5 and Figure 7.7 illustrate nicotine's acute pharmacological effects at "normal" doses, or at doses that everyday smokers, tobacco chewers, or snuff users typically ingest, for example. Because of nicotine's biphasic effects, its effects at higher doses would tend to be more depressant than are the effects listed in Table 7.5 or Figure 7.7.

TABLE 7.5 Acute Pharmacological Effects of Nicotine

General CNS Stimulant

- Increases behavioural activity
- May produce tremors
- Stimulates vomiting centre in brain stem (tolerance to this effect develops quickly)
- Stimulates release of antidiuretic hormones from hypothalamus, increasing fluid retention
- Reduces muscle tone by reducing activity of afferent nerves from muscles
- Enhances alertness, learning, and memory

Other Actions

- Increases heart rate, blood pressure, and contraction of the heart
- Initiates dilation of arteries, if they are not atherosclerotic, to meet heart's increased oxygen demand caused by nicotine

Source: Adapted from Julien (2005) and Taylor (2001).

A major point to notice is that nicotine has ACH-like effects (see Table 7.5), which agrees with its ACH agonist action: nicotine has major CNS stimulant action, although these effects are not as intense as what is observed with cocaine and amphetamines. Nicotine's enhancing effects on alertness, learning, and memory are of considerable importance to us because these effects may account for part of nicotine's reinforcing effects in humans. It is important to note that nicotine deprivation in smokers tends to result in impaired performance on cognitive tasks, but administration of nicotine reverses that impairment. Reversal of cognitive impairment, therefore, could play a part in maintaining cigarette use (Heishman, Taylor, & Henningfield, 1994; Parrott, 1998).

Another point to notice is nicotine's autonomic effects, particularly on the cardiovascular system. The stimulation of the heart and its resultant increased demands for oxygen underlie the association of nicotine and heart disease. In this regard, a less-than-adequate supply of oxygen to the heart may result in chest pain (angina) or a heart attack (Julien, 2005).

Nicotine is classified as a stimulant drug, but people who use it often report decreased arousal. That is, the perception is that nicotine has a calming effect and nicotine users find this effect reinforcing (Todd, 2004). The reasons for this perception of lowered arousal are complex. One factor may be nicotine's acute effect of relaxing the skeletal muscles (also see Jones, 1987b). Another pharmacological reason is nicotine's biphasic action: At higher doses, its effects are more depressant.

Pharmacology is only part of the explanation of how aroused people feel when they use nicotine. One of the sedating psychological effects of smoking is the smoker's perception of successfully coping with stress while smoking, which suggests that individuals' beliefs about nicotine's effects influence their reaction to smoking cigarettes (Abrams & Wilson, 1986; Juliano & Brandon, 2002). More fundamentally, personality research suggests that arousal and the perception of stress reduction are independent factors, so they are positively related on occasion, not surprisingly (Parrott, 1998). Along these same lines, nicotine use often is associated with pleasant social situations like parties. Many other secondary (associated) effects of nicotine use exist and can contribute to users' perceptions at times that the drug has calming effects.

A final acute effect of nicotine is its relationship to lower body weight. Nicotine decreases one's appetite for sweet foods and increases the amount of energy the body uses both while it is resting and while it is exercising (Jaffe, 1990; West & Russell, 1985). These effects of nicotine use help to explain the common finding that quitting smoking is associated with weight gain. The nicotine–body weight relationship is noteworthy to us for a couple of reasons. First, the association of smoking with body weight may affect adolescents' decisions to start smoking. Austin and Gortmaker (2001) found that frequency of dieting among middle-school girls (which implies concern about weight control) was directly related to the probability that they would start smoking within the next two years. In addition, among adults who already smoke, the perception that smoking controls weight is a powerful motivator for continuing to smoke and for resuming smoking after stopping for a period of time (Pomerleau & Saules, 2007). The motivation seems to be particularly strong among women (McKee et al., 2005), although weight gain also has been associated in men who resume smoking after stopping for a period of time (Borelli et al., 2001). However, researchers from the University of Montreal (O'Loughlinal et al., 2008) conducted a longitudinal study over five years that examined the growth and development of almost 1300 Montreal teens. They found that teenage girls aged 12–17 who smoked were no more likely to lose weight than their nonsmoking counterparts. In addition, the researchers found that teenage boys who smoked were about one inch shorter than nonsmoking teenage boys.

Nicotine's Dependence Liability

In the late 1980s the conclusion by both the U.S. Surgeon General and the Royal Society of Canada that nicotine is physically addicting stunned many people, although knowledge that physical dependence on nicotine can develop had been around for years. The shock of the report probably lay in the public's failure to view nicotine as a "serious" drug like cocaine or heroin. Yet, the circumstances are most conducive for developing both psychological and physical dependence on nicotine.

Nicotine's CNS-stimulating effects, coupled with the frequent perception that it is sedating, are powerfully reinforcing to humans. Nicotine remains a highly accessible drug in spite of the numerous taxes levied on its purchase over the years. In addition, although the number of social settings where nicotine use is acceptable has decreased, enclaves of social support for its use remain in North America.

Nicotine's CNS-stimulating effects, coupled with the frequent perception that it is sedating, are powerfully reinforcing to humans.

The rapid rise and fall of nicotine blood levels creates the demand for many nicotine reinforcements a day. For smokers, each inhalation results in a drug reinforcement that must be replaced quickly because of a rapid fall in the blood level of nicotine. For two-pack-a-day smokers, estimates average 300 nicotine reinforcements a day, which equals about 110 000 a year.

Reasons such as these make psychological dependence on nicotine so likely once use of the drug starts. Many social and environmental associations with nicotine use strengthen the psychological dependence. Additionally, strong incentive to continue using the drug is added when people become physically dependent on it. Use must continue in order to avoid unpleasant withdrawal symptoms or to escape such symptoms if they begin. Use of nicotine under such conditions is strengthened through negative reinforcement. Therefore, pharmacological, psychological, and social/environmental variables combine to make nicotine a drug with high-dependence liability. Indeed, it now is generally agreed that smokers smoke, tobacco chewers chew, and snuffers snuff primarily for the effects of nicotine (Jarvik et al., 2000).

Effects of Chronic Tobacco Use

Chronic or long-term use of tobacco products is associated with life-threatening diseases. The seriousness of these consequences is reflected in precedent-setting legislation enacted in Canada in 1997. As of 2000, part of the law requires cigarette packs to display gruesome pictures of possible long-term consequences of

FIGURE 7.8
Anatomy of a cigarette package

Source: Health Canada. *Tobacco Product Labeling*. Health Canada, 2009. Reproduced with permission of the Minister of Public Works and Government Services 2012.

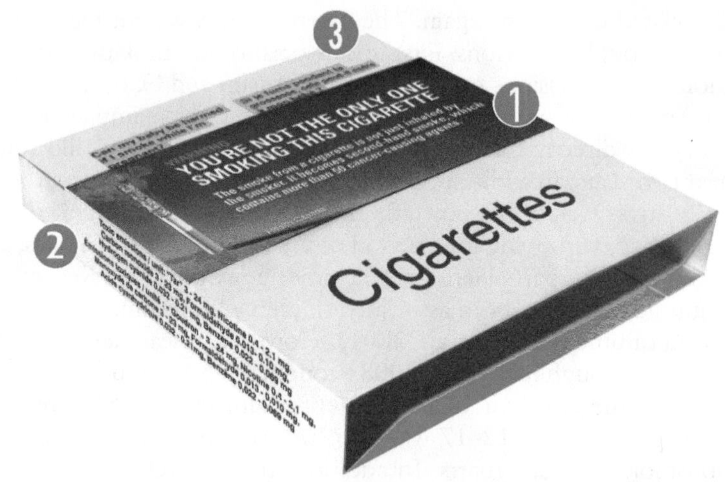

The Tobacco Act requires that certain information be displayed on packages of all tobacco products: 1) Graphic health warnings; 2) Toxic emissions statement; and, 3) Health information messages.

Health Canada. *Health Labels for Cigarettes and Little Cigars*. Reproduced with permission of the Minister of Public Works and Government Services 2012.

Examples of graphic health warnings on cigarette packages.

smoking, such as a lung tumour or a mouth with oral cancer. The pictures must cover 50 percent of the front and back of each pack. Figure 7.8 shows the anatomy of a cigarette package in Canada. Each cigarette package must contain one of 16 health warnings that describe the diseases or dangers of cigarette smoke. A colour picture accompanies these warnings. The photos (to the left) show some examples of these warnings. Currently, the Canadian government is proposing new legislation that will require larger and more graphic warnings on cigarette packages. Cigarette packages must also contain a toxic emissions statement that reports the emission levels of six toxic chemicals: nicotine, tar, carbon monoxide, formaldehyde, benzene, and hydrogen cyanide. Figure 7.9 illustrates the compounds that are often found in cigarettes. Finally, each cigarette package must contain health information about the risks of tobacco use or tips on quitting smoking. These are usually found on the inside of the package (Health Canada, 2010). The Canadian legislation is part of an international trend to use the cigarette (and cigar and smokeless tobacco) package itself to reduce the world's health care burdens by helping people either to stop smoking or not to initiate it (National Cancer Council of Australia, 2006).

We begin this section with a discussion of the effects of chronic cigarette smoking because that is the dominant way tobacco is used. In Canada, smoking contributes to more than 45 000 deaths a year. This makes cigarettes and tobacco the leading cause of preventable deaths in Canada. The story is the same in the United States, where more than 430 000 people who smoke will die each year—almost 1200 people a day. Woloshin, Schwartz, and Welch (2002) made this figure more personal by comparing rates of death from different diseases among adults 20 years of age and older who currently smoke or who never smoked. These researchers computed the chances of dying in the next 10 years for a given medical problem for different age groups, and used the 1998 National Center for Health Statistics Multiple Cause-of-Death Public-Use files for their computations. For women, there were some diseases for which the probability of dying in the next 10 years does not differ at any age between smokers and nonsmokers. For example, at age 30, the chance of dying of breast cancer in the next 10 years is 0.001 for both groups, and at age 45, it is 0.004. For other diseases, however, there are big differences between the groups. At age 45, six of 1000 (0.006) women smokers are likely to die of a heart attack compared with two of 1000 (0.002) nonsmokers. At age 55, the counterpart numbers are 24 (0.024) and seven (0.007). The disparity continues with further aging: at age 80, the numbers are 453 (0.453) and 90 (0.090). For all causes of death, at age 30, the numbers are 14 (0.014) for smokers and seven (0.007) for nonsmokers; at age 45, they are 50 (0.050) and 26 (0.026); at age 55, 125 (0.125) and 66 (0.066); and at age 80, 950 (0.950) and 581 (0.581).

FIGURE 7.9 What is in your cigarette?

=
Over 4000 chemicals
Over 70 cancer-causing chemicals including Arsenic, Benzene, Formaldehyde, Nickel, and Lead
The poisonous gas Hydrogen Cyanide
Fine particles that damage the respiratory system

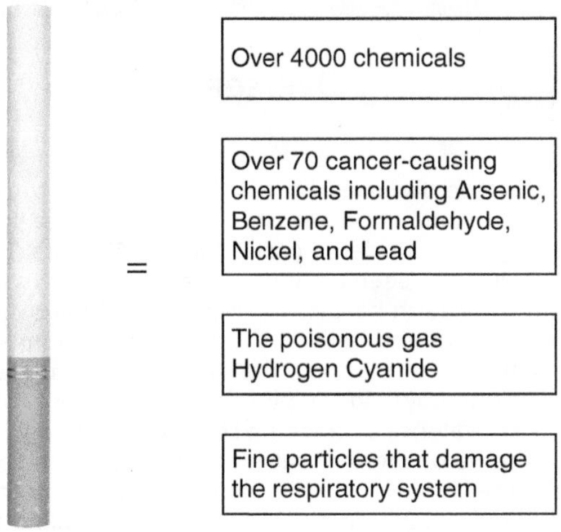

Source: Shutterstock

The picture is similar for men. Smokers and nonsmokers did not differ in projected death rates from diseases like colon or prostate cancer, and they did not differ in rates of death by accidents. However, for death by heart attack, stroke, or lung cancer, the disparities in death rates were large and evident from age 30 to old age. The proportions of death from all causes at age 30 were 0.030 for smokers and 0.013 for nonsmokers; at age 45, they were 0.091 and 0.039; at age 55, 0.125 and 0.066; and at age 80, 0.950 and 0.650. Statistics like these are represented in cost-of-illness studies.

4.3 million men and women worldwide die prematurely due to their cigarette smoking.
Ezzati & Lopez (2003)

All the data we cited on the health consequences of chronic cigarette smoking are for Canada and the United States only. However, 4.3 million men and women worldwide die prematurely due to their cigarette smoking (Ezzati & Lopez, 2003). The problem is not estimated to resolve itself. In February 2008, the World Health Organization (WHO) issued a report estimating that, in the 20th century, 100 million people around the world died prematurely due to smoking; by the year 2100, the WHO projects 10 times that number, or one billion premature deaths due to smoking worldwide (see the Drugs and Culture Box 7.1).

Tar, Nicotine, and Carbon Monoxide

Cigarette smoking damages health because of the constituents of tobacco smoke. The three main culprits are tar, nicotine, and carbon monoxide, and cigarette smokers face continual exposure to them for years. For example, a two-pack-a-day smoker could be seen with cigarette in hand, mouth, or ashtray 13.4 hours a day, taking about 400 puffs and inhaling as much as 1000 milligrams of tar. Carbon monoxide appears to facilitate many of the disease processes associated with smoking. This is due to carbon monoxide's advantage over oxygen in binding to hemoglobin, which carries oxygen from the lungs to the tissues in the body. Exposure to even small amounts of carbon monoxide reduces the amount of hemoglobin available for binding to oxygen

A two-pack-a-day smoker could be seen with cigarette in hand, mouth, or ashtray 13.4 hours a day, taking about 400 puffs and inhaling as much as 1000 milligrams of tar.

DRUGS AND CULTURE BOX 7.1

Smoking Overseas

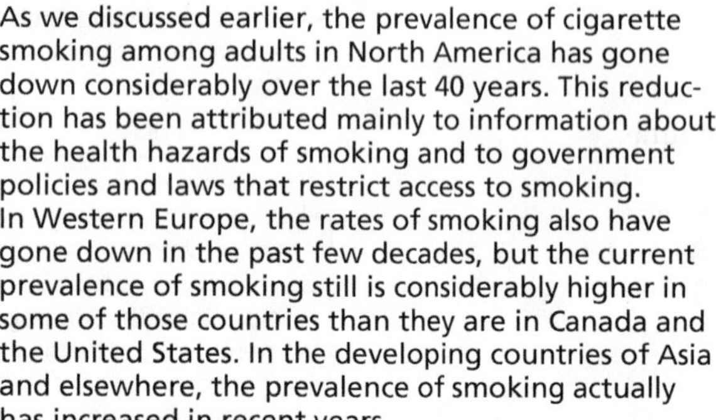

As we discussed earlier, the prevalence of cigarette smoking among adults in North America has gone down considerably over the last 40 years. This reduction has been attributed mainly to information about the health hazards of smoking and to government policies and laws that restrict access to smoking. In Western Europe, the rates of smoking also have gone down in the past few decades, but the current prevalence of smoking still is considerably higher in some of those countries than they are in Canada and the United States. In the developing countries of Asia and elsewhere, the prevalence of smoking actually has increased in recent years.

Of course, the knowledge about the effects of smoking on health that is available to North Americans is available to the governments of other countries as well. Thus, it seems that cultural, social, and financial factors account for the continued and sometimes increased popularity of smoking around the world. For example, one reason that sounds very Western, culturally speaking, is that smoking is viewed as a personal choice that may cause some harm but not that much. As such, society and governments alike should tolerate smoking. In France, smoking is very much a part of café life and lends an intellectual aura to smokers. In China and Japan, smoking is a symbol of liberation from restrictive female gender roles. Finally, in countries like Italy and China, the governments are, at best, ambivalent about their citizens' smoking. Although these governments are aware of the health risks of smoking, they also control tobacco product distribution and sales in their respective countries. Countries with such monopolies on tobacco have a financial incentive to keep people smoking.

The financial and health implications of smoking trends overseas are profound. This is especially true for developing nations. These countries offer major new market opportunities for the North American tobacco industries, which face increasing government regulation and an uncertain adult market at home. China, which is the largest cigarette producer and consumer in the world, has an estimated 500 000 to 750 000 smoking-related deaths a year (Lam et al., 1997; Lopez, 1998). The estimate reaches three million deaths a year by the time today's young smokers reach middle and old age.

Given what is known about cigarette smoking, what do you see as the major ethical, social, and financial factors that must be considered in deciding on a government's smoking laws? How much weight do you think should be given to each of these factors?

and thereby deprives the body's tissues of oxygen. The brain and heart are especially vulnerable to this action of carbon monoxide because they depend on aerobic respiration for proper functioning (Blum, 1984).

Most of the cancer-causing substances in smoke are in tar, which is the material that remains after cigarette smoke is passed through a filter. A cigarette typically contains 0.3 milligrams to 2.0 milligrams of nicotine (cigars yield nine to 12 times more). When cigarettes are smoked and inhaled, about 20 percent of the nicotine is absorbed, compared with 2.5–5 percent when smoke is drawn into the mouth and then exhaled. That virtually all cigarette smokers inhale is one reason (other than sheer numbers) that cigarette smoking, as opposed to cigar or pipe smoking is the major cause of diseases related to tobacco use.

Canadian Intense Method
A technique that uses a laboratory machine to test levels of compounds in cigarettes. It is more realistic because it takes larger puffs of cigarette smoke more frequently than other methods.

In Canada, cigarette manufactures are required by law to print the levels of tar, nicotine, carbon monoxide, hydrogen cyanide, formaldehyde, and benzene in cigarette smoke. These levels are measured using both the standard ISO method for testing cigarettes and the **"Canadian Intense Method"** (also referred to as the Health Canada "Realistic Smoking" test) to derive the results. Both methods use a laboratory smoking machine, but with the Canadian Intense Method, the machine draws larger puffs, more frequently, and if any ventilation holes are present on the cigarette, these are blocked. Figure 7.10 shows the tar levels of du Maurier cigarettes, the most popular cigarette brand in Canada for both the ISO and Canadian Intense Method.

FIGURE 7.10 Tar levels of du Maurier cigarettes as shown on package labels and as measured by Health Canada "Realistic Smoking" test (mg/cigarette)

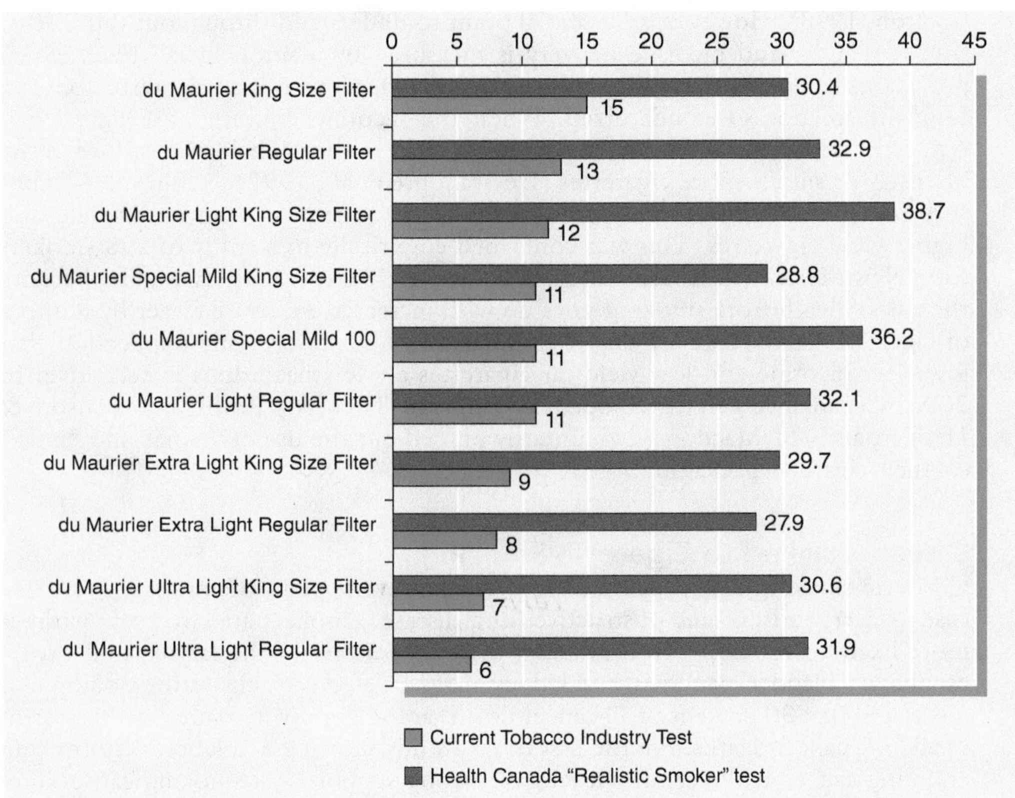

Source: Physicians for a Smoke-Free Canada.

The amount of tar and nicotine delivered in North American brand-name cigarettes has declined considerably. For example, in 1968, the average tar and nicotine yields of cigarettes produced in the United States were 21.6 mg and 1.35 mg respectively. In 1978, these contents were 16.1 mg and 1.11 mg; in 1988, they were 13.3 mg and 0.94 mg; and in 1998, 12.0 mg and 0.88 mg (Federal Trade Commission, 2001). These averages cover a range of values for "light" versus "regular" versus "ultra" brands. According to a report published by the Lorillard Tobacco Company in February 2009, each Newport Lights Box 80s cigarette has 9.0 mg of tar and 0.80 mg of nicotine, each Newport Medium Box 80s cigarette has 12.0 mg of tar and 1.00 mg of nicotine, and each Newport Regular Box 80s cigarette has 18.0 mg of tar and 1.30 mg of nicotine. A similar range is evident in cigarettes manufactured in other countries, too. For example, Endo et al. (2009) reported the tar and nicotine levels of the 10 most popular cigarette brands in Japan. The tar and nicotine levels were determined by following the testing procedures of the International Organization for Standardization (ISO), whose protocol is aligned with that of the FTC. As previously discussed, Canadian cigarette brands publish tar and nicotine levels according to far more strict protocol called the Canadian Intense Method that results in far higher estimates of tar and nicotine levels than those of either the FTC or the ISO. The findings for the Japanese brands ranged from 0.90 mg of tar and 0.20 mg of nicotine for each "Pianissimo" cigarette, to 14.80 mg of tar and 1.11 mg of nicotine for each "Seven Stars" cigarette.

Reduced delivery of tar and nicotine from cigarettes seems like a good thing, given what we know about their contribution to serious disease. Indeed, the American public perceives that cigarette brands with low tar and nicotine yields are healthier (Cotton, 1993). However, an essential point to understand throughout this discussion is that tar and nicotine delivery is measured by a smoking machine, which puffs consistently in the same controlled way regardless of the cigarette content. Humans are not so standardized. When the nicotine content of a cigarette is reduced, smokers consciously or unconsciously either inhale the smoke more intensely or smoke more cigarettes (DeGrandpre et al., 1992). The result is exposure to similar amounts of toxic substances in the smoke from lower-yield and higher-yield cigarettes. This was confirmed empirically in a study of 298 smokers from New Mexico (Coultas, Stidley, & Samet, 1993). It is a critical finding because the risk of death from smoking goes up with increased exposure either by number of cigarettes smoked or by depth of inhalations. Therefore, any implication that low-yield nicotine and low-yield tar cigarettes are less hazardous is deceptive. In 2006, Canadian cigarette companies, Imperial Tobacco, Rothmans, Benson & Hedges, and JTI-Macdonald voluntarily phased out the use of "light" and "mild" on their cigarette packaging.

Diseases Linked to Cigarette Smoking

Cigarette smoking kills because it leads to the development of coronary heart disease, cancer, and chronic obstructive lung disease. Smokers are two to four times more likely to develop coronary heart disease. Cancers of the larynx, oral cavity, esophagus, bladder, pancreas, and kidney are associated with cigarette smoking—so associated that 30 percent of all cancer deaths are caused by it, as are 80–90 percent of all lung cancer deaths. For the first time, a study showing a link between smoking and lung cancer at the cellular level gave strong support that smoking causes lung cancer (Denissenko et al., 1996). Finally, smoking causes 80–90 percent of chronic obstructive lung diseases, such as **emphysema**. Fortunately, the risk of contracting these diseases decreases with time away from cigarettes. If smokers can manage to quit smoking, then their risk of illness and death drops considerably and continues to decline with subsequent years of abstinence from smoking (Huxley et al., 2007; Williams et al., 2002).

emphysema
Disease of the lung characterized by abnormal dilution of its air spaces and distension of its walls. Frequently, heart action is impaired.

Many of the statistics on cigarette smoking and health have been based on studies done with men. However, large numbers of women began the habit after World War II, and they soon fell prey to similar health damages (USDHHS, 1987b). This upsurge likely was due in part to the tobacco industry's specific targeting of women in their advertising campaigns and to their design of cigarettes to suit women's product preferences (Henningfield, Santora, & Stillman, 2005). The rate of death due to lung cancer in Canadian women in 1996 was 77 percent greater than it was in 1985, and lung cancer displaced breast cancer as the leading cancer-related cause of death for women in the 1980s (Center for Disease Control and Prevention, 1993; Ernster, 1993; Health Canada, 1999; Physicians, 2011). According to Health Canada, every 35 minutes a Canadian woman dies as a result of smoking.

Women also face some unique health consequences of smoking. For example, women who smoke are at higher risk of cervical cancer, unwanted side effects of using oral contraceptives, and early menopause (Ernster, 1993). Furthermore, smokers who are pregnant incur a higher risk of spontaneous abortion, preterm births, low-weight babies, and fetal and infant deaths. If the infant is born healthy, there still is risk from nicotine present in the mother's milk (USDHHS, 1987b, 2001).

Other Tobacco Products and Health

The use of other tobacco products is not risk-free. Pipe and cigar smokers also have higher death rates than nonsmokers. The differences are not as large as the comparisons we cited for cigarette smokers, however, because pipe and cigar smokers tend to consume less tobacco and tend not to inhale (World Health Organization, 1999). A review of studies conducted around the world showed some mixed evidence, but, overall, it appears that users of snuff and other kinds of smokeless tobacco are more likely to get oral cancer and types of noncancerous oral disease than are nonusers and nonsmokers (Bofetta et al., 2008). Another finding from the Bofetta et al. review was that cigarette smokers who switched from cigarettes to "spit" (chewing) tobacco still were at considerably higher risk to incur various cancers than were individuals who changed from cigarette smoking to no tobacco use at all. It seems that the risk for cancer is lower for smokeless tobacco users than for cigarette smokers, but smokeless tobacco use is not risk-free for cancer.

Passive Smoking (Secondhand Smoke)

It once was thought that smokers were harming only themselves. However, we know now that if you merely stay in the vicinity of people smoking, then you absorb nicotine, carbon monoxide, and other elements of tobacco smoke, although in lesser amounts than if you were actively smoking. You are essentially smoking passively if your body is the recipient of the toxins of another person's tobacco smoke. There are two types of passive smoking or secondhand smoke: mainstream smoke, which is inhaled and exhaled by people who smoke; and sidestream smoke, which is emitted directly from the lit end of a cigarette. Sidestream smoke is the most toxic. It contains almost twice the nicotine, three times more benzopyrene, six times as much toluene, and 50 times more dimethylnitrosamine as mainstream smoke. Sidestream smoke represents at least half of all secondhand smoke. Secondhand smoke is a class-A carcinogen. For reference, other Group A carcinogens include arsenic, asbestos, benzine, and radon. In 2008, secondhand smoke killed 1,203 people in Canada (96 infants under the age of one, 746 deaths due to heart attacks, and 361 deaths due to lung cancer). After smoking and indoor exposure to radon, secondhand smoke is the third leading cause of lung cancer in Canada (Canadian Council for Tobacco Control, 2007). Age is no barrier to passive smoking; its effects can be felt by anyone from young children to older adults. In 2010, 11 percent of Canadian households reported that at least one person smoked inside the home every day or almost every day and nine percent allowed smoking inside. Forty-three percent of households in which smoking was allowed in the home or where someone smoked regularly inside the home placed some restriction on it. Nationally, five percent of children from birth to 11 years and eight percent of children aged 12–17 years were regularly exposed to secondhand smoke at home (CTUMS, 2011).

In 2008, secondhand smoke killed 1203 people in Canada.

Moreover, research has shown that the fetus is exposed to significant amounts of nicotine if a nonsmoking mother is regularly exposed to cigarette smoke during the gestation period (Eliopoulos et al., 1994), and that such exposure can harm the fetus (Grant, 2005). More than one-third of all sudden infant deaths are linked to the mother's smoking (Canadian Council for Tobacco Control, 2007). Children whose parents smoke are more likely than children whose parents do not smoke to have bronchitis and pneumonia as well as some impaired pulmonary function (Rees, Gregory, & Connolly, 2006; World Health Organization, 1999); these childhood illnesses may extend into adulthood (David et al., 2005). Secondhand smoke is also a key issue in the workplace (See Drugs and Culture Box 7.2). Many Canadian service industry employees are exposed to secondhand smoke in their workplace. Chemical concentrations in secondhand smoke are, on average, four to six times higher in bars and 1.6–2.0 times higher in restaurants than offices where smoking is

DRUGS AND CULTURE BOX 7.2

Secondhand Smoke: The Story of Heather Crowe*

Since the 1970s tobacco companies had been aware of the dangers of secondhand smoke. A few Canadian municipalities introduced the first restrictions on secondhand smoke in the 1970s. By the 1980s the scientific evidence was clear that secondhand smoke caused lung cancer and other diseases. More municipalities started to introduce stronger and stronger legal protections from secondhand smoke in the 1980s and 1990s. Victoria became the first large city in Canada to ban smoking in all indoor workplaces and public places under its jurisdiction in 1999. By 2002, only two more large cities had followed Victoria's lead: Waterloo in 2000 and Ottawa in 2001.

Then, in the summer of 2002, a waitress in Ottawa named Heather Crowe was diagnosed with third stage lung cancer. Heather had never smoked. She did not live with smokers. For almost all of her 40-year career she had worked up to 60 hours a week in smoky bars, restaurants, and banquet halls. "The air was blue where I worked," said Heather. Her diagnosis and near-certain death sentence that accompanied it transformed Heather from a hard-working ordinary Canadian into a tireless campaigner for laws that would protect all workers in Canada from secondhand smoke. The rest of 2002 was a series of firsts for Heather.

She became the first worker to win full compensation from the Ontario Workplace Safety and Insurance Board for lung cancer, contracted by 40 years of exposure to secondhand smoke at work. She became the first person to make a dramatic testimonial television advertisement for Health Canada. In just 30 seconds, she simply and dramatically told her story to Canadians. "I'm dying. I'm dying of secondhand smoke," she said. Then she volunteered her time with Physicians for a Smoke-Free Canada and criss-crossed Canada to speak to federal, provincial, and municipal politicians; community groups; and high school students about the importance of passing laws to protect workers from secondhand smoke. Wherever she went, new by-laws or laws frequently followed to provide exactly the kind of protection that she wanted. She told politicians her compelling and simple wish: "I want to be the last person to die from secondhand smoke at work." And the politicians responded. While scientific evidence, popular support, and other factors undoubtedly all played a part in their political decisions, it was frequently hearing Heather's story firsthand that spurred them on to ban smoking in workplaces and public places. Following Heather's visits, all territories and provinces and the federal government eventually banned smoking in indoor public places and workplaces.

- Nunavut & Northwest Territories—May 2004
- Manitoba—October 2004
- New Brunswick—October 2004
- Newfoundland and Labrador—July 2005
- Ontario—May 31 2006
- Quebec—May 31 2006
- Nova Scotia—December 2006
- Federal jurisdiction—November 2007
- Alberta—January 2008
- British Columbia—March 2008
- Yukon—May 2008
- Saskatchewan—January 2005 (public places); May 2009 (workplaces)
- Prince Edward Island—September 2009

All Canadians now enjoy full protection from secondhand smoke in public places and indoor workplaces. Tragically, Heather did not live to see her dream come true. She passed away on May 22, 2006. However, her legacy lives on, enshrined in legislation in all 14 federal, provincial, and territorial jurisdictions in Canada. More than any other single person, Heather made Canadian public places and workplaces smoke-free.

*This story of Heather Crowe is taken from Collishaw, 2009, pp. 63–66.

Source: Neil Collishaw. *History of Tobacco Control in Canada.* Physicians for a Smoke-Free Canada. 2009. Pg. 63.

allowed. The risk of lung cancer is 50 percent higher for service industry workers than the general population (Canadian Council for Tobacco Control, 2007). Researchers who followed 32 000 healthy nonsmoking female nurses for 10 years found that regular exposure to cigarette smoke almost doubled the nurses' chances of developing heart disease (Kawachi et al., 1997). While the *Non-Smokers' Health Act* bans smoking in federal workplaces, it permits the use of designated smoking rooms (DSRs) and designated smoking areas (DSAs). In 2005, 68 percent of Canadians were employed where smoking was completely restricted, while almost 15 percent of Canadians aged 12 and older reported that they were regularly exposed to cigarette smoke in public areas (CCHS, 2006). Figure 7.11 shows where this exposure to secondhand smoke most often occurs. This figure also shows a decrease in overall exposure to secondhand smoke. This decrease reflects Canadian attitudes about smoking. For example, a 2006 poll found that 31 percent of Canadians believed that smoking should be restricted to private residences, 23 percent believed it should be banned altogether, and 39 percent believed that smoking should be permitted in social settings (such as restaurants and bars) in a completely separate smoking area.

Passive smoking is no less of a problem in other parts of the world. A report from the University of California–Berkeley showed that, in 2002, over 48 000 women in China died from ischemic heart disease and lung cancer caused by passive smoking (Yang, 2005). This compares to the 47 300 Chinese women who died that year from the same diseases caused by active smoking.

Of further concern is "thirdhand" smoke. One study showed that the toxins in tobacco smoke linger (Winickoff et al., 2009). Therefore, going outside of

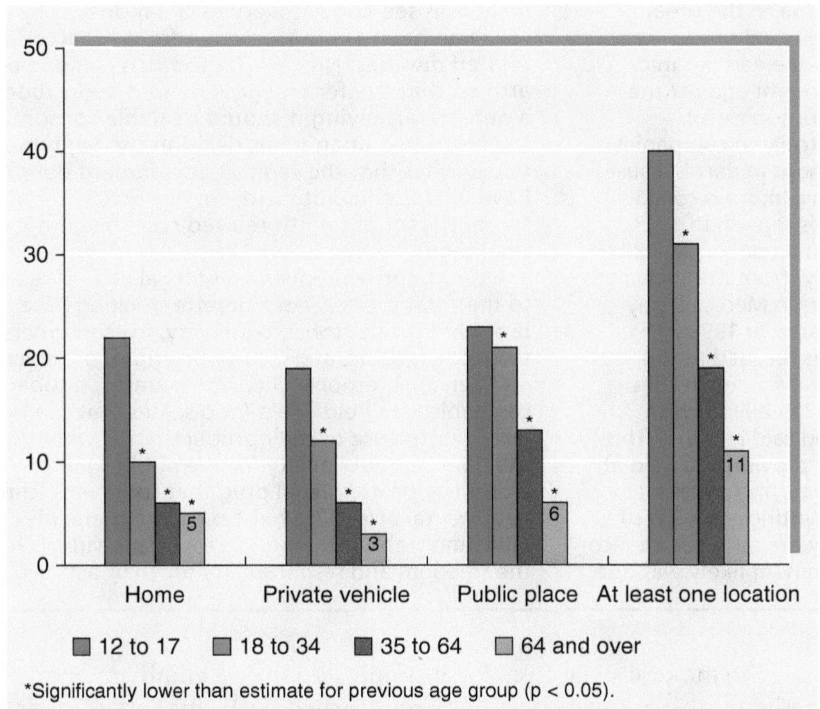

FIGURE 7.11
Percentage of non-smokers regularly exposed to second-hand smoke, by type of location and age group, household population aged 12 or older, 2005

Source: Statistics Canada. *Smoking and Diabetes Care: Results of the CCHS Cycle 3.1* (2005). Catalogue No. 82-621-XIE. No. 002.Chart 12. Pg. 43.

CONTEMPORARY ISSUE BOX 7.3

Cigarette Smoking and Health: Who's Responsible?

In the United States, smokers began filing lawsuits against cigarette companies as early as the 1950s. They claimed that the companies were responsible for the smokers' poor health. Until the 1980s, all these cases had failed and the tobacco industry never paid a cent in damages. Their trump card was the 1965 U.S. Federal Cigarette Labeling and Advertising Act that took effect in 1966. Federal courts had always claimed that this act pre-empted the tobacco industry from responsibility for the health consequences of smoking, at least for any smoking done on or after January 1, 1966. Furthermore, juries had tended to perceive that smokers were responsible for their own decisions regarding smoking.

Great attention was given to a smoker's lawsuit filed in 1983 by a New Jersey woman. In 1988, a jury awarded $400 000 to the husband of the woman, who died in 1984 of lung cancer. This landmark decision was overturned in 1990 by an appeals court, which ruled that whether the woman had seen or believed tobacco industry advertisements before 1966 had not been proven. The woman's family continued to fight, but they dropped their suit in November 1992, at least partly due to the great financial cost of pursuing it. Individual smokers and their families filed other suits in the early to mid-1990s. However, legal action brought against the tobacco industry generally was unsuccessful.

Class action suits against the tobacco companies have been more successful, perhaps in part because groups of individuals tend to have more resources than any one person does. In this regard, in 1997, both Florida and Mississippi won damages ($11.3 billion and $3.3 billion, respectively) from the tobacco industry to cover the states' costs in Medicaid payments for smoking-related illnesses. In 1999, the omnibus tobacco settlement was reached as the attorneys general of 46 states and five territories signed an agreement totaling $206 billion, with tobacco companies to settle Medicaid lawsuits. This accord also has numerous other provisions aimed at preventing young people from starting smoking in the first place, as well as underwriting the costs of treating individuals who already are addicted to nicotine. The omnibus tobacco settlement likely was due primarily to revelations that the tobacco industry concealed early knowledge about the relationship between smoking and serious health problems.

In 2011, the Canadian Supreme Court heard two cases involving the possible responsibility of the Canadian government in tobacco-related costs. Case 1 was a class action suit brought forward by smokers in British Columbia. They requested that Imperial Tobacco Group Ltd. return the money that they had spent on "light" or "mild" brands of their cigarettes. The plaintiffs maintained that the company's description of cigarettes as "light" or "mild" was misleading. Imperial Tobacco asked the court to add the federal government as a defendant because the health department encouraged the development and promotion of light cigarettes and vouched for the relative safety of light brands. In addition, according to Imperial Tobacco, the Canadian government collected licence fees and royalties on tobacco strains developed by Canada for use in light cigarettes.

The second case involved a 2001 suit brought forward by the British Columbia government against 14 tobacco manufacturers. The BC government was seeking recovery of the money they had spent on health care stemming from tobacco-related diseases. Nine of the tobacco companies argued that the federal government be included as a defendant, saying it should be liable for some of the costs. In a unanimous decision the Supreme Court ruled that the federal government does not have to share liability with the tobacco companies for monetary or health-related costs resulting from smoking (Mayeda, 2011).

Overall, the consequences of legal actions related to the chronic effects of cigarette smoking have been profound for the tobacco industry, for consumers of tobacco products, and for our principles of choice and personal responsibility. For example, if tobacco companies are held liable for diseases that can be traced to the use of their products, then what does that imply about liability for the public's use of alcohol as another legal drug that could have chronic detrimental effects? What would the companies' liability imply about the principle that individuals have the freedom and responsibility for their actions?

the home to smoke a cigarette, for example, does not eliminate the problem, because the toxins in tobacco smoke are returned with smokers in their hair or clothes, even though the cigarette has been extinguished. Thirdhand smoke is especially a problem for young children, whose immune systems are not fully developed.

Image courtesy of The Advertising Archives

Cigar and pipe smokers also have higher death rates than nonsmokers.

Treatment of Cigarette Smoking

In this section, we consider ways to stop smoking. Although stopping the use of other tobacco products also is an important topic, we again focus on cigarette smoking because it accounts for the vast majority of tobacco use and because it has been the major subject by far in the literature on ways to stop nicotine use. We will discuss the treatment of nicotine dependence in more detail in Chapter 14.

In reviewing nicotine's acute effects, you saw how easily a person might acquire and keep the habit of tobacco use. In reviewing the health consequences of chronic tobacco use, you may have wondered why anyone would continue to use tobacco products. Yet, of course, many people do continue, despite wanting to quit; others find quitting easier.

Adults say they quit smoking for a variety of reasons. These reasons may be categorized broadly as "intrinsic motivation" and "extrinsic motivation" (Curry, Wagner, & Grothaus, 1990). Examples of intrinsic reasons are a fear of getting sick, feeling in control, and proving that quitting is possible (for the individual). Extrinsic reasons include stopping others from nagging, being forced by others to quit, and saving money (McBride et al., 2001).

relapse
A term from physical disease; return to a previous state of illness from one of health. As applied to smoking, it means the smoker resumes smoking after having abstained for some amount of time.

Researchers (e.g., Lichtenstein, 1982; Shiffman et al., 1996) also have summarized the determinants of smoking **relapse**, which is a major problem in smoking treatment and in treatment of the substance-use disorders in general. Smoking relapse determinants include nicotine withdrawal symptoms, stress and frustration, social pressure, alcohol use, and weight gain. Furthermore, Pomerleau (1997) suggested that people with psychiatric problems such as depression, anxiety, bulimia, and attention deficit/hyperactivity disorder have a higher prevalence of smoking and a lower rate of quitting smoking successfully than do people without such problems.

In Canada, tobacco related costs are $17.5 million a year, with $2.6 billion in health care costs and $2.4 billion in sick days.

The Necessity of Formal Treatment

The rate of smoking in North America has decreased over the past 20 years. So, the question is: do we need formal treatments for smoking?

In answering this question, we must consider several points. Although most people stop smoking without help, they tend to succeed only after multiple attempts. Perhaps you have heard the comment attributed to Mark Twain: "Quitting smoking is easy; I've done it many times." Indeed, with or without formal treatment, success at stopping smoking is more likely with more previous tries at quitting. Another important statistic is the rate of "spontaneous remission." Briefly, this refers to the rate of "cure" (in other words, stopping smoking) during a given time period without any formal treatment. Although data on spontaneous remission are basic to evaluating treatment effectiveness, they unfortunately are extremely hard to collect. For cigarette smoking, Abrams and Wilson (1986) estimated that the rate of spontaneous remission ranges from three percent to 14 percent. Formal treatments have to do better than that rate to prove their worth.

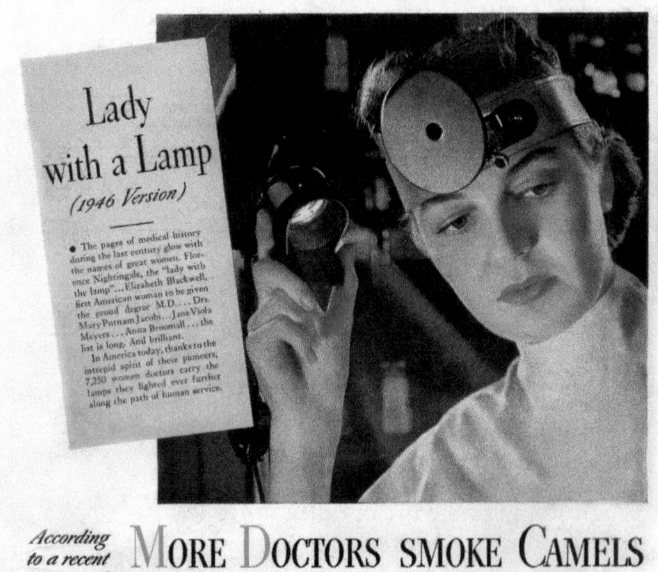

Apic/Getty images

The health message of this 1930s advertisement stands in stark contrast to current thinking.

Another set of statistics to consider in deciding whether formal treatments of smoking are necessary are the economic and social costs of cigarette smoking. In Canada, tobacco related costs are $17.5 million a year, with $2.6 billion in health care costs and $2.4 billion in sick days (Ontario Tobacco Research Unit, 2002). This figure does not begin to reflect the human suffering of patients and their families that goes with contracting cancer, heart disease, and other diseases associated with chronic tobacco use.

Add to this the finding of a 1991 study of men and women in three different communities that showed that quitting smoking, even at a later age, prolongs life. The increased longevity is due to a quick reduction in the risk of major smoking-influenced illnesses (LaCroix et al., 1991). Similarly, Anthonisen et al. (2005) reported the findings from a follow-up of adult smokers with chronic obstructive pulmonary (lung) disease who had received intensive smoking cessation therapy 14.5 years earlier.

DRUGS AND CULTURE BOX 7.4

The Cost of Contraband Cigarettes in Canada

In 2008 the Canadian Government established the RCMP Contraband Tobacco Enforcement Strategy and a new government Task Force led by Public Safety Canada. The mandate of the Task Force is to provide the recommendations that will reduce the trade of contraband tobacco. The contraband tobacco market in the 1990s was a result of stiff taxes placed on smoking. In the last decade, the largest quantity of illicit tobacco found in Canada has come from Aboriginal reserves and territories located on both sides of the Canada–U.S. border, most often on the U.S. side of Akwesasne, in Kahnawake Quebec, and in Tyendinaga and Six Nations in Ontario. Contraband tobacco can come from several sources, including that which is

- unlawfully/lawfully manufactured in the United States and then smuggled into Canada;
- unlawfully manufactured in Canada, mainly on First Nations reserves and territories;
- diverted tax-exempt products;
- counterfeit tobacco products and international brands entering the country illegally via sea container; and,
- stolen tobacco products (e.g., convenience store and cargo thefts, truck high-jackings).

It is estimated that about 30 percent of tobacco purchased in Canada is bought illegally. In Quebec and Ontario, where most of the problem lies, the rates are 40 percent and 50 percent, respectively. The problem is not yet improving, and an estimated 13 billion illegal cigarettes were bought in 2008, up from 10 billion a year earlier. Contraband tobacco is especially appealing because of its low cost, which makes it easily affordable for teenagers to purchase. The Centre for Addiction and Mental Heath (2009) reports that Canadian teens are buying cheaper contraband cigarettes in large numbers paying only one-third of the cost of a legitimate or name brand pack of cigarettes. The study asked 2849 teens in secondary schools across Canada about their smoking choices. The results showed that 17.5 percent use First Nations or Native brand cigarettes, with the highest rates in Ontario (26.3 percent) and Quebec (30 percent). Figure 7.12 shows the RCMP seizures of contraband tobacco between 1994 and 2008.

FIGURE 7.12 RCMP seizures of contraband tobacco between 1994 and 2008

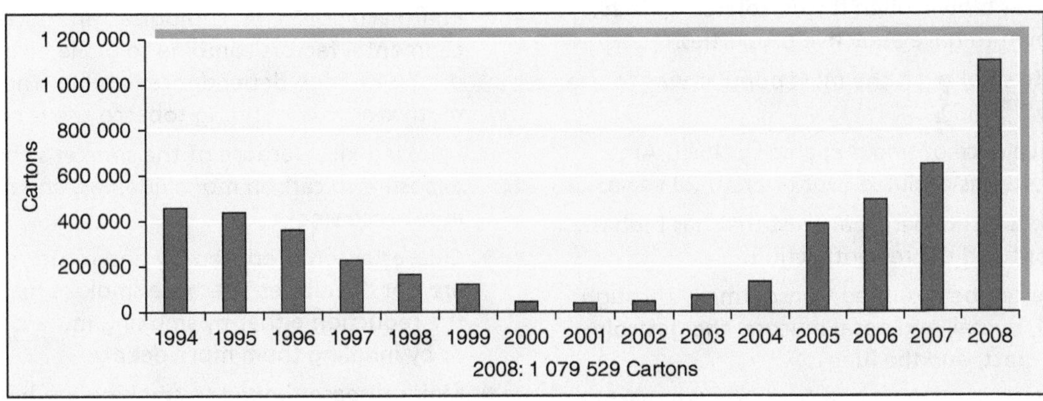

Source: *Report On The Status Of The Contraband Tobacco Situation In Canada*. Found at: http://www.publicsafety.gc.ca/prg/le/ct-rpt-eng.aspx. 2009. Reproduced with the permission of the Minister of Public Works and Government Services [2011].

The results showed that over 21 percent of the individuals who had received smoking cessation treatment sustained their status as nonsmokers, compared to about five percent of the individuals who had not received the treatment. Moreover, the percentages of individuals who had died at 14.5 years from all causes were significantly lower in the smoking treatment group compared to the rates for the group without treatment. Therefore, it seems that if smoking treatments increase the rate of smoking cessation compared to what people do on their own, then they would be more than worth their cost.

Nicotine is a strongly reinforcing drug to humans and can be quickly addicting. Nicotine does have some "adaptive" acute effects, such as improved sensory and cognitive functioning, but most attention has been paid to the negative health consequences of chronic nicotine use through smoking cigarettes. As a result, the emphasis today is on how to stop people from using nicotine. The best way to do this is by continuing the information campaigns and other "macro-environmental" methods, such as banning smoking in public places, which have advanced the overall decline in the prevalence of smoking and other use of tobacco among North American adults. Along these lines, programs aimed at youth who have not begun to use tobacco are the best investments because tobacco use is hard to stop once started. We will continue to discuss the treatment methods for tobacco use in Chapter 15.

SUMMARY

- Nicotine occurs naturally in only one source: the tobacco plant. The major commercial tobacco products are cigarettes, cigars, snuff, chewing tobacco, and pipe tobacco.
- Western Europeans discovered tobacco when they saw Native Americans in the New World smoking dried tobacco leaves. The Europeans seized the idea and spread it throughout Europe and Asia.
- Until about 1860, tobacco was widely believed to have medicinal properties. Nicotine's "medical cover" was blown when it was isolated in 1828, and shown to have addictive properties.
- Cigarette smoking is the most popular way to use tobacco.
- The prevalence of smoking among North American adults has declined over the past 20 years.
- Nicotine is a cholinergic agonist that has biphasic (stimulant and depressant) action.
- Nicotine can be absorbed transdermally through the oral, buccal, and nasal mucosa; the gastrointestinal tract; and the lungs.
- By inhalation, nicotine in tobacco smoke reaches the brain in seven seconds. Brain levels thus rise rapidly, but then they fall rapidly because nicotine is quickly distributed to other sites of action. Nicotine is metabolized primarily in the liver and eliminated mostly in urine.
- Functional tolerance to nicotine's effects is acquired quickly. Dispositional tolerance to nicotine also seems to develop.
- Nicotine induces physical dependence.
- Nicotine's acute effects involve the CNS and ANS. It tends to have stimulant effects at lower doses but more depressant effects at higher doses.
- Despite its classification as a stimulant, users often perceive nicotine as having calming, relaxing effects.
- Nicotine's suppressant effect on body weight is an important motivation for smoking, especially in women.
- Pharmacological, psychological, and social/environmental factors combine to make nicotine a drug with high dependence liability. The major motivator in continuing tobacco use is nicotine.
- Smoking kills because of the smoker's chronic exposure to carbon monoxide, tar, and nicotine in tobacco smoke.
- Cigarettes with reduced tar and nicotine levels are not "healthier" because smokers make up for the reduction either by smoking more cigarettes or by inhaling them more deeply.
- Major diseases linked to smoking are heart disease, chronic obstructive lung disease, and cancers of various types.
- In the last three decades, women have had rates of smoking-related diseases similar to those of men. Some smoking-related health risks are unique to women.
- Because of the negative health consequences of passive smoking, there has been an increase in banning and restricting smoking in public places.

Key Terms

Canadian Intense Method p. 158
emphysema p. 160
nicotine poisoning p. 150
relapse p. 166

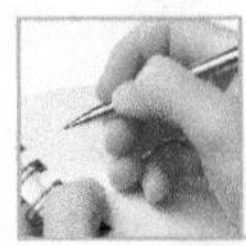

Essays/Thought Questions

1. Nicotine's dependence liability is high, and how its chronic use affects health is widely known. Why, then, do you think that use of this drug remains legal in much of the world?
2. Based on our knowledge about the effects of secondhand smoke, would a total ban on smoking cigarettes in public places violate the Charter of Rights and Freedoms in Canada?
3. What advice would you give a 15-year-old who has just begun smoking? How would this advice change if the person was 25 years old? 50 years old?
4. Do you think that the Canadian federal and provincial governments should share the expenses for tobacco-related health issues, along with the tobacco companies? Why or why not?

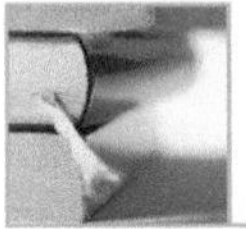

Suggested Readings

Brecher, E.M. (1972). *Licit and illicit drugs*. Mount Vernon, NY: Consumers Union.

Cotton, P. (1993). Low tar cigarettes come under fire. *Journal of the American Medical Association, 270*, 1399.

Fiori, M.C., Keller, P.A., & Curry, S.J. (2007). Health system changes to facilitate the delivery of tobacco dependence treatment. *American Journal of Preventive Medicine, 33*, S349–S356.

U.S. Department of Health and Human Services. (2008). *Treating tobacco use and dependence*. Clinical practice guideline. Rockville, MD: U.S. Department of Health and Human Services.

CHAPTER 8

Caffeine

Did You Know

?

- About 90 percent of the world's population consumes caffeine regularly.
- When body weight is taken into account, children aged one to five have the highest caffeine exposure after adults.
- Smokers metabolize caffeine more quickly than nonsmokers.
- You can become intoxicated from caffeine; this is called caffeinism.
- Caffeine elevates mood and can improve performance on tasks; both factors reinforce its use.
- Caffeine is found in many medications.
- The average Canadian consumes 210 mg of caffeine a day.
- The Netherlands has the highest caffeine consumption at 414 mg/day while Nigerians consume only 4 mg/day.

Caffeine, theophylline, and theobromine are three chemically related compounds that occur naturally in more than 60 species of plants. These compounds are called the methylxanthines and are classified as alkaloids. An alkaloid is a compound that is of botanical origin, contains nitrogen, and is physiologically active (Levenson & Bick, 1977; Syed, 1976). Because of its overwhelming popularity, we emphasize caffeine in our discussion. This should not be taken to suggest that the other methylxanthine drugs are of no importance, however. Like caffeine, theophylline is a mild central nervous system (CNS) stimulant, although it is less active than caffeine. Theobromine is the least active of the three drugs as a CNS stimulant. Popular products that contain caffeine may also contain different amounts of the other methylxanthines. Tea contains theophylline, though in considerably smaller proportion than caffeine. Milk chocolate actually contains a higher proportion of theobromine than of caffeine. Table 8.1 gives the caffeine concentrations in coffee, tea, energy drinks, chocolate, and other foods and products.

TABLE 8.1 Caffeine Concentration in Beverages, Energy Drinks, Foods, and Medications

Source	Caffeine Concentration (mg/oz)	Total Caffeine (mg)
Beverages		
COFFEE		
Coffee, brewed (8 oz)	17	135
Coffee, roasted and ground, filter drip (8 oz)	22	179
Coffee, roasted and ground, percolated (8 oz)	15	118
Coffee, roasted and ground, decaffeinated (8 oz)	0.4	3
Coffee, instant (8 oz)	9.5–13	76–106
Coffee, instant, decaffeinated	0.6	5
Coffee, espresso (1.5 oz)	51	77
TEA		
Average blend (8 oz)	5	43
Green (8 oz)	4	30
Instant (8 oz)	2	15
Leaf or bag (8 oz)	6	50
Decaffeinated (8 oz)	0	0
COCOA PRODUCTS		
Chocolate milk (8 oz)	1	8
1 envelope hot-cocoa mix (8 oz)	0.6	5
COLA BEVERAGES		
Coca-Cola Classic (12 oz)	3	35
Pepsi-Cola (12 oz)	3	38
Dr. Pepper (12 oz)	3	41

(continued)

Mountain Dew—Canada (12 oz)	0	0
Mountain Dew—USA (12 oz)	4.5	54
Canada Dry Ginger Ale (12 oz)	0	0
Energy Drinks		
Red Bull (8.3 oz)	10	80
Monster (16 oz)	10	160
Rockstar (16 oz)	10	160
Full Throttle (16 oz)	9	144
No Fear (16 oz)	11	174
Amp (8.4 oz)	9	75
SoBe Adrenaline Rush (8.3 oz)	9.5	79
Tab Energy (10.5 oz)	9	95
HIGHER CAFFEINE ENERGY DRINKS		
Wired X505 (24 oz)	21	505
Fixx (20 oz)	25	500
BooKoo Energy (24 oz)	15	360
Wired X344 (16 oz)	21.5	344
SPIKE Shooter (8.4 oz)	36	300
Cocaine Energy Drink (8.4 oz)	33	280
Jolt Cola (23.5 oz)	12	280
LOWER CAFFEINE ENERGY DRINKS		
Bomba Energy (8.4 oz)	9	75
Whoop Ass (8.5 oz)	6	50
HIGH CONCENTRATION ENERGY DRINKS		
Ammo (1 oz)	171	171
Powershot (1 oz)	100	100
Foods		
Candy, milk chocolate (1 oz)	7	7
Candy, sweet chocolate (1oz)	19	19
Candy, dark chocolate (1 oz)	20–25	20–25
Baking chocolate, unsweetened (1 oz)	25–58	25–58
Chocolate cake (2.8 oz)	13	36
Chocolate brownies (1.5 oz)	7	10
Chocolate mousse (3.2 oz)	5	15
Chocolate pudding (5.1 oz)	2	9

Prescription Medications (1 tablet)	
APCs (aspirin, phenacetin, caffeine)	32
Cafergot	100
Darvon Compound	32
Fiorinal	40
Migral	50
Over-the-Counter Preparations (1 tablet)	
Anacin	32
Aspirin	0
Tylenol	0
Cope, Easy-Mens, Midol	32
Vanquish	32
Excedrin	65
Pre-Mens	66
Dristan	30
Vivarin	200
No-Doz	100
No-Doz Maximum Strength	200
Dexatrim	200
Stay Awake	200
Ultra Pep-Back	200
Awake	100

Source: Adapted from multiple sources, including MedicineNet.com; The Vaults of Erowid (www.erowid.org): Energy Fiend (www.energyfiend.com): Reissig, Strain, & Griffiths (2009).

We begin our review of caffeine by presenting the sources of caffeine and a brief history of its use. We then discuss current prevalence statistics. Following that, we describe caffeine's pharmacological action, development of tolerance to and physical dependence on caffeine, and caffeine's acute and chronic effects. We conclude with a review of some therapeutic uses of caffeine and other major methylxanthine drugs.

Sources of Caffeine

Most people take their caffeine orally, as is apparent in Table 8.1, which highlights the wide range of caffeine products that adults and children consume regularly. Compounds synthesized to treat some medical problems also contain caffeine, even though caffeine is not always of direct benefit in alleviating the problem symptoms. Table 8.1 does not present another source of caffeine—illicit street drugs (Gilbert, 1984). For example, over-the-counter pain medications such as Anacin and Excedrin contain caffeine and frequently are used as filler to adulterate street drugs like heroin and cocaine.

History of Caffeine Use

The plants that contain the methylxanthines have been used to make popular beverages since ancient times. "Ancient" probably means at least back to the Stone Age (Rall, 1990a). Many stories, some mythical, attempt to explain how these beverages were created. For example, coffee supposedly was discovered in Arabia by a holy man. It seems that goats in a herd had been jumping around at night instead of sleeping, apparently because they had been nibbling on the beans of the coffee plant. The holy man got a brilliant idea that beans from the same plant could help him endure his long nights of prayer. It was a small next step to the first cup of coffee (Blum, 1984). Tea, on the other hand, supposedly dates back to 2737 BCE. Legend has it that Chinese Emperor Shen Nung was boiling water when the leaves from a nearby bush fell into the pot, producing the first pot of tea.

Table 8.1 shows that caffeine is found in some of our most popular beverages and foods. In Chapter 7, we noted that during the time of Columbus Europe knew nothing of these caffeine-containing substances. In fact, the only psychoactive substance that 15th-century Europeans did seem to know about was alcohol. All this changed with the ventures of the explorers and others from Europe. Explorers found coffee in Arabia, Turkey, and Ethiopia. In China, they found tea. In West Africa, they found the kola nut. In Mexico and much of Central and South America, they found the cacao plant, which is the source of chocolate. Other sources of teas were discovered in parts of North and South America. Travellers brought their discoveries home to Europe and then spread them across other continents.

Like other drugs, caffeine was not always well received by societies when it was introduced. For example, when the Mohammedans tried caffeine to stay awake during their long vigils, the orthodox priests were not pleased with the innovation. However, official punishments and attempts to kill coffee trees were not enough to stop coffee from becoming as popular among Arabian Moslems as tea is among the Chinese. Similar negative sanctions against coffee drinking in Egypt and Europe met with the same failure.

Caffeine, nicotine, and alcohol have been seen as having a greater effect on human civilization than all other nonmedical psychoactive substances combined (Levenson & Bick, 1977). Caffeine stands out among these three drugs because of its ubiquitous use around the world and because it is a **"cradle-to-grave drug"** (Kenny & Darragh, 1985, p. 278). That is, caffeine commonly is used nonmedically by young children and adults alike, which is true of no other psychoactive substance.

cradle-to-grave drug
A term used to denote a drug's popularity and use throughout the lifespan.

Prevalence of Caffeine Consumption

Good estimates of caffeine consumption around the world are not nearly as available as estimates for other drug use, even though caffeine use is more widespread (Barone & Roberts, 1996). Finding good worldwide estimates is difficult for several reasons. For one, due to the fact that people consume caffeine in many different products, they find it hard—say, in a survey—to provide accurate data on all their caffeine use over a given time period. The surveys that have been done are, accordingly, expensive to conduct and thus are limited in numbers of respondents. Furthermore, finding good caffeine consumption survey data outside of North America and Europe is hard (James, 1991). Collecting good estimates of caffeine consumption is also difficult because some products are prepared in ways that can alter the caffeine content. For example, coffee-brewing methods affect caffeine content. The caffeine content is higher for boiled than for percolated coffee (D'Amicis & Viani, 1993).

Despite these problems, estimates of caffeine consumption have been derived, typically based on survey data or on a country's import figures for a given caffeine-containing product. The estimated average consumption of caffeine per capita worldwide is around

70 milligrams (mg) per day (Gilbert, 1984). However, countries vary considerably in per capita caffeine consumption and in the sources of that consumption, ranging from four mg/person/day to 414 mg/person/day. Table 8.2 shows per capita caffeine consumption estimates for a number of countries. In Canada people average 210 mg per day of caffeine consumption, with the vast majority of that amount accounted for

TABLE 8.2 General Estimates of Caffeine Use from around the World

	(in mg/person/day)			
Country	**Caffeine from Coffee**	**Caffeine from Tea**	**Caffeine from Cocoa**	**Caffeine from All These Sources**
Argentina	43	1	5	49
Australia	202	29	0	232
Brazil	26	1	4	31
Canada	**180**	**18**	**12**	**210**
Denmark	354	15	21	390
Egypt	5	53	1	58
Finland	322	6	1	329
France	215	8	16	239
Germany	292	9	12	313
India	1	26	0	27
Ireland	81	127	5	213
Kuwait	49	112	13	173
Netherlands	369	38	6	414
Nigeria	1	2	1	4
Norway	379	8	13	400
Paraguay	51	1	3	55
Poland	100	33	8	141
Russian Federation	26	40	7	72
Saudi Arabia	14	13	2	28
South Africa	15	23	1	40
Sweden	388	12	7	407
Switzerland	275	11	1	288
United Arab Emirates	74	87	5	167
United Kingdom	92	96	14	202
United States	143	12	12	168
Venezuela	135	0	4	139

Note: Not included in this table is caffeine consumption from maté, a tealike beverage consumed mainly in several South American countries. It is prepared by steeping dried leaves of the yerba maté plant in hot water. With regards to the listed estimates of caffeine consumption, the following amounts should be added for the following countries: Argentina, 52 mg/person/day; Brazil, 10 mg/person/day; and Paraguay, 101 mg/person/day.

Source: Adapted from Fredholm et al. (1999), p. 85.

Creatista, 2009/Shutterstock.com

Coffee is the most popular source of caffeine in Canada.

by coffee consumption (See Drugs and Culture Box 8.1). Table 8.3 shows how many caffeinated beverages Canadians consume by age group and type of beverage. The world's top per capita rates of caffeine consumption are the Scandinavian countries—Finland, Sweden, Denmark, and Norway—along with the Netherlands, which ranks number one at 414 mg per person per day, predominantly via coffee consumption.

Tea is the dominant source of caffeine in the United Kingdom, and the same is true for its close neighbour, Ireland. Kuwait and the United Arab Emirates also rank

DRUGS AND CULTURE BOX 8.1

Canada's Love Affair with Coffee

Canadians love coffee. Coffee is the number one beverage of choice for Canadian adults (after water): 81 percent of Canadians drink coffee occasionally and 63 percent drink it daily. In 2003 the Coffee Association of Canada conducted a Canada-wide survey to evaluate the coffee habits of Canadians. They found that the Canadian men and women are equally likely to be coffee drinkers, averaging 2.6 cups of coffee per day. However, men tend to drink slightly more coffee than women. About half (51 percent) of all coffee consumption happens at breakfast and another 16 percent occurs through the rest of the morning. Coffee consumption is fairly evenly distributed throughout the rest of the day (nine percent at lunch, 10 percent in the afternoon, eight percent at dinner, and seven percent in the evening). Only nine percent of Canadians drink decaffeinated coffee.

Most Canadians enjoy their coffee at home (66 percent), 12 percent is consumed at work, 16 percent is consumed or purchased at eating places, and five percent is consumed in other places such as hospital, schools, hockey rinks, and other institutions. Drinking coffee in-transit increased from two percent in 1999 to seven percent in 2003.

Coffee consumption varies across Canada. Quebec has the greatest coffee consumption with 70 percent of people in Quebec drinking coffee daily, followed by the Prairies (67 percent), British Columbia (61 percent), Ontario (60 percent), and the Atlantic region (53 percent).

Source: Coffee Association of Canada. *Highlights: 2003 Canadian Coffee Drinking Study.* 2003.

TABLE 8.3 Average Daily Consumption (in Grams) of Selected Beverages, by Age Group and Gender, Total Household Population Aged 19 or Older, Canada Excluding Territories, 2004

	19–30		31–50		51–70		71 or older	
Beverage	**Men**	**Women**	**Men**	**Women**	**Men**	**Women**	**Men**	**Women**
Coffee	227[*]	183	451[*†]	375[†]	474[*]	364	365[*†]	270[†]
Tea	105[*]	136	131[*†]	178[†]	174[*†]	227[†]	246[†]	262[†]
Regular Soft Drinks	304[*]	142	193[*†]	97[†]	115[*†]	62[†]	37[†]	29[†]
Diet Soft Drinks	32	44	61[†]	69[†]	53	55[†]	39[E*]	13[E†]

Notes:

[*] significantly different from estimate for women of same age ($p < 0.05$)

[†] significantly different from estimate for same sex in preceding age group ($p < 0.05$)

[E] use with caution (coefficient of variation 16.6 percent to 33.3 percent)

Source: Garriguet, D. (2008) *Beverage consumption of Canadian adults.* Statistics Canada. Catalogue no. 82-003-X Health Reports.

high on per capita caffeine consumption through their tea consumption. Brazil is the world's leading producer of coffee (more than 25 percent of the total), but its citizens' primary caffeine source is maté, a type of tea grown in South America (James, 1991).

Cocoa is produced primarily in Africa. In 2010, 3.6 million tonnes of cocoa were ground worldwide. The majority of cocoa consumption occurs in developed countries. For example, Europeans are the world's largest cocoa consumers consuming an average total of almost 1 200 000 tonnes of cocoa between 1998 and 2000. North Americans are the second largest consumers of cocoa, averaging almost 500 000 tonnes during that same time. In general, cocoa consumption has been increasing worldwide (FAO, 2011). Since the early 1980s, the level of caffeinated coffee consumption has risen only slightly. Therefore, whatever decline in caffeine consumption may have occurred from drinking less caffeinated coffee was compensated for to some degree by drinking more soft drinks.

The contribution of soft drinks to total caffeine consumption is significant. One U.S. study showed that in 1962 one-third of the population said they had consumed soft drinks the day before, but currently, around two-thirds said they had. Nevertheless, it will be important in future surveys on caffeine consumption to focus greater attention to soft drink and energy drink consumption so as to obtain the most accurate estimates. For example, the Frary, Johnson, and Wang (2005) study mentioned earlier included the contribution of soft drink consumption to their estimates of per capita caffeine consumption (in the U.S.) and found a rate of 193 mg per person per day, 25 mg per person per day higher than the rate provided in Table 8.2.

In Canada, caffeine consumption varies by age, as shown in Table 8.3. Caffeine consumption appears to peak between 31 and 50 years of age. Health Canada (2011) recommends a maximum caffeine intake of 400 mg (equivalent to three 8oz cups of coffee). However, as Figure 8.1 shows, more than 20 percent of men and about 15 percent of women in the 31-to-70 age range exceeded the 400 milligram per day, paralleling the intake reported for coffee. However, for a "dose" of caffeine

FIGURE 8.1
Percentage with usual daily caffeine intake greater than 400 milligrams, by gender and age group, household population aged 19 or older, Canada excluding territories, 2004

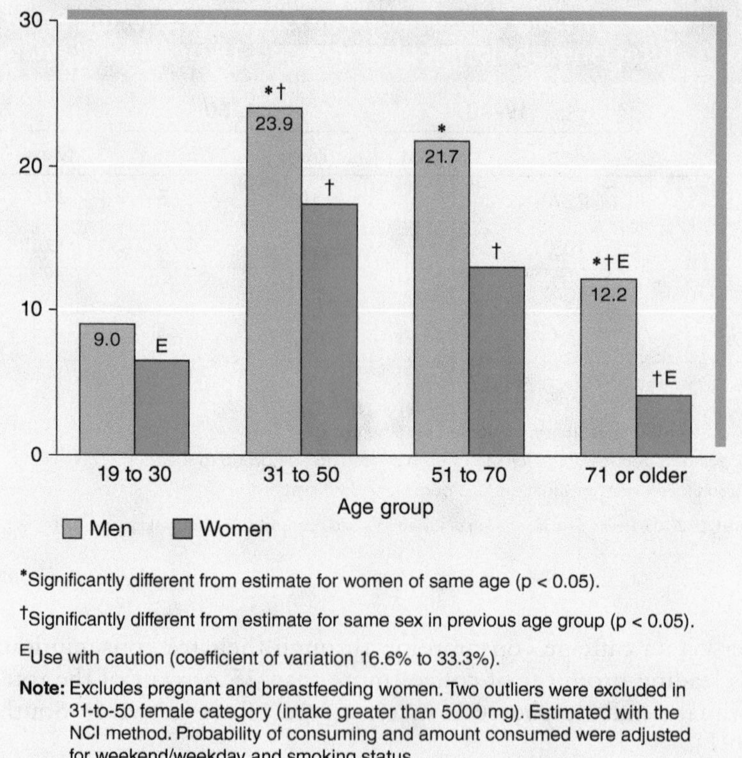
30
20
10
0
*†
23.9
†
*
21.7
†
*†E
12.2
9.0
E
†E
19 to 30
31 to 50
51 to 70
71 or older
Age group
Men
Women
*Significantly different from estimate for women of same age (p < 0.05).
†Significantly different from estimate for same sex in previous age group (p < 0.05).
EUse with caution (coefficient of variation 16.6% to 33.3%).
Note: Excludes pregnant and breastfeeding women. Two outliers were excluded in 31-to-50 female category (intake greater than 5000 mg). Estimated with the NCI method. Probability of consuming and amount consumed were adjusted for weekend/weekday and smoking status.

Source: Statistics Canada, Beverage consumption of Canadian adults, *Health Reports*, Catalogue 82-003-XIE2008004, Vol. 19 No. 4, December 2008.

consumed, which takes into account body weight (see Chapter 4), children aged one to five have the highest exposure to caffeine after adults aged 18 and older (Greden & Walters, 1992). Table 8.4 shows Health Canada's recommended caffeine intake by age. Coffee is the major source of caffeine for adults, and soft drinks are the major source for children and adolescents (Frary, Johnson, & Wang, 2005) (see also Drugs and Culture Box 8.2 and Table 8.4).

TABLE 8.4 Health Canada's Recommended Daily Intake of Caffeine by Age Group

Age Group	Recommended Maximum Caffeine Intake (mg/day)
Adult (18+)*	400
*Women who are planning to become pregnant, pregnant women, and breast feeding mothers	300
Children: 4–6 years	45
Children: 7–9 years	62.5
Children: 10–12 years	85

Source: *Caffeine in Food.* Health Canada, 2010. Minister of Public Works and Government Services Canada, 2011.

DRUGS AND CULTURE BOX 8.2

Canadian Children and Caffeine

Studies show that children all over the world regularly consume pharmacologically active amounts of caffeine. This pattern of use combines with our knowledge about the high degree of caffeine exposure in young children (because of their lower body weights) to raise serious concerns about children's use of caffeine. Despite the potential seriousness of this problem, little is known about caffeine effects in children (Hughes & Hale, 1998; Temple, 2009). What research is available suggests that children are not more or less sensitive than adults to caffeine's action in the body (James, 1991).

Children's use of caffeine is a major concern for two reasons. First, caffeine is very popular among young people, as reflected in the surge in children's consumption of "high-energy" (high-caffeine) beverages. Goldstein and Wallace's (1997) exploratory study provided evidence for what may be a caffeine withdrawal syndrome in children (ages 11 to 12). The children's major source of caffeine was soft drinks. Second, caffeine exposure in children is high compared to that of adults. In addition, little is known about the long-term effects of children's caffeine use.

Health Canada (2011) recommends that children under the age of 12 consume no more than 2.5 milligrams of caffeine per kilogram of body weight. Health Canada does not have sufficient data to propose recommendations for adolescents, but they suggest using the same formula to calculate the daily maximum caffeine intake. According to Health Canada, this more conservative calculation may be more appropriate because the maximum adult caffeine dose (400 mg/day) may be too high for lighter weight adolescents or for younger adolescents who are still growing. The daily dose of 2.5 mg/kg body weight would not cause adverse health effects in the majority of adolescent caffeine consumers, although older and heavier weight adolescents may be able to consume adult doses of caffeine without suffering adverse effects. These recommendations would limit children's caffeine intake to about one to two cans of cola a day.

Interestingly, in 2010, Health Canada lifted its ban on injecting synthetic caffeine into soft drinks that were not darkly coloured (i.e., not "cola" soft drinks). Now, manufacturers can add caffeinated to ginger ale, 7-UP, Sprite, and fruit flavoured sodas, such as Orange Crush. The Canadian government is restricting the amount of caffeine that can be added to non-cola soft drinks to 150 parts per million, which is 75 percent of the amount that is allowed in colas. They maintain that this will not pose any health risks as long as consumers adhere to Health Canada's recommendations for maximum daily intake.

Currently in Canada there are no mandatory labelling requirements for caffeine content in beverages or food. To address this concern given their recent decision to allow synthetic caffeine in non-cola soft drinks, Health Canada (2011) has proposed the following labelling guidelines to the industry:

- When the food additive caffeine is added to a beverage, the caffeine content of that beverage should be expressed on the product label in milligrams (mg) of caffeine per stated serving size.
- When the food additive caffeine is added to a beverage that also has added to it an ingredient that naturally contains caffeine, all sources of caffeine should be taken into account in order to express total caffeine content on the product label in milligrams (mg) of caffeine per stated serving size.
- If an ingredient that is a relatively unknown source of caffeine (e.g., guarana, yerba maté) is added to a food, the total caffeine content of that food should be indicated on the product label in milligrams (mg) of caffeine per stated serving size.
- The product's caffeine content statement should be placed outside and directly beneath the nutrition facts panel and should read as follows: Caffeine Content: __mg per "stated serving size."
- Caffeinated versions of carbonated "soft drinks" that have not previously been permitted to contain the food additive caffeine and which consumers would not expect to contain caffeine should bear a statement "Contains Caffeine" on the label's principal display panel if the intention is to market and present the product under the same brand name. The product should carry the statement for a sufficient period of time to alert consumers to the fact that the product is now caffeinated.
- As always, manufacturers should ensure that all labelling information is presented in a clearly visible and legible manner and is compliant with all Health Canada and Canadian Food Inspection Agency labelling requirements.
- The above guidelines do not apply to foods/ingredients that are well known sources of caffeine (e.g., coffee, tea, and chocolate).

What do you think about Health Canada's decision to lift the ban on synthetic caffeine in non-cola soft drinks? What factors do you think they considered? Do you agree with the proposed labelling requirements?

Source: Health Canada. *Preliminary Guidance for Industry on the Labeling of Caffeine Content in Prepackaged Foods.* Found at http://www.hc-sc.gc.ca/fn-an/legislation/guide-ld/etiquetage-caf-labelling-eng.php

In summary, people of all races and social classes worldwide consume caffeine. Estimates are that about 90 percent of the world's population regularly consumes products that contain caffeine, with coffee, tea, and soft drinks being the most common sources (James, 1991). Trends in recent years in overall caffeine use are difficult to specify because of the measurement problems we referred to earlier, along with limited attention to the consumption of products such as soft drinks, energy drinks, caffeinated water, and caffeine-containing herbal supplements. Nevertheless, there is no question that caffeine is the world's most preferred drug.

THIS IS YOUR BRAIN ON CAFFEINE

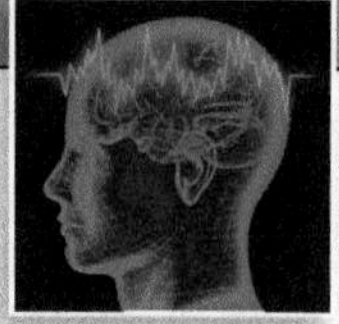

For many years, caffeine's effects were thought to be a result of the drug's inhibition of the enzyme phosphodiesterase. However, the phosphodiesterase theory fell out of favour following the realization that caffeine acts only at doses much higher than the typical dose required for pharmacological effects in humans, which is about 200 milligrams (Snyder & Sklar, 1984). The explanation for caffeine's acute effects most accepted now is the adenosine hypothesis (Daly & Fredholm, 2004; Fisone, Borgkvist, & Usiello, 2004). Adenosine is a chemical that the body produces; it is an inhibitory neurotransmitter (see Chapter 3). Adenosine receptors are in the central and peripheral nervous systems. Adenosine leads to behavioural sedation, regulation of oxygen delivery to cells, dilation of cerebral and coronary blood vessels, and production of asthma (Julien, 1996). Adenosine increases the flow of oxygen and makes us feel sleepy. Caffeine and the other methylxanthines occupy adenosine receptors and then block the action of that transmitter. This prevents us from feeling sleepy and we become more alert and energetic.

- In the normal functioning of the nervous system, neurotransmitters are released into the synaptic cleft by vesicles in terminal buttons of sending neurons. Many are taken up by receptor sites in receiving neurons.
- In the process called *reuptake*, sending neurons typically reabsorb excess molecules of neurotransmitters.
- Caffeine is an adenosine antagonist. It blocks the activity of adenosine, by binding to adenosine receptors. The result is that adenosine cannot do its job, which is to prepare our bodies for sleep. Instead, we become alert and energetic.

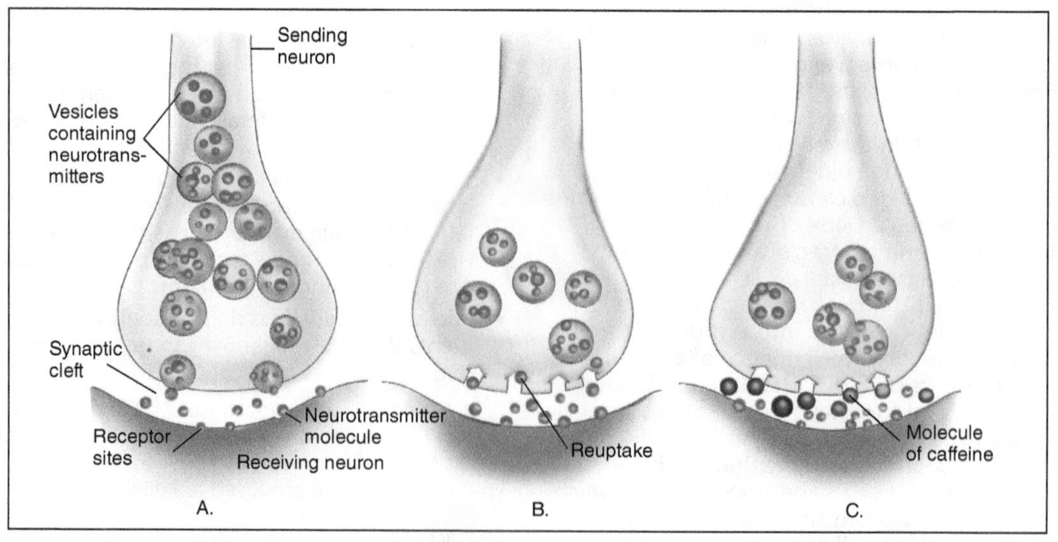

Pharmacokinetics

Absorption

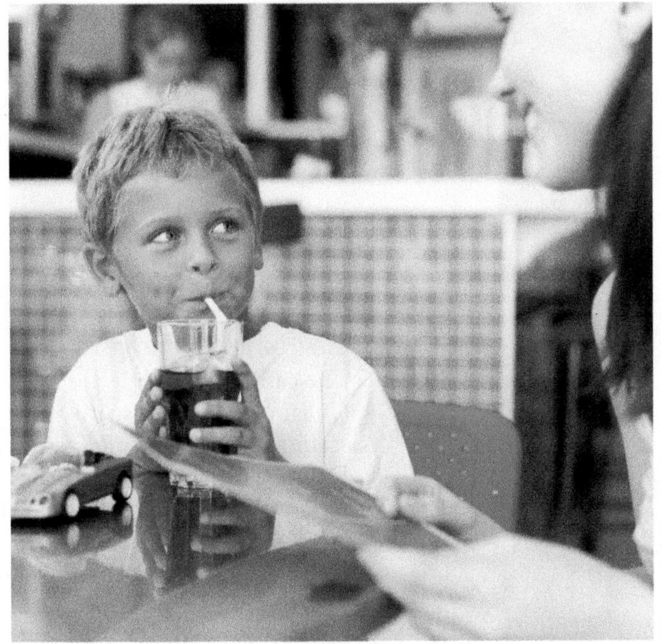
© Exactostock/SuperStock

Children one to five years of age have the highest exposure to caffeine by dose, next to adults aged 18 and older.

Caffeine is rapidly absorbed from the gastrointestinal tract. The drug quickly reaches the brain because it can pass through the blood–brain barrier. The half-life of caffeine in the blood varies widely among people and ranges from about 21.5 to 71.5 hours (Blum, 1984; Julien, 1998; Leonard, Watson, & Mohs, 1987; Lorist & Tops, 2003). Peak levels of caffeine occur 15 to 45 minutes after the drug is taken and sometimes depend on the source (Snel, Tieges, & Lorist, 2004). For example, one study (Marks & Kelly, 1973) involved three healthy men who were given an average of 155 milligrams of caffeine in the form of Coca-Cola, tea, or coffee. The men's plasma levels of caffeine were then charted for two hours. The peak levels of caffeine were higher for tea and coffee and were reached within 30 minutes of ingestion. The peak for Coca-Cola was lower and did not occur for about an hour. After two hours, the plasma level of caffeine for the cola was higher than for tea or coffee and was still at a level comparable to its peak. In a later study of 13 individuals who averaged more than 450 milligrams of caffeine consumption a day, however, no differences in peak caffeine level reached or in time to reach peak level were found among coffee, cola drinks, and caffeine capsules (Liguori, Hughes, & Grass, 1997).

Distribution

Caffeine is equally distributed in total body water and freely crosses the placenta to the fetus (Julien, 1998). Therefore, after consumption, the concentration of caffeine is similar throughout the body.

Metabolism and Excretion

The liver does most of the metabolizing of caffeine. The drug is excreted almost entirely by the kidneys—less than 10 percent in pure form and the rest in metabolites. Very small proportions of caffeine are also excreted in feces, saliva, semen, and breast milk. Of interest is the variance among people in caffeine metabolism and excretion from the body. For example, the rates of these processes are slower in people who have been using caffeine over a shorter period of time (Leonard, Watson, & Mohs, 1987). Other differences in metabolism and excretion are caused by liver disease (it slows the process), pregnancy (slows), and use of oral contraceptives (slows). On the other hand, those who smoke cigarettes metabolize caffeine more quickly (Julien, 1998). One study showed that ex-smokers' blood levels of caffeine more than doubled from what they were when they drank the same amount of coffee before they quit smoking (Benowitz, Hall, & Modin, 1989). Other therapeutic drugs interact with caffeine to increase or decrease its metabolism and excretion.

Tolerance and Dependence

Caffeine long was considered a strange drug because of its unorthodox potential for inducing tolerance and physical dependence (Gilbert, 1976). Evidence of a distinct caffeine withdrawal syndrome has been available for some time; indeed, an individual's pattern of using caffeine can meet the DSM-IV criteria for drug dependence that we described in Chapter 1 (Strain et al., 1994). The evidence for tolerance to caffeine is far less clear, however. The usual picture for drugs is the reverse—they can induce tolerance without dependence but rarely dependence without tolerance.

Caffeine Withdrawal

The caffeine withdrawal symptoms most consistently reported are headache and fatigue (Juliano & Griffiths, 2001). Other withdrawal symptoms have been documented in studies by Goldstein, Kaizer, & Whitby (1969), and are summarized in reviews by Dews, O'Brian, and Bergman (2002) and Juliano and Griffiths (2004). Their subjects reported symptoms of caffeine abstinence that included depression, decreased alertness, less contentment and relaxed mood, decreased activity and energy, greater sleepiness and drowsiness, and increased irritability. These findings have been replicated in experimental studies (Evans & Griffiths, 1999). Furthermore, these experiments show that physical dependence can develop with an exposure of 300 milligrams of caffeine a day for only three consecutive days. Withdrawal symptoms can range from mild to severe and begin within 12 to 24 hours of cessation of caffeine use (Comer et al., 1997; Nehlig, 2004). They may last about a week (Griffiths & Woodson, 1988a; Hughes et al., 1992). A large survey of people who ingest caffeine on a daily basis found that 11 percent report withdrawal symptoms upon cessation of caffeine use (Dews et al., 1999).

Tolerance

The contradictions about tolerance to caffeine that abound in the experimental findings are probably a result of poor research methods, such as not specifying caffeine use patterns in subjects (Curatolo & Robertson, 1983). In general, tolerance probably does develop to caffeine's effects on renal function, sleep, and other physiological functions, such as blood pressure and heart rate. On the other hand, little tolerance seems to develop to caffeine's stimulant effects (Hogan, Hornick, & Bouchoux, 2002).

Confusion about caffeine tolerance also results from ignoring differences among people in what is an "acceptable" level of caffeine. Differences between high- and low-caffeine users in the acute effects of a dose of caffeine in children and adults have been attributed to differences in the degree of acquired tolerance. However, some better-controlled studies offer another explanation. One reason people are heavier or lighter caffeine users is their individual ability to tolerate caffeine. This interpretation is always an alternative in studies that fail to specify long-term patterns of caffeine consumption in the experimental participants. The best strategy is to measure caffeine use and effects in the same people over a period of time.

Acute Effects of Caffeine

Caffeine's primary action is stimulation of CNS activity but, as we saw, caffeine is distributed freely throughout the body. Such distribution is evidenced by caffeine's actions outside the CNS: contraction of striated muscle, including the heart;

relaxation of smooth muscle, especially the coronary arteries, uterus, and bronchi; diuretic effects on the kidneys; a stimulating effect on respiration at higher doses; elevation of basal metabolism; and various endocrine and enzymatic effects (Levenson & Bick, 1977; Rall, 1990a). Caffeine's effects on the body's systems provide good evidence for the blockade of adenosine receptors as its mechanism of action because caffeine's effects essentially are opposite to those of adenosine (Leonard, Watson, & Mohs, 1987).

Behavioural and Psychological Effects

Mood

The CNS-stimulation action of caffeine elevates mood. A large amount of research has shown that moderate doses of caffeine are reliably associated with feeling energized, creative, efficient, confident, and alert (Fredholm et al., 1999; Temple, 2009). This effect was anecdotally documented in a quote from the will of Dr. William Dunlap, who died in 1848: "I leave John Caddle a silver teapot, to the end that he may drink tea therefrom to comfort him under the affliction of a slatternly wife" (Gilbert, 1976, p. 77). The acute mood-elevating effects of caffeine account for much of the popularity that coffee and tea have as morning wake-up beverages. It also has been speculated that many people who are afflicted with significant depression "medicate" themselves by using caffeine products. Figure 8.2 illustrates the side effects associated with caffeine.

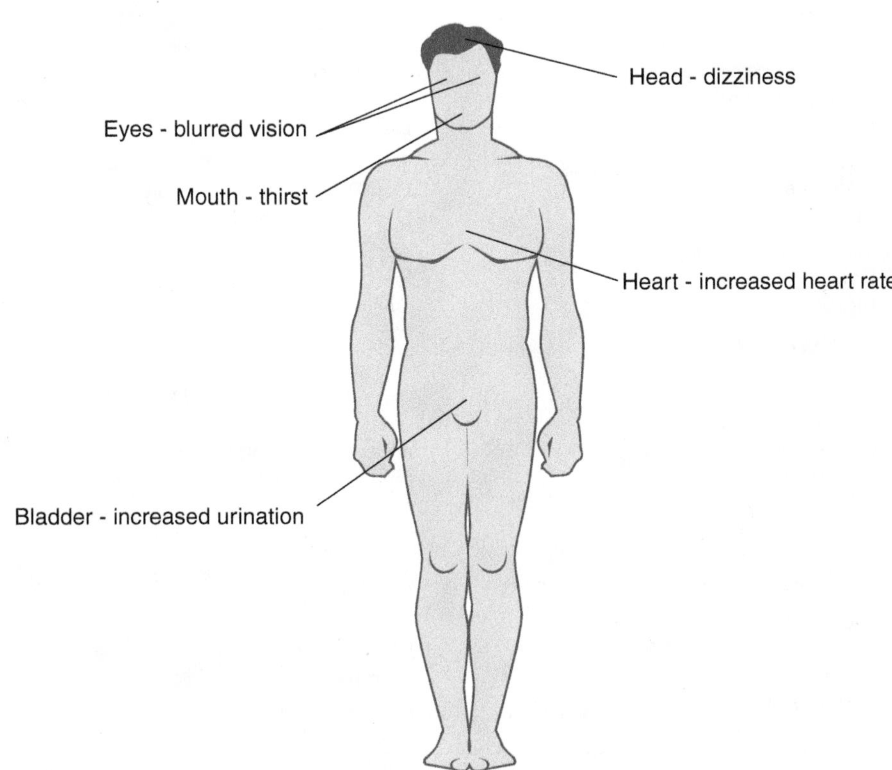

FIGURE 8.2 Side effects of caffeine

Source: Zubada/Shutterstock

Performance

Caffeine's effects on human task performance are complicated. Table 8.5 lists some of the major performance effects of caffeine. The table shows that the range of caffeine effects is wide, and many of them are stimulative (also see Smit & Rogers, 2000; Smith, 2002). It should be noted that one of the major ways caffeine improves task performance is by decreasing fatigue and increasing vigilance so that, over time, performance does not drop below what is typical for a person (Institute of Medicine, 2001). Such action is in contrast to pushing performance above what is normal for a person. In addition, the complexity of caffeine's effects is illustrated in the choice reaction time task. Caffeine impairs the decision-making part of the task but improves the motor component. The drug's effects are different

TABLE 8.5 Caffeine's Acute Effects on Human Performance

Performance Variable	Effect of Caffeine
Physical endurance	
Bicycle ergometer	
—Fixed load	Increases
—Progressive load	No effect
Motor skills	
Rapidity and accuracy	Decreases at higher doses; increases at lower doses
Eye-hand coordination	Decreases
Vigilance	
Visual	
—Night driving analogue	Increases
—Target scanning:	
low coffee users	Decreases
high coffee users	No effect
Reaction time	
Simple reaction time	Decreases (speeds up)
Choice reaction time	
—Decision time	Increases (slows down)
—Motor time	Decreases
Verbal tests	
Graduate Record Exam practice test	
—Speed and accuracy:	
extroverts	Increases with higher doses
introverts	First increases and then decreases with higher doses
Time stress accuracy	
—Extroverts	Increases
—Introverts	Decreases
Accuracy	
—Low impulsives	Increases (in the A.M.), decreases (in the P.M.)
—High impulsives	Decreases (in the A.M.), increases (in the P.M.)

Source: With kind permission from Springer Science+Business Media: Sawyer, D. A., Julia, H. L., and Turin, A. C. (1982). "Caffeine and human behavior: Arousal, anxiety, and performance effects," *Journal of Behavioral Medicine*, Vol. 5, pg. 415-439. © 1982 Plenum Publishing.

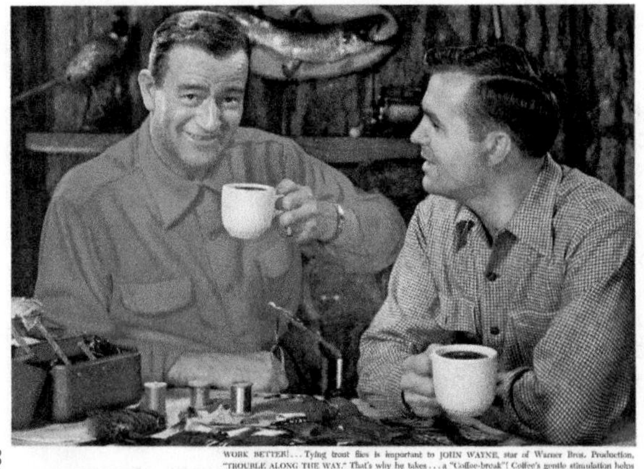

Image Courtesy of The Advertising Archives

Yuri Arcurs/Shutterstock

Caffeine's enhancing effects on the performance of various cognitive and motor tasks make it a popular drug in the workplace.

even for different components of the same task. The inconsistency in the findings about caffeine effects is probably due in part to the different methods experimenters have used. Also, caffeine's effects depend not only on the drug's pharmacological action but also on the dose of the drug, the setting in which it is used, and the personality of the user. This is represented in Table 8.5 by findings such as verbal test accuracy (the last entry in the table), which caffeine affects according to the personality of the subject (impulsiveness) and the setting (time of day) (Sawyer, Julia, & Turin, 1982). Finally, there is evidence that caffeine enhances athletic performance, including perceived exertion and endurance (Burke, 2008; Ganio et al., 2009; Hogervorst et al., 2008; Hudson et al., 2008; Jones, 2008).

energy drinks
Beverages that contain large doses of caffeine, and other ingredients such as sugar, vitamins, herbal stimulants, and amino acids.

CONTEMPORARY ISSUE BOX 8.3

On the Issue of Energy Drinks

Energy drinks are canned or bottled beverages that contain large doses of caffeine. Other ingredients often include sugar, B vitamins, amino acids (e.g., taurine), and herbal stimulants such as guarana and ginseng. At present, literally hundreds of brands of energy drinks are being distributed worldwide.

The amount of caffeine in energy drinks varies considerably. The top-selling brands (including Red Bull, Monster, Rockstar, Full Throttle, No Fear, Amp, SoBe Adrenaline Rush, and Tab Energy) have comparable caffeine concentrations (ranging from around nine mg/oz to 11 mg/oz) (Reissig, Strain, & Griffiths, 2009). However, the amount of caffeine contained in a can or bottle of these brands has more variability because they contain anywhere from 8.3 ounces (Red Bull, with 80 mg of total caffeine) to 16 ounces (No Fear, with 174 mg of total caffeine). Also being marketed are energy drinks with considerably higher levels of caffeine, ranging in caffeine concentrations of 11.9 mg/oz (in the 23.5 oz Jolt Cola, resulting in

(continued)

280 mg of total caffeine) to 35.7 mg/oz (in the 8.4 oz SPIKE Shooter, resulting in 300 mg of total caffeine) (ibid.). The energy drink leaders in terms of total caffeine are the 24 oz Wired X505 (at 505 mg) and the 20 oz Fixx (at 500 mg).

For the most part, energy drinks contain considerably higher concentrations of caffeine than coffee or tea (beverages that are typically consumed at a much slower pace than energy drinks), or soft drinks such as Coca-Cola, Pepsi-Cola, or even Mountain Dew (which contains 54 mg of caffeine).

Regulation

Given the high amounts of caffeine in energy drinks, it is not surprising that Norway and Denmark have banned them, while Sweden only allows energy drinks to be sold in pharmacies for medicinal purposes. In Canada energy drinks are classified as "Natural Health Products." According to the Natural Health Product (NHP) regulations products must carry a product licence number somewhere on the can. This indicates that the product is considered safe if used according to the instructions on the label. However, the products can continue to be sold without a Natural Product Number. Currently, the U.S. has no regulation on energy drinks. Curiously, by way of contrast, the U.S. Food and Drug Adminitration does monitor caffeine containing over-the-counter products such as NoDoz (containing 100 mg caffeine per tablet), requiring warning labels despite the total caffeine content being much lower than that contained in the majority of energy drinks. The lack of oversight is also surprising because the health consequences of energy drink consumption (including long-term consequences) are not known. (Keep in mind that consumers of energy drinks include adolescents and even children!) Also unknown are the potential impact of the other ingredients in energy drinks, alone or in conjunction with the caffeine.

Marketing

Energy drinks are predominantly marketed to adolescents and young adults, with claims of enhancing alertness and providing an energy boost. In some cases, energy drinks have been marketed in the context of improving endurance and performance (including athletic performance) and even weight loss. Many such claims appear to be offered without much in the way of substantiation.

A considerable amount of the advertising of energy drinks is geared toward young males, with the suggestion that the beverages will enhance strength, vigor, and virility. Recent research by Dr. Kathleen Miller on energy drink consumption has provided some interesting insights on this topic. Her research suggests a relationship between drinking energy drinks and "toxic jock behaviour," characterized with hypermasculine attitudes and excessive risk taking. Miller (2008) found that frequent energy drink consumers (drinking energy drinks six or more days per month) were considerably more likely to have smoked cigarettes, abused prescription drugs, or been in a serious physical fight in the past year. The frequent consumers also reported drinking alcohol, have alcohol-related problems, and using marijuana about twice as often as nonconsumers. In addition, they were more likely to engage in other risk taking, including unsafe sex, not using a seatbelt, participating in extreme sports, and doing something dangerous on a dare. The associations with smoking, drinking, alcohol problems, and illicit prescriptions were found for white students but not black students. According to Miller, these findings overall suggest that frequent energy drink consumption may serve as a useful screening indicator to identify students at risk for a broader "problem behaviour syndrome."

Combining Energy Drinks and Alcohol

Mixing energy drinks such as Red Bull with alcohol has become increasingly popular among young people, who often believe that this combination will improve their stamina while partying, or their physical performance more generally. Indeed, a popular drink today in a number of clubs is Red Bull and vodka. This popularity led several alcohol beverage producers to market alcoholic energy drinks, although these companies recently ceased this practice.

A research team in Brazil recently studied the effects of combining alcohol with Red Bull (Ferreira et al., 2006). In an interview reported in *Science Daily* (March 30, 2006), Oliveira de Souza-Formigoni, one of the study authors, stated that "[y]oung people believe that Red Bull and other energy drinks avoid the sleepiness caused by alcoholic beverages and increase their capacity to dance all night." In their study, they assessed the effects of ingesting alcohol alone, an energy drink alone, or alcohol and an energy drink (Red Bull) combined. For each participant, sensations of intoxication and measures of motor coordination and visual reaction time were assessed.

Two key findings emerged. First, drinking alcohol and Red Bull together reduced the *perception* of headache, weakness, dry mouth, and motor coordination impairment. Second, Red Bull did not significantly reduce alcohol-related deficits on the measures of motor coordination and visual reaction time.

The take-home message is clear. The combined use of Red Bull and alcohol decreases sensations of sleepiness and tiredness, but it does not reduce the harmful effects of alcohol on motor performance. In fact, the combined use of these beverages might be harmful, as some drinkers may believe they are less impaired than they actually are.

Overall, it seems that caffeine's acute effects at lower doses are what sustain the world's use of beverages such as coffee and tea (Griffiths & Woodson, 1988a; James, 1991). Although caffeine's effects at low doses are not so intense as, say, cocaine's, its reinforcing properties are strong enough to make it the world's most popular drug.

Interactions among Caffeine, Nicotine, and Alcohol

Caffeine, nicotine, and alcohol are the world's most popular drugs, and many people use them in combination (Koslowski et al., 1993; Steptoe & Wardle, 1999). An important question, therefore, is what the interactive effects of these compounds are. It seems, for example, that smokers smoke fewer cigarettes after they drink coffee compared with when they have not had coffee (Hepple & Robson, 1996). This effect is stronger for lighter caffeine users. Another effect of nicotine is in the excretion of caffeine from the body, which occurs more than 50 percent faster in smokers than in nonsmokers (Benowitz, Hall, & Modin, 1989; Sawyer, Julia, & Turin, 1982). Furthermore, how individuals react to nicotine may be associated with how they react to caffeine and alcohol (Perkins et al., 2001).

One study (Lowe, 1988) suggests that everyday forgetfulness has something to do with the state-dependent effects of caffeine, nicotine, and alcohol in combination. In the first study, 24 men and women college undergraduates who were smokers and drinkers were given a moderate dose of vodka and two cigarettes to smoke. They were exposed to a list of 19 items about a route on a map and then had to recall the items in successive tests until they achieved 14 correct items. On the day of their next session, the participants were randomly assigned to one of four drug conditions: alcohol and nicotine (control condition), alcohol and nicotine placebo, alcohol placebo and nicotine, or alcohol placebo and nicotine placebo. The participants then were asked to recall as many of the 19 items as they could from their first experimental session. The results showed no recall decrement (between the Day 1 and the Day 2 score) for those who had alcohol and nicotine on both days. However, recall scores decreased significantly for participants in the other three groups. These "dissociative" or state-dependent effects seemed attributable to alcohol and, to a lesser extent, nicotine.

The next study by Lowe (1988) was the same as the first except that 16 undergraduates who drink coffee and alcohol participated and caffeine was substituted for nicotine. The results of this study showed state-dependent effects for alcohol and caffeine. Because the major recall decrements occurred in people who had no caffeine the second day, even if they drank alcohol, it seems the state-dependent effect was mostly due to caffeine.

Acute Toxic Effects of Caffeine

Health professionals have recently given a lot of attention to caffeine intoxication, or **caffeinism** (Hogan, Hornick, & Bouchoux, 2002). An example of a case of caffeinism will give you an idea of the phenomenon*:

> A 27-year-old nurse requested an evaluation at an outpatient medical clinic because of lightheadedness, tremulousness, breathlessness, headache, and irregular heartbeat occurring sporadically about two to three times a day. The symptoms had developed gradually over a three-week period. The nurse said there were no precipitating stresses. The physical exam was within normal limits, except that an electrocardiogram showed premature ventricular contractions.

caffeinism
Caffeine intoxication that may occur after the consumption of more than 600 mg of caffeine in a given day. It can cause symptoms such as muscle twitching, disordered thought and speech, and cardiac arrhythmia.

* Adapted from Greden, 1974, pg. 1090-1091, American Psychiatric Press, Inc.

At her final session with the evaluating internist the nurse was referred to an outpatient psychiatric clinic with the diagnosis of anxiety reaction, probably due to fear that her husband would be transferred by the military to be stationed in Vietnam. However, the nurse did not accept this diagnosis and searched for a dietary cause of her symptoms. After about 10 days she had linked her symptoms to coffee consumption.

With the recent purchase of a new coffee pot the nurse had been drinking 10 to 12 cups of strong black coffee a day—more than 1000 mg of caffeine. She stopped drinking coffee, and within 36 hours virtually all of her symptoms disappeared, including the cardiovascular irregularities.

Note that the symptoms occurred in the nurse apparently as a result of her consuming more than 1000 mg of caffeine a day. As with other caffeine effects, however, people differ in how much caffeine they can ingest before they experience symptoms of intoxication. For example, caffeinism has been reported following consumption of as little as 250 mg of caffeine in a day, which is not much more than the average for adults in Canada (210 mg/day). Generally, ingesting 600 mg of caffeine a day greatly increases the chances of developing caffeinism (Kenny & Darragh, 1985).

Consuming more than 1000 mg of caffeine a day increases the risk of experiencing even more severe toxic symptoms, including muscle twitching, rambling flow of thought and speech, cardiac arrhythmia, periods of inexhaustibility, and psychomotor agitation (American Psychiatric Association, 1987). Other symptoms that have been reported are ringing in the ears and seeing flashes of light. Figure 8.3 illustrates the symptoms of caffeinism. The lethal dose of caffeine when it is taken orally is about 10 grams for adults and 100 mg/kg for children (Leonard, Watson, & Mohs, 1987). The adult lethal dose is equal to about 75 cups of coffee, 125 cups of tea, 200 colas, or 100 No-Doz tablets. Reports of death due to caffeine overdose are rare. Much more

FIGURE 8.3
Caffeinism

Source: Zubada/Shutterstock

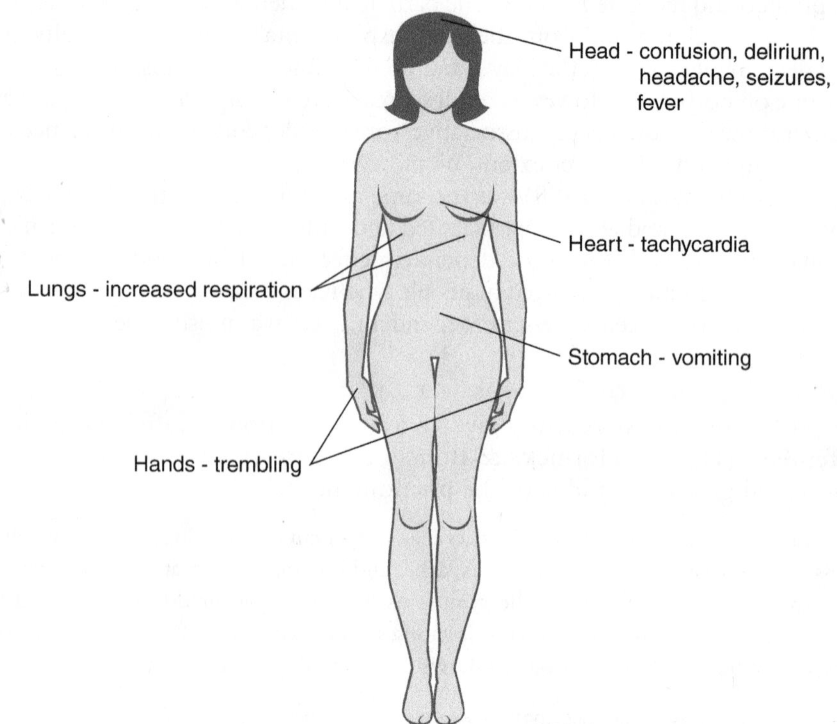

common is people appearing for treatment of acute overexposure to caffeine. In fact, caffeinism may be viewed as a more extreme case of acute overexposure to caffeine (James, 1991). Keep in mind, however, caffeine overexposure occurs most infrequently given the commonality of its use.

Chronic Effects of Caffeine Use

The chronic effects of caffeine have been studied primarily for major medical problems, and the research has produced some inconsistent findings. For example, a retrospective study (Infante-Rivard et al., 1993) found a positive relationship between reported caffeine intake one month before and during pregnancy and loss of the fetus. In another longitudinal study, however, no relationship was found between caffeine consumption during the first three months of pregnancy and damage to the fetus, including spontaneous abortion (Mills et al., 1993). Health Canada recommends that pregnant women comsume no more that 300 mg of caffeine a day. High levels of caffeine intake among women attempting to become pregnant can be associated with lower rates of conception (Temple, 2009). Research on other medical problems has suggested there is no consistent relationship between caffeine consumption and cancer, myocardial infarction, or cardiovascular disease (Abbott, 1986; Grobbee et al., 1990; Nkondjock, 2009; Temple, 2009; van Dam, 2008). An exception might exist among people with slow caffeine metabolism, based on a recent report indicating that coffee intake was associated with an increased risk of nonfatal myocardial infarction in this subgroup of coffee drinkers (Cornelis et al., 2006).

One study on postmenopausal women discovered a positive relationship between the lifetime amount of caffeinated coffee consumed and osteoporosis (Barrett-Connor, Chang, & Edelstein, 1994). In this study, drinking two cups of coffee a day was associated with decreased bone mineral density, a measure of osteoporosis. However, the relationship between coffee and osteoporosis was negated in women who said they drank at least one glass of milk a day during the ages between 20 and 50. More recent research also suggests that the little effect that caffeine consumption might have on bone density can be reversed or counteracted by including small amounts of milk in the diet (Lloyd et al., 2000).

Some studies have shown an association between serum cholesterol levels and caffeine consumption: As one level goes up, the other one also tends to rise. Level of serum cholesterol is related to atherosclerosis. The caffeine–cholesterol research illustrates the complexity of linking chronic drug use to medical problems and is one reason caffeine research in particular has yielded so many inconsistent findings. When researchers consider coffee intake as the source of caffeine, the caffeine–cholesterol relationship seems to depend on how the coffee is brewed. It appears that when coffee is boiled—as is common, for example, in Norway—the caffeine–cholesterol link holds up. The link disappears when the coffee is made by drip-filtering (Bak & Grobbee, 1989; Urgert et al., 1996).

Caffeine consumption seems to be associated with other symptoms that are less major but are experienced more commonly. Abbott (1986) cited a survey of 4558 Australians that concerned caffeine ingestion and the occurrence of indigestion, palpitations, tremor, headache, and insomnia. The more caffeine respondents ingested, the more likely they were to report these symptoms (the average consumption for the sample was 240 mg a day).

In terms of potential health benefits of coffee, there are indications that coffee consumption may help prevent several chronic diseases, including liver disease,

Parkinson's disease, and type 2 diabetes mellitus (Higdon & Frei, 2006). In one study, Klatsky et al. (2006) found an ingredient in coffee that appears to protect against liver cirrhosis, especially alcoholic cirrhosis. The cause of the apparent protective effect was not clear. There is some speculation that caffeine is playing a central role. However, the protective effect was not found among tea drinkers (although there were fewer tea drinkers relative to coffee drinkers). In another domain, no clear evidence exists for a causal relationship between caffeine consumption and peptic ulcer (Council on Scientific Affairs, 1984). Recently, a large study of women found that coffee consumption was not associated with an increased risk of hypertension (in fact, it appeared to be protective among the heaviest coffee consumers studied) (Winkelmayer et al., 2005). Interestingly, though, the women who consumed caffeine via soft drinks did have an increased risk for hypertension, although how much of this effect is attributable to the caffeine was not clear. In other research, coffee consumption has regularly been found to reduce risk of type 2 diabetes mellitus (Temple, 2009), although caffeine itself does not appear to be the mechanism accounting for this benefit. Finally, there are some indications that caffeine may provide some protections to the development of Alzheimer's disease (Eskelinen et al., 2009; Rosso, Mossey, & Lippa, 2008).

In summary, based on the apparent infrequency of acute caffeine overexposure and research on its chronic effects, caffeine is considered a relatively safe drug. However, because more minor symptoms occur with higher levels of caffeine consumption (but still within the range of typical use patterns, as indicated earlier in the Australian study), it has been recommended that caffeine consumption be moderated. Furthermore, some individuals, such as pregnant women, particularly benefit by keeping their caffeine consumption at a low to moderate level. In addition, there is an ongoing concern over the caffeine intake associated with energy drinks, particularly among children and teenagers. The absence of data on the effects of such intake, especially in the longer term, has led to calls for adding warning labels to energy drinks or even regulating the amount of caffeine they can contain. Another example is people who suffer from certain psychiatric disorders characterized by high levels of anxiety (see Chapter 13). It appears, for instance, that people who have been diagnosed as having generalized anxiety disorder are hypersensitive to the effects of caffeine, and the drug may exacerbate the anxiety symptoms (Bruce et al., 1992). You can connect this finding with the case study we cited that involved mistaking caffeinism for an anxiety reaction.

Therapeutic Uses of Caffeine

Caffeine is also used in a variety of prescription and over-the-counter medications. Caffeine is very much a part of the medications used to treat a range of ailments. In fact, other methylxanthines also have therapeutic value. You can better appreciate this by looking at the different xanthines used to achieve a preferred pharmacological action. The differences among the xanthines in their effects are based on slight differences in their chemical structure. For example, aminophylline, a cardiac and bronchial dilator that contains theophylline (found in tea), is used to treat both cardiac and bronchial asthma. Theobromine (found in cocoa) causes diuresis (Graham, 1978). Caffeine is the most common drug (highest concentrations found in coffee), as it is part of many remedies for headaches and colds. Its mild stimulant properties help to counteract some of the side effects of medications for those ailments (Gilbert, 1976). Caffeine can also be used as a respiratory stimulant for premature infants

(Graham, 1978). Caffeine also is in appetite-suppressant medications because of its diuretic effects (Snyder & Sklar, 1984).

Conclusions

Caffeine is an extremely important drug because of its widespread use. Overall, it also seems to be a relatively safe drug. Despite the many years of research that have been devoted to caffeine, however, we still have a lot to learn about it. Probably the most essential research concerns developing better ways to obtain accurate measures of caffeine consumption. Such advances would help us answer important research questions. For example, we need to know more about the long-term effects of caffeine use in children, the development of tolerance to caffeine, and the prevalence of more minor symptoms of higher, but not extreme, levels of caffeine use. Another question is how caffeine affects people in special populations, such as those who are medically or psychiatrically ill.

Finally, Sawyer, Julia, and Turin (1982) made the excellent point that much of the research on caffeine has been done with healthy volunteers who have consumed only well-specified single doses of caffeine. Little information exists on the cumulative effects on task performance during, say, one day of caffeine use, although studies are beginning to address this question (Hindmarch et al., 2000). Such information is important because that is most people's pattern of caffeine use. Similarly, caffeine effects in combination with other commonly used drugs need more attention. Lowe's (1988) findings on state-dependent learning and alcohol, caffeine, and nicotine suggest that significant practical questions can be answered by such research.

SUMMARY

- Caffeine and other methylxanthine drugs occur naturally in more than 60 species of plants. Caffeine is the world's most popular drug, and humans have used it since ancient times. Many everyday products that children or adults consume contain caffeine.
- Health Canada recommends that adults consume no more than 400 mg of caffeine a day.
- Overall, coffee is the major source of caffeine, but tea is the dominant source for many countries. In the last 20 years, soft drinks and energy drinks have emerged as other significant sources of caffeine.
- Total caffeine consumption does not seem to vary by characteristics of people, except for age.
- When we factor in body weight, children aged one to five have the highest exposure to caffeine, after adults aged 18 and older.
- Caffeine's mechanism of action seems to be blocking of adenosine receptor sites.
- Caffeine is rapidly absorbed from the gastrointestinal tract and is distributed throughout the body. Its half-life in the blood ranges from 2.5 to 7.5 hours.
- Caffeine is metabolized primarily in the liver and is almost entirely excreted in the urine.
- A clear withdrawal syndrome has been identified for caffeine, and there is evidence for the development of tolerance to some of caffeine's effects.
- The acute effects of caffeine include diuresis, stimulation of the heart and CNS, relaxation of smooth muscles, and stimulation of gastric acid.
- Because many people use caffeine, nicotine, and alcohol in some combination, knowing how each of these drugs interacts with the other two is important.
- Acute caffeine intoxication is called caffeinism. Caffeinism is most likely to occur with a dose of 600 mg or higher. The higher the dose of caffeine, the more severe the symptoms.
- Overall, caffeine is a relatively safe drug, but important research questions remain about long-term caffeine use and health.

Key Terms

caffeinism p. 187

cradle-to-grave drug p. 174

energy drinks p. 185

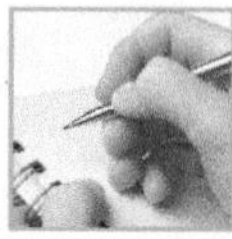

Essays/Thought Questions

1. Research provides us with good evidence that individuals may build a physical dependence on caffeine. Is this a reason to impose any restrictions, warning labels, or other controls on caffeine use? Why or why not?
2. Why has it proved difficult to obtain reliable information on caffeine consumption in the general population by use of survey research methods?

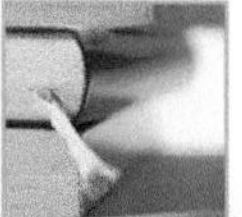

Suggested Readings

Coe, S.D., & Coe, M.D. (1996). *The true history of chocolate*. London: Thames & Hudson.

Hogan, E.H., Hornick, B.A., & Bouchoux, A. (2002). Communicating the message: Clarifying the controversies about caffeine. *Nutrition Today, 37,* 28–36.

CHAPTER 9

Marijuana

Did You Know

?

- Hemp was the first agricultural crop subsidized by the Canadian government.
- Marijuana is the most frequently used illicit drug in Canada.
- 44 percent of Canadians have tried marijuana.
- In 2007, Canada had the highest rate of marijuana use in the industrialized world.
- Marijuana metabolites can be detected in the body for up to 30 days.
- Marijuana cigarettes have more tar and cancerous agents than tobacco cigarettes.
- Cannabis has long been used for medicinal and psychotherapeutic purposes.
- In 2001, Canada became the first country to legalize medical marijuana.
- Marijuana does not enhance social skills or induce aggression or violence.

Cannabis sativa, more commonly known as marijuana, is a hemp plant that grows freely throughout the world. The cannabis plant has been harvested for its fibre since the Mesolithic, or Middle Stone Age (Walton, 2001). These strong hemp fibres were employed in the production of rope, clothes, and ship sails. Today, cannabis is harvested for paper and clothing. As early as pre-historic times the resin of the cannabis plant was known for its psychoactive effects—a notoriety that continues today. In fact, the cannabis plant is so well known for its psychoactive effects that the term *marijuana* is thought to be based on the Portuguese word *mariguango*, which translates as "intoxicant." Marijuana, incidentally, is not the same as hashish, although both are derived from the *Cannabis sativa* plant. Marijuana is the leafy top portion of the plant, whereas hashish is made from the dust of the resin that the hemp plant produces for protection from the sun and heat and for maintaining hydration. Plants that grow in warmer climates produce greater amounts of the resin, which generally has stronger psychoactive effects.

We begin this chapter with a historical overview of marijuana, followed by sections on the epidemiology of current marijuana use; its mechanisms of action; tolerance and dependence; and information on absorption, distribution, metabolism, and excretion. Following this are discussions concerning the physical, psychological, and social/environmental effects of marijuana. The chapter's final section provides an overview of the medical and psychotherapeutic uses of marijuana.

Historical Overview

As previously stated, the cannabis plant has been used since the Middle Stone Age (Walton, 2001). Archeologists at a Taiwanese site discovered pots made of fibres presumed to be from the cannabis plant. The earliest known references to the use of cannabis for its pharmacological properties are attributed to Shen Nung in about 2800 BCE. Shen Nung was a mythical Chinese emperor and pharmacist who purportedly shared knowledge of the medicinal uses of cannabis with his subjects. It has been speculated that cannabis was used in this period in China for sedating, treating pain and illness, countering the influences of evil spirits, and gaining its general psychoactive effects (Abel, 1980; Nahas, 1973).

Rodehi/Dreamstime LLC

The marijuana plant.

Cannabis use gradually spread from China to surrounding Asian countries. Of particular note was its adoption in India, where cannabis served a religious function. The *Atharva Veda*, one of the oldest books of Hinduism, includes it as one of the five sacred plants (Aldrich, 1977). This gave cannabis the protection and reverence engendered by cultural or religious acceptance. Not until much later did cannabis use spread to the Middle East and then on to North Africa. During this expansion, hashish was first identified. The use of hashish dates to around the 10th century among the Arabs and to the 11th century in Egypt (Abel, 1980).

Cannabis appears to have been used for its intoxicating effects in these parts of the world for an extended time. Not until the 19th century did the Western world begin to be exposed to cannabis, primarily through descriptions of the hashish experience in medical writings and the popular press. The use of cannabis was introduced to Great Britain primarily by William O'Shaughnessy, an Irish physician. In India, he observed the medical applications of cannabis and described them in his writings. Suggestions regarding the use of cannabis were made in France by Dr. Jacques Moreau, a physician who thought it could be used in the treatment of mental illness (Bloomquist, 1971). Subsequently, the use and effects of cannabis were described in detail in the works of other French authors. Perhaps most notable was Théophile Gautier, a famous and influential poet and essayist, who was introduced to cannabis by Moreau. Gautier graphically described his initiation into *Le Club des Hachichins* (The Hashish Club), which met in Paris in the exclusive Hotel Pimodan in the 1840s. The hashish consumed was contained in a sweetmeat called Dawamesc. Gautier's descriptions of the drug effects were graphic (some excerpts from his writings are presented in the Contemporary Issue Box 9.1). His descriptions of the hashish experiences included elements of mystery, intrigue, joy, ecstasy, fear, and terror.

CONTEMPORARY ISSUE BOX 9.1

Learning from the Past: Gautier's Experiences at The Hashish Club

As noted in the text, the Frenchman Théophile Gautier wrote in graphic detail of his experiences using hashish in the 1840s. These drug-use descriptions are of interest to us today for several reasons. They provide an opportunity for us to observe the similarities in the marijuana experience then and now, at least as described by those who write of their experiences. In addition, these descriptions allow us to observe the use of drugs in different cultures. In the present case, the user is a French hashish user, the setting is a club in Paris, and the time is the mid-19th century.

The hashish Gautier and his friends used was contained in a sweetmeat (a food rich in sugar, such as candied or crystallized fruit) called Dawamesc, which they ate at the Paris hotel that housed *Le Club des Hachichins* (The Hashish Club). The drug-laced sweetmeat was eaten before dinner. After dinner, sitting in a large drawing room, Gautier (1844) described the scene:

> Solitude reigned in the drawing room, which was studded with only a few dubious gleams; all of a sudden, a red flash passed beneath my eyelids, innumerable candles burst into light and I felt bathed in a warm, clear glow. I was indeed in the same place, but it was as different as a sketch is from a painting: everything was larger, richer, more gorgeous. Reality served as a point of departure for the splendors of the hallucination. (Solomon, 1966, p. 126)

This period was followed by a state Gautier labelled "fantasia," after which *al-kief* was experienced:

> I was in that blessed state induced by hashish which the Orientals call al-kief. I could no longer feel my body; the bonds of matter and spirit were severed; I moved by sheer willpower in an unresisting medium.
>
> Thus I imagine the movement of souls in the world of fragrances to which we shall go after death. A bluish haze, an Elysian light, the reflections of an azure grotto, formed an atmosphere in the room through which I vaguely saw the tremblings of hesitant outlines; an atmosphere at once cool and warm, moist and perfumed, enveloping me like bath water in a sort of enervating sweetness. When I tried to move away, the caressing air made a thousand voluptuous waves about me; a delightful languor gripped my senses and threw me back upon the sofa, where I hung, limp as a discarded garment.
>
> Then I understood the pleasure experienced by the spirits and angels, according to their degree of perfection, when they traverse the ethers and the skies, and how eternity might occupy one in Paradise. (Solomon, 1966, pp. 130–131)

Al-kief was replaced by a nightmarish stage in which Gautier felt fear, fury, and aspects of paranoia. Then, finally, around five hours after entering The Hashish Club, the drug effects ended:

> The dream was at an end.
>
> The hashisheen went off, each in his own direction, like the officers in *Marlborough Goes to War*.
>
> With light steps, I went down the stairs that had caused me so much anguish, and a few moments later I was in my room, in full reality; the last vapors raised by the hashish had vanished. (Solomon, 1966, p. 135)

Source: Théophile Gautier, "Le Club des Hachichin." *Revue des Deux Mondes.* 1846.

Despite what appeared to some as attractive features of cannabis and hashish, the use of this drug did not immediately catch on in Europe. In fact, using cannabis for its psychoactive properties did not become widespread in Europe until the 1960s, when it was reintroduced by, among others, tourists from the United States (Bloomquist, 1971).

Cannabis in the New World

The presence of cannabis in the New World dates to 1545, when the Spaniards brought it to Chile. In the North American colonies, the Jamestown settlers in Virginia raised the cannabis plant for fibre in 1611. Not long after, this hemp product was firmly entrenched as a basic staple crop and was cultivated by George Washington, among many others. Cannabis was harvested in New England starting in 1629; it remained a core U.S. crop until after the Civil War. The centre of hemp production was Kentucky, where it was a major crop product for decades. In Canada, similar initiates were implemented in the early 1800s, and hemp became the first agricultural crop subsidized by the government. By the 1820s, Canada had six hemp mills and subsidies for continued growth, new machinery, and repairs. However, by the end of the 19th century Canada's hemp industry was all but abandoned in favour of the less labour-intensive cotton crop.

Despite its widespread presence, the marijuana plant was relatively unknown as a mind-altering substance. But it was known for its medicinal properties. Between 1840 and 1900 cannabis was used in medicinal practice throughout North America, and more than 100 papers were published in the Western medical literature recommending it for various illnesses and discomforts. The first physician to introduce cannabis to Western medicine was W.B. O'Shaunghnessy. He introduced cannabis to Western medicine in 1841 after observing its use in India and performing experiments on animals to satisfy himself that it was safe for human use. Soon after its introduction to North America, physicians began to prescribe cannabis for a variety of physical conditions such as rabies, migraines, rheumatism, epilepsy, depression, tetanus, and as a muscle relaxant. Cannabis became so common in medicinal use that, eventually, cannabis preparations were sold over the counter in drug stores (Spicer, 2002). However, by the end of the 19th century the medicinal use of cannabis fell as a result of several factors, including, inconsistent potency levels, the increased use of opiates and soluble drugs made possible by the invention of the hypodermic needle, and the development of drugs such as aspirin and barbiturates.

Further complicating the use of cannabis was the growing realization of its psychoactive effects. In 1857, Fitz Hugh Ludlow published the book *The Hasheesh Eater*, which detailed his cannabis-eating experiences over a four-year period beginning at around age 16. Ludlow lived in the town of Poughkeepsie, north of New York City in the Hudson River Valley. He spent much of his time with a friend named Anderson, an **apothecary**, and often experimented with the varied substances in Anderson's drugstore. One day, Anderson pointed out to Ludlow a new arrival: a marijuana extract from Tilden and Co. Ludlow began experimenting with the substance. At first, he experienced no immediate drug effects, but he described the onset of effects after several hours as follows:

apothecary
A pharmacist.

> Ha! what means this sudden thrill? A shock, as of some unimagined vital force, shoots without warning through my entire frame, leaping to my fingers' ends, piercing my brain, startling me till I almost spring from my chair. I could not doubt it. I was in the power of the hasheesh influence. (Ludlow, 1857/1979, p. 20)

Ludlow continued his experimenting, graphically describing the varied cannabis effects. For example, in a chapter titled "The Kingdom of the Dream," he noted:

> The moment that I closed my eyes a vision of celestial glory burst upon me. I stood on the silver strand of a translucent, boundless lake, across whose bosom I seemed to have been just transported. A short way up the beach, a temple, modeled like the Parthenon, lifted its

> spotless and gleaming columns of alabaster sublimely into a rosy air—like the Parthenon, yet as much excelling it as the godlike ideal of architecture must transcend that ideal realized by man. (Ludlow, 1857/1979, p. 34)

Ludlow also identified two "laws of the hasheesh operation." The first was that "after the completion of any one fantasia has arrived, there almost invariably succeeds a shifting of the action to some other stage entirely different in its surroundings" (pp. 36–37). The second law was that "after the full storm of a vision of intense sublimity has blown past the hasheesh-eater, his next vision is generally of a quiet, relaxing, and recreating nature" (p. 37).

Although, Canadians did not widely use cannabis for psychoactive purposes until the middle of the 20th century, American recreational use of cannabis began to grow considerably during the 1920s. Edward M. Brecher, in The Consumers Union Report on *Licit and Illicit Drugs* (1972), attributes this increase to alcohol prohibition. He writes, "Not until the Eighteenth Amendment and the Volstead Act of 1920 raised the price of alcoholic beverages and made them less convenient to secure and inferior in quality did substantial commercial trade in marijuana for recreational use spring up" (1972, p. 410). In New York City, for example, a number of marijuana **tea-pads** (estimated at more than 500 in Harlem alone) opened in the early 1920s, generally in a room or apartment. As described by Mayor LaGuardia's Committee on Marihuana (1944),

tea-pads
Historically, places where people gathered to smoke marijuana. The sites could be anything from a rented room to a hotel suite.

> The "tea-pad" is furnished according to the clientele it expects to serve. Usually, each "tea-pad" has comfortable furniture, a radio, Victrola or, as in most instances, a rented nickelodeon. The lighting is more or less uniformly dim, with blue predominating. An incense burner is considered part of the furnishings. The walls are frequently decorated with pictures of nude subjects suggestive of perverted sexual practices. The furnishings, as described, are believed to be essential as a setting for those participating in smoking marihuana. (p. 10)

The Committee went on to note:

> The marihuana smoker derives greater satisfaction if he is smoking in the presence of others. His attitude in the "tea-pad" is that of a relaxed individual, free from the anxieties and cares of the realities of life. The "tea-pad" takes on the atmosphere of a very congenial social club. The smoker readily engages in conversation with strangers, discussing freely his pleasant reactions to the drug and philosophizing on subjects pertaining to life in a manner which, at times, appears to be out of keeping with his intellectual level.... A boisterous, rowdy atmosphere did not prevail and on the rare occasions when there appeared signs indicative of a belligerent attitude on the part of a smoker, he was ejected or forced to become more tolerant and quiescent. (p. 10)

The origins of the practice of smoking marijuana in North America are not clear, but most agree that one of the earliest introductions was through Mexican labourers crossing the border into the United States. The greatest extent of use was in New Orleans, also in the early 1920s. In fact, New Orleans was a central dispensing arena for marijuana as late as the 1930s. The marijuana could be sent up the Mississippi River to river ports and then distributed throughout the country. According to Nahas (1973), marijuana was available in the larger cities by 1930, although its use was limited to primarily black Americans, not infrequently jazz musicians.

There was little public concern over the use of marijuana during this period, with one notable exception. In 1926, a series of articles was printed in two New Orleans newspapers. They sensationally "exposed" the "menacing" presence of marijuana and attributed a number of crimes and heinous acts to use of the drug. Although many of these lurid reports were ridiculous and fabricated, a Louisiana law mandating a maximum penalty of a $500 fine and/or six months imprisonment for conviction of possession or sale of marijuana was passed the next year. This law had little effect on the sale or use of marijuana in New Orleans, however, except for a possible moderate increase in the price of a marijuana cigarette (Brecher, 1972).

Even though marijuana had not threatened to enter the mainstream of American life, additional government and legal action continued into the next decade. Much of this activity was promoted by Harry J. Anslinger, who became director of the Federal Bureau of Narcotics in 1932. Anslinger was convinced that marijuana represented a major threat to the safety and well-being of the country. He successfully encouraged many states to restrict the trafficking and use of marijuana. In 1930, only 16 states had statutes prohibiting the use of marijuana; by 1937, virtually all states had such statutes.

Anslinger's efforts culminated in the 1937 passage of the Marijuana Tax Act. The act did not officially ban marijuana; rather, it acknowledged the medicinal uses of marijuana and permitted the prescription of marijuana following payment of a licence fee of $1 per year. Any other possession or sale of marijuana was strictly outlawed. Punishments for violation were a $2000 fine, five years of imprisonment, or both. Anslinger's efforts overall were successful in reducing the legal spread of marijuana; in the following year, only 38 physicians paid the $1 licence fee to prescribe marijuana (Brecher, 1972). Furthermore, Anslinger's efforts set the stage for progressively stricter penalties for marijuana sale and possession in the ensuing years.

A year later, the Canadian Opium and Narcotics Act came into effect. Internationally, cannabis began to be controlled in 1961 by the United Nations *Single Convention on Narcotic Drugs, 1961*, requiring states to adopt the necessary legislative and regulatory measures in order to limit the production, distribution, and use of prohibited substances to medical and scientific purposes. Canada both signed and ratified the convention in 1961 and the United States later acceded to the convention in 1967 (Spicer, 2002). Since that time the use of cannabis for medicinal or recreational purposes has been a hotly debated topic in many countries, including Canada. Table 9.1 provides a timeline of key issues in Canadian cannabis use and legislation.

TABLE 9.1 Key Issues in Canadian Cannabis Use and Legislation

1800s	Canada has a strong hemp industry. Hemp becomes the first agricultural crop subsidized by the government.
1840–1900	Cannabis is used in medicinal practice throughout North America.
1923	Canadian Opium and Narcotics Act comes into effect, which prohibits marijuana use.
1930s	Canadians are NOT using cannabis for recreational purposes.
1930–1946	25 convictions for cannabis possession in all of Canada.
1960s–1970s	Canada signs the United Nations *Single Convention on Narcotic Drugs*. There is a dramatic increase in cannabis use among Canadians. The maximum penalty for possessing small amounts of cannabis is six months in prison and a $1000 fine for a first offence. In 1962 the Royal Canadian Mounted Police reported only 20 cases connected with cannabis. In 1968 the number of cannabis related cases had risen to over 2300, and in 1972 there were nearly 12 000 cannabis convictions in Canada. Cannabis use among Canadian students approaches 25 percent, with 1979 being a peak year in which over 30 percent of students in grades 7, 9, 11, and 13 reported use in the previous 12 months.
Early 1970s	The Le Dain Commission was appointed in Canada to undertake a complete and factual study of marijuana use and its effects. It concluded that, "Canada's prohibition laws had only served to create a sub-culture with little respect for the law and law enforcement, as well as diverting law enforcement capability, clogging the judicial system, and providing a base of funds for organized crime.

1978–1979	In 1978, another report, commissioned on marijuana laws, recommended, once again, that marijuana be decriminalized and legalized. In 1979, Prime Minister Joe Clark and the Progressive Conservative government gave notice in its Throne Speech that it intended to reform the Criminal Code provisions regarding cannabis, but the Conservative Government was defeated before making these revisions. The newly elected Liberal government signs the UN's Convention on Psychotropic Substances and halts all plans to legalize marijuana.
1980s	In the U.S., the Reagan-Bush administration carries out 'The War on Drugs' campaign. In Canada, this U.S. initiative affects marijuana use: levels of use stabilize and decrease among youths; marijuana is now a private and personal activity, done at home and out of sight of friends, coworkers, and family members.
1987	Canada's Drug Strategy is implemented to address both the supply and demand reduction strategies and programs in enforcement, and treatment and prevention programming were funded. Some say that at the time, this may have been the most severe cannabis censorship strategy in the world.
1990s	Cannabis use rises in Canada. In 1993–1994 cannabis use increases from 4.2 percent to 7.4 percent. In 1996–2000 cannabis use among 18–29-year-olds increases from 18 percent to 28 percent.
Mid 1990s	The rise of a cannabis decriminalization movement is joined by hundreds of recreational smokers who say that Canada's laws against cannabis are outdated and out of step with the rest of the Western world. Many governments in a number of European countries, including the Netherlands, Germany, Italy, and Spain, have now decided not to prosecute for possession of cannabis for personal use.
1994	Joe Strobel, an Ontario farmer, is granted a federal licence to grow 10 acres of marijuana for research into the plant's industrial agricultural potential.
1997	The Canadian Government passes the *Controlled Drugs and Substances Act,* which consolidates marijuana laws previously found in the Narcotic Control Act and Parts III and IV of the Food and Drugs Act.
2000	In 2000 over 30 000 Canadians are charged with simple possession of marijuana, according to the Senate Committee on Illegal Drugs. Ontario's court of appeal rules that banning marijuana for medicinal purposes violates the Canadian Charter of Rights and Freedoms. Striking down a federal law prohibiting the possession of less than 30 grams, the court rules the law violates the rights of the sick to use the drug for medical purposes. Health Canada approves the Cannabis Medical Access Project, launching the country's first legal marijuana growing facility. A deep, abandoned mine shaft beneath a northern Manitoba lake, larger than three football fields, is chosen for the high-security operation.
2001	The Marihuana Medical Access Regulations makes Canada the first country in the world to legalize the use of marijuana by people suffering from terminal illnesses and chronic conditions.
2002	The Special Senate Committee on Illegal Drugs releases its final report which concludes marijuana is less harmful than alcohol and should be governed by the same sort of regulations that control tobacco. The House of Commons Special Committee on Non-Medical Use of Drugs releases its final report, recommending decriminalization of possession of small amounts of marijuana. Charges against two volunteers at a medical marijuana club are thrown out of a Quebec Court. Judge Gilles Cadieux dismissed possession and trafficking charges, citing a contradiction between a law allowing the ill to use marijuana, and another prohibiting a legal source of the drug.
2003	Ontario Justice Douglas Phillips suggests marijuana possession laws are no longer valid, in his decision to dismiss two drug charges against a 16-year-old Windsor boy. The Ontario Court of Appeal rules that the new regulations provide acceptable access to medical marijuana, thus re-criminalizing possession of marijuana for recreational purposes. Later that year, the Supreme Court rules that our marijuana laws "do not violate the Charter of Rights and Freedom and its protection of life, liberty and security of person."
2007	47 000 people are arrested for possession of marijuana; this is about half of all drug arrests in Canada for that year.
April 2011	An Ontario Superior Court judge strikes down Canada's laws prohibiting the possession and production of marijuana, giving the federal government 90 days to fix the country's medical marijuana program before the ruling comes into effect and effectively legalizes cannabis.
August 2011	The Federal Government fails to provide the Ontario Court of Appeals with an amended medical marijuana program.

Sources: Spicer (2002); CTV News (2003); Canada On-line (2011); Hathaway (2011); Cannabis Culture (2011); Centre for Addiction and Mental Health (2009) and Queen's Policy Review (2011).

Epidemiology

Marijuana is the most widely used illicit drug in the Western world and the third most commonly used recreational drug after alcohol and tobacco (Iversen, 2000). According to the World Health Organization, it also is the illicit substance most widely cultivated, trafficked, and abused.

For a number of years, the United Nations has been compiling annual surveys of worldwide drug use, including cannabis. Reflecting the difficulties and uncertainties associated with developing estimates of the number of people who use drugs (such as the quality of the data gathered and the methodologies used to sample populations), the latest United Nations estimates are presented in ranges, reflecting the lower and upper estimates indicated through the array of surveys available. In their 2009 report (covering 2007), the United Nations estimated that between 142.6 and 190.3 million people between the ages of 15 and 64 had used cannabis in the past year, representing between 3.3 percent and 4.4 percent of the world's population (UN Office on Drugs and Crime, 2009b).

Looking at specific regions of the world, surveys have found that the highest per capita rate of use has been in Oceania (the countries and territories in the Pacific Ocean, including Australia), where between 11.0–11.5 percent of adults reported past-year use. Past-year prevalence estimates for other regions were 7.0–7.1 percent for the Americas, 5.4–10.5 percent for Africa, 5.2–5.4 percent for Europe, and 1.6–2.3 percent for Asia. Past-year cannabis use estimates for subregions include 9.3–15.6 percent for west and central Africa, 10.5 percent for North America, 7.7 percent for western/central Europe, 4.3–6.7 percent for the Caribbean, 3.4 percent for South America, and 2.9–3.1 percent for eastern Europe (UN Office on Drugs and Crime, 2009b).

Stockphoto4u/iStockphoto.com

There has been growing concern over the use of marijuana by young people.

As in most other countries, marijuana is the most frequently used illicit drug in Canada. In fact, in 2007 Canada had the highest rate of marijuana use in the industrialized world—a rate four times greater than the global rate of use (UN, 2007). According to the Centre for Addiction and Mental Health (2009), 44 percent of Canadians say they have used marijuana at least once in their lifetime. Cannabis use among Canadian youth is of particular concern: 17 percent of students in grades 7–9 report having tried cannabis, while 29 percent of 15–17-year-olds and almost half of 18–19-year-olds report past-year cannabis use. Provincial surveys show that 25–33 percent of junior high and high school students use cannabis and three to five percent of students use cannabis daily. Overall, daily cannabis use has increased over the long-term. In addition, Canadian boys report the highest rates of frequent (more than 40 times in their lifetime) cannabis use, compared to other countries.

Despite the prevalence of marijuana use, the Canadian Alcohol and Drug Use Monitoring Survey (CADUMS, 2010) reports that cannabis use among both adults and youth has decreased since 2004. For example, the prevalence of past-year cannabis use by Canadians 15 years and older decreased from 14.1 percent in 2004 to 10.7 percent in 2010; while past-year cannabis use by 15–24-year-olds decreased from 37.0 percent in 2004 to 25.1 percent in 2010.

CONTEMPORARY ISSUE BOX 9.2

Marijuana as a Gateway to Other Drug Use

The gateway or "stepping stone" theory of drug use posits that the use of licit and illicit substances follows a predictable pattern. This theory of stages receives considerable attention during debates on the legalization of marijuana. Opponents of legalization argue that marijuana use is the first step on a path that leads to the use of—and potentially addiction to—drugs such as heroin and cocaine. As it turns out, research by Johnson (1973), Fergusson and Horwood (2000), and others has shown that the vast majority of marijuana users do not go on to become heroin addicts.

Nevertheless, substance use does appear to follow a uniform sequence of drugs. One of the earliest studies (Kandel, 1975) found that alcohol use among high school students was a necessary stepping-stone between nonuse of drugs and use of marijuana. This finding was replicated in research conducted at the New York State Research Institute on Addictions (Welte & Barnes, 1985; Windle, Barnes, & Welte, 1989). High school students (white, black, and Hispanic) tend to use drugs in the same sequence: alcohol, marijuana, and then the so-called hard drugs (such as cocaine, crack, hallucinogens, and heroin). In a later study, Kandel and Yamaguchi (1993) found that crack users almost always had used marijuana earlier. Indeed, only 10 percent of crack users in high school had not previously used marijuana. Adler and Kandel (1981) found similar patterns in the sequence of drug use among adolescents in Israel and France.

More recently, researchers at the Center on Addiction and Substance Abuse at Columbia University found that teenagers who experimented with alcohol, cigarettes, and marijuana were more likely than other youths to use cocaine and other "hard drugs." The report noted that 17 percent of children (aged 12 to 17) who had used marijuana had tried cocaine as well; five percent of those who drank alcohol and six percent of those who smoked cigarettes also had tried cocaine. Similarly, Fergusson and his colleagues (Fergusson & Horwood, 2000; Fergusson, Boden, & Horwood, 2006) found that marijuana use among New Zealanders was strongly related to the use of other forms of illicit drugs. Use of marijuana almost without exception preceded other illicit drug use, and more frequent marijuana users (using more than 50 occasions a year) were 140 times more likely to use other illicit drugs than those not using marijuana. Hall and Lynskey (2005) concluded that there was a reasonably strong association between regular and early cannabis use and other illicit drug use.

It is important to keep a couple of things in mind when interpreting these stepping-stone data. First, and perhaps most important, not everyone who uses alcohol will subsequently use marijuana, and not everyone who uses marijuana will subsequently use other illicit drugs. (Indeed, in both cases, most will not.) Second, people who start using marijuana after previously using alcohol typically do not stop using alcohol. Instead, both substances can be in the person's drug-use repertoire. Finally, consider that an alternative to the gateway theory has been proposed. Called the "correlated vulnerabilities" theory, it suggests that the so-called "stepping-stone" pattern of substance use is explained by the common characteristics (i.e., a general predisposition to use drugs) of those who use cannabis and other drugs (Hall & Lynskey, 2005; Morral, McCaffrey, & Paddock, 2002).

The studies mentioned have implications for people who work in the areas of prevention and drug policy. As one example (and you probably can imagine others), these studies suggest that people who do not use marijuana for the most part will not use "hard drugs" such as cocaine or heroin. Prevention efforts that focus on not using marijuana potentially will decrease the pool of marijuana users who will subsequently use other drugs.

With 25 percent of Canadian youth having smoked marijuana in the last year, the question of marijuana's safety for young people comes to the forefront. For example, McGill University reseracher s (Bambicoa, Nguyena, Katza, & Gobbi, 2009) report that daily marijuana use can lead to depression and anxiety among teenagers. Further, they suggest that the neurological changes caused by daily marijuana use may be irreversible.

Elena Ioachim/Shutterstock

A bud of marijuana.

Methods of Use

Marijuana and hashish have been administered in a number of ways in their use as psychoactive agents. For example, they were ingested in India centuries ago in liquid and food form. People can also experience the psychoactive effects of marijuana by chewing marijuana leaves. However, the most common procedure for ingesting cannabis in this country has been and remains smoking, typically in cigarette (**joint**) form. Inhalation through cigarettes is also the most efficient method for absorption of cannabis. Other methods of smoking marijuana include water pipes (often called bongs) or blunts (a cigar that is emptied of tobacco and refilled with marijuana). The smoking of blunts has increased in popularity among American urban youth (Ream et al., 2008) and may present some unique health risks, given the combined intake of the marijuana and tobacco (as the cigar wrapper is a tobacco leaf). For example, smoking marijuana in a tobacco leaf appears to increase the risks of marijuana by enhancing carbon monoxide exposure and increasing heart rate, relative to smoking marijuana in joint form (Cooper & Haney, 2009).

Eric Gevaert/Shutterstock

Chunks of hashish.

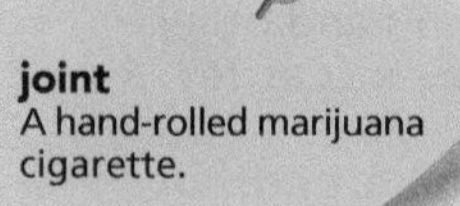

joint
A hand-rolled marijuana cigarette.

cannabinoids
The more than 60 chemical compounds present in cannabis. One is delta-9-tetrahydrocannabinol (better known as THC).

delta-9-tetrahydrocannabinol
The principal active cannabinoid in marijuana responsible for the psychoactive effects.

Active Ingredients

The first chemical analysis of cannabis apparently was performed in 1821 (Mechoulam, 1973). Since then, studies have shown cannabis to be a complex plant. More than 400 individual chemical compounds have been identified in the plant. Over 60 of these chemicals, collectively called **cannabinoids**, are unique to the cannabis plant (El Sohly, 2002). Continued research will probably identify additional cannabis chemical compounds and cannabinoids.

Despite years of study, the principal psychoactive agent in cannabis was not isolated until 1964. This substance has been labelled **delta-9-tetrahydrocannabinol** but is more commonly known as D-9-THC, or simply THC. The THC compound was first reported by Gaoni and Mechoulam (1964), two researchers working in Israel. Research since 1964 has shown that the D-9-THC cannabinoid accounts for the vast majority of the known specific pharmacological actions of marijuana. Although THC is the prime psychoactive agent in cannabis, other cannabinoids, such as cannabidiol and cannabinol, can be biologically active and can modify THC effects. However, they tend not to be psychoactive in and of themselves.

The Psychotropic Effects of Marijuana

The psychotropic actions of marijuana occur in the brain and are a result of the drug's effect on chemical neurotransmission. Much of the early research in this area (typically performed with animals) focused on the effects of marijuana on acetylcholine, a chemical transmitter involved in memory. THC in relatively small doses has been shown to decrease the turnover in acetylcholine, particularly in the hippocampus, resulting in a

CONTEMPORARY ISSUE BOX 9.3

Potency of Cannabis

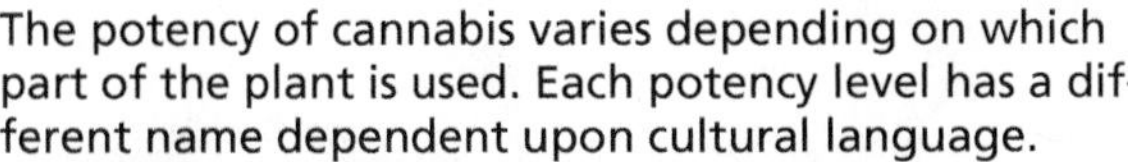

The potency of cannabis varies depending on which part of the plant is used. Each potency level has a different name dependent upon cultural language.

1. Mild Potency: Marijuana (Europe and North America), Mariguango (Mexican) Dagga (South Africa), Kif (North Africa), Bhang (India). The flowering leaves of ripe male and female hemp plants secrete a sticky resin which is the source of all, or almost all, of the THC (delta-1-tetrahydrocannabinol, the ingredient which reproduces in man all the mind-altering effects that follow smoking or eating marijuana or hashish) in cannabis. In this form of cannabis use, the leaves, and sometimes the stems and even seeds or entire plants are ground up and smoked or baked into cookies. The potency varies with the THC content. Bhang is a little different as it usually involves only leaves, is drunk, and is usually somewhat richer in THC than North American marijuana.
2. Intermediate Potency: Ganja (India). The dried flowering tops of cultivated plants are covered with THC as a result of not having released their seeds. These are harvested and used in 'ganja'. Ganja is usually smoked; however it is also drunk or baked into sweets. Outside of India, it is virtually unknown.
3. High Potency: Charas (India), Hashish (Arabia and North America), Hashishi (Syria). Almost all of the THC is contained in the resin on the leaves near the flowering tops. The resin is scraped off of the leaves, pressed into blocks, and usually smoked. Hashish is about 10 times as powerful as marijuana and is the only cannabis derivative that has the capacity to produce hallucinogenic and psychotomimetic effects with any regularity. An Indian pharmacologist, Chopra (1933, pp. 78–79), has described another method of harvesting charas:

   > Sometimes men, naked, or dressed in leather suits or jackets, passed through the fields of *cannabis sativa* rubbing and crushing roughly against the plants early in the morning just after sunrise when a fall of dew has taken place. The resinous material that sticks on is then scraped off them and forms the charas resin of commerce.

Other common names for cannabis include *grifa* in Spain and Mexico; *anascha* in Russia; *kendir* in Tartar; *konop* in Bulgaria and *konope* in Poland; *momea* in Tibet; *kanbun* in Chaldea; *dawamesk* in Algeria; *liamba* or *maconha* in Brazil; and *bust* or *sheera* in Egypt.

The potency of marijuana is a hotly debated topic in many countries, including Canada. The general consensus is that the potency of cannabis has, in general, increased since the 1970s. For example, in the United States, marijuana is considerably stronger than that used three decades ago (eight percent to 10 percent THC is now the average versus around two percent in 1980) (El Sohly et al., 2000; Iverson, 2000; McLaren et al., 2008). Comparable figures are reported for marijuana smoked in the United Kingdom. Higher THC potency is generally found in "homegrown" cannabis—that is, marijuana grown in large-scale domestic indoor environments (Iversen, 2000). The THC content in sinsemilla (a seedless variety of marijuana) is now in the range of 10–20 percent and sometimes reaches 30 percent (Pijlman et al., 2005). Similar variations and increasing average potencies have been found as well for hashish. A third form of cannabis is **hash oil**, a concentrated liquid marijuana extract derived from the cannabis plant using solvents. This oil has been available on the streets for a number of years and is more potent than the marijuana leaf material or resin. Estimates are that hash oil can contain as much as 60 percent THC, although the potency is more generally found to be around 20 percent (Iversen, 2000).

However, other research suggests that there has not been an increase in the potency of cannabis. For example, the European Monitoring Centre for Drugs and Drug Addiction (2004), conducted a comprehensive review of available evidence in Europe, the United States, Australia, and New Zealand, and concluded that reports of increased potency of cannabis are not valid.

Source: *Historical and cultural uses of cannabis and the Canadian "marijuana clash."* Leah Spicer. Prepared for the Senate Special Committee on Illegal Drugs. 2002. Reproduced with the permission of the Library of Parliament, 2012.

decrease in neurotransmitter activity. Similar inhibitory effects of THC have been observed on a variety of neurotransmitters, including L-glutamate, GABA, noradrenaline, dopamine, and 5-HT (Iversen, 2003). In addition, THC facilitates release of the neurotransmitter serotonin and produces changes in the dopamine system, thus enhancing activation of movement.

hash oil
A potent distillate of marijuana or hashish. It first appeared in the United States in 1971 and can contain up to 60 percent THC.

Although specification of the drug action remains somewhat speculative, important advances are occurring. Foremost among these has been research on THC receptors in

FIGURE 9.1
Where marijuana acts in the brain

Source: © Alice Y. Chen, 2004 for Scientific American.

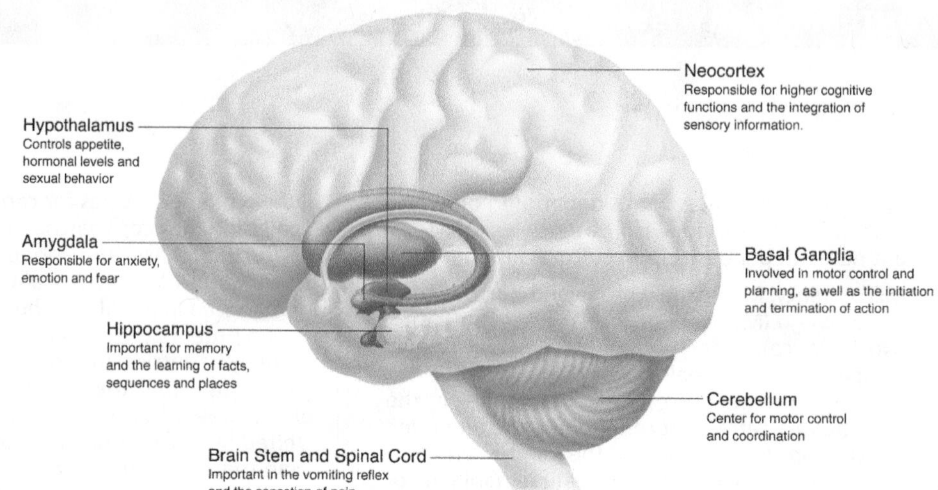
Neocortex
Responsible for higher cognitive functions and the integration of sensory information.
Hypothalamus
Controls appetite, hormonal levels and sexual behavior
Amygdala
Responsible for anxiety, emotion and fear
Basal Ganglia
Involved in motor control and planning, as well as the initiation and termination of action
Hippocampus
Important for memory and the learning of facts, sequences and places
Cerebellum
Center for motor control and coordination
Brain Stem and Spinal Cord
Important in the vomiting reflex and the sensation of pain

the brain (Adams & Martin, 1996; Iversen, 2003). Figure 9.1 shows the areas of the brain affected by marijuana use. Two types of cannabinoid receptors (called CB1 and CB2) have been identified (Devane et al., 1988; Herkenham et al., 1990; Matsuda et al., 1990; Munro, Thomas, & Abu-Shaar, 1993). These receptors are uniquely stimulated by THC. CB1 receptors are located predominantly in brain areas that control memory, cognition, the motor system, and mood. CB2 receptors are most prevalent in the immune system. These cannabinoid receptors regulate the release of dopamine.

Research on cannabinoid receptors opened the door to efforts to study pathways in the brain that may be involved in cannabinoid actions and to the search for naturally occurring chemicals in the body (called endogenous chemicals) that normally would interact with the identified receptors. One research team (Devane et al., 1992) identified such a chemical (named "anandamide" from the Sanskrit word for "bliss") that binds to the same receptors on brain cells as do cannabinoids. When anandamide binds to these receptors it turns off the release of inhibitory neurotransmitters that ordinarily prevent the release of dopamine into the synapse. Thus, the binding of anandamide causes the release of dopamine. Anandamide breaks down quickly and does not produce the "high" experienced with marijuana. Researchers now are using the compound anandamide to study how the cannabinoid receptors affect functions such as memory, movement, hunger, and pain, which are affected by marijuana use. Another endogenous chemical identified as interacting with cannabinoid receptors is 2-arachidonoyl-glycerol, or 2-AG (Pertwee, 2002; Sugiura et al., 2000).

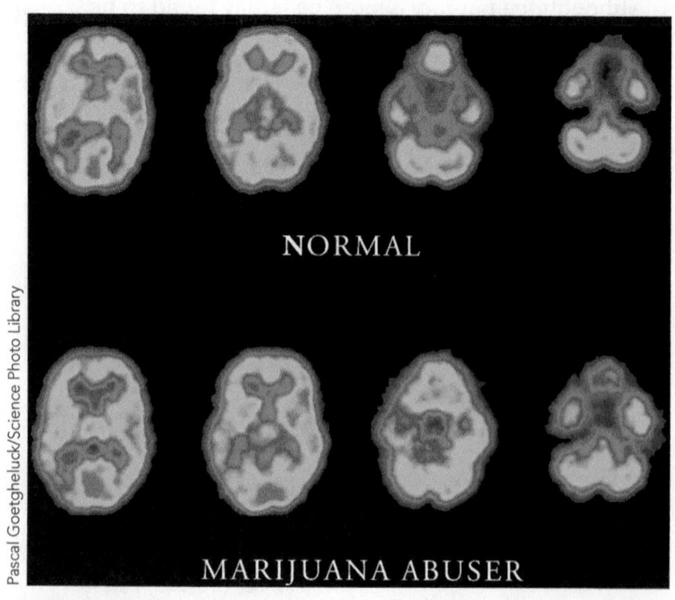
NORMAL
MARIJUANA ABUSER

Pascal Goetgheluck/Science Photo Library

PET scan showing blood flow of marijuana abuser and nonuser ("normal") control.

Newer research methods, such as positron emission transaxial tomography (PET), which assesses cerebral blood flow, have opened new avenues for exploring marijuana effects. For example, it has been shown that THC increases blood flow in most brain regions in both the cerebral cortex and deeper brain

THIS IS YOUR BRAIN ON MARIJUANA

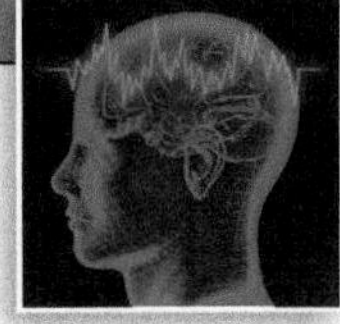

A. In the normal functioning of the nervous system, neurotransmitters are released into the synaptic cleft by vesicles in terminal buttons of sending neurons. Many are taken up by receptor sites in receiving neurons.

B. In the process called *reuptake*, sending neurons typically reabsorb excess molecules of neurotransmitters.

C. THC, the active ingredient in marijuana, acts like anandamide and binds to cannabinoid receptors in the brain. When this happens it stops inhibitory neurotransmitters from blocking the release of dopamine. Thus, dopamine is released into the synapse.

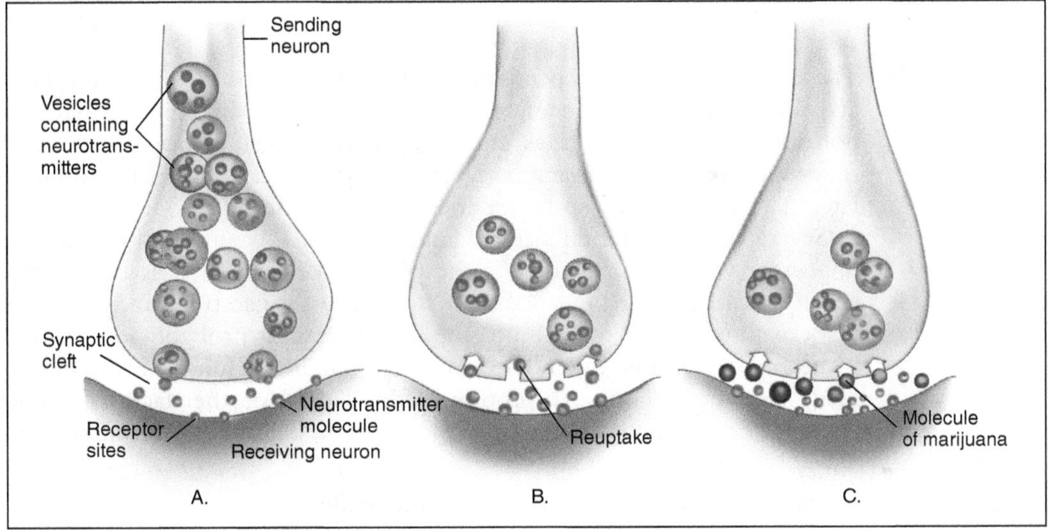

S. Rathus, S. Maheu, & S. Veenvliet. *PSYCH, 1e.* © 2012 Nelson Education Ltd. Reproduced by permission. www.cengage.com/permissions

structures (Iversen, 2000; Quickfall & Crockford, 2006). Such blood flow is greatest in the frontal cortex (Matthew et al., 1997), which is critical to "executive" brain functions. Other recent research has focused on identifying and investigating areas of the brain that have greater densities of cannabinoid receptors, such as the cerebral cortex.

Tolerance and Dependence

Tolerance to cannabis has been well documented in animal species (for example, Agurell et al., 1986; Harris, Dewey, & Razdan, 1977). The evidence for tolerance to cannabis in humans is less clear, with many studies indicating tolerance but a number of others not. Some of the discrepancies in the human studies can be attributed to the dose of marijuana and the duration of use being studied. Tolerance is more likely to occur with higher doses used over longer periods of time. Research has typically been done in controlled laboratory settings, where the doses and frequencies of use studied are generally much greater than those reported by marijuana users in the general population. The mechanisms by which tolerance occurs are still unknown. There is an ongoing debate as to whether physical dependence can occur in the context of marijuana use. Some have argued that there is no significant withdrawal syndrome identifiable (Compton et al., 1996; Smith, 2002), and certainly no clustering of withdrawal indicators as identified for other substances such as alcohol or heroin. Jones (1980), on the other hand, described several aspects of dependence associated with sustained heavy use of marijuana. These aspects entailed sleep disturbance, nausea, irritability, and restlessness following cessation of marijuana use. It has been more recently posited that these symptoms reflect a reliable and clinically significant withdrawal syndrome (Budney et al., 2004); however, debate continues as to whether these symptoms are more indicative of a psychological as opposed to physical dependence on marijuana. At present, it appears that aspects of physical dependence, when they occur, are most likely to be associated with sustained heavy use of marijuana.

Pharmacokinetics

Absorption

The absorption of THC depends primarily on the mode of consumption. The most rapid and efficient absorption of marijuana occurs through smoking. Inhalation results in absorption directly through the lungs, and the onset of the THC action begins within minutes. Assessments of blood plasma reveal that peak concentrations occur 30 to 60 minutes later. The drug effects can be experienced for two to four hours (see Figure 9.2).

Several factors can influence the amount of THC absorbed through smoking. One important variable, of course, is the potency of the cannabis being smoked. Only about half of the THC available in a marijuana cigarette is in the smoke, and the amount ultimately absorbed into the bloodstream is probably less. Another variable is the amount of time the inhaled smoke is held in the lungs; the longer the smoke is held, the more time for absorption of the THC. Another factor influencing intake is the number of people who share the cigarette because more smokers may decrease

FIGURE 9.2
Effects of marijuana

Source: Zubada/Shutterstock

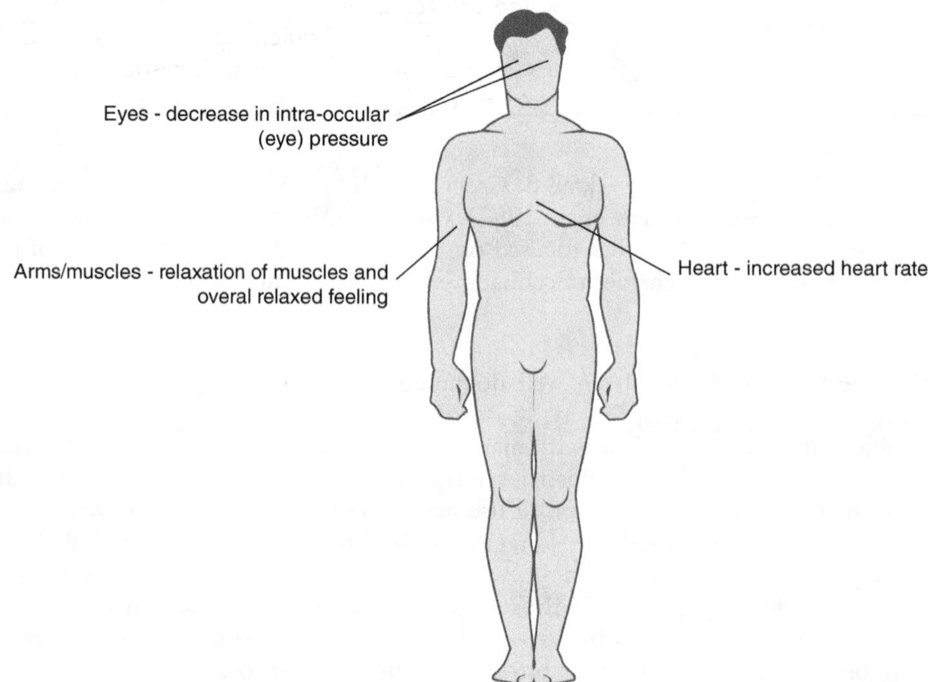

the amount of marijuana available to any one user. The amount of THC in a marijuana cigarette that is actually absorbed by smoking averages around 20 percent, with the other 80 percent is lost primarily through combustion, sidestream smoke, and incomplete absorption in the lungs (Iversen, 2000).

Oral ingestion of marijuana is much slower and relatively inefficient. The onset of action is longer than when smoked, taking as long as an hour. The marijuana is absorbed primarily through the gastrointestinal tract, and peak plasma levels can be delayed for as long as two to three hours following ingestion. An important difference from absorption through smoking is that blood containing orally ingested marijuana goes through the liver before going to the brain. The liver processes or clears much of the THC so that lesser amounts have the opportunity to exert action in the brain. The drug effects following oral ingestion can be experienced for longer periods of time, however, generally four to six hours. The dose needed to create a comparable high when orally ingested is estimated as three times greater than that needed when smoking.

Distribution, Metabolism, and Excretion

Using peak plasma THC levels to assess cannabis effects can be misleading because the psychoactive cannabinoids are highly lipid-soluble; that is, the cannabinoids are lipids and this means that they are almost entirely insoluble in water. The cannabinoids instead are a dark, viscous, oil-like substance. Plasma levels of THC decrease rapidly because the THC is deposited in the tissues of various organs, particularly those that contain fatty material. Assessments of organs following cannabis ingestion reveal marked concentrations of THC in the brain, lungs, kidneys, and liver. Thus, even when blood levels of THC are zero, the levels of THC in other organs can be substantial. Also, THC is capable of crossing the placental barrier and reaching the fetus.

As noted, THC is carried through the bloodstream and deposited within various organs. The THC is then metabolized to less active products over time. Although this process occurs primarily in the liver, it can occur in other organs as well. The THC metabolites are excreted slowly through the feces and urine. Approximately half of the THC is excreted over several days and the remainder by the end of about a week. However, some metabolites of the THC, a number of which may still be active in the system, can be detected in the body at least 30 days following ingestion of a single dose and in the urine for several weeks following chronic use.

DRUGS AND CULTURE BOX 9.4

Secondhand Marijuana?

In Chapter 7 we discussed the issue of secondhand tobacco smoke on health. But, is it possible to get high from secondhand marijuana? In 1998, Canadian snowboarder Ross Rebagliati tested positive for marijuana at the Olympics in Nagano, Japan, and his gold medal was taken away. Rebagliati protested his disqualification from the games and the loss of his medal. He claimed that the THC found in his urine was due to secondhand exposure to marijuana smoke. His medal was returned five days later because marijuana was not explicitly banned in the Olympics. At the time Rebagliati's story grabbed news headlines and sparked interest in the consequences of secondhand marijuana use. Today, there is still considerable debate about whether secondhand smoke can lead to THC levels high enough for detection in a nonuser. While some research (e.g., Morland, et al., 1985; Westin & Slordal, 2009) indicates that this is indeed possible, other research suggests otherwise (e.g.., Hayden, 1991). Of bigger concern are the health consequences associated with secondhand marijuana exposure. According to the Canadian Cancer Society (2009) experts believe that exposure to secondhand marijuana smoke is at least as harmful as secondhand tobacco smoke.

Physiological Effects

Acute Effects

Although cannabis produces physiological effects, most of these actions are different for different users, not only in strength or intensity of the effect but also in duration. In general, as shown in Figure 9.2, the acute physiological effects of marijuana in a healthy individual are not dramatic. In fact, the LeDain Commission (1972) reported the "short-term physiological effects of a typical cannabis dose on normal persons are generally quite benign, and are apparently of little clinical significance," a finding often reported in subsequent research.

The most commonly experienced effects are cardiovascular. Predominant among these is injection of the conjunctiva, or bloodshot eyes. This effect, a result of vasodilation, is most obvious about an hour after smoking, and it is generally dose-related. Although some cite a concomitant dilation of the pupil, research does not support this claim. It appears more likely that the dilation is a consequence of smoking the marijuana in a darkened room. There does, however, tend to be a cannabis-induced sluggish reaction to light.

The second most common cardiovascular effect is an increase in heart rate and pulse rate (Grotenhermen, 2007; Kelly, Foltin, & Fischman, 1993). Both of these effects last for about an hour, and each appears to be dose-related. The peak heart rate occurs around 20 minutes after smoking. In addition to these effects, blood pressure tends to become slightly elevated. No evidence indicates that these effects create any permanent damage within the normal cardiovascular system (Institute of Medicine, 1982; Workshop on the Medical Utility of Marijuana, 1997).

Another general effect following cannabis use is a generalized decrease in motor activity. The only real exception to this is the talkative behaviour of many following smoking. Some users also report drowsiness. Cannabis use also can have a marked effect on sleep stages, tending in part to decrease the total REM sleep achieved. However, this effect typically occurs only with higher doses of cannabis.

Other effects have also been reported, but they tend to be minor or infrequent and often variable from person to person. These other effects include (but are not limited to) dry mouth, thirst, fluctuations in respiration and body temperature, hunger or "the munchies" (peaking two to three hours after smoking), nausea, and headache or dizziness.

Longer-Term Effects

Data on the longer-term effects of marijuana unfortunately are sparse and difficult to interpret. The research that has been conducted has focused on four central systems: respiratory, cardiovascular, immune, and reproductive.

Respiratory System

Little controlled research has been done on the long-term effects of smoking cannabis. Proper lung functioning appears to be altered as a consequence of smoking cannabis, but much of this impairment, such as airway obstruction, is reversed following abstinence from smoking. Marijuana cigarettes contain more tar than tobacco cigarettes. Additionally, cannabis tar contains greater amounts of cancerous agents than does tobacco tar (Jones, 1980). Canadian researchers, David Moir and colleagues (2007) used smoking machines to compare marijuana smoke to tobacco smoke. They found that ammonia levels were 20 times higher in the marijuana smoke than in the tobacco smoke. It also contained three to five times higher levels of hydrogen cyanide, nitric oxide, and certain aromatic amines. Additional Canadian research (Maertens et al., 2009) examined the toxicity of marijuana smoke and tobacco smoke to cells and DNA and found that marijuana smoke caused more cellular and DNA damage compared to tobacco smoke (which caused chromosomal damage). This is particularly noteworthy because marijuana smokers (in an effort to maximize the effects of the drug) inhale deeply and hold the smoke in their lungs. The long-term consequences unfortunately are not known. One difficulty in specifying these effects is that cannabis smokers frequently also smoke cigarettes, and separating the effects of the two substances is difficult. Nevertheless, the possibility of irreversible lung damage due to marijuana smoking remains.

Cardiovascular System

The vast majority of cardiovascular effects associated with cannabis smoking were described earlier in this section as short term (or acute). No evidence shows that smoking marijuana produces deleterious cardiovascular effects among healthy individuals. The acute effects produced (for example, increased heart rate) are, however, potentially dangerous among people who have existing cardiovascular problems, such as abnormal heart functioning or atherosclerosis.

Immune System

Although some of the early research on this topic was contradictory, it appears now that cannabis poses no significant long-term threat to the immune system. Thus, although cannabis can act as an immunosuppressant and decrease resistance to some viruses and bacteria, its clinical significance among otherwise healthy individuals remains questionable. The mechanism through which this immune dysfunction occurs has not yet been defined.

Reproductive System

Studies using animals and humans suggest that cannabis does disrupt the reproductive system in both males and females. For example, chronic marijuana use has been associated with decreases in the number of sperm and sperm motility among men. The potential effects of these disruptions on fertility are difficult to specify. Frequent use of cannabis by women may produce nonovulatory menstrual cycles, in which menstruation is not preceded by the release of an ovum. As in the males, the delayed effects of these disruptions on fertility are not known. In reviews, researchers (Budney, Moore, & Vandrey, 2004; Ehrenkranz & Hembree, 1986; and Zimmer & Morgan, 1997) concluded that disruptions in reproductive function are not obvious, although subtle alterations may be operative.

Of more concern are possible teratogenic effects. The active agents present when marijuana is smoked readily cross the placental barrier and expose a fetus to an array of cannabinoids. Although few data are available for humans, it does not appear that major birth malformations result. This does not mean significant effects cannot occur, however. The use of marijuana by pregnant women is associated with increased risk of premature birth, shorter body length, and lower infant birth weight (e.g., Day & Richardson, 1991; Fried, 1986). A more recent concern is that children born to mothers who used marijuana during pregnancy may be at greater risk of developing certain forms of childhood cancer (Grufferman et al., 1993; Robison et al., 1989). In addition, newborn infants whose mothers used marijuana during pregnancy have been noted to exhibit tremor, startle response, and altered visual responses (Jones, 1980), although the functional impact of these effects has not been determined.

Longer-term consequences also have been reported. Children exposed to marijuana prenatally were found to show deficits on a sustained attention task at age six (Fried, Watkinson, & Gray, 1992), and to be more impulsive, hyperactive, and delinquent at age 10 (Goldschmidt, Day, & Richardson, 2000). The prudent advice is to not use cannabis during pregnancy.

Summary of Longer-Term Effects

It appears the majority of effects associated with marijuana use are more acute than chronic and that longer-term effects tend to be reversible with the termination of drug use. Significant exceptions may occur, however. Smoking marijuana may be found to be linked to various respiratory disorders, including cancer. Most of the negative effects found are correlated with higher doses and frequency of use than those described by most cannabis smokers in this country. Nevertheless, these indications are tentative and await confirmation from more systematic and controlled research. In addition, marijuana use has been linked to the development of schizophrenia (see Drugs and Culture Box 9.5).

DRUGS AND CULTURE BOX 9.5

Cannabis and Psychosis

Recently, there has been great interest in the link between cannabis use and psychosis, such as schizophrenia. At present, Health Canada is funding a national project implemented by the Schizophrenia Society of Canada (SSC) entitled *Cannabis and Psychosis: An Awareness Strategy for Youth*. The goal of this project is to increase awareness and understanding of the relationship between cannabis use and psychosis from the perspective of youth. Schizophrenia affects one in every 100 Canadians. If you use marijuana regularly, your chances of developing schizophrenia may be twice as great as someone who does not smoke marijuana. If you use marijuana before the age of 16, you are four times as likely to become schizophrenic (SSC, 2011). However, while these statistics may give the impression that there is a causal link between cannabis use and schizophrenia, the story is not that simple. As noted by the SSC, the research on this topic supports three possible explanations for the link between cannabis use and psychosis:

1) The Contributing Cause Hypothesis:
   Cannabis-->Psychosis
   (psychosis is a consequence of cannabis use)
2) The Self-Medication Hypothesis:
   Psychosis-->Cannabis
   (cannabis use is a consequence of psychosis)
3) The Vulnerability Hypothesis:
   Cannabis<-->Psychosis
   (cannabis use may be a stressor/trigger for individuals at high-risk/vulnerable for psychosis)

The SSC goes on to note that that there is little evidence to support the idea that cannabis use is a necessary cause for psychosis given that statistics have failed to show that all adults with psychosis related illnesses used cannabis as a young person. Further, cannabis is not a sufficient cause of psychosis either because the majority of adolescent users did not develop psychosis in adulthood. Therefore, the most likely explanation is that cannabis is a component cause, among other possible causes that lead to psychosis.

At present time, cannabis is best viewed as a modifiable risk factor both in individuals who are vulnerable to develop psychosis and in the time of the onset of psychosis. This means that young people who are identified as being at-risk for developing psychosis should avoid cannabis. This is not to say that avoiding cannabis will prevent a psychotic episode from occurring all together (many studies estimate that there would be an eight percent reduction in diagnoses of schizophrenia if cannabis was 100 percent abstained from) but it would certainly help improve prognosis. In addition, avoiding cannabis may delay the onset of psychosis, or even prevent it all together. The SSC recommends further investigation into the link between cannabis and psychosis from etiological and public education perspectives, stating that knowledge about these issues will help us treat those suffering from psychosis.

You can find more information at http://www.cannabisandpsychosis.ca/index.php?id=69.

Psychological Effects

Although cannabis can produce the varied effects previously noted, most marijuana users use the drug to experience its psychological effects, some of which are reported consistently and others more idiosyncratically. The psychological effects that marijuana users generally experience can be divided into three domains: behavioural, cognitive, and emotional.

Some cannabis effects, especially those associated with the "marijuana high" that users describe, are learned. This learning process has been described in detail by Becker (1953, 1963). According to Becker, the first step is mechanical, when the smoker learns to inhale the smoke and hold it in the lungs to maximize intake and absorption. The second step is to learn to perceive the effects of the cannabis, which can be physical as well as psychological. The final step described by Becker is learning to label these effects as pleasant. This learning process accounts for the frequent finding that experienced users are more sensitive to cannabis effects than novice smokers are.

Behavioural Effects

The most common behavioural effect is a generalized decrease in psychomotor activity and decrements in some domains of psychomotor performance. These effects appear to be dose-related, with more pronounced changes associated with greater amounts of marijuana taken in. The general decrease in motor activity appears to be pervasive, and the state is described as associated with feelings of relaxation and tranquility. The only exception to this effect appears to be speech because marijuana use is associated with rapid or slurred speech, circumstantial talk, and loquaciousness. These speech effects often are observed more in the early smoking phase, followed by the more traditional relaxation.

Although relaxation and a sense of well-being are the usual responses to cannabis, some users first experience a stage in which they feel excited and restless. Fairly soon, however, these users virtually always experience a transition to the relaxation stage. Furthermore, despite feeling relaxed, users sometimes also feel their senses are markedly keener. Many users, for example, describe more intense perceptions of touch, vision (especially in perceiving colours), hearing, and smell. The research cited to support these reports is not strong, though. Finally, other research has shown a decreased sensitivity to pain during marijuana intoxication.

Concomitant with the feelings of relaxation and decreased motor activity is a subtle impairment in some areas of psychomotor performance. There appear to be dose-related dysfunctions in motor coordination, signal detection, and the ability to monitor a moving object. The data on reaction time are not conclusive. Taken together, these findings have implications for driving a motor vehicle after using cannabis. Laboratory studies that use a driving simulator have revealed detrimental effects of marijuana on driving skill. Some of these impairments may be cognitively mediated in that drivers under the influence of marijuana showed impaired judgment and concentration along with other general driving skills. Others have suggested that some of the detriments in driving skill may result from decreased vigilance and thus less awareness of peripheral stimuli. Therefore, it appears that cannabis can cause psychomotor impairment and that this impairment becomes more apparent in tasks that require thinking and concentration.

The influence of marijuana on sexual behaviour and functioning is not fully understood, but its effects vary considerably from user to user. Some report that sexual pleasures are more intense and enjoyable when using marijuana, whereas others describe a disinterest in sex. Those who report increased sexual pleasure when smoking probably are responding to the enhanced sensory sensitivity that frequently accompanies marijuana use. The drug itself produces no known specific physiological response that stimulates sexual drive or performance. Long-term or heavy use of marijuana has been associated with temporary impotence among men and temporary decreases in sex drive among women.

Cognitive Effects

Two primary cognitive consequences of cannabis intoxication have been documented. The first is impaired short-term memory and the second is the perception that time passes more slowly.

The impairment in short-term memory seen following cannabis use can occur with intake of a fairly low dose (Deahl, 1991). The degree of impairment increases rapidly with the complexity of the memory task. This effect has been observed with various types of stimuli, such as word lists and conversational materials. More generally, the evidence indicates that cannabis intake impairs multiple aspects of memory, including the encoding, consolidation, and retrieval of information (Grotenhermen, 2007; Ranganathan & D'Souza, 2006).

The mechanisms of marijuana's effects on memory have not been specified, but Paton and Pertwee (1973) have identified several possibilities. The first cause simply may be that the user is not motivated to attend to or to retrieve the material presented. Although this hypothesis is plausible, indications suggest participants in these experiments perceive the tasks administered as a challenge and respond actively to the task demands. A second possibility is that the perceptual changes created by cannabis produce a "curtain of interference" that blocks or hinders intake or retrieval of material. The third hypothesis proposed by Paton and Pertwee (1973) is that marijuana causes a decreased ability to concentrate and attend to the material presented. This mechanism was advocated by Abel (1971) and by DeLong and Levy (1974). These latter researchers have proposed a model of attentional processes as a central key in understanding the cognitive effects of cannabis. Finally, cannabis drug action may interfere with the neurochemical processes that operate in memory and retrieval operations. The exact factor, or set of factors, remains unknown, but it is likely that they operate in concert to affect short-term memory. However, likely mechanisms include cannabis effects on long-term potentiation and long-term depression and the inhibition of neurotransmitter (GABA, glutamate, acetylcholine, dopamine) release.

Altered perception of the passage of time is the second common cognitive effect of cannabis (Chait & Pierri, 1992). This is perhaps best described in statements like "a few minutes seemed to pass like hours." The effect has been noted in both surveys and the experimental literature. However, the time distortion is not as pronounced in the research reports as it is in more subjective self-reports that marijuana users provided.

Other cognitive effects of marijuana have been reported but not as consistently as those already described. One effect is decreased ability to attend and concentrate so that the user is easily distracted. Many users report that cannabis produces racing thoughts and "flight of ideas," in which various (and sometimes seemingly random) ideas "fly" in and out of the mind. Another perception sometimes reported is enhanced creativity. Writers and painters have especially noted this. Finally, some cannabis users describe occasional feelings of "unreality" (see Hollister, Richards, & Gillespie, 1968) and the attachment of increased meaning to events or objects not previously perceived as important. Most of the effects noted are short-term.

The effects of long-term cannabis use on cognitive functioning have received much less attention. Research in this area has been increasing, although providing a mixed picture so far. Solowij (1998), for example, reported that a longer history of use was associated with greater cognitive impairment, even after stopping marijuana use. Messinis et al. (2006) found that frequent marijuana users (smoking four or more joints per week) performed worse than nonusers on several measures of cognitive functioning, including divided attention (paying attention to more than one task at a time) and verbal fluency. Among the marijuana users, those who had used marijuana for 10 or more years had more difficulties with their thinking abilities than those who had used marijuana for five to 10 years. Other recent studies comparing the cognitive functioning of current heavy users, former heavy users, light users, and nonusers have not found such a relationship (Lyketsos et al., 1999; Pope et al., 2001). Pope et al. (2001) found that intellectual impairment associated with heavy marijuana use is apparently reversible with abstinence. More generally, the available research on persistent cognitive effects from long-term marijuana use is, at best, equivocal (Grant et al., 2003; Van Amsterdam, van der Laan, & Slangen, 1996).

Emotional Effects

Positive emotional changes following cannabis intake are cited frequently as key motivators to smoke marijuana. Alterations in mood can occur, but there is uncertainty regarding the extent to which these are direct drug effects. A host of nonpharmacological factors can contribute to the drug effects experienced (Adesso, 1985; Zinberg, 1984). Chief among these nondrug influences are past experiences with cannabis, attitudes about the drug, expectancies regarding the drug-use consequences, and the situational context of drug use. These factors must be considered in conjunction with the dose of THC absorbed to understand the emotional changes attributed to the drug.

The typical emotional response to cannabis is a carefree and relaxed state. This feeling has been described in various ways: euphoric, content, happy, and excited. It frequently includes laughter and loquaciousness and may take on the character of a dreamlike state. Most generally, the response is viewed as pleasant and positive. It appears the intensity of the response is positively correlated with the dose.

It is noteworthy that negative emotional feelings, such as anxiety or dysphoria, are more common than might be expected. Additionally, a variety of somatic consequences have been experienced, including headache, nausea, and muscle tension; less frequently reported are suspiciousness and paranoid ideation. About a third of marijuana users at least occasionally experience some negative effects; however, the effects can be transitory. A user may fluctuate between experiencing these negative feelings and the more positive states described earlier. Also, the negative effects often are reported more by inexperienced cannabis users.

In recent years, there has been an increased focus on the relationship between cannabis use and various mental health outcomes, such as schizophrenia, anxiety disorders, and depression. A review of the literature on this issue concluded that cannabis use increases one's risk for psychotic behaviour outcomes (including schizophrenia), and not just among heavy users (Moore et al., 2007). In this regard, they found that marijuana users had around a 40 percent higher chance of developing a psychotic condition later in life, relative to nonusers (although the risk is fairly low overall). Although the data used to address this issue do not prove that marijuana use increases the risk for psychosis (instead, it could be something else about cannabis users, such as their use of other drugs or particular personality traits), the association is still noteworthy. A comparable relationship between cannabis use and anxiety disorders and depressive disorders was not found in the Moore et al. (2007) study. In another report, however, a modest link between cannabis use and the risk for a later episode of depression was found (van Laar et al., 2007). The mechanisms underlying these relationships are not known, although they do not appear to be related to cannabis-induced changes in brain anatomy (DeLisi, 2008; Linszen & van Amelsvoort, 2007). Instead, the positive relationship may reflect the impact of cannabis on the dopaminergic pathway, perhaps especially among genetically vulnerable individuals (Di Forti et al., 2007).

Social and Environmental Effects

Three hypothesized social and environmental consequences of cannabis use have received attention: the role of marijuana in enhancing interpersonal skills, the effect of cannabis on aggression and violence, and the role of marijuana use in what has been called the **amotivational syndrome**.

amotivational syndrome Loss of effectiveness and reduced capacity to accomplish conventional goals as a result of chronic marijuana use.

Many young users of marijuana have said they use the drug because it enhances their social skills and allows them to be more competent in social situations. Although insufficient data are available to evaluate it fully, this claim has not been supported by the available research. Rather, what seems to occur is that users either are more relaxed in the situation and thus perceive less anxiety or interpret their behaviour differently while under the influence of marijuana. In any event, marijuana does not seem to significantly enhance competence in social situations.

A longstanding claim regarding cannabis use, dating in this country to 1920s, newspaper articles in New Orleans cited previously, is that marijuana causes users to be aggressive and violent. The overwhelming conclusion drawn from data, including surveys, laboratory investigations, and field studies, however, is that cannabis use is not causally related to increased aggression (Institute of Medicine, 1982). When aggression is observed, it probably is more a function of the beliefs and characteristics of the individual drug users (Cherek et al., 1993). In fact, levels of aggression actually decrease following cannabis use.

Perhaps the most controversial social/environmental consequence of cannabis use is the amotivational syndrome. The term was used independently in the late 1960s by McGlothlin and West (1968) and Smith (1968) to describe the clinical observation "that regular marijuana use may contribute to the development of more passive, inward turning, amotivational personality characteristics" (McGlothlin & West, 1968). Based on case reports, the phenomenon was most likely to be seen among younger users who were using marijuana daily or heavily. The list of behaviours proposed as part of the syndrome includes apathy, decreased effectiveness, lost ambition, decreased sense of goals, and difficulty in attending and concentrating.

Although there does not seem to be much question that these characteristics cluster in some marijuana users, the causal influence of cannabis is not clear (Brick, 1990). Also, there is some debate about just how commonly the syndrome occurs, with some citing it as fairly infrequent (Duncan, 1987). In addition, anthropological investigations of heavy cannabis users in other countries generally have not found the presence of the amotivational syndrome (for example, Carter, 1980; Carter & Doughty, 1976; Comitas, 1976; Duncan, 1987; Page, 1983), and laboratory studies on cannabis use in humans have not supported the hypothesized syndrome (Foltin et al., 1989; Foltin et al., 1990). Furthermore, survey studies do not always find the differences between marijuana users and nonusers that would be expected if marijuana caused this clustering of effects. And, the amotivational syndrome has been seen in youths who do

CONTEMPORARY ISSUE BOX 9.6

AMP: Combining Embalming Fluid and Marijuana

There is seemingly no end to the number of ways in which a drug can be used or abused. Sometimes the effects of a drug are much more pronounced when the drug is taken, for example, intravenously versus orally. Sometimes the way a substance is prepared has an effect on how and what effects are experienced. One dramatic example of changing the preparation of a psychoactive substance is the drug known as AMP in the 1980s and now also called "dank." AMP/dank is marijuana soaked in embalming fluid or formaldehyde (the fluid's main ingredient) and dried before being smoked. Ivan Spector, a physician at Baylor College of Medicine in Texas, first described this in the clinical literature in 1985.

According to Spector, who provided case examples of patients seeking treatment after they smoked AMP, these users showed some profound psychiatric effects and impairments. Several of them reported they "immediately felt as if a transparent field has been placed between them and their surroundings." Among the symptoms associated with AMP intoxication are a slowed sense of time, memory impairment, disorientation, paranoid thoughts, anxiety, confusion, disordered thought and difficulties in reality testing, and tremor. Physiological components in the response to AMP intake include elevated blood pressure, hypersalivation, tachycardia, and psychomotor excitement.

It may be instructive to describe one of the cases seen by Spector. A 35-year-old woman, called Ms. D., was presented for treatment three days after smoking AMP. She felt anxious, was tremulous, was salivating excessively and sweating, and had a racing heartbeat. All of this followed closely the actual AMP smoking. Several hours later, she exhibited psychomotor retardation, secluded herself, reported she could not think well, lost all motivation, and described paranoid thoughts. Ms. D. also described hallucinations in which she saw blood on the walls. After three days, many of these complaints disappeared, with the exception of the anxiety and tremulousness. She was treated with an antianxiety medication, and the discomfort cleared within several days.

Ms. D's scenario was similar to those of the other AMP users described in the report, and we can offer two conclusions. One is that any given drug can be prepared in ways that markedly influence its effect on the user. For example, in some areas, the formaldehyde is combined with the drug PCP before soaking the marijuana so as to increase the high. This form of preparation has been referred to as "fry." A second conclusion is that drug users may be in a situation in which the drug they are using is not quite what they thought it was. Some AMP users reported they were given AMP by friends who told them it was only marijuana.

not use marijuana and is often not seen in other daily users of marijuana. Thus, both preexisting personality characteristics and some drug effects together probably account for the clustering labelled the amotivational syndrome, when it occurs.

Medical and Psychotherapeutic Uses

History of Therapeutic Use

Cannabis has a long history of use for medical and health purposes, with the earliest documented use attributed to Shen Nung in the 28th century BCE. As we noted earlier, Shen Nung purportedly recommended that his people use cannabis for its medicinal benefits. The earliest physical evidence of marijuana used as a medicine was uncovered recently by Israeli scientists who found residue of marijuana buried with the body of a young woman who apparently died in childbirth 1600 years ago. They suggested that the marijuana was used to speed the birth process and to ease the associated pain. Indications that cannabis had been used during childbirth had been found earlier in Egyptian papyri and Assyrian tablets (Martin et al., 1993). More systematic uses of cannabis as a therapeutic agent did not occur until the 1800s. For example, the Paris physician Jacques Moreau used cannabis in the mid-1800s to treat mental illnesses. (Recall that Moreau supplied the cannabis used by Gautier at *Le Club des Hachichins.*) Much greater

FIGURE 9.3
First time applications received per month for authorization to possess under the Marihuana Medical Access Regulations (MMAR)

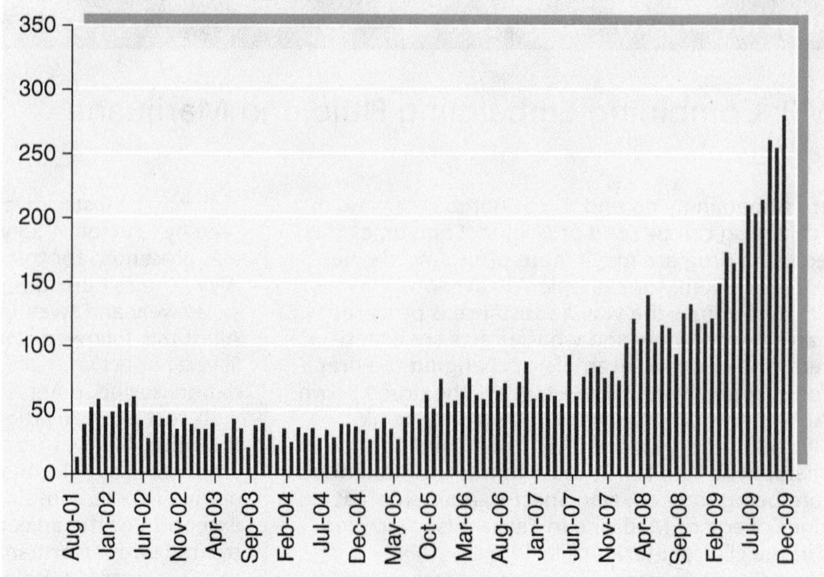

Source: *Marijuana for Medical Purposes*. Health Canada, 2010. Minister of Public Works and Government Services Canada, 2011.

legitimization of the medical use of marijuana was provided by Dr. William O'Shaughnessy, the Irish physician who, in an 1838 treatise, described the use of cannabis to treat such problems as rheumatism, pain, rabies, convulsions, and cholera.

Cannabis also was used widely in North America for many complaints. It was recognized as a therapeutic drug well into the 1900s, for treating neuralgia, gout, rheumatism, rabies, cholera, convulsions, hysteria, mental depression, delirium tremens, and insanity.

Well into the 1930s cannabis was an ingredient in a variety of over-the-counter medicines, such as remedies for stomach pain and discomfort, restlessness, and coughs (Iversen, 2000). One company marketed cannabis cigarettes for the treatment of asthma. These medicinal uses of cannabis rapidly began to decline, however, for two reasons. The first was the advances made in medicine and specific knowledge about various diseases and their treatments. The second factor was the Marijuana Tax Act of 1937. This legislation, along with the Canadian Opium and Narcotics Act, markedly decreased prescribed medicinal uses of marijuana. Since that time there has been great debate and controversy about the merits of marijuana to treat illness and whether to legalize marijuana for medical use.

Canada's role in legalizing medical marijuana has been precedent setting. As stated in Table 9.1, Canada became the first country in the world to legalize the use of marijuana for terminal and chronic illnesses. The request for medical marijuana has increased every year since 2001 (see Figure 9.3 above). In 2010, 4884 Canadians were authorized to have marijuana for medical purposes. Figure 9.4 illustrates the provincial breakdown of medical marijuana users in Canada.

FIGURE 9.4 **Geographical distribution of authorizations to possess under the Marihuana Medical Access Regulations (MMAR)**

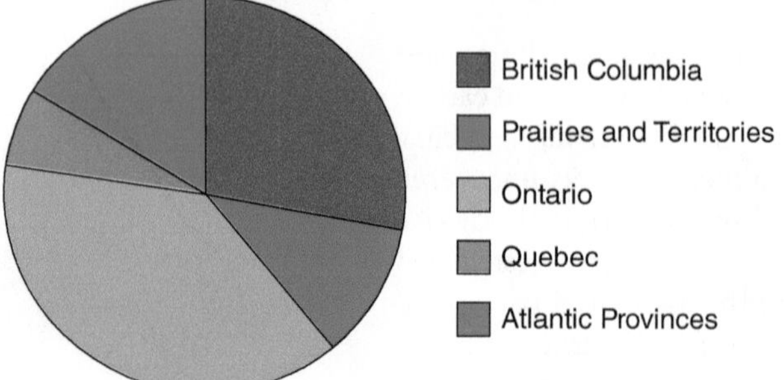

Source: *Marijuana for Medical Purposes*. Health Canada, 2010. Minister of Public Works and Government Services Canada, 2011.

Health Canada, the body that regulates the MMAR, states on their website the following key information about medicinal marijuana use in Canada:

> There are two categories of people who can apply to possess marijuana for medical purposes:
>
> *Category 1:* This category is comprised of any symptoms treated within the context of providing compassionate end-of-life care; or the symptoms associated with the specified medical conditions listed in the schedule to the Regulations, namely:
>
> - Severe pain and/or persistent muscle spasms from multiple sclerosis;
> - Severe pain and/or persistent muscle spasms from a spinal cord injury;
> - Severe pain and/or persistent muscle spasms from spinal cord disease;
> - Severe pain, cachexia, anorexia, weight loss, and/or severe nausea from cancer;
> - Severe pain, cachexia, anorexia, weight loss, and/or severe nausea from HIV/AIDS infection;
> - Severe pain from severe forms of arthritis; or
> - Seizures from epilepsy.
>
> Applicants must provide a declaration from a medical practitioner to support their application.
>
> *Category 2:* This category is for applicants who have debilitating symptom(s) of medical condition(s), other than those described in Category 1. Under Category 2, persons with debilitating symptoms can apply to obtain an *Authorization to Possess* dried marihuana for medical purposes, if a specialist confirms the diagnosis and that conventional treatments have failed or judged inappropriate to relieve symptoms of the medical condition. While an assessment of the applicant's case by a specialist is required, the treating physician, whether or not a specialist, can sign the medical declaration.

The marijuana grown under contract for Health Canada by Prairie Plant Systems (PPS) is grown under very strict, controlled and documented conditions. The product is tested to determine its THC content, its content in 28 metals including heavy metals such as lead, arsenic and mercury and for the presence of mould spores. In addition, the product is irradiated prior to distribution to eliminate any viable mould spores. This is a process that is also used in the Netherlands, the only other country that grows and provides access to marijuana for therapeutic purposes. The PPS product meets or surpasses all of the requirements established by Health Canada for natural health products. Since there have never been specific standards developed for marijuana, natural health products standards are used in both Canada and the Netherlands*.

> Patients have the option of purchasing dried marihuana and/or seeds in order to grow. A packet of 30 seeds will cost $20, plus applicable taxes. The dried marihuana costs patients $5 gram, plus applicable taxes.
>
> Dried marihuana is not covered by provincial health insurance plans because it is not an approved therapeutic drug under the Food and Drug Act. Authorized persons should contact their local health insurance authorities and their private health insurance providers directly for information about coverage.

* Health Canada. *Medical Use of Marijuana*. Found at http://www.hc-sc.gc.ca/dhp-mps/marihuana/index-eng.php. Reproduced with the permission of the Minister of Public Works and Government Services, 2011.

Persons who are authorized to possess and/or produce marihuana for medical purposes can however, claim the costs of their marijuana supply as a medical expense for tax purposes provided they have receipts from the Government of Canada (for Health Canada product) or from their designated producer.

In addition, researchers are exploring the use of synthetic products (such as dronabinol [trade name Marinol] and nabilone [Cesamet]) that chemically resemble the cannabinoids because they provide the active elements of THC in a more stable manner (see Joy, Watson, & Benson, 1999; Sussman et al., 1996). Synthetics also can provide better solubility. Unfortunately, a downside to the synthetics is the absence of the rapid effect experienced when marijuana is smoked. When synthetic THC is taken orally, it is broken down prior to entering the bloodstream and absorption thus is delayed. A recent development with promise is a cannabis oral spray (trade name Sativex), which has been approved in several countries for use as a painkiller for sufferers of multiple sclerosis. Sativex also holds promise for alleviating pain associated with rheumatoid arthritis and may even suppress the disease. Sativex has also shown some promise in animal research for improving memory loss in Alzheimer's disease. Figure 9.5 shows some of the potential therapeutic uses of marijuana.

The discovery of the cannabinoid receptor by Devane and his colleagues (described earlier) has important implications for future medical and psychotherapeutic uses of cannabis. The identification of the cannabinoid receptor also has advanced knowledge about the neurobiology of cannabis abuse. Perhaps more importantly in the context of therapeutics, it has opened wide investigation of compounds related to the endogenous cannabinoid system for potential applications with multiple disorders (de Fonseca & Schneider, 2008). For example, a medication based on the cannabinoid CB1 receptor, the antagonist rimonabant, is being used in the treatment of complicated obesity. Other medications based on the endogenous cannabinoid system are now in development or under evaluation.

FIGURE 9.5
Therapeutic uses of marijuana

Source: Zubada/Shutterstock

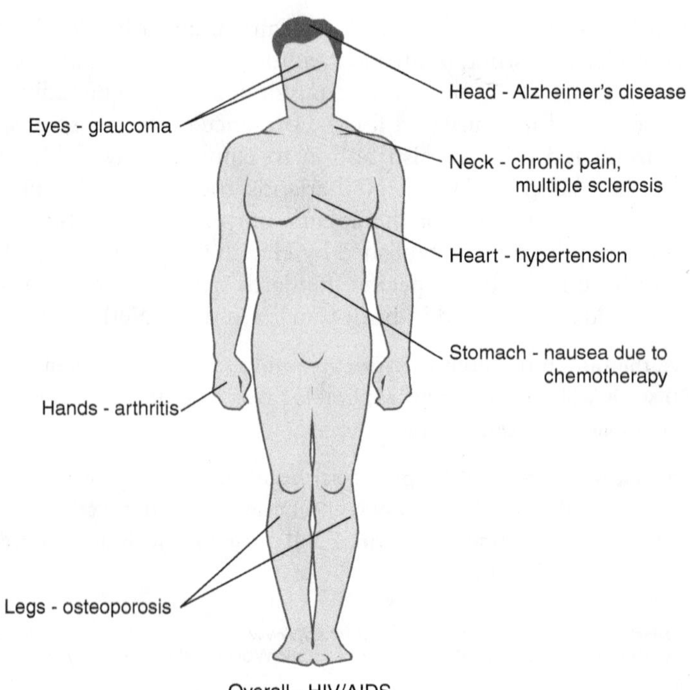

Nausea and Vomiting

Cannabis and THC synthetics have been used to counter the nausea and vomiting frequently associated with chemotherapies (and some radiation treatments) for cancer. These side effects, which can last for several hours or even several days, often are not ameliorated by traditional antiemetic medications (although significant advances are being made in the development of more powerful antisickness drugs). Researchers in the 1970s began more systematic study of the antinausea and antivomiting effects of THC (usually administered orally), and their results were favourable. This research, incidentally, followed anecdotal reports by chemotherapy patients that their private use of marijuana had reduced the aversive side effects of their treatments.

Positive outcomes have emerged in subsequent research. Furthermore, there are indications that children undergoing cancer chemotherapy may particularly benefit from orally administered high doses of cannabinoids (see Abrahamov, Abrahamov, & Mechoulam, 1995; Martin et al., 1993). More recent studies have included the use of THC synthetics. The main drawback to the use of cannabis and THC synthetics is the resultant mental effects, which some patients have viewed as uncomfortable and disorienting. Nevertheless, many patients undergoing chemotherapy find the THC side effects an acceptable price to pay for reduced side effects. Only limited research is being conducted, despite the classification of synthetic THC as a Schedule III drug, which means some medical value is recognized. The synthetic had once been classified as a Schedule I drug, meaning it was a prohibited substance with no recognized medical benefit. Marijuana not in synthetic form remains a Schedule I drug. Meanwhile, advances have been occurring with newer antiemetic drugs, not cannabis-based, that have been well tolerated and effective.

Cachexia

Cachexia is a disorder in which an individual physiologically "wastes away," often due to HIV infection or cancer. Based partly on anecdotal reports that marijuana use is associated with increased frequency and amount of eating, it has been proposed that patients with cachexia use marijuana to stimulate appetite and thus weight gain. These anecdotal reports have some empirical support. Plasse et al. (1991) found a relationship between marijuana ingestion and appetite. Accordingly, some individuals who have disorders that include cachexia have been turning to marijuana to stem the tide of weight loss and to gain weight. Abrams et al. (2003), for example, found that smoked marijuana or oral THC each effectively induced weight gain among HIV-infected adults. A caution on the use of smoked marijuana is that patients with HIV, for example, might be uniquely vulnerable to any immunosuppressive effects of the drug (Joy et al., 1999). More study in this area appears justified (Robson, 2001).

Glaucoma

Glaucoma is a generic term used to denote ocular diseases that involve increases in intraocular pressure. This pressure damages the optic nerve and represents the leading cause of preventable blindness in the world; 400 000 Canadians are affected by glaucoma; 67 million people are affected worldwide. Although drug and surgical interventions are available, their effectiveness is variable.

Cannabis has been shown to decrease intraocular pressure (Joy et al., 1999), although patients have experienced side effects regardless of whether the cannabis was administered orally, through injection, or by smoking (Hepler & Petrus, 1976; Merritt et al., 1980). These side effects include increased heart rate and psychological effects. Some effects dissipate with extended exposure to the cannabis. Of more concern, marijuana may also reduce blood flow to the optic nerve and possibly exacerbate the loss of vision.

The mechanisms through which the cannabis reduces intraocular pressure have not been determined. Cohen and Andrysiak (1982) suggested that cannabis dilates the vessels that drain excess fluids from the eyeball. This draining is thought to prevent fluid buildup and the resultant pressure that causes optic nerve damage.

Clinical research on the potential benefits of cannabis as a treatment for glaucoma is continuing, with two emphases. The first is on developing synthetic formulas that reduce side effects, and the second emphasis is on modes of application. Particular attention is given to developing a topical preparation that could be applied directly onto the eye. Meanwhile, most experts believe that existing non-THC medications have equal or greater benefit in the treatment of glaucoma (Amar, 2006; Joy et al., 1999).

Other Uses

Dr. Mark Ware, assistant professor at McGill University in Montreal, examined the effectiveness of marijuana in treating chronic pain. In his study (Ware, 2010), 21 men and women who had chronic nerve pain (neuropathic pain) were monitored for two months while they received different doses of cannabis: a placebo (zero percent THC), 2.5 percent THC, six percent THC, and 9.4 percent THC. He found that the highest dosage decreased participants' pain compared to the placebo. Additional research is examining the use of Ajulemic acid, a synthetic analog of THC, as a pain-reliever that does not produce feelings of being "high" (Burstein et al., 2004; Karst et al., 2003).

Cannabis and THC synthetics have also been used to a lesser extent or in exploratory fashion in the treatment of several other disorders, such as muscle spasticity, convulsant activity, epilepsy, chronic pain, insomnia, hypertension, asthma, anxiety, Tourette's syndrome, and depression. However, the data in support of these uses so far have been preliminary or mixed, and more research is needed to specify the potential utility of cannabis in these areas.

SUMMARY

- The plant *Cannabis sativa* is more commonly known as marijuana. It once was harvested primarily for its fibre but now is most often grown for its psychoactive effects.
- Marijuana is the leafy top portion of the plant, and hashish is made from the resin the plant produces for protection from the sun.
- The use of cannabis for its intoxicating effects appears to have been centred in Asia, the Middle East, and North Africa for an extended period of time before Europe was exposed to these effects in the 19th century.
- Cannabis in the New World dates to 1543, when the Spaniards brought it to Chile. The cannabis plant was raised in the American colonies for its fibre.
- Marijuana is the most frequently used illicit drug in Canada. The most common and efficient procedure for ingesting cannabis is smoking.
- The principal psychoactive agent in cannabis, isolated in 1964, is delta-9-tetrahydrocannabinol, more commonly known as D-9-THC or simply THC.
- The onset of THC action occurs within minutes of inhalation, and peak concentrations occur 30 to 60 minutes later. The effects usually are experienced for two to four hours. Most of the THC metabolites are excreted slowly, approximately half within several days and the remainder by the end of about a week. Some metabolites can be detected in the body for up to and beyond 30 days.
- The main actions of marijuana occur in the brain and result from the drug's effect on neurotransmitters. Although specification of the drug action remains speculative, recent advances include work on THC receptors in the brain.
- Tolerance, when it occurs, is most likely when high doses of cannabis are used over extended periods of time. Dependence on cannabis has

been documented, although there is debate as to whether this dependence is more psychological than physical.

- Cannabis has long been used for medicinal and psychotherapeutic purposes. Today, it is used mostly to reduce nausea and vomiting associated with cancer chemotherapies and as an appetite stimulant among patients with cachexia.
- The acute effects of marijuana generally are benign. They include bloodshot eyes, increased heart rate and pulse rate, and decreased motor activity.
- Research on the long-term effects of marijuana is sparse. Some effects associated with long-term marijuana use appear to be reversible with termination of its use. There may be significant exceptions, such as the possible association between marijuana and lung cancer.
- Psychological effects of cannabis include decreased psychomotor activity, happy feelings and relaxation, impaired short-term memory, and altered time perception.
- Marijuana has not been shown to enhance social skills or to induce aggression or violence. The data on cannabis causing an amotivational syndrome are mixed. Both preexisting personality characteristics and drug effects probably account for what has been labelled the amotivational syndrome.

Key Terms

amotivational syndrome p. 214
apothecary p. 196
cannabinoids p. 202
delta-9-tetrahydrocannabinol p. 202
hash oil p. 203
joint p. 202
tea-pads p. 197

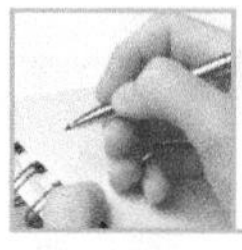

Essays/Thought Questions

1. Should marijuana be legalized, or at least markedly decriminalized? Would the use of marijuana increase? What would be the advantages and disadvantages to society as a whole?
2. What do you think might be the critical determinants of a person's decision to use marijuana?
3. Would you use marijuana for medical purposes? What factors would you consider when making this decision?

Suggested Readings

Becker, H.S. (1953). Becoming a marihuana user. *American Journal of Sociology, 59*, 235–242.

Booth, M. (2003). *Cannabis: A history*. New York: St. Martin's Press.

Earleywine, M. (2002). *Understanding marijuana: A new look at the scientific evidence*. New York: Oxford University Press.

Hall, W., & Pacula, R.L. (2003). *Cannabis use and dependence*. Cambridge: Cambridge University Press.

Iversen, L.L. (2000). *The science of marijuana*. New York: Oxford University Press.

Joy, J.E., Watson, S.J., & Benson, J.A. (1999). *Marijuana and medicine: Assessing the science base*. Washington, DC: National Academy Press.

Ludlow, F.H. (1857/1979). *The hasheesh eater, being: Being passages from the life of a Pythagorean*. San Francisco: City Lights Books.

CHAPTER 10

Hallucinogens

Did You Know

?

- Hallucinogens profoundly affect mood, thinking, and physiological processes.
- There are four subgroups of hallucinogens.
- LSD was discovered by accident.
- Canadians were pioneers in LSD research.
- Peyote is legal in Canada, but mescaline is not.
- LSD and Ecstasy were once used in psychotherapy.
- PCP and Ketamine are used as anesthesia for animals.
- Seven percent of Canadian youth have used salvia.

Among the most fascinating, but also confusing, classes of drugs is the group called hallucinogens. These drugs are fascinating because they can alter consciousness in profound and bizarre ways. They are at the same time confusing because so many different drugs act in a variety of ways as hallucinogens and because these drugs have been named and classified in many different ways over the years. Called "phantastica" by Lewin (1964), hallucinogens have gone through dozens of name changes. Some researchers have used the term *psychotomimetics* because of the belief that these drugs mimic the symptoms of functional psychoses such as schizophrenia. This usage is rare today; it is now clear that although intriguing similarities exist the effects of hallucinogens differ in many respects (to be considered later) from natural psychosis. During the 1960s, advocates of hallucinogen use referred to them as *psychedelics*, a term coined by one of the pioneers of LSD research, Humphrey Osmond. Osmond, who worked in Canada, defined psychedelic as "mind-expanding or mind-revealing" (Stevens, 1987), but whether LSD or other hallucinogens actually possess such properties is controversial at best, and we avoid the term for that reason.

We are left with the term *hallucinogen*, but even this term is misleading. It does focus attention on hallucinations and other alterations in perception, and indeed most of the drugs in this category generally do produce sensory disturbances or alterations that can be considered hallucinogenic. However, that is certainly not the only effect these drugs produce. Hallucinogens exert profound effects on mood, thinking processes, and physiological processes as well. Hallucinogens alter nearly all aspects of psychological functioning, and the phrase "altered state of consciousness" describes these drugs better than any we have considered.

Hallucinogens alter nearly all aspects of psychological functioning, and the phrase "altered state of consciousness" describes these drugs better than any we have considered.

An additional complexity is that more than 90 different species of plants and many more synthetic agents can produce these kinds of effects (Siegel, 1984). To simplify this complex group of drugs, we divide them on the basis of their effects and mechanisms of action into four different subgroups to be treated separately. Table 10.1 summarizes the subgroups of hallucinogens.

TABLE 10.1 Subgroups of Hallucinogens

Subgroup	Example	Neorotransmitter(s) Affected	Physiological Effects
Serotonergic Hallucinogen	LSD, Mescaline, Psilocybin	Serotonin	Produce vivid visual hallucinations and additional effects on consciousness
Methylated Amphetamines	MDA, MDMA (ecstasy)	Dopamine Norepinephrine Serotonin	Produce altered mood and consciousness; little or no sensory change
Anticholinergic Hallucinogens	Atropine, Scopolamine	Acetylcholine	Produce dreamlike trance with little or no memory of the experience
Dissociative Anesthetics	PCP (angel dust), Ketamine	Glutamate	Produce surgical anesthesia; individual remains semiconscious

serotonergic hallucinogens
A class of drugs that includes LSD and drugs with similar effects and mechanisms of actions.

mescaline
An LSD-like hallucinogen found in the peyote cactus.

psilocybin
An LSD-like hallucinogen found in mushrooms.

The first and historically most important group is referred to as the **serotonergic hallucinogens**. This category includes the synthetic compound lysergic acid diethylamide (LSD) and related drugs, such as **mescaline** (from the peyote cactus) and **psilocybin** (from certain mushrooms), along with many other less well-known compounds. These drugs all produce vivid visual hallucinations and a variety of other effects on consciousness. Numerous experiments suggest that, despite differing chemical structures, these drugs also have in common the action of influencing serotonergic transmission in the brain (Meyer & Quenzer, 2005).

The second class of hallucinogens includes MDA and MDMA (Ecstasy), referred to as the **methylated amphetamines**. As the name suggests, these drugs are structurally related to amphetamine (as is mescaline). MDA and MDMA produce alterations in mood and consciousness with little or no sensory change. Like amphetamine and cocaine, these drugs act on dopamine, norepinephrine, and serotonin synapses, but their effects are most potent on the serotonergic system (Iversen, 2008).

methylated amphetamines
A class of drugs including MDA and MDMA (Ecstasy).

anticholinergic hallucinogens
A class of drugs including atropine and scopolamine.

dissociative anesthetic
A class of drugs including PCP and ketamine.

A third class of hallucinogens, called the **anticholinergic hallucinogens**, is less familiar to most people and includes drugs such as atropine and scopolamine found in plants such as mandrake, henbane, belladonna, and jimsonweed. These drugs produce a dreamlike trance in users from which they awaken with little or no memory of the experience. The drugs in this class act on cholinergic synapses of the brain (Meyer & Quenzer, 2005).

A fourth class of hallucinogens includes phencyclidine (PCP or angel dust) and the related compound ketamine. These are often referred to as the **dissociative anesthetics** because of their ability to produce surgical anesthesia while an individual remains at least semiconscious. Dissociative anesthetics are thought to act through a receptor that influences activity of the excitatory amino acid neurotransmitter, glutamate (Balazs, Bridges, & Cotman, 2006).

Finally, one of the most widely used hallucinogens in recent years is salvinorin A, a chemical found in a plant in the sage family (*Salvia divinorum*) and often referred to as diviner's sage or just salvia. Almost completely unknown a decade ago, salvia is not currently a federal controlled substance; however, Health Canada has recently recommended that it be banned (Canada Gazette, 2011), and the Canadian Federal Government has proposed that salvinorin A be added to Schedule III of the *Controlled Drugs and Substances Act. This would essentially make salvia an illegal substance (Health Canada, 2011).* Although relatively little is known about salvinorin A, it appears to act differently on the brain from any of the previously known hallucinogens by affecting specialized opiate receptors known as kappa receptors. As a result, we classify it as a kappa hallucinogen.

Serotonergic Hallucinogens: LSD and Related Compounds

Early History

Tables 10.1 and 10.2 lists some of the major drugs that are thought to obtain their hallucinogenic properties by altering serotonin function in the brain. LSD is the prototype hallucinogen of this class, but drugs with effects similar to those of LSD were used long before LSD was synthesized. As you can see in Table 10.2, LSD-like

TABLE 10.2 Serotonergic Hallucinogens

Drug	Botanical Source	Area Found	Other Names
Lysergic acid diethylamide (LSD)	Synthetic, but derived from the ergot fungus	Ergot native to Europe	Acid, many others
Ibogaine	Iboga plant: *Tabernanthe iboga*	Africa	—
Psilocybin	Mushrooms of genus *Psilocybe, Conocybe, Panaeolus,* and *Stropharia*	Throughout the world	Teonanacatl
Dimethyltryptamine (DMT)	Virola tree: *Virola calophylla* and other species	South America	Yakee, yopo
Mescaline	Peyote cactus: *Lophophora williamsii*	Mexico and Southwest U.S.	Peyote
Harmaline, Harmine	Ayahuasca vine: *Banisteriopsis caapi, Banisteriopsis inebrians*	South America	Yagé
Lysergic acid amide	Morning glory seeds: *Rivea corymbosa, Ipomoea violacea*	Throughout the world	Ololuiqui

hallucinogens are found in a wide variety of plants. The hallucinogenic properties of these plants were primarily discovered and used by the Indian peoples of Central and South America (an exception is ibogaine, which was discovered and used by tribal peoples of Africa). Historians and anthropologists have reconstructed the uses to which these hallucinogenic plants were put and these are worth some consideration here.

When the Spanish ***conquistadores*** began to explore and colonize Mexico and other parts of Central and South America, they encountered new civilizations with customs and religious practices unfamiliar to Europeans. Among these practices was the use of hallucinogenic plants in religious ceremonies. One of the earliest documentations was by Fernando Hernandez, the royal physician to the king of Spain (Stewart, 1987). In 1577, he studied the plants the Aztecs used and noted the use of peyote cactus (referred to as peyotl), psilocybe mushrooms (called teonanacatl), and morning glory seeds (called ololuiqui). Although each of these plants contains a different drug, all produce vivid visual hallucinations, and the Indians took the visions as oracles that could reveal the future and solve other mysteries, help in decision making, and aid the medicine man or shaman in healing the sick (see the Drugs and Culture Box 10.1).

Although mescaline is a Schedule II drug under the Canadian Controlled Drugs and Substances Act, peyote is specifically exempt.

The Aztec and Mayan peoples called the psilocybe mushrooms ***teonanacatl***, which means "flesh of the gods," and as one might guess from that name, the mushrooms were viewed as sacred. Mushroom icons found in Mayan ruins dating back to before 1000 BCE suggest that the use of the sacred mushroom was an ancient practice (Schultes, 1976).

DRUGS AND CULTURE BOX 10.1

Peyote

Peyote may have been the most widespread hallucinogenic drug in the New World, which is surprising given that the range of the peyote cactus is limited to a relatively small area of northern Mexico and southwestern Texas. The Aztecs used peyote in their rituals, and de Sahagun noted, "Those who eat or drink it see visions either frightful or laughable..." (Stewart, 1987, p. 19). Peyote, like ololiuqui and sacred mushrooms, was forbidden to the Indians by the Spaniards, who regarded its use for religious purposes as blasphemous. Thus, the use of all these agents persisted only "underground," and little is known of them before the 20th century. The peyote religion, Peyotism, spread widely during the 18th and 19th centuries, however, to unite most Indian tribes in western Mexico and the United States. It was not until the early 20th century that Peyotism came to Canada. Its popularity peaked in the 1940s and steadily decreased afterwards (Shields, 2007).

The southwestern tribes gathered peyote by cutting the cactus at the soil line, leaving the root intact. The cactus was sliced and dried into hard "buttons." These buttons could be transported great distances without losing their potency, and indeed they found their way to Native American tribes living throughout the West and as far north as Minnesota and Wisconsin. The ritual itself is almost identical regardless of the tribe studied. The all-night ceremony takes place in a large tepee where the participants sit in a circle around a fire, eating peyote buttons and drinking peyote tea. They smoke tobacco in cigarettes or a pipe. The night is spent chanting, singing, praying, and later on discussing and interpreting the peyote-induced visions. These ceremonies are still conducted today by some Native American people, much as they were many centuries ago (Stewart, 1987).

In Canada, Native Americans can legally take peyote. Although mescaline is a Schedule II drug under the Canadian Controlled Drugs and Substances Act, peyote is specifically exempt.

Wildlife/Peter Arnold Inc.

Mescaline comes from the peyote cactus, *Lophophora williamsii*.

In South America, a number of different hallucinogenic plants traditionally have been used in much the same way as peyote and psilocybin were used farther north. Two hallucinogens, harmine and harmaline, are found in the bark of the vines *Banisteriopsis caapi* and *B. inebrians*. These plants are known as *ayahuasca* and *caapi* by indigenous people of the western Amazon area of Brazil, Colombia, Peru,

Psilocybin comes from mushrooms such as this *Psilocybe cubensis.*

Ecuador, and Bolivia. Local names for the drink made from the bark of these vines are *yagé*, *pinde*, and *dapa*. These plants are used in healing ceremonies, initiation rites, and other rituals. It is said that the plants provide users with telepathic powers, but this claim has no scientific support (Schultes, 1976), and in fact, the effects are similar to those of the other serotonergic hallucinogens. Another group of South American plants used for their hallucinogenic properties includes the various species of the Virola tree (*Virola calophylla*, *V. calophylloidea*, and *V. theiodora*) of Brazil, Colombia, and Venezuela. The bark of these trees is taken as a snuff called yopo that contains the hallucinogen dimethyltryptamine (DMT), and DMT is also one of the active compounds in yagé preparations. The effects of DMT are consistent with those noted previously except that DMT has a shorter duration of action (Riba et al., 2001). Virola snuff is taken by some Amazon tribes in a funeral ritual in which the powdered bones of the deceased are consumed along with the snuff (Schultes, 1976).

Recent History

Despite the long history of hallucinogenic drug use, these drugs had virtually no impact on mainstream European or North American culture until the 1960s, when hallucinogen use exploded. The history of the "psychedelic movement" began in Basel, Switzerland, where Albert Hofmann, a chemist working in Sandoz Laboratories, discovered LSD in 1938. The story of this discovery is presented in Contemporary Issue Box 10.2.

In 1938, Albert Hofmann discovered LSD—by accident.

The discovery of LSD eventually led to an explosion in interest and research on this new drug. Much of this early research was conducted in Canada at the University of Saskatchewan. One especially noteworthy team, known as the "Saskatchewan group," have been hailed as pioneers in the field of LSD research. They included Abram

CONTEMPORARY ISSUE BOX 10.2

The Discovery of LSD

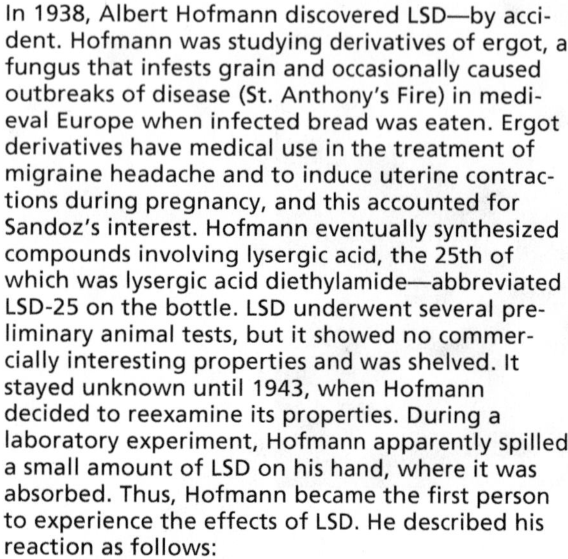

In 1938, Albert Hofmann discovered LSD—by accident. Hofmann was studying derivatives of ergot, a fungus that infests grain and occasionally caused outbreaks of disease (St. Anthony's Fire) in medieval Europe when infected bread was eaten. Ergot derivatives have medical use in the treatment of migraine headache and to induce uterine contractions during pregnancy, and this accounted for Sandoz's interest. Hofmann eventually synthesized compounds involving lysergic acid, the 25th of which was lysergic acid diethylamide—abbreviated LSD-25 on the bottle. LSD underwent several preliminary animal tests, but it showed no commercially interesting properties and was shelved. It stayed unknown until 1943, when Hofmann decided to reexamine its properties. During a laboratory experiment, Hofmann apparently spilled a small amount of LSD on his hand, where it was absorbed. Thus, Hofmann became the first person to experience the effects of LSD. He described his reaction as follows:

> I was forced to interrupt my work in the laboratory in the middle of the afternoon and proceed home, being affected by a remarkable restlessness, combined with a slight dizziness. At home I lay down and sank into a not unpleasant intoxicated-like condition, characterized by an extremely stimulated imagination. In a dreamlike state, with eyes closed... I perceived an uninterrupted stream of fantastic pictures, extraordinary shapes with intense, kaleidoscopic play of colors. (Hofmann, 1980, p. 15)

Hofmann decided the bizarre experience must have been due to contact with LSD, so he decided to test that hypothesis with an experiment. He reasoned that LSD must be very potent to have produced such effects through an accidental exposure, and he measured out for oral administration 250 micrograms—a minute amount by the standards of drugs known at that time. What Hofmann could not have known is that LSD is *so* potent that this dose was at least twice as potent as the normal effective dose (25–125 micrograms).

After taking the drug, Hofmann (1980) noted in his journal: "Beginning dizziness, feeling of anxiety, visual distortions, symptoms of paralysis, desire to laugh" (p. 16). At this point, Hofmann was overcome by the drug and could no longer write. He asked his assistant to escort him home, and he later wrote about his LSD trip:

> On the way home, my condition began to assume threatening forms. Everything in my field of vision wavered and was distorted as if seen in a curved mirror.... Finally we arrived at home safe and sound, and I was just barely capable of asking my companion to summon our family doctor and request milk from the neighbors... as a nonspecific antidote for poisoning.
>
> My surroundings had now transformed themselves in more terrifying ways. Everything in the room spun around, and assumed grotesque, threatening forms. They were in continuous motion, animated, as if driven by an inner restlessness. The lady next door, whom I scarcely recognized, brought me milk.... She was no longer Mrs. R., but rather a malevolent, insidious witch with a colored mask.... (pp. 16–17)

Later, as the intensity of the drug effects began to subside, Hofmann reported enjoying the hallucinations and altered thought processes. After he recovered and made his report to Sandoz, many other experiments followed.

Hoffer, Humphrey Osmond, and Duncan Blewett. The timeline in Table 10.3 outlines some of the key contributions made by these Canadian researchers in the 1950s and 1960s.

By the early 1960s, many people had tried LSD, and it was beginning to generate some publicity. One user was movie star Cary Grant, who said in an interview that his LSD psychotherapy changed his whole life and brought him true peace of mind. Another famous user, Henry Luce, head of Time Inc., said he talked to God under LSD's influence. The British author Aldous Huxley, who earlier had tried peyote and written a book about his experiences (*The Doors of Perception*, 1954), promoted LSD and other hallucinogenic drugs as leading to

TABLE 10.3 Timeline of Key Events in LSD Research in Canada

1950	• Humphrey Osmond begins using mescaline in his treatment of schizophrenic patients in London, England.
1951	• Osmond comes to Canada and becomes the Superintendent at Saskatchewan Hospital in Weyburn. • He suggests that our bodies may be capable of producing hallucinogenic compounds, which in turn, may lead to the symptoms of schizophrenia. • Osmond comes across the research of Abram Hoffer.
1956	• Osmond coins the term "psychedelic."
1960s	• LSD's effects on the mind begin to spread, leading to an increased interest in the drugs among, not only scientists, but other intellectuals as well as artists. Many travel to Saskatchewan to experience these effects firsthand. • Timothy Leary takes LSD for the first time after being influenced by the work of the Saskatchewan group.
Late 1960s	• In 1966, the television program *W-5* broadcasts actress Pamela Hyatt undergoing therapy with LSD. The next year a young man commits suicide while on LSD. • Opposition Leader John Diefenbaker asks the Canadian government to ban the use of LSD; the Canadian government bans LSD in 1967. • All research by the Saskatchewan group stops.

Source: Minds Eye Entertainment.

the next step in human evolution! But the most influential of the early LSD users were Harvard psychologist Timothy Leary and writer Ken Kesey (see Contemporary Issue Box 10.3).

The use of LSD did not vanish, but it did decline throughout the 1980s. Then LSD use, along with other hallucinogens, increased once again in the 1990s. For example, a U.S. national survey of high school seniors showed increases in reported LSD use through the early part of that decade, reaching a peak in 1996, when 8.8 percent reported having used LSD during the past year. LSD use has declined substantially since then with only 2.7 percent of America's high school seniors reporting use of LSD during 2008 (Johnston et al., 2009a). Current statistics from the CADUMS (Health Canada, 2009) indicate 0.9 percent of Canadians used hallucinogens, including salvia. This was a statistically significantly decrease from 2008, when 2.1 percent of Canadians reported using hallucinogens.

In Canada, it is illegal to produce, distribute, or possess hallucinogens. However, hallucinogens, including LSD, have become associated with the "club" scene and "raves" are often occasions for hallucinogen drug use. In 2009, 4.4 percent of youth had used hallucinogens (Health Canada, 2009). Although MDMA or Ecstasy is generally considered the prototypical "club drug," LSD is used as well. For example, in one study of clients in treatment for substance abuse (Hopfer et al., 2006), LSD use was reported by nearly half (48.6 percent) of those under 18 years old, as compared to 32.3 percent reporting MDMA use. Among older clients (18–32 years), the pattern

In 2009, 4.4 percent of youth had used hallucinogens.

CONTEMPORARY ISSUE BOX 10.3

Learning from the Past: The Early "Celebrity" of LSD

Timothy Leary and his Harvard associate Richard Alpert (who later became known as religious writer Baba Ram Das) had taken LSD and other hallucinogens and become convinced of their psychological and spiritual value. What began as legitimate experiments, including work on the possible beneficial effects of hallucinogens on prison inmates, began to look suspiciously like LSD parties involving Harvard faculty, students, and an assortment of celebrities and intellectuals. At some point, Leary had stepped out of his role as a scientist and had become the leader of a social and religious movement. Calling himself "High Priest," Leary claimed LSD was a ticket for a trip to spiritual enlightenment. He exhorted an entire generation to "Turn on. Tune in. Drop out" (Stevens, 1987). Leary left Harvard under duress in 1963, but continued to proselytize for LSD and in fact became a media celebrity. Harassment by law enforcement officials continued to increase Leary's eminence, and he became viewed as something of a martyr, winning new converts as a curious nation heard more and more about the wonders of LSD.

On the West Coast, LSD was popularized by Ken Kesey, author of *One Flew over the Cuckoo's Nest*, and his "merry pranksters." As recounted by Wolfe (1969), Kesey's "acid tests" were large parties where hundreds of people were "turned on to LSD" in a single night. LSD began to make an impact on the emerging hippie subculture, particularly through the music of groups like the Grateful Dead, Jefferson Airplane, Jimi Hendrix, and others whose music became known as "acid rock." Eventually, The Beatles became part of the movement, and the surreal images of songs such as "Lucy in the Sky with Diamonds" had the entire Western world talking about, if not using, LSD.

By the late 1960s, LSD had become the most controversial drug in the world. As many as two million people in the United States had tried LSD, but the positive statements about LSD were counterbalanced by increasing negative publicity. LSD was claimed to cause chromosome damage, and users were said to be likely to have mutant children. It was said to cause insanity, suicide, acts of violence, and homicidal behaviour (Stevens, 1987). All of this controversy led to a decline in LSD use in the 1970s and 1980s, but perhaps equally important was a loss of faith in the LSD mystique and the recognition that spiritual enlightenment produced by LSD was a false hope. As Hunter S. Thompson (1971) put it in his chronicle of the era:

> This was the fatal flaw in Tim Leary's trip. He crashed around America selling consciousness expansion without ever giving a thought to the grim meat-hook realities that were lying in wait for all the people who took him too seriously.... Not that they didn't deserve it: No doubt they all Got What Was Coming To Them. All those pathetically eager acid freaks thought they could buy Peace and Understanding for three bucks a hit. But their loss and failure is ours, too. What Leary took down with him was the central illusion of a whole life-style that he helped to create... a generation of permanent cripples, failed seekers, who never understood the essential old-mystic fallacy of the Acid Culture: the desperate assumption that somebody—or at least some force—is tending that Light at the end of the tunnel. (pp. 178–179)

was similar, with 42.9 percent reporting LSD use compared with 37.0 percent using MDMA (ibid.). LSD remains a significant issue in North America today.

Serotonergic Hallucinogens

The mechanisms by which hallucinogens such as LSD produce visual hallucinations and alterations of consciousness seem to be related to the neurotransmitter serotonin. The first bit of evidence was suggested by the chemical structures of some of the major hallucinogens. LSD, psilocybin, and many of the other drugs listed in Tables 10.1 and 10.2 have similar chemical structures that resemble that of the naturally occurring transmitter serotonin (see Figure 10.1). The structural similarity led to the notion that LSD and related compounds might act by mimicking serotonin and thus activate serotonin receptors in the brain. This hypothesis has now received considerable support. For example, it has been shown that LSD and the related hallucinogens bind to

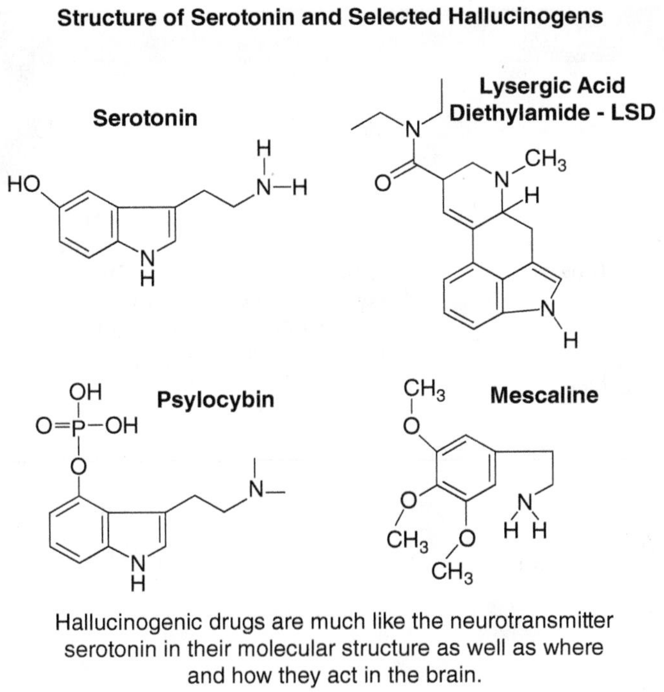

Structure of Serotonin and Selected Hallucinogens

Hallucinogenic drugs are much like the neurotransmitter serotonin in their molecular structure as well as where and how they act in the brain.

FIGURE 10.1
The chemical structure of some common hallucinogens is similar to serotonin

certain subtypes of serotonin receptors (5-HT2A receptors) and that this effect correlates strongly with the potency of the drug as a hallucinogen (Iversen et al., 2009; Nichols, 2004).

One problem with this analysis that has puzzled researchers is the structure of mescaline. As shown in Figure 10.1, mescaline's chemical structure is different from the others; in fact, mescaline is far more similar to amphetamine than to LSD. For this reason, it has often been classified as having a different mechanism from LSD. Unlike amphetamine (and the methylated amphetamines like MDA, discussed later), however, mescaline produces vivid visual hallucinations virtually identical in form to those of LSD. Further evidence for a common mechanism of action between LSD and mescaline comes from studies on tolerance. Tolerance to all the effects of LSD develops fairly rapidly, and the same is true for mescaline. In addition, there is cross-tolerance between LSD, mescaline, and other drugs of this class (Abraham, Aldridge, & Gogia, 1996), suggesting a common mechanism of action. Finally, mescaline, like LSD, is an agonist at the specialized group of serotonin receptor subtypes called 5-HT2A receptors, providing further support that these receptors play an important role in mediating the visual hallucinations common to all the drugs in this class (Meyer & Quenzer, 2005).

As we noted in Chapter 3, serotonin is distributed widely in the brain. This may account for the enormously varied effects of LSD-like hallucinogens. Serotonin is thought to play an important role in mood, which is consistent with the powerful emotional effects of these drugs. The precise areas of the brain responsible for the hallucinogenic actions of these drugs remain open to debate. Interestingly, many drugs that affect serotonin do *not* produce hallucinations (e.g., MDMA, SSRI antidepressants), and thus many questions remain regarding just how serotonergic hallucinogens produce their remarkable effects on visual experience (Iversen et al., 2009).

THIS IS YOUR BRAIN ON HALLUCINOGENS

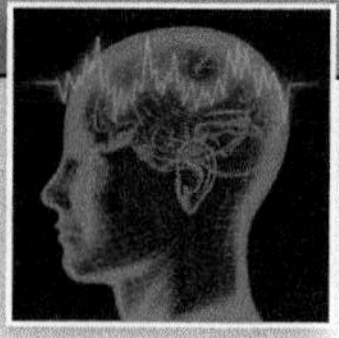

A. In the normal functioning of the nervous system, neurotransmitters are released into the synaptic cleft by vesicles in terminal buttons of sending neurons. Many are taken up by receptor sites in receiving neurons.

B. In the process called *reuptake*, sending neurons typically reabsorb excess molecules of neurotransmitters.

C. LSD binds to serotonin receptors in the brain. LSD does not always interact with serotonin receptors in the same way. That is, sometimes LSD acts like an excitatory neurotransmitter and sometimes it acts as an inhibitory neurotransmitter.

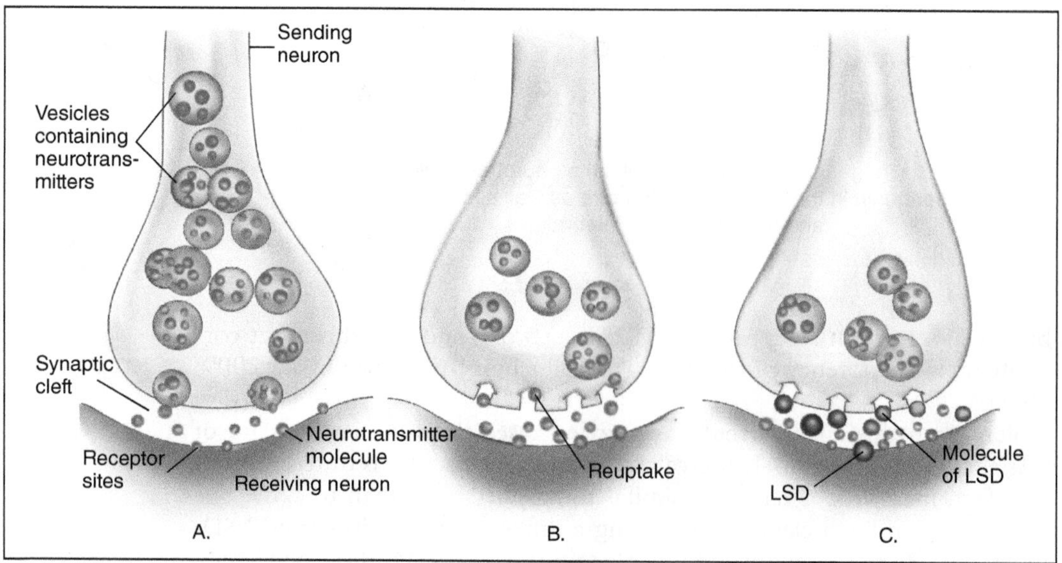

S. Rathus, S. Maheu, & S. Veenvliet. *PSYCH, 1e.* © 2012 Nelson Education Ltd. Reproduced by permission. www.cengage.com/permissions

Pharmacokinetics of Serotonergic Hallucinogens

As we have noted, all the hallucinogens that act on serotonin receptors have similar effects. However, these drugs differ widely in potency, duration of action, and other pharmacokinetic variables. LSD is the most potent of the class, with oral doses as small as 25 micrograms producing effects. Street doses range from about 12 to 350 micrograms and are prepared by placing a small amount of LSD solution in a gel (windowpane), in a tablet, or, most commonly, on paper (blotter) with colourful cartoon designs (Dal Cason & Franzosa, 2003). LSD is rapidly absorbed, and subjective effects are usually noted within 20 to 60 minutes after consumption. The drug is distributed throughout the body and readily penetrates the blood–brain barrier. The effects of LSD persist for eight to 12 hours, and the drug is rapidly metabolized and eliminated from the body. Figure 10.2 shows the physical effects of LSD. Even the most sensitive techniques can detect LSD or its metabolites in urine for no longer than 72 hours after use (Hawks & Chiang, 1986). Although the hallucinogen found in morning glory seeds (lysergic acid amide) is similar to LSD, it is far less potent—perhaps 10 percent as strong as LSD (Julien, Advokat, & Comaty, 2008).

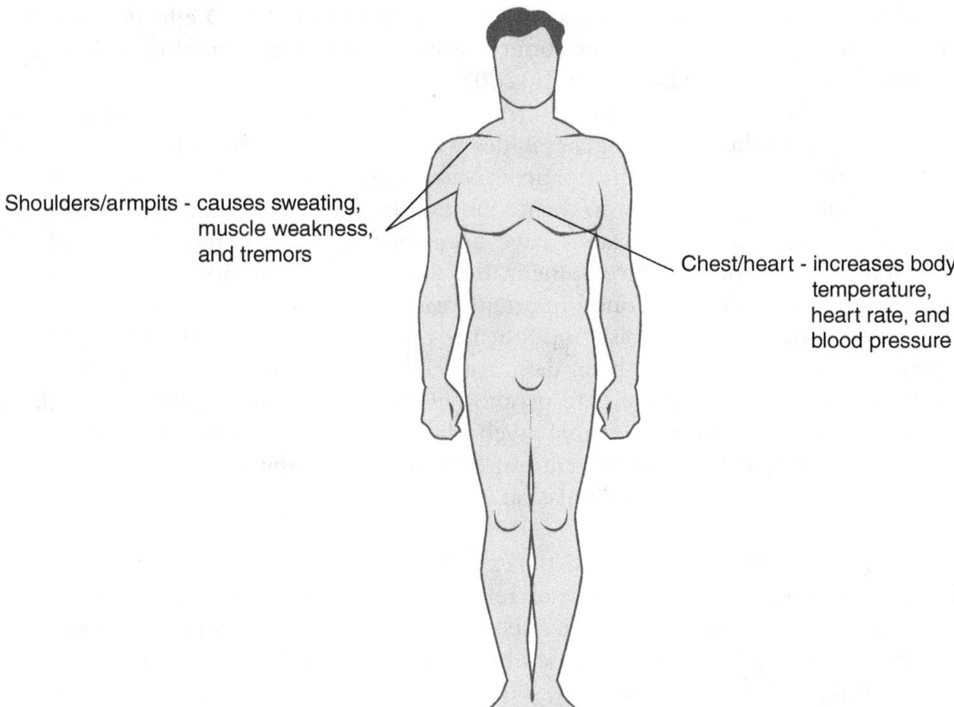

FIGURE 10.2
The physical effects of LSD

Source: Zubada/Shutterstock

People normally take psilocybin orally by either eating the mushrooms or drinking a brew containing them. It is difficult to specify doses because the amount of psilocybin varies depending on the species of mushroom, among other things. Typically, five to 10 grams of mushrooms are taken, which contain 10 to 20 milligrams of psilocybin. Thus, psilocybin is about one percent as potent as LSD. The duration of action is about four to six hours. As is true of virtually all the serotonergic hallucinogens, tolerance develops to both LSD and psilocybin, and both show cross-tolerance with each other as well as with other members of the class (Grinspoon & Bakalar, 1979).

Mescaline is normally taken by consuming peyote buttons, as described. Usually five to 20 buttons are eaten, delivering 200 to 800 milligrams of mescaline. Mescaline is about 1/3000 as potent as LSD, with 200 milligrams considered an effective dose. Duration of action is about 10 to 14 hours (Strassman, 2005).

Less information is available about the other serotonergic hallucinogens, but most are similar. One noteworthy exception is dimethyltryptamine (DMT), which is usually taken by using the bark of the Virola as a snuff or by smoking. Its effects begin within minutes of use but persist for only about 60 minutes (Dal Cason & Franzosa, 2003).

Psychotherapeutic Uses

LSD and the related hallucinogens historically have been thought to have two applications in psychotherapy but neither is well accepted today. One notion was that LSD produced a model psychosis and that psychotherapists would benefit from having experiences similar to those of their patients. It is true that hallucinations, unusual affective reactions, and loss of reality contact are characteristics of both schizophrenia and hallucinogenic experiences, but there also are important differences. For example, the hallucinations experienced under the influence of LSD are primarily visual, whereas those of schizophrenics are usually auditory (Strassman, 2005), so the subjective experiences of the psychotic are certainly not identical to those of the hallucinogen user. An intriguing similarity is that chlorpromazine and the other antipsychotics used

Hallucinogens may yet provide clues about the biochemistry of mental disorders.

in the treatment of schizophrenia are effective antagonists of LSD effects. Thus, hallucinogens may yet provide clues about the biochemistry of mental disorders (e.g., Marona-Lewicka, Thisted, & Nichols, 2005).

Paradoxically, the other major application of hallucinogens has been its use as an adjunct to psychotherapy. The general idea was that therapists would be able to learn important information when their patients were using LSD and that the patients would be better able to gain insight into their condition because LSD could break down ego defences. Many extravagant claims have been made about the benefits of LSD for mental health and spiritual development, but the use of LSD in psychotherapy gradually has declined. Although one important reason for this was the political climate, another was that most therapists thought the potential risks of LSD outweighed the benefits. In fact, it never has been demonstrated scientifically that the use of LSD is superior to placebo as an adjunct to psychotherapy. Some therapists think these drugs deserve further evaluation as possible psychotherapeutic agents (Grinspoon & Bakalar, 1983; Strassman, 2005), but the current controversy has shifted to the related drug MDMA or Ecstasy (see a later discussion in this chapter).

Effects of Serotonergic Hallucinogens

The physiological effects of LSD and related hallucinogens are generally similar to those of amphetamine and cocaine; that is, they are sympathomimetic. Thus, the effects include pupil dilation, increased heart rate and blood pressure, increased body temperature, and increased sweating (Grinspoon & Bakalar, 1979).

Experiences with hallucinogens are tremendously variable among individuals and may vary from one experience to the next for a single individual.

The psychological effects are more difficult to characterize. Experiences with hallucinogens are tremendously variable among individuals and may vary from one experience to the next for a single individual. Common to all the serotonergic hallucinogens are profound changes in visual perception, although there is some consistency in the types of visual changes that occur. Many were summarized by Albert Hofmann (1980) in his account of his first LSD trip described earlier:

> Kaleidoscopic fantastic images surged in on me, alternating, variegated, opening, and then closing themselves in circles and spirals, exploding in colored fountains, rearranging and hybridizing themselves in constant flux. It was particularly remarkable how every acoustic perception, such as the sound of a door handle or a passing automobile, became transformed into optical perceptions. Every sound generated a vividly changing image, with its own consistent form and color. (p. 19)

The spiral explosions and vortex patterns Hofmann described have been noted by Siegel (1992) to be among the most common forms in hallucinogenic experiences. Siegel calls them form constants because they are reported so frequently, not only in drug-induced states but also in hallucinations experienced by people with medical conditions such as migraine headache and high fever. Siegel noted another form constant, the lattice pattern: a checkerboard pattern that appears in an otherwise plain surface. The experience of sensing a sound stimulus as a visual one that Hofmann described is called **synesthesia**, and others have reported it as well. Other visual effects are flashing lights, increased brightness and saturation of colours, trails or plumes around objects, and the sense of movement in stable objects (for example, the wall breathes or moves rhythmically). Visual patterns may be seen as familiar or unfamiliar images that may be perceived as in motion (see Strassman, 2005, for a review).

synesthesia
An effect sometimes produced by hallucinogens that is characterized by the perception of a stimulus in a modality other than the one in which it was presented (for example, a subject may report "seeing" music).

There is a good bit more to the "trip" than just a light show, however. Other perceptions may be altered. Mood is extremely labile, and bizarre cognitive experiences occur (Stevens, 1987). Some examples of such experiences are described in the

Contemporary Issue Box 10.4. Although the descriptions recounted are quite different, they do reveal some similarities. All are characterized by strong affect, although the nature of the emotional state varies. All involve "magical" thinking and, particularly in the last two, events are fraught with cosmic significance. If the visions are terrifying (as in the second quote), the subject may behave in a psychotic manner; this is usually referred to as a bad or bum trip. The insights, enlightenments, and beliefs that occur and seem so significant during the trip often turn out to be trivial or false afterward. For example, users are often convinced they possess telepathic or clairvoyant abilities under the influence of the drug, but when tested, these abilities are not present. Nonetheless, it is easy to see how such experiences must have led prescientific cultures to attach mystical and religious significance to hallucinogens.

Adverse Effects of Serotonergic Hallucinogens

The LSD controversy revolves around the adverse effects of its use. One major concern about LSD use involved the claim that it produced chromosome damage—that those who used the drug, male or female, would stand a high risk of having deformed children. This concern was based on a study that found that LSD produced chromosome breaks in white blood cells artificially cultured in the laboratory. The study raised fears that LSD also might damage human gametes (Cohen & Marmillo, 1967). However, breaking chromosomes in white cells in a test tube under high doses of LSD has not been shown to generalize to in vivo conditions. After considerable research into this question, there is no convincing evidence that LSD (or any other serotonergic hallucinogen) increases birth defects in offspring when taken in normal doses (Wiegand, Thai, & Benowitz, 2008). As with most drugs, however, there is risk of fetal damage if taken by pregnant women (Grinspoon & Bakalar, 1979).

CONTEMPORARY ISSUE BOX 10.4

Descriptions of the Subjective Effects of LSD

Many attempts have been made to describe the effects and experiences produced by LSD. Such accounts are remarkably diverse, often confusing, and sometimes contradictory, yet some features are common. The following are vivid recollections given by well-known LSD users, illustrating the variety of the experience.

> I looked into the glass of water. In its swirling depths was a vortex which went down the center of the world and the heart of time.... A dog barked and its piercing howl might have been all the wolves in Tartary.... At one moment I would be a giant in a tiny cupboard, and the next, a dwarf in a huge hall. (Humphrey Osmond on mescaline, in Grinspoon & Bakalar, 1979, p. 100)

> I was lying on my back on the floor. Then the room itself vanished and I was sinking, sinking, sinking. From far away I heard very faintly the word "death." I sank faster, turning and falling a million light years from the earth. The word got louder and more insistent. It took shape around me, closing me in. "DEATH... DEATH... DEATH." I thought of the dread in my father's eyes in his final hours. At the last instant before my own death I shouted, "No." Absolute terror, total horror. ([Richard] Lingeman on LSD, in Grinspoon & Bakalar, 1979, p. 112)

> Now a series of visions began. The imagery appeared to synchronize with the phonograph music.... I envisioned myself at the court of Kubla Khan... at a concert being held in an immense auditorium... in some futuristic Utopia... at Versailles... at a statue of Lincoln.... I felt myself engulfed in a chaotic, turbulent sea.... There were a number of small boats tossing on the raging sea... [I was] in one of these vessels... we came upon a gigantic figure standing waist-deep in the churning waters.... His facial features were graced by an unforgettable look of compassion, love, and concern. We knew that this was the image of God. We realized that God, too, was caught in the storm. ([Stanley] Krippner on psilocybin, in Grinspoon & Bakalar, 1979, pp. 100–101)

Other adverse effects of LSD and related hallucinogens are more cause for concern. An important problem has been acute panic or paranoid reactions to the drug. These bad trips can leave individuals in an acute psychotic state during which they may harm themselves or others. The frequency of bad trips is difficult to estimate, but it was high enough in the 1960s to lead to the widespread development of walk-in crisis centres where victims could be brought for reassurance (talking the subject down) and, if necessary, hospital referral. Bad trips appear to be less frequent today, perhaps because

DRUGS AND CULTURE BOX 10.5

Hallucinogenic Ibogaine: New Rx for Addiction?

Tabernathe iboga is a shrub native to West Africa. Several tribal groups in the region made up of Cameroon, Congo, and Gabon have used this plant for many centuries for its hallucinogenic properties. The bark of the iboga root is eaten in ceremonies by members of the Bwiti religion who believe that the plant produces divine visions and permits them to commune with their ancestors. Iboga contains a number of psychoactive chemicals, but the critical component isolated from the bark preparation seems to be the chemical ibogaine. Although ibogaine is generally classified as a serotonergic hallucinogen (see previous discussion), recent studies have suggested that its neurochemical actions may be more complex, including effects on glutamate, endorphin, and dopamine pathways (Vastag, 2005). In recent years, ibogaine has become quite controversial because of claims that it may be of value in the treatment of addiction. Anecdotes from ex-addicts who believe that ibogaine visions helped in their recovery from dependency on alcohol, cocaine, and heroin have circulated since the 1960s, and although interest in this possibility has increased in recent years, there has been very little research on it. Most treatment experts are skeptical of these claims, but certainly studies are needed. As Frank Vocci, director of anti-addiction drug development for the National Institute on Drug Abuse (NIDA), put it: "There's basically a vast uncontrolled experiment going on out there" (Vastag, 2005, p. 345). Some data show that ibogaine can reduce alcohol consumption in rats (Rezvani et al., 2003), but until controlled clinical outcome studies are available, ibogaine treatment will remain controversial.

Daniel Lainé/Documentary Value/Corbis

Hallucinogenic iboga root is eaten by West Africans who follow the Bwiti religion.

more is known about how to prevent them. The psychological state of the user and the environmental setting are important. For example, one of the few documented LSD suicides took place after a man was administered LSD without his knowledge in an experiment conducted by the CIA in the 1950s (Grinspoon & Bakalar, 1979). Being exposed to the drug without foreknowledge is apparently frightening and disturbing. Individuals seem to be less likely to have bad trips if they are aware and frequently reminded that they are under the influence of a drug. A calm and comfortable setting and low doses of LSD are thought to reduce the frequency of bad trips as well, although bad trips may occur even under the best of circumstances (Abraham, Aldridge, & Gogia, 1996).

Another problem associated with LSD use is a phenomenon known as the **flashback**. Flashbacks are a reexperience of some aspect of a hallucinogenic trip that may have occurred months or even years before. The nature of the experience usually involves visual disturbances such as flashes of colour, trails in the visual field, or fleeting perceptions in the peripheral field of view. Flashbacks are often brought on by stress, fatigue, entering a dark environment, or marijuana use (Abraham, Aldridge, & Gogia, 1996). In a review, Halpern and Pope (2003) noted that it is difficult to estimate the frequency of flashbacks. In most cases, it appears that users do not find their flashbacks to be problematic, and so, no doubt, many go unreported. In unusual cases, flashbacks can be frequent and severe and may disrupt the individual's life. The DSM-IV diagnosis of hallucinogen persisting perception disorder is applied to such cases. Very rarely, the visual distortions are nearly constant and may reflect permanent loss of serotonergic neurons. Treatment with antipsychotics or benzodiazepines may relieve the symptoms of such cases (Halpern & Pope, 2003; Young, 1997).

flashback
A sudden recurrence of an LSD-like experience.

LSD also has been linked to long-term psychiatric disorders. Perhaps the most publicized and horrifying example is Charles Manson and his "family." The Manson family used LSD heavily, but it is unclear what role, if any, the drug played in the development of their psychopathology and subsequent mass murders. When one is confronted with a psychotic individual who has used LSD, it is difficult to determine whether LSD caused the psychosis or the person was psychotic to begin with and LSD made the symptoms more flagrant. To complicate matters further, most users of LSD who are diagnosed as psychotic have extensive histories with other drugs as well, and the role these other drugs may have played is rarely certain. It generally is agreed that hallucinogens may precipitate or exacerbate psychosis or emotional disturbance in certain vulnerable individuals.

LSD has also been linked to chronic psychiatric disorders in rare cases. Then, the controversy focuses on the precise role of LSD and related hallucinogens. Some have argued that LSD may be capable of producing psychosis even in the absence of other predisposing conditions, but the general consensus seems to be that, when chronic psychiatric problems occur following serotonergic hallucinogen use, it generally involves individuals who had already been diagnosed with or have manifested psychotic or prepsychotic symptoms before the drug use (Halpern & Pope, 1999; Wiegand, Thai & Benowitz, 2008).

Methylated Amphetamines

Overview

MDMA (Ecstasy) has become perhaps the most controversial illegal drug in our society today. One reason was its rapid increase in popularity in the late 1990s. Prior to 1996, the annual high school senior survey undertaken in the United States did not even have a specific category for MDMA; in that year, 4.6 percent of America's high school seniors reported having used it during the past year. That number rose explosively, doubling by 2001, when 9.2 percent reported using it; after that peak, however, use declined and has leveled off in recent years (Johnston et al., 2009a). One important reason for this decline is the publicity about the many adverse effects of MDMA, including claims that it may produce brain damage and death. These claims, in turn, have generated considerable controversy and a tremendous amount of research on MDMA in the past few years. We discuss this in some detail because of the importance of this drug on college and university campuses today.

MDMA is one of a group of drugs known as methylated amphetamines because of their chemical structures. Dozens of drugs fall into this category, and the more well-known variations are listed in Table 10.4. These drugs are often categorized with the serotonergic hallucinogens, and indeed their chemical structures resemble that of mescaline. In addition, they influence serotonin transmission, and also dopamine and norepinephrine (Morton, 2005). DOM (2,5-dimethoxy-4 methylamphetamine) not only resembles mescaline in structure but also produces similar effects, including visual hallucinations.

The others (MDA, MDMA, MDE) are more similar to amphetamine in effects (see Chapter 5) and differ from the serotonergic hallucinogens in that they produce few or no visual hallucinations. The effects of MDA and MDMA seem to be primarily a mild euphoria accompanied by openness, feelings of warmth and empathy, and lack of defensiveness. These properties led some psychotherapists to advocate the use of these drugs, particularly MDMA, as an adjunct to therapy. Some scientists classify MDMA with the hallucinogens, others with the amphetamines, and still others consider these drugs as belonging to a unique category (Cohen, 1998).

History and Epidemiology

MDMA came to be known as the "love drug" because users reported positive feelings toward others and increased empathy as part of the drug experience.

Methylated amphetamines were developed in the early 1900s, but attracted little attention until relatively recently. For example, MDMA was patented in 1914, by Merck Pharmaceuticals in Germany, but the drug was not marketed or even much studied until many years later (Iversen, 2008). DOM was first reported on the street in the late 1960s, when its potent hallucinogenic effects and very long duration of action (as long as 24 hours) led to many bad trips. MDA also surfaced on the street about this time, but it had a better reception. It was called "mellow drug of America" because it has fewer perceptual effects than LSD. The use of MDA declined along with LSD in the 1970s, whereas MDMA began to increase in popularity. In 1976, an estimated 10 000 doses of MDMA were used in the United States. In 1985, the Drug Enforcement Agency (DEA) estimated that 30 000 doses were distributed per month in one Texas City alone (Stock, 1986).

TABLE 10.4 Methylated Amphetamines

Chemical Name	Abbreviation	Street Names
2,5-dimethoxy-4 methylamphetamine	DOM	STP
3,4-methylenedioxyamphetamine	MDA	love drug, mellow drug of America
3,4-methylenedioxymethamphetamine	MDMA	Ecstasy, XTC, Adam
N-ethyl-3,4-methylenedioxyamphetamine	MDE	Eve

Source: Johnston, L. D., O'Malley, P. M., Bachman, J. G., & Schulenberg, J. E. (2009). *Monitoring the Future—National Results on Adolescent Drug Use: Overview of key findings, 2008* (NIH Publication No. 09-7401). Bethesda, MD: National Institute on Drug Abuse.

What accounted for this enormous increase? During this period, there was considerable interest in the potential value of MDA and MDMA in psychotherapy, and publicity about the therapeutic benefits of MDMA made it attractive. It did not hurt public relations for the drug to pick up the nickname "Ecstasy." Indeed, MDMA came to be known as the "love drug" because users reported positive feelings toward others and increased empathy as part of the drug experience.

Ecstasy tablets.

Jbouzou/Dreamstime LLC

Until 1985, MDMA was a legal drug in the USA. Although MDA was a Schedule I drug, its close relative MDMA had not yet been classified. Thus, dealers preferred the low risks associated with the designer drug Ecstasy. In the face of the explosive rise in MDMA use, coupled with animal research implicating the drug in brain damage, however, the DEA classified MDMA as Schedule I in 1985, on an emergency basis. Amid considerable controversy over whether MDMA had legitimate medical uses, this decision was affirmed in 1986, and MDMA was permanently placed in Schedule I (Holland, 2001). In Canada MDMA is a Schedule III drug, which means that you need a prescription or licence to legally possess it.

MDMA grew in popularity as it became associated with the "club" or "rave" subcultures. Originating in Europe in the late 1980s, the rave movement swept rapidly through North America, and indeed much of the world, in the 1990s (Holland, 2001). Raves were usually large-scale, all-night dance parties featuring "techno," "house," or "trance" musical styles often accompanied by light shows. Alcohol was rarely associated with raves; rather, the "club drugs" tended to be drugs like MDMA, methamphetamine, Ritalin (see Chapter 5), LSD, and GHB (see Chapter 13). Bright fluorescent clothing and jewellery along with paraphernalia such as pacifiers (to avoid teeth grinding or bruxism, a side effect of MDMA) were common, and the settings varied from empty warehouses, airplane hangers, and open fields to smaller venues such as clubs. The popularity of raves declined in the late 1990s, but by the early 2000s, MDMA was the fastest-growing illicit drug across North America, western Europe, and Australia (Inciardi, 2002), and had become known as the prototype of club drugs. Even considering the recent decline in use noted among U.S. high school seniors, MDMA remains one of the world's most popular recreational drugs. After marijuana, it is the most widely used illegal drug in Europe, and more than eight million people are thought to have used MDMA at least once (Morton, 2005). Figure 10.3 shows that MDMA production is very high in Canada, which is the primary source of MDMA for the USA (National Drug Intelligence Center, 2009).

FIGURE 10.3 MDMA labs in Canada

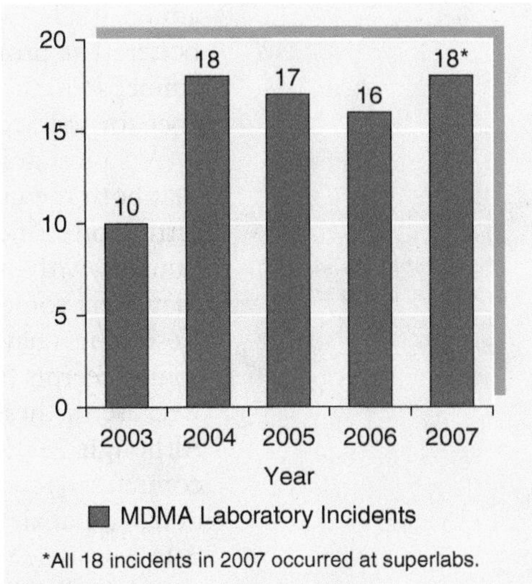

Source: National Drug Intelligence Center.

Jim Arbogast/Corbis Yellow/Corbis

The club scene is associated with LSD and Ecstasy.

Effects of Methylated Amphetamines

The effects of MDMA, MDA, and MDE are similar enough to be discussed together (DOM effects are like those of mescaline or LSD and are not considered further). These drugs are usually taken orally but can be injected or absorbed intranasally (snorted). They are absorbed rapidly, and their duration of action is about six to eight hours. The neural mechanisms of action involve increased release of monoamines, particularly serotonin. MDMA also blocks the reuptake of serotonin and, to a lesser extent, dopamine. Thus, there is an initial overall increase in serotonin and dopamine activity after taking the drug, but this is followed after several hours by a marked decrease in serotonin activity (Iversen, 2008). At effective doses (75 to 150 mg for MDMA, 50 to 150 mg for MDA, 1 to 2 mg for MDE), these drugs produce clear sympathomimetic effects, including increased heart rate, blood pressure, and pupil dilation. Additional physical effects include muscle tension, teeth grinding (bruxism), increased body temperature, appetite suppression, and insomnia—effects remarkably similar to those of amphetamine (Freedman, Johanson, & Tancer, 2005). The psychological effects claimed for these drugs are euphoria, increased emotional warmth and empathy, lowered defensiveness, and increases in verbal behaviour (Bravo, 2001). Hallucinations are uncommon or absent at ordinary doses. Few experiments have directly compared the psychological effects of MDMA to amphetamine, but Tancer and Johanson (2003) studied young adults under various doses of both drugs. Participants reported stronger reinforcing effects for MDMA than amphetamine at all doses tested, and they also consistently reported that they liked MDMA better. The profile of MDMA effects were generally quite similar to those of amphetamine, so in the Tancer and Johanson (2003) study, the main difference was a preference for the MDMA drug effect over amphetamine.

The combination of drug and setting produces effects that users sometimes describe as a trancelike state with feelings of peace and unity.

A clinical description of this sort does not capture the allure of MDMA. Remember that both the user and the setting determine the effects of any drug. For MDMA, the setting often includes the pulsing rhythm of techno music, strobe lights, dancing, and bonding with other individuals. The combination of drug and setting produces effects that users sometimes describe as a trancelike state with feelings of peace and unity. Researchers have interviewed hundreds of MDMA users about their experiences, and some excerpts from their descriptions are given in the Contemporary Issue Box 10.6. Because of these desirable effects, some users develop a pattern of heavy, binge use. Although MDMA is not associated with dramatic physical withdrawal symptoms, commonly reported aftereffects include drowsiness, muscle pain, depression, paranoia, and anxiety (Hegadoren, Baker, & Bourin, 1999). These effects typically dissipate within a few days but can be more persistent in some cases.

The belief that MDMA might enhance communicative ability and empathy and decrease defensiveness led some therapists to advocate the use of these drugs as an

CONTEMPORARY ISSUE BOX 10.6

Voices of Ecstasy

Cohen (1998) and Iversen (2008) have published several descriptions of MDMA users' experiences on the drug. The following are some brief excerpts:

> "Ecstasy is more or less a happy speed."
>
> "All I wanted to do was smile. I was so wide awake, and I felt love for everything and everyone."
>
> "Pure energy. Happy energy. I felt tingly all over. It felt good to be touched. Being touched was so intense."
>
> "It made me able to let my guard down and reveal my true self. I did experience mood fluctuations (ups and downs)."
>
> "Everyone was my friend. I don't think that anything could have brought me down. I loved it."
>
> "I had a bad experience. I felt like I was surrounded by water and drowning. It must have been panic."
>
> "Floating, flying, highly sexual. I felt like I was on this really high mountain and I just wanted to stay there."
>
> "It was the most euphoric experience of my life."

adjunct to psychotherapy. The logic was much the same as that described for LSD therapy, but because MDMA does not produce hallucinations or the dissociation of LSD, it was seen as less likely to produce adverse reactions. Although some therapists involved in this work reported that MDMA was beneficial (Naranjo, 2001; Riedlinger & Montagne, 2001), controlled studies are lacking and thus little experimental evidence supports the value of MDMA (or any other drugs of this class) in psychotherapy. Recent years have seen a renewed interest in the possibility of MDMA therapy, and controlled trials are underway to determine whether MDMA is of value in the treatment of posttraumatic stress syndrome and other psychological disorders (e.g., Bouso et al., 2008).

Toxicity

The increased use of MDMA in the late 1990s was associated with reports of toxic reactions and deaths. Toxic reactions include dehydration, heatstroke and heat exhaustion, muscle breakdown, kidney failure, stroke, seizures, and heart attacks (Eede et al., 2009; Ghatol & Kazory, 2009). Most toxic reactions to MDMA occur after high doses or multiple doses (stacking) have been ingested, but in some cases, serious reactions and even deaths have occurred after relatively low doses (Hegadoren, Baker, & Bourin, 1999; Schifano, 2004). The toxic effects of MDMA are often related to elevated body temperature, and the pharmacological effects of the drug may be compounded by intense physical activity of users and by the high temperatures of many clubs. Users are often advised to drink fluids to avoid dehydration and overheating, but some MDMA emergency cases have involved collapse due to low sodium levels, possibly caused by excessive fluid intake altering the salt balance (Schifano, 2004). Complicating our ability to evaluate toxic reactions to MDMA is the fact that tablets sold on the street as MDMA often contain other drugs that may also be toxic in some cases. Adulterants are so common in street MDMA that one organization (DanceSafe) maintains a website with pictures of commonly sold MDMA tablets along with the results of their chemical analysis. Many different compounds have been revealed in these analyses; among the more common adulterants in samples posted in the first half of 2009 were benzodiazepines, methamphetamine, caffeine, ketamine, and dextromethorphan. Interestingly, many of the samples contained no active chemical at all (see Parrott, 2004)!

Residual Effects of MDMA

One of the major controversies about MDMA and other methylated amphetamines concerns the possibility that they may produce long-term damage of certain brain structures. The report sounding the alarm (Ricaurte et al., 1985) showed that, after several administrations of high doses of MDA, rats had a depletion of serotonin apparently caused by the degeneration of serotonergic neuron terminals. Similar results have now been reported for MDMA in several species, including primates, and it appears that the neurotoxic effects can be produced after a single high dose (20 mg/kg) is administered or after several lower doses (five mg/kg) are administered over consecutive days (Bauman, Wang, & Rothman, 2007). One criticism of this work is that even the doses considered moderate in these animal studies are higher than doses generally used on the street. This point is somewhat difficult to evaluate in that MDMA tablets vary enormously in the dose contained. In a worldwide survey, Parrott (2004) found that most pills sold as MDMA contained an average of 70 to 100 mg MDMA, which would deliver between one to two mg/kg to an adult human depending on body weight. This is below the dose range shown to be neurotoxic in nonhumans. However, some tablets have contained up to 300 mg (according to information on www.dancesafe.org), and many users take multiple tablets during the course of an evening; two or three tablets could certainly deliver a dose capable of producing neurotoxic effects. Indeed, some users report commonly taking 15 or more tablets in a night, and this would likely produce doses well above those shown to produce long-term serotonin deficits in nonhumans (Schifano, 2004). Of course, human users may take lower doses of MDMA but take them many times, intermittently, over many years, and we do not yet know what neural consequences may occur following this pattern of use. How rapidly neurons recover from the toxic effects of the drugs is also open to debate, but one study showed effects that persisted for as long as seven years after drug administration in primates (Hatzidimitriou, McCann, & Ricaurte, 1999). As noted in Chapter 3, serotonin is a neurotransmitter that modulates sleep, mood, and many other functions, so depletion of serotonin could lead to serious problems. Thus, whether MDMA produces these neurotoxic effects in humans is a critical issue.

As you might imagine, in recent years, many researchers have attempted to determine whether MDMA users show evidence of brain damage or other residual effects. Numerous studies have used brain imaging technology such as PET and SPECT techniques (see Chapter 3) and consistently have found reductions in serotonergic functioning between heavy MDMA users and controls; however, there is also evidence that the serotonin system recovers from these effects after a period of abstinence (McCann et al., 2005; Selvaraj et al, 2009).

Although Ecstasy users do show evidence of serotonin neurotoxicity, the functional significance of these neural changes has been controversial. Dozens of studies have compared MDMA users and controls on tests of mood, psychopathology, memory, and attention. In many of these studies, heavy users of MDMA showed more evidence of sleep problems, depressed mood, and memory as well as related cognitive deficits when compared to nonusers (see Morton, 2005, for a review). Of course, these studies have many interpretive problems. For example, the accuracy of the drug histories used to form the groups is open to question. As noted, many different drugs are sold as MDMA, and some of these may produce more toxicity than MDMA alone.

It is also difficult to determine from study results whether the differences between users and nonusers are actually caused by MDMA. MDMA users may differ in many respects from the nonusing control sample, and these other differences may influence the measured variables. For example, most MDMA users also use other drugs, and in many studies, the MDMA user group differs from the control group with respect to overall drug use—not just MDMA. The potential importance of such a confound has been demonstrated in some recent studies. Parrott et al. (2001) studied 618 polydrug users and 150 nonusers in England and Italy. In keeping with the studies reviewed here, they found that heavy MDMA users showed more evidence of psychopathology than nonusers. However, drug users who did not report using MDMA did not differ from MDMA users in psychopathology, so the role of MDMA use was unclear. These findings have been replicated by Daumann et al. (2004) and by a study that focused on depressive symptoms (Roiser & Sahakian, 2004). In summary, frequent MDMA users generally show more psychopathology (particularly depression) than controls who do not report use of illegal drugs, but when compared to polydrug users or marijuana users who do not use MDMA, these differences tend to disappear.

Similar results have been obtained with respect to cognitive impairments associated with MDMA use. For example, several studies (Croft et al., 2001; Dafters, Hoshi, & Talbot, 2004; de Sola et al., 2008) have compared groups of MDMA users (who also reported marijuana use) with groups of participants who reported only marijuana use and with control groups who did not use drugs on various neuropsychological tests. MDMA users performed more poorly than controls on tests of attention and memory, but the participants who used marijuana only were equally impaired. These studies suggest that the memory deficits often reported in MDMA users might have been caused by their coincident use of marijuana. However, other researchers have found that MDMA users showed more severe deficits on memory and other cognitive tasks than control participants matched for drug use other than MDMA (Dafters, 2006; Daumann et al., 2005; Halpern et al., 2004), so it remains possible that MDMA use may play a role.

In sum, the jury is still out on what long-term effects are associated with MDMA use. Although scientific opinion does not support the "horror scenarios of our kids' brains rotting out by the time they were 30" touted by the media in the 1990s (Iversen, 2008), neither does it support the notion that MDMA is a safe drug. On the contrary, MDMA and related drugs pose risks of acute toxic effects and possible deficits in neuropsychological functioning, particularly among heavy users.

Anticholinergic Hallucinogens

Atropine and **scopolamine** are drugs that block acetylcholine receptors in the brain. In low doses these drugs are used for a variety of medical purposes, and atropine in particular has been in the news because it is standard issue to troops in the Middle East where there is risk of nerve gas attack. Deadly nerve gases (sarin and soman) are toxic because they inhibit the enzyme that breaks down acetylcholine, and as an acetylcholine antagonist, atropine is an antidote if administered rapidly after exposure. However, drugs like atropine and scopolamine also can produce hallucinogenic effects. They are found in a number of plants known throughout the world and have a long history of use. Hundreds of years before the birth of Christ, the ancient Greeks at the oracle of Delphi used plants containing scopolamine and atropine. In the Middle Ages, such plants were included in the infamous witches' brews. Plants such as belladonna, also called deadly nightshade (*Atropa belladonna*), mandrake (*Mandragora officinarum*), henbane (*Hyoscyamus niger*) of Europe, jimsonweed (*Datura stramonium*), and other plants of the *Datura* genus from the New World have been eaten for their hallucinogenic properties (Schultes, 1976). Although these drugs are not widely used for witchcraft today, *Datura* is allegedly one of the ingredients in zombie powder in Haiti (Davis, 1988).

atropine
An anticholinergic hallucinogen found in certain plants.

scopolamine
An anticholinergic hallucinogen found in certain plants.

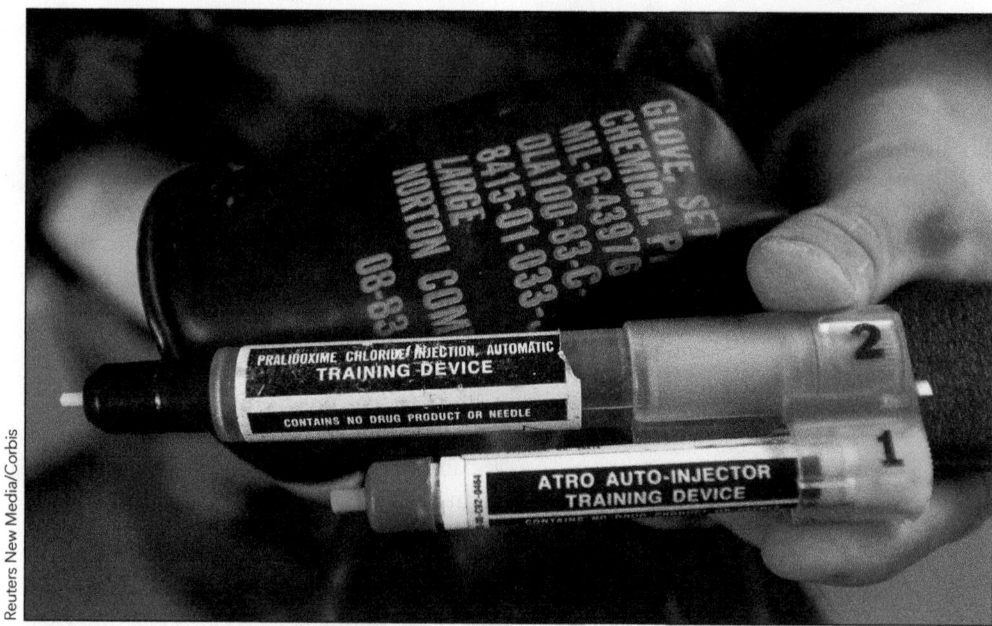

Atropine auto-injections are provided to soldiers who are at risk of nerve gas attacks.

Anticholinergic hallucinogens produce a variety of physiological effects, including dry mouth, blurred vision, loss of motor control, and increased heart rate and body temperature. These drugs can be fatal as they cause respiratory failure at doses only slightly higher than the effective dose (Grinspoon & Bakalar, 1979). The psychological experience appears to be a dreamlike trance or stupor. Users seem delirious and confused but may be able to describe visions if asked. A unique feature of the drugs of this class is that memory of the drug experience is poor, and users may be unable to recall any details of the experience. These drugs are rarely seen on the street today.

One additional plant to be discussed in this section is the fly agaric mushroom (*Amanita muscaria*). Fly agaric contains several different hallucinogenic chemicals, including muscarine, which is a cholinergic agonist, and muscimole, a hallucinogen that may be similar to the LSD-like drugs. Although rarely used today, the mushroom represents one of the earliest forms of hallucinogen use. Fly agaric grows throughout much of Europe and Asia, and it may have been the mysterious "Soma" described in the Hindu *Rig-Veda* more than 2000 years ago. The *Rig-Veda* describes the rather bizarre practice of recycling the drug effect by drinking the urine of the intoxicated individual. Muscimole is the only hallucinogen known that passes unchanged through the system into the urine (Wasson, 1979). The effects of the mushroom are unique among hallucinogens. Users of the fly agaric typically fall into a stupor for several hours during which they experience visions, and later they experience intense euphoria and energy accompanied by visual hallucinations (ibid.).

phencyclidine A dissociative anesthetic.

ketamine A dissociative anesthetic.

Dissociative Anesthetic Hallucinogens

History

The final class of hallucinogens to be considered is a large group, but only two of its members, **phencyclidine** (PCP, angel dust) and its close analogue **ketamine** (special K, vitamin K), have been used enough to warrant discussion here. PCP was synthesized in 1956, and was tested as an anesthetic because it had pronounced tranquilizing effects. With animals, it produced a general anesthesia that left the animal conscious but not feeling pain, even during surgery. In clinical trials of PCP and ketamine with humans, however, some patients experienced hyperexcitability, delirium, and visual disturbances. Thus, these drugs were largely abandoned for human use, although both were marketed for use as anesthetics and tranquilizers in veterinary medicine (Dal Cason & Franzosa, 2003; Linder, Lerner, & Burns, 1981). Both PCP and ketamine are classified as Schdeule I drugs under Canada's Controlled Drugs and Substances Act, and are therefore illegal substances.

PCP emerged in the 1970s as a street drug of preference. Sold under a variety of names, including "angel dust," "hog," "horse tranquilizer," and "lovely," it was often taken as sprinkled powder on a cigarette or joint. Although PCP also is effective taken orally and can be injected, smoking remains the most popular route of administration. By the early 1980s, some surveys were finding that more than 20 percent of America's high school students had tried PCP. Because of the high incidence of dangerous side effects, PCP became a notorious drug and its use declined. The high school senior surveys indicated that the number of high school seniors who used PCP through the 1990s was near three percent, and by the 2008 survey, this was down to 1.8 percent reporting they had tried the drug (Johnston et al., 2009a).

Although PCP is no longer extensively used in veterinary medicine, ketamine remains quite popular in this regard, and ketamine abuse appears to be increasing as it is often included among the "club" drugs. Most of the ketamine or "special K" that appears on the street today is diverted from veterinary supplies and is seen as a crystalline powder or in solution. It can be snorted, injected, taken orally, or smoked (Jansen, 2004). Ketamine has not yet been included in the senior survey, so less is known about current levels of use. In one study, Hopfer et al. (2006) reported that over 18 percent of young clients (18 to 32 years old) in treatment for substance abuse had used ketamine, making it one of the popular club drugs used in this population.

Pharmacokinetics

The mechanism of PCP and ketamine action involves antagonism of a subset of receptors for the excitatory amino acid glutamate (Balazs, Bridges, & Cotman, 2006). PCP is absorbed rapidly after smoking or injection, with peak blood concentrations noted 5 to 15 minutes after smoking. In contrast, peak concentrations are reached two hours after oral administration. The drug remains in the system unmetabolized for more than two days, and PCP is detectable in urine for several weeks after a single use (Hawks & Chiang, 1986).

Effects of PCP and Ketamine

A moderate dose (one to 10 mg) of the dissociative anesthetics produces feelings of euphoria and numbness resembling alcohol intoxication. Speech may be slurred, and generally there is motor discoordination. Users may be catatonic and rigid with a blank stare or may be aggressive and hyperactive. Effects include profuse sweating, increased heart rate and blood pressure, and rapid jerky eye movements called nystagmus (Linder, Lerner, & Burns, 1981; Young, Lawson, & Gacono, 1987). Subjects often report blurred vision or double vision but rarely visual hallucinations. Rather, there are changes in perception of body image, distortions of the tactile senses, and sometimes dreamlike visions. Consider these descriptions from PCP users:

> It's weirdly hallucinogenic. It makes you go, boy that's steep stairs I have to climb there, that you realized you climb in five minutes you know, and stuff, and it actually feels like you're going to float off the couch and stuff, you know. Your arm is over somewhere. I can

remember like crawling down the stairs because the only thing that I trusted was my fingers and my knees....

The most frequent hallucination is that parts of your body are extremely large or extremely small. You can imagine yourself small enough to walk through a keyhole, or you can be lying there and all of a sudden you just hallucinate that your arm is twice the length of your body. (Feldman, Agar, & Beschner, 1979, p. 133)

My body image was distorted beyond recognition—fantastically elongated pipe-cleaner legs and arms, spindly E.T.-like fingers, and morphing alien-insect head in the mirror.... (Jansen, 2004, p. 75)

These effects, described as being in the "K-hole," normally last four to six hours but are variable and, particularly after high doses, may persist for days or weeks. Overdoses (more than 20 mg) may result in seizures, prolonged coma, and sometimes death from respiratory failure (Carroll, 1990). Like LSD, anesthetic hallucinogens may produce transient psychotic states or "bad trips." Toxic psychosis produced by PCP and ketamine is often characterized by paranoia and sometimes violence and may persist for several days (Young, Lawson, & Gacono, 1987). Long-term cognitive impairments have also been reported for PCP and ketamine (Morgan et al., 2004). Talking the subject down from a bad trip with these drugs generally is difficult. Physical restraint and intensive medical care are often necessary. Dissociative anesthetics are far more likely than other hallucinogens to produce medical or psychiatric complications (Boutros & Bowers, 1996; Morgan et al., 2004; Young, Lawson, & Gacono, 1987).

Salvinorin A (Salvia)

Salvia's appeal is greatest among Canadian youth, with 7.3 percent reporting that they had used salvia.

Salvia divinorum is a plant in the sage family that has been cultivated by the Mazatec people of southern Mexico and used in religious ceremonies for many centuries. Traditionally, salvia was ingested by chewing the leaves or drinking a tea brewed from them. Today, the leaves are often dried and smoked, and concentrated extracts are also available for oral use or smoking. Use of salvia was virtually unheard of 10 years ago in North America, but use has grown rapidly in recent years. In 2009, 1.6 percent of Canadians aged 15 years and older reported that they had used salvia in their lifetime, and 0.2 percent reported using it in the past year. But, salvia's appeal is greatest among Canadian youth, with 7.3 percent reporting that they had used salvia.

Ted Kinsman/Photo Researchers, Inc.

Salvia divinorum.

The hallucinogenic effects of salvia are relatively short-lived (generally less than 30 minutes in duration), but are often intense and produce a trancelike state. Figure 10.4 illustrates the effect of salvia. The effects include visual hallucinations and other sensory disturbances and impaired motor control. Although this is often reported as pleasant, frightening experiences that resemble the bad trips associated with some of the types of hallucinogens reviewed previously can also occur. The active chemical

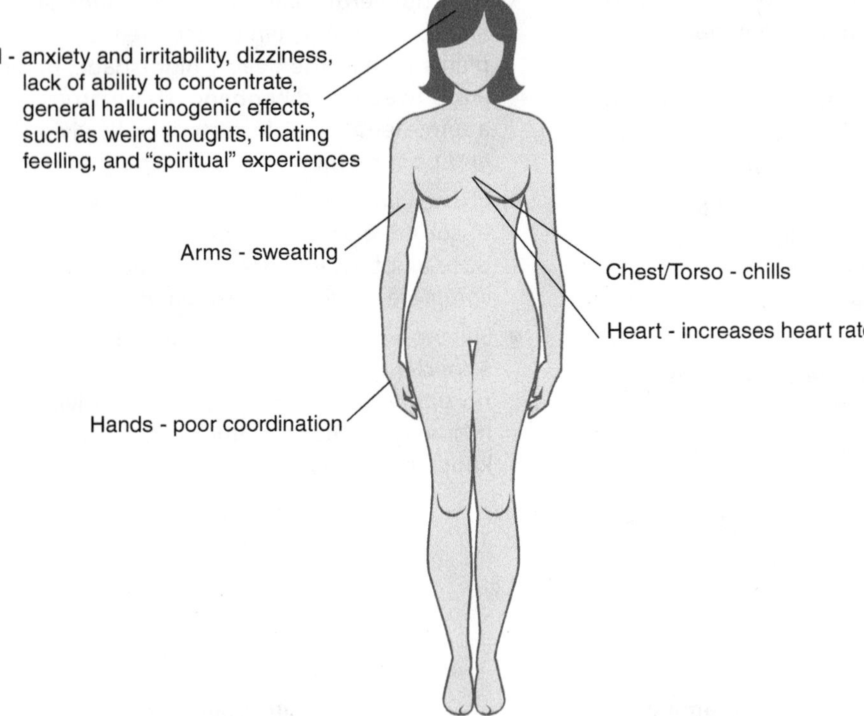

FIGURE 10.4
Salvia's effect on the body

Source: Zubada/Shutterstock

in salvia is a compound called salvinorin A. Effective in doses of 100 to 500 micrograms, it is considered to be the most potent of any naturally occurring hallucinogen (Julien, Advokat, & Comaty, 2008). The mechanism of salvinorin A action is also quite unlike any of the hallucinogens reviewed previously, but rather appears to act as an agonist of a subset of opioid receptors called kappa receptors (Butelman et al., 2009). Little is known about the functions of these kappa receptors. They are not the same receptors that produce the pleasurable effects of opiate drugs reviewed in Chapter 12, but they are thought to be involved in regulating pain. There is considerable scientific interest in salvinorin A as it may open the door to learning more about the functions of the kappa receptor system in the brain. In the meantime, very little is known about the possible adverse or long-term effects of salvia use. Given the increasing popularity of the drug, it is currently under review and it would not be surprising to see salvia become a federally scheduled drug in the near future.

SUMMARY

- Hallucinogens are a group of drugs that have the capacity to alter perceptual, cognitive, and emotional states.
- Hallucinogens may be divided into four classes: serotonergic hallucinogens, methylated amphetamines, anticholinergic hallucinogens, and dissociative anesthetics.
- Serotonergic hallucinogens include drugs such as LSD, psilocybin, and mescaline. Psilocybin comes from mushrooms of the *Psilocybe* genus, and mescaline from the peyote cactus. These drugs have a long history of use by early Indian peoples for religious purposes.
- LSD is a synthetic compound. Its hallucinogenic properties were discovered by the Swiss chemist Albert Hofmann, but it was made popular by counterculture figures such as Timothy Leary and Ken Kesey.

- LSD and the other drugs in this class affect serotonergic neurons. They are sympathomimetic drugs as well.
- The psychological effects of these drugs are diverse but include visual hallucinations, alterations of mood and thought, and dreamlike visions.
- Many adverse effects have been linked to LSD and other drugs in this class, including acute psychotic reactions (bad trips), flashbacks, and long-term psychological deficits.
- Methylated amphetamines include drugs such as MDA and MDMA (Ecstasy). These drugs are sympathomimetic and produce many other effects similar to LSD but generally do not produce visual hallucinations.
- Anticholinergic hallucinogens include atropine and scopolamine, which are chemicals found in plants such as the deadly nightshade, mandrake, jimsonweed, and henbane. These drugs produce a semi-sleep state characterized by vivid visions and poor memory of the experience later.
- Phencyclidine (PCP) and ketamine are classified as dissociative anesthetic hallucinogens. They produce a potent intoxication at moderate doses and complete surgical anesthesia at higher doses.
- Salvinorin A is a hallucinogenic chemical found in a species of plant in the sage family (*Salvia divinorum*) and is often referred to as diviner's sage. It is unique among hallucinogens in acting on kappa receptors in the brain.

Key Terms

anticholinergic hallucinogens p. 224
atropine p. 243
dissociative anesthetic p. 224
flashback p. 237
ketamine p. 244
mescaline p. 224
methylated amphetamines p. 224
phencyclidine p. 244
psilocybin p. 224
scopolamine p. 243
serotonergic hallucinogens p. 224
synesthesia p. 234

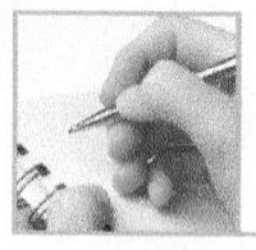

Essays/Thought Questions

1. Why might a person decide to use hallucinogens? Would this decision be based on similar or different factors than those considered for other drugs such as marijuana or alcohol?
2. Do you think salvia should be illegal? What factors should you consider when making this decision?
3. MDMA production is very high in Canada. What strategies could the federal and provincial governments use to decrease the production of MDMA? What roles could media, law enforcement, schools, and local city councils play?

Suggested Readings

Iversen, L. (2008). *Speed, ecstasy, Ritalin: The science of amphetamines.* Oxford: Oxford University Press.

Laing, R. (2003). *Hallucinogens: A forensic drug handbook.* London: Academic Press.

CHAPTER 11

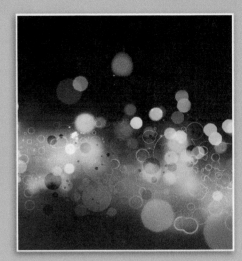

Opiates

Did You Know

?

- Opium is produced from the sap of the poppy plant, and it has been used for medicinal purposes for centuries.
- The major medical use for opiate drugs is in the treatment of severe pain.
- Opiates depress respiration, lower body temperature, and cause capillary constriction. They induce a pleasurable euphoria as well as relieve pain.
- Morphine and codeine are chemicals directly derived from opium.
- The use of "dirty" needles is now one of the major causes of HIV/AIDS transmission.
- Heroin inhibits sexual arousal.
- Doda (poor man's heroin) use is a growing problem in Canada.
- Alcohol and other depressant drugs act synergistically with heroin and other opiates; these combinations are often fatal.

As indicated in historical overviews in earlier chapters, psychoactive drugs can be double-edged swords in their potential for improving the human condition, on one hand, and their capacity to cause destruction to individuals and society on the other. No group of drugs captures this paradox more dramatically than the class of drugs we call opiates, which includes opium, morphine, heroin, and related compounds. Opiate drugs have been used for centuries to relieve pain and, when introduced to Europe, were hailed by physicians as a godsend. One of the first European physicians to use opium to relieve pain and suffering in his patients, Thomas Sydenham, wrote in 1680: "Among the remedies which it has pleased Almighty God to give man to relieve his sufferings, none is so universal and so efficacious as opium" (Gay & Way, 1972, p. 47). Even today, opiate drugs remain the most potent painkillers available to physicians, yet we now recognize the other edge of the opiate sword—the ability of opiates to produce severe dependence. Heroin is viewed as the prototype addictive drug, and illegal use and traffic in heroin are major international problems. Thus, many of the general concerns regarding psychoactive drugs emerge in bold relief in a consideration of opiates.

History of the Opiates

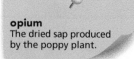

opium
The dried sap produced by the poppy plant.

Early History

Opium comes from *Papaver somniferum*, one of the many species of the poppy plant. The opium poppy is native to the Middle East, in the areas that border the Mediterranean Sea, but it is now cultivated extensively throughout Asia and the Middle East. Contrary to the experiences of Dorothy in *The Wizard of Oz*, however, simply walking through a poppy field will not cause sleep or euphoria. Rather, special procedures must be followed to extract opium from the poppy. The petals fall after the poppy blooms, leaving a round seedpod the size of an egg. If the seedpod is scored lightly with a knife, it secretes a milky white sap. After drying, this sap forms a thick, gummy, brown substance that is called **opium**. A person experiences the effects of opium by consuming the substance orally or by smoking it.

Mafoto/Dreamstime LLC

Opium exudes from incisions of the poppy pod.

The use of crude opium preparations is truly an ancient practice. There is evidence that the Sumerian and Assyrian civilizations cultivated and used opium as long ago as 6000 years. The ancient Egyptians had discovered medical uses for opiates 3500 years ago, as documented in the "Therapeutic Papyrus of Thebes" (Scott, 1969). The Greek and Roman civilizations also used opium for a variety of medical purposes. The great Greek physician Galen (130–201 CE) noted the following uses for opium:

> [Opium]...resists poison and venomous bites, cures chronic headache, vertigo, deafness, epilepsy, apoplexy, dimness of sight, loss of voice, asthma, coughs of all kinds, spitting of blood, tightness of breath, colic, the iliac poison, jaundice, hardness of the spleen, stone, urinary complaints, fevers, dropsies, leprosies, the troubles to which women are subject, melancholy and all pestilences. (Scott, 1969, p. 111)

Although this quote may seem more a testament to the ignorance of medical problems of this age, certainly the remarkable **analgesia** (pain relief) of opium must have made it seem helpful for many disease states. In fact, opiate drugs do have special cough-suppressant and antidiarrheal properties in addition to their analgesic actions, and they are used in modern medicine for these purposes.

analgesia
Pain relief produced without a loss of consciousness.

The use of opium for medical and recreational purposes became widespread among the Islamic peoples of the Middle East. This may have been because the Koran's explicit prohibition of the use of alcohol and some other drugs did not include opiate use (Latimer & Goldberg, 1981). To this day, the use of opiates is less censored than that of alcohol among many Muslims. By the 9th century, Arab traders spread the use of opium to India and China, where the practice of smoking opium developed. Dependence on opium was first recognized as a problem in China as well, with the first edict against opium issued in 1729. However, China already had so many opium addicts that the demand remained very high. In spite of the ban on importing opium into China, British ships continued to trade opium grown in India for Chinese tea, and this activity was the basis for the Opium Wars between China and Great Britain in the middle of the 19th century (see Chapter 2).

Opiate Use in the 19th Century

Opium dependence was a serious problem in China by the beginning of the 19th century, but it was not yet seen as such in Europe or North America. Although opium was readily available in laudanum and various patent medicines, it almost always was in liquid form and taken orally (a practice called opium eating, even though it was really opium drinking) rather than smoked. It was used mostly for medical purposes. Developments during the century brought the addictive properties of opiate drugs to the awareness of Western societies. As noted in Chapter 2, opium preparations were readily available and completely legal in 19th-century Europe and North America. The pleasurable properties of opium soon led to its widespread use for nonmedical reasons. The pleasures of opium were extolled in a book written by the British poet Thomas De Quincey, *The Confessions of an English Opium-Eater*, published in 1822. De Quincey's book praised the effects of opium and included several famous quotes, including "...thou hast the keys of Paradise, O just, subtle and mighty opium!" (Scott, 1969, p. 52). Westerners were slow to recognize that "eating" opium could prove just as addictive as smoking it, but concern about opium became more widespread, as tomes such as De Quincey's fueled its use. By the late 1800s, opium use had spread throughout society, affecting such noted literary and scientific figures as Elizabeth Barrett Browning, Samuel Coleridge, William Halstead, Walter Scott, and Percy Shelley, to name a few. It was becoming recognized that opium dependence was not limited to the Chinese.

Pharmacological developments added to the problems. In 1803, the German pharmacist F.W. Serturner developed a process that separated morphine from opium. Morphine is the major active chemical in opium (codeine is another opiate drug found in opium) and is about 10 times more potent than crude opium. Serturner experimented with morphine and was so impressed with the blissful, dreamlike state it induced that he named the chemical after Morpheus, the Greek god of dreams. Morphine became widely available in the mid-1800s, and with the concomitant development of the hypodermic syringe, injected morphine became a major dependence problem in Europe and North America. Because of the rapid and potent pain-relieving properties of injectable morphine, it was the treatment of choice during recovery from severe wounds. However, withdrawal from the morphine was often more difficult

Morphine is the major active chemical in opium.

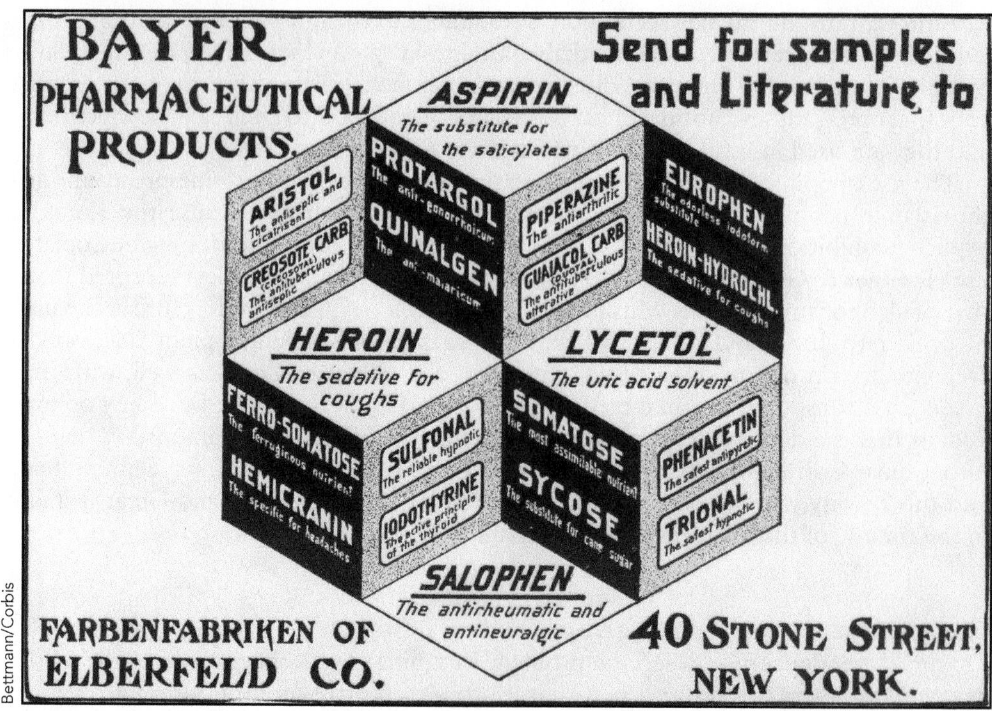

Bettmann/Corbis

Patent medicines of the 19th century frequently contained opiates such as heroin.

Because this new compound was so powerful, it was viewed as a new treatment with "heroic" possibilities and was christened heroin.

heroin
A drug produced by chemically processing morphine. It is more potent than morphine and has become the major opiate drug of abuse.

than recovery from the wound. For example, morphine dependence was so common among soldiers on both sides during the Civil War in America that it was often called "soldier's disease."

In 1874, British chemist Alder Wright published reports of experiments that produced a new chemical compound based on an alteration of morphine: diacetylmorphine. Wright's discovery went unnoticed until 1898, when the great German pharmacologist Heinrich Dreser (who also discovered aspirin) rediscovered the compound and noted that it was twice as potent as morphine. Because this new compound was so powerful, it was viewed as a new treatment with "heroic" possibilities and was christened **heroin**. Heroin was used immediately as a cough suppressant and pain reliever. Not until many years later was it recognized that heroin was even more likely than morphine to produce dependence.

Opiate Use in the 20th Century and Today

During the 20th century, there was growing awareness of the danger and pervasiveness of opiate dependence which led to a number of legal changes in the United States and Canada. In the United States, these culminated in the 1914 Harrison Narcotics Act. Of course, the Harrison Act did not completely eliminate the nonmedical use of opiates and, in fact, it marked the beginning of drug crime in America. Illegal opiate use meant opium and heroin were smuggled into the country. This resulted in an escalation of prices and a change in the type of person who became or remained addicted to opiates. The Harrison Act placed the control of opiate drugs in the hands of physicians; determination of whether an addict had a valid medical need for opiates was exclusively the physician's decision. However, legislative interpretations ruled that a physician must not prescribe opiates unless doses could be shown to be decreasing over time (1915), that opiates must not be prescribed to addicts (1917), and that heroin must not be prescribed at all (1924) (Kramer, 1972). After the legitimate channels for obtaining drugs were blocked for many addicts, they turned to a growing black market to maintain their addiction.

In Canada, the introduction of the Opium Act in 1908 was this country's first drug prohibition legislation. Later, in 1929, the Opium and Narcotic Drug Act became Canada's main instrument of drug policy, which lasted for over 40 years. The 1960s and 1970s were marked by an increase in illicit drug use in both Canada and the United States, which led to further criminalization and stiffer penalties associated with drug possession and use (Riley, 1998). Opiate use has certainly changed since the Opium and Narcotic Drug Act was introduced in Canada, and the Harrison Act was introduced in the United States. One major change is simply the number of individuals who use opiates. In Canada, opioid pain relievers were the most commonly pharmaceutical used in 2010. One in five Canadians (aged 15 years and older) reported its use in the last 12 months (Health Canada, 2010). Another major change is in the demographics of opiate use. Prior to legislation, opiate addiction cut across social classes, but when opiates became illegal, they began to be used mainly in large cities where organized crime provided a supply. Heroin quickly emerged as the addict's drug of choice. In addition, addicts tended more and more to be young, poorly educated men of lower socioeconomic status (James & Johnson, 1996), although heroin use has since made inroads in other populations.

In Canada, opioid pain relievers were the most commonly pharmaceutical used in 2010. One in five Canadians (aged 15 years and older) reported its use in the last 12 months.

A huge criminal apparatus for producing and supplying heroin was spawned in the wake of these legislations. Today, most heroin comes from poppies grown in Southwest Asia. Afghanistan produces more than 90 percent of the world's opium (see Contemporary Issue Box 11.1), with lesser amounts coming from Laos and Burma, according to the United Nations Office on Drugs and Crime (2009). The opium is processed to heroin and transported to Europe or Mexico before being smuggled into the United States and Canada.

Afghanistan produces more than 90 percent of the world's opium.

Street heroin is adulterated or cut many times as it changes hands on the way from the producer to the importer to those who sell to individual users, and it may vary enormously in quality. If sophisticated chemical production and refining techniques are used, uncut heroin can be quite pure and appears as a white odourless powder that can be injected, smoked ("chasing the dragon"), or taken intranasally (snorted). On the other hand, crude processing techniques may yield much lower-quality heroin. For example, black tar heroin, produced in Mexico, is a dark brown or black substance that may be tarlike or hard. It is generally too impure to be smoked or even to dissolve in water and has to be melted to be injected (Ashton, 2002). Even high-quality heroin may be adulterated (cut) with cheap adulterants such as baking powder, caffeine, quinine, or even talcum powder to increase the dealer's profit. Heroin remains a large and important source of illegal revenue, which helps recruit participants in organized crime.

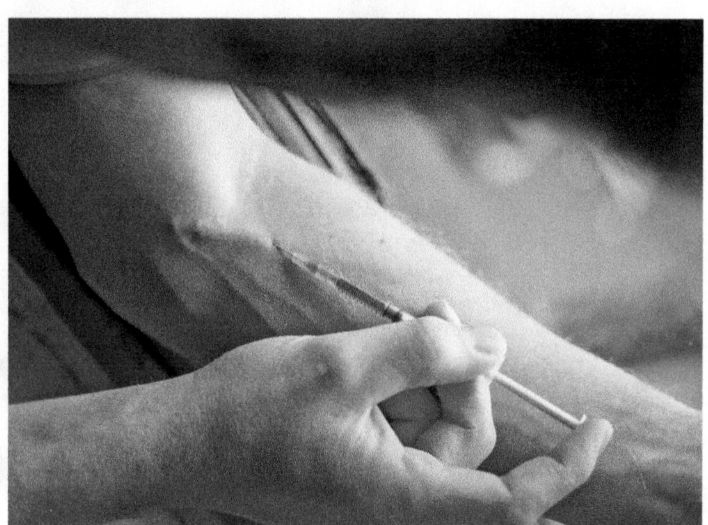

Corbis

Heroin is often administered via intravenous injection.

Many heroin addicts become involved in criminal activity to support their habit. At first, the cost of heroin may appear relatively low to addicts who use the drug occasionally for "kicks." But in the words of an addict interviewed by Smith and Gay (1972): "It's so good, don't even try it once." Many users find that

CONTEMPORARY ISSUE BOX 11.1

Poppies in Afghanistan: The Taliban and the Heroin Trade

Most Americans knew little about Afghanistan or the Taliban prior to September 11, 2001, but those who follow the heroin trade have focused on Afghanistan for decades. Afghanistan has long been a major area of opium production, but the "golden triangle" of Southeast Asia (Burma, Laos, and Thailand) historically dominated opium production. By 1999, though, Afghanistan had become the undisputed world leader in opium production despite being an Islamic state ruled by the Taliban, which publicly opposed opium use. In 1999, the Taliban representative to the United States, Abdul Hakeem Mujahid, said, "We are against poppy cultivation, narcotics production and drugs, but we cannot fight our own people" (Bartolet & Levine, 2001, p. 85). Even before 9/11, the United States accused the Taliban of profiting from opium and heroin production, and using those profits to fund terrorist activities. Under pressure from the United Nations, the Taliban announced bans on poppy cultivation in 1997, 1998, and 2000, but there was little evidence of any decreased production. In 2001, though, a ban was put into place that apparently really did reduce poppy production. Cynics have pointed out that the Taliban was simply trying to increase prices by temporarily cutting the supply; however, whatever the reason, when the Taliban lost control of Afghanistan, the poppy made a comeback.

In this war-ravaged and economically depressed nation, growing opium is one of the few ways that farmers can make a living. Afghan President Hamid Karzai has urged his people to declare jihad (holy war) on drug production, but opium farming still accounts for nearly half of the domestic economy, and Afghanistan supplies over 90 percent of the world's heroin (United Nations Office on Drugs and Crime, 2009a). In recent years, the resurgent Taliban has gained control of poppy production again, and it is estimated that hundreds of millions of dollars from opium sales are being used to fund the insurgency against U.S. forces and the Karzai government (Moreau, 2009).

Harvesting opium in Afghanistan.

they take the drug more and more frequently, and because tolerance develops rapidly to heroin and other opiates, higher doses are soon required to produce the desired effect. Soon the cost of maintaining the growing habit virtually forces addicts to engage in criminal activities. Here is part of an interview with a street addict from San Francisco:

> [Heroin]...is the mellowest downer of all. You get none of the side effects of speed and barbs. After you fix, you feel the rush, like an orgasm if it's good dope. Then you float for about four hours; nothing positive, just a normal feeling, nowhere. It's like being half asleep, like watching a movie; nothing gets through to you, you're safe and warm. The big thing is, you don't hurt. You can walk around with rotting teeth and a busted appendix and not feel it. You don't need sex, you don't need food, you don't need people, you don't care. It's like death without permanence, life without pain. For me, the only hard part is keeping in H, paying my connection, man. I know these rich cats who can get good smack and shoot it for years and nothing happens, but me, you know, it's a hustle to stay alive. I run about a $100, $150-a-day habit, so I have to cop twice that much to keep my fence happy.... (Luce, 1972, p. 145)

In another testimonial on heroin, the great guitarist, Eric Clapton, describes his fall into addiction this way:

> I assumed I was in some way immune to it and wouldn't get hooked. But addiction doesn't negotiate and it gradually crept up on me like a fog.... It was so insidious. It took over my life without my really noticing. (Clapton, 2007)

In fact, heroin addiction is a hard way to live. Consider the findings of a study that followed 581 heroin addicts over a period of 33 years (Hser et al., 2001). Half of these individuals died during the study period, 50 to 100 times the death rate in the general population of the same age. Of the surviving addicts at the end of the period, 20 percent were still using heroin (and another 10 percent refused to be tested) and 14 percent were in prison.

Why is the life span of a heroin addict so short? Addicts are at great risk for disease and death from AIDS, hepatitis, and other diseases spread by sharing contaminated needles (see Contemporary Issue Box 11.2). It is estimated that there are around 125 000 injection opiate users in Canada (Fischer, Rehm, Patra, & Cruz, 2006).

The National Institute on Drug Abuse estimates that heroin overdose is responsible for more than 1000 deaths every year. Overdose deaths most commonly occur when heroin or another opiate drug is combined with alcohol or another depressant drug due to synergy, but another factor is that different concoctions of street heroin can vary enormously in potency. Between 2006 and 2007, a rash of overdose deaths in the Eastern and Midwestern United States were traced to a mixture of heroin and fentanyl, a short-acting but highly potent opioid combination called "fefe," that has recently appeared in these parts of the country (Shenfeld, 2006). Between 2007 and 2008, a combination of heroin and cold medications called "cheese" resulted in numerous overdose deaths in Texas.

The National Institute on Drug Abuse estimates that heroin overdose is responsible for more than 1000 deaths every year.

Researchers have noted that opiate users are aware of these increased risks to their health. In a study conducted by researchers at the University of Toronto (Millson et al., 2004), 143 opiate users were asked to respond to a questionnaire that examined their perceived health status. The results indicated that opiate users perceived their mental and physical health as worse than both the general population and individuals with minor and serious medical problems. However, they did rank their health as comparable to those suffering from mental illnesses.

Another issue involving opiate drug use is "designer" heroin. Designer heroin is produced illicitly by chemists who design or develop chemical analogues to heroin.

CONTEMPORARY ISSUE BOX 11.2

Fatal Attraction: Intravenous Drug Use and AIDS

Intravenous (IV) drug users may inject cocaine or methamphetamine, but the majority are heroin addicts. They may be young or old, black or white, male or female, but one thing they have in common is a great risk for developing acquired immune deficiency syndrome, or AIDS. In the early 1980s, male homosexuals were the major group at high risk for AIDS, but the number of drug-related AIDS cases has risen so sharply that they now account for more than 25 percent of all AIDS cases (NIDA, 2005). The magnitude of the problem is substantial. In 2008, 65 000 individuals were living with HIV or AIDS in Canada. The number of new cases of HIV or AIDS was between 2300 and 4300 Canadians, with individuals who inject drugs accounting for 17 percent of these new cases (Public Health Agency of Canada, 2009). The story is similar in other countries. A recent study of IV drug users in New York City (Davis et al., 2006) found that nearly a quarter (23.9 percent) was infected with the human immunodeficiency virus (HIV). Moreover, it is not just the users who are involved. The virus does spread among heterosexuals, and the babies born of HIV-positive mothers will usually develop AIDS as well.

An ironic aspect of this tragedy is that it is so avoidable. IV drug users are at dual risk for HIV infection because they are likely to engage in both risky sex and the common practice of sharing needles. According to the Public Health Agency of Canada, roughly 14.5 percent of participants in their "Enhanced Surveillance of Risk Behaviours among Injecting Drug Users in Canada" study (2006) reported borrowing needles for injection, most often from a close friend or sex partner. In addition, 32.0 percent of users reported passing on their injecting equipment to others, and 18.2 percent of participants reported passing used needles to someone else. Using a needle contaminated with the blood of someone who has HIV leads to direct blood-to-blood transmission, which involves a very high risk of infection. If sterile needles were used, this risk would be eliminated. Health care workers are striving to send the message out to IV drug users that they should avoid sharing needles, or clean them with bleach if sharing is necessary. Canada has been a leader in establishing clean needle exchanges for drug users. The first official needle exchange program began in 1989 in Vancouver, British Columbia. Shortly after, similar programs were established in other major cities, such as Toronto and Montreal. By 2004 there were over 100 exchange programs across Canada. According to the Centre for Addiction and Mental Health (CAMH), needle exchange programs (NEPs) are beneficial because they reduce the transmission of disease. Further, they do not increase injection drug use nor the number of needles discarded. Unfortunately, sharing needles has become part of the "culture" for users. IV drug use often occurs in "shooting galleries," places where people gather to inject and enjoy the effects of the drug. In another attempt to reduce the spread of disease among drug users, Vancouver opened North America's only legal shooting gallery in 2003. It provides a safe place and clean "tools" for addicts to shoot up, and it saves lives. In one year, the facility handled over 100 overdoses with no deaths (CBC, 2004).

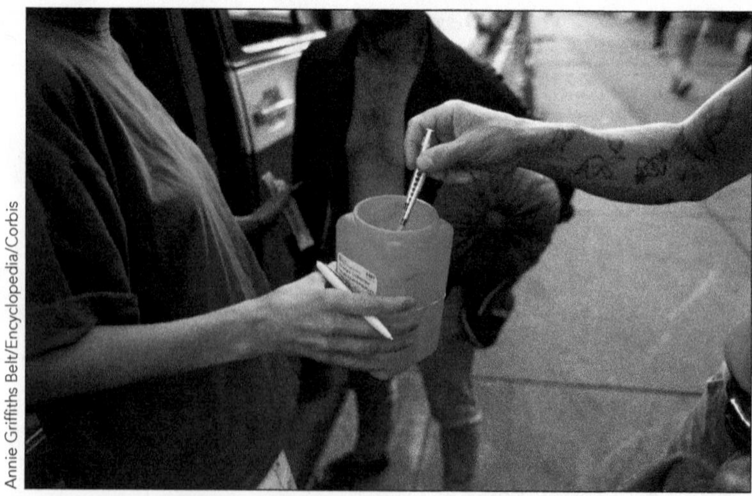

Annie Griffiths Belt/Encyclopedia/Corbis

Needle exchange programs are designed to reduce the spread of needle-borne diseases.

These new compounds are untested but usually produce effects similar to those of heroin or other opiates. Most designer heroin compounds are derivatives of the powerful opioid, fentanyl. One problem with these fentanyl derivatives (often sold on the street as "China white") is that they may be 10 to 1000 times more potent than heroin. Thus, the risk of overdose death is greater. Another problem posed by designer compounds is chillingly illustrated by an episode from the 1980s, when an underground chemist in the San Francisco Bay area began to produce a designer heroin called MPPP. Apparently, due to poor laboratory technique, some portion of his product was a closely related but highly toxic compound called MPTP. The error was discovered when a number of young drug users were hospitalized with complete paralysis. At first the cause of this epidemic of paralysis was a mystery. The symptoms were similar to those of advanced Parkinson's disease. However, because Parkinson's is a disease of the elderly, only an inspired guess by a physician named William Langston solved the puzzle. He tried to use L-dopa with these "frozen" addicts. The L-dopa was successful enough that the paralyzed patients were able to at least talk a little. Eventually, they were identified as heroin addicts who had tried the misdesigned heroin, MPTP.

Designer opiates create new dangers for users. Specifically, these drugs are more potent than the original drug and the added compounds are dangerous in themselves. Two of the most common designer drugs are fentanyl and meperidine (Demerol). Fentanyl is 50 times more potent than heroin. It can stop respiration: ..."users have been found dead with the needle used to inject the drug still in his or her arm" (NIDA, 2011).

We now know that MPTP selectively attacks and rapidly destroys the substantia nigra, which leads to symptoms of advanced Parkinson's disease (see Chapter 3). The addicts who became victims of MPTP have sustained permanent damage, although L-dopa has reduced some symptoms (Langston, 2002). A couple of important points: First, the tremendous hazard associated with designer drugs is obvious. Because these drugs are not tested in animals or screened by the FDA, they pose serious risks to users. Second, designer drugs can produce brain damage without overt symptoms. Many people who were exposed to MPTP only once or twice probably do not show any Parkinson's symptoms at present. Nonetheless, some damage to the substantia nigra has occurred. As these people lose more cells during the normal aging process, they may reach the 80 percent threshold and may yet pay the price by developing premature Parkinson's disease (ibid.).

Not all heroin casualties are due to overdose or toxicity from designer drugs. As an example, Jerry Garcia of the Grateful Dead died of poor health complicated by years of heroin addiction in a drug detox centre in 1996. Many believed Nirvana singer Kurt Cobain's 1994 suicide was related to his inability to kick his heroin habit. His journal, published posthumously in 2002, is a chronicle of his struggle to get off heroin during the final years of his life. He wrote:

> I remember someone saying if you try heroine [sic] once you'll become hooked. Of course I laughed and scoffed at the idea but I now believe this to be very true. Not literally, I mean if you do dope once you don't instantly become addicted, it usually takes about one month of everyday use to physically become addicted. But after the first time your mind says ahh that was very pleasant as long as I don't do it every day I won't have a problem. The problem is it happens over time.... (Cobain, 2002)

Despite the well-publicized dangers, heroin use remains a tragic problem throughout North America. One reason is that the abundance of relatively pure and very potent heroin on the street has made the drug available to be snorted or smoked as well as injected. In fact, snorting or smoking heroin has become the method of choice for administering heroin among a generation of users who are younger and have a higher socioeconomic status than was once the case (Durrant & Thakker, 2003). Some estimates indicate that the United States may have as many as 900 000 heroin addicts. Although this number may seem small relative to more widespread drug problems like alcoholism and nicotine dependence, heroin has a significant impact on society (Inciardi, 2002).

Prescription Opiate Abuse

Illicit use of prescription opiates more than tripled from the 1990s to the present.

Although heroin use has levelled off over the past decade, overall abuse of opiate drugs went up dramatically during this period. The reason is because of the explosive increase in prescription opiate drug use (Compton & Volkow, 2006). Illicit use of prescription opiates more than tripled from the 1990s to the present. According to the World Health Organization, 2.8 million people in Europe and the United States are addicted to opiates such as heroin, and more than two million in the U.S. alone are dependent on prescription opioid medications. Canadians rank third in the world in the use of prescription opioids, just behind the U.S. and Germany (CBC, 2010). Table 11.1 shows a list of prescription opiates available in Canada.

TABLE 11.1 Prescription Opiates Available in Canada

Opioid Active Ingredient	Product Names
Butorphanol	APO-Butorphanol PMS-Butorphanol
Codeine	Atasol 282 Tablets 292 Tablets Codeine Contin-controlled Release Coactifed Exdol Tylenol with Codeine No. 1 Tylenol with Codeine No. 2 Tylenol with Codeine No. 3 Tylenol with Codeine No. 4
Fentanyl	Duragesic
Hydocodone	Dalmacol Hycodan Tussionex
Hydromorphone	Dilaudid Hydromorph Contin-controlled release Hydromorph.IR
Meperidine	Demerol
Morphine	Doloral 1 (Syrup and Tablets) MS Contin M-Eslon Kadian Statex
Oxycodone	Oxy.IR Oxycontin Percocet Percodan Endocet Supeudol
Pentazocine	Talwin
Propoxyphene	Darvon

Source: Health Canada, *It's Your Health: Opioid Pain Medications Frequently Asked Questions*, Health Canada, 2009. Reproduced with the permission of the Minister of Health, 2011.

Along with increased use of prescription opiates has come an increased number of drug treatment admissions and emergency room mentions involving these drugs (Subramaniam & Stitzer, 2009). The rate of overdose deaths involving prescription opiates has also gone up and has actually been higher than rates associated with heroin in recent years (Wu, Pilowsky, & Patkar, 2008). Several prescription opiate painkillers have been part of this trend, but the most publicized of these has been OxyContin. OxyContin was introduced by the pharmaceutical firm Purdue Pharma in the mid-1990s. There was no particular reason to expect it to become a significant abuse problem. The generic drug in OxyContin, oxycodone, is not new. It is a synthetic opiate found in Percodan and other prescription painkillers that have been on the market for decades. The difference is that OxyContin was designed to treat severe and chronic pain, and so it contains a higher dose of oxycodone. Whereas Percodan might contain five milligrams of oxycodone and has a relatively short duration of action, OxyContin formulations contain 20 to 160 milligrams of oxycodone in time-release form so that a single pill has a duration of action up to 12 hours. This formulation makes OxyContin a highly effective pain reliever, but illicit users discovered that they could crush the OxyContin tablet to produce a powder they could inject or snort. This practice releases all of the oxycodone at once and thus delivers a large dose of opiate immediately to the user.

These large doses available in a single tablet are particularly dangerous. OxyContin abuse, addiction, and lethal overdose all skyrocketed in the early 2000s. In 2001, the United States announced a national strategy to crack down on OxyContin use. Under pressure, Purdue Pharma, which made more than $4 billion on OxyContin sales between 2001 and 2003 (Tolman, 2005), discontinued the high-dose (160 mg) OxyContin pill in 2001 but continues to market 20-, 40-, and 80-mg tablets, and widespread diversion and abuse of the drug continues. In September 2007, Purdue Pharma paid $20 million in civil penalties to 26 states and the District of Columbia and $600 million in fines for misrepresenting the abuse liability of OxyContin.

The demographics of prescription opiate misuse are somewhat different than those we noted with heroin. One important feature is that nonmedical use of prescription opiates is far more widespread among young people. As an illustration, consider that although recent national high school senior surveys noted decreases in most illicit drug use over the past several years, use of OxyContin and other prescription opiates actually went up (see Figure 11.1; Johnston et al., 2009a). In fact, as Figure 11.1 shows, overall use of prescription opiates by high school seniors rose dramatically from 1991 to the present, and similar trends were noted in surveys of adults as well (Compton & Volkow, 2006). Although some of this trend is due to OxyContin use (which was not asked about specifically on the survey until 2002), use of other prescription opiates increased as well, notably hydrocodone (Vicodin) (Cicero, Inciardi, & Munoz, 2005). Other demographic trends are interesting as well. For example, heroin use is more widespread among males, whereas prescription opiate use is slightly more common among females (Green et al., 2009). In a large scale study, Wu, Pilowsky, and Patkar (2008) found that nearly 10 percent of U.S. adolescents between the ages of 12 and 17 reported nonprescribed use of prescription opiates. The drugs used included in order of frequency: Darvocet/Darvon, Vicodin/Lortab, codeine, Percocet/Percodan, and OxyContin, with other opiates less frequently reported. Although illicit use of opiates was part of a pattern of use of alcohol and other drugs for some adolescents, fully 25 percent of the sample reported only using prescription opiate drugs. Thus, illicit use of prescription opiate drugs has emerged as a major new drug issue in the late 2000s.

FIGURE 11.1 Percentage of high school seniors reporting illicit/nonmedical use in the past year

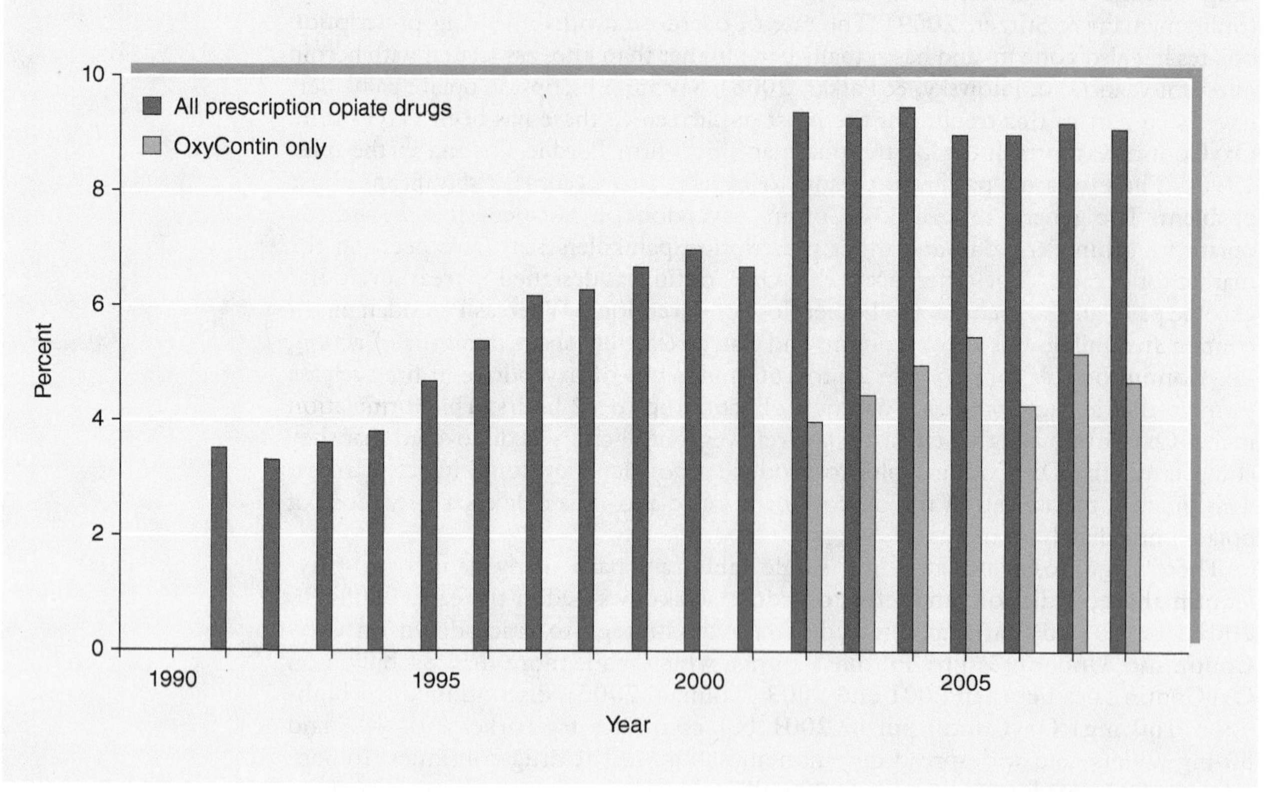

Source: Johnston et al., 2009a.

In Canada, opioid pain medications are regulated by the Controlled Drugs and Substances Act (CDSA). Under the CDSA, it is illegal to:

- carry out activities related to prescription opioid pain medications without a licence, unless you are a patient with a prescription from a licensed health care provider;
- sell or even give away your prescription opioid pain medication to someone else; and
- "double doctor," which is seeking a prescription for an opioid pain medication from more than one doctor in a short period of time without telling the others.

The pharmaceutical industry (including manufacturers, wholesalers and distributors), hospital pharmacies, retail pharmacies, and practitioners must also report any incidence of loss and theft of opiate drugs to Health Canada (Heath Canada, 2009).

How Do Opiates Work?

Absorption

As noted, opiate drugs may be taken into the body in a variety of ways. Most are readily absorbed from the gastrointestinal tract, although a given dose has a greater effect if it is injected intravenously. Most opioids also are absorbed through the nasal mucosa and lungs. Thus, opium and pure forms of heroin are often smoked, and heroin frequently is taken intranasally. Opiates are also absorbed after intramuscular or subcutaneous administration.

On the street, for example, heroin may be injected intravenously ("mainlining") or subcutaneously.

Rock singer Courtney Love was sentenced to rehabilitation to recover from opiate addiction.

Sam Mircovich/Reuters/Corbis

Distribution, Metabolism, and Excretion

Once in the bloodstream, opioids are distributed throughout the body and accumulate in the kidneys, lungs, liver, spleen, digestive tract, and muscles, as well as the brain. With some opiates, such as morphine, only a small amount penetrates the blood–brain barrier. In fact, the main difference between morphine and the more potent drug heroin is that heroin is more lipid-soluble and thus more readily penetrates the blood–brain barrier. Once in the brain, heroin is converted to morphine. So heroin is essentially a more effective package for delivering morphine to the brain than is morphine itself.

Most opiate drugs are rapidly metabolized in the liver and excreted by the kidneys. Excretion of opiates is fairly rapid, with 90 percent excretion within a day after taking the drug. However, traces of morphine may remain in urine for two to four days after use (Hawks & Chiang, 1986). Figure 11.2 shows some of the short-term effects of heroin.

Discovery of Endorphins

One of the most exciting developments in the neurosciences was the breakthrough in the understanding of the neural mechanisms of action of opiate drugs in the 1970s. Research on this topic led to the discovery of a class of brain chemicals called the endorphins, which function as neurotransmitters. It is now believed that heroin,

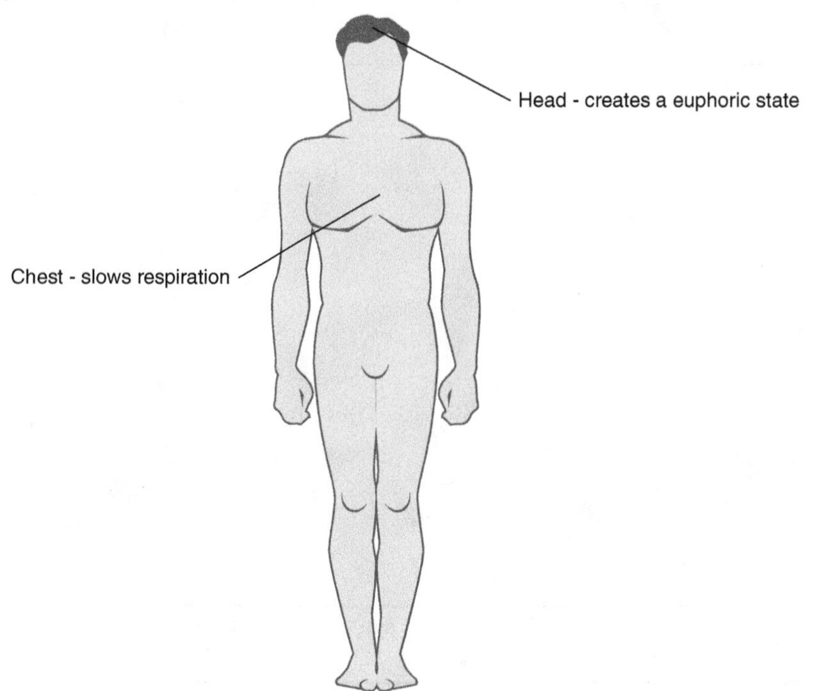

FIGURE 11.2
Short-term effects of heroin

Source: Zubada/Shutterstock

morphine, and other opiate drugs produce their effects by triggering activity in the brain's endorphin systems (Goldstein, 2001; Meyer & Quenzer, 2005).

naloxone
A short-acting opiate antagonist.

In the 1960s, chemists discovered that making a slight change in the morphine molecule resulted in a chemical that did not produce any of the standard opiate drug effects (pain relief, euphoria) but instead reversed or blocked the effects of morphine and other opiate drugs. This compound is called **naloxone** and may be described as an opiate antagonist. When naloxone is given to a patient who is suffering from an overdose of heroin or morphine, it completely reverses the effects of those drugs.

THIS IS YOUR BRAIN ON OPIATES

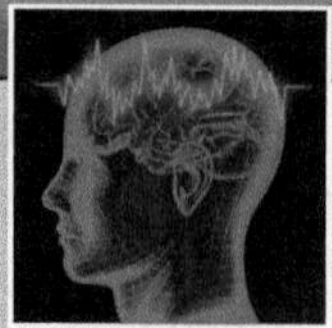

In the early 1970s, two researchers at Johns Hopkins University in Baltimore—Candace Pert and Solomon Snyder—reported they had discovered brain receptors that responded selectively to opiate drugs; these were dubbed "opiate receptors" (Pert & Snyder, 1973). The existence of opiate receptors was of great interest. Figure 11.3 illustrates how these opiate receptors may work and the effects of opiates on our brain and nervous system. One might reasonably wonder why there would be neurons in the brain that responded to such drugs. Did nature somehow intend us to be heroin addicts? Neuroscientists had a different notion. They believed the presence of such receptors must mean that some natural brain chemicals have morphine-like structure and properties. The search was on for the "brain's own opiates," and, in 1975, several such chemicals were discovered (Snyder, 1989). Although several morphine-like substances (beta-endorphin, enkephalin, and dynorphin are the most important compounds) are found in the brain, these complex peptide molecules are referred to collectively as endorphins, a contraction of *endogenous morphine*.

- In the normal functioning of the nervous system, neurotransmitters are released into the synaptic cleft by vesicles in terminal buttons of sending neurons. Many are taken up by receptor sites in receiving neurons.
- In the process called *reuptake*, sending neurons typically reabsorb excess molecules of neurotransmitters.
- Opiates, such as heroin, bind to opiate receptors in the brain. This stops the inhibitory neurotransmitters from blocking the release of dopamine, and dopamine floods the synapse.

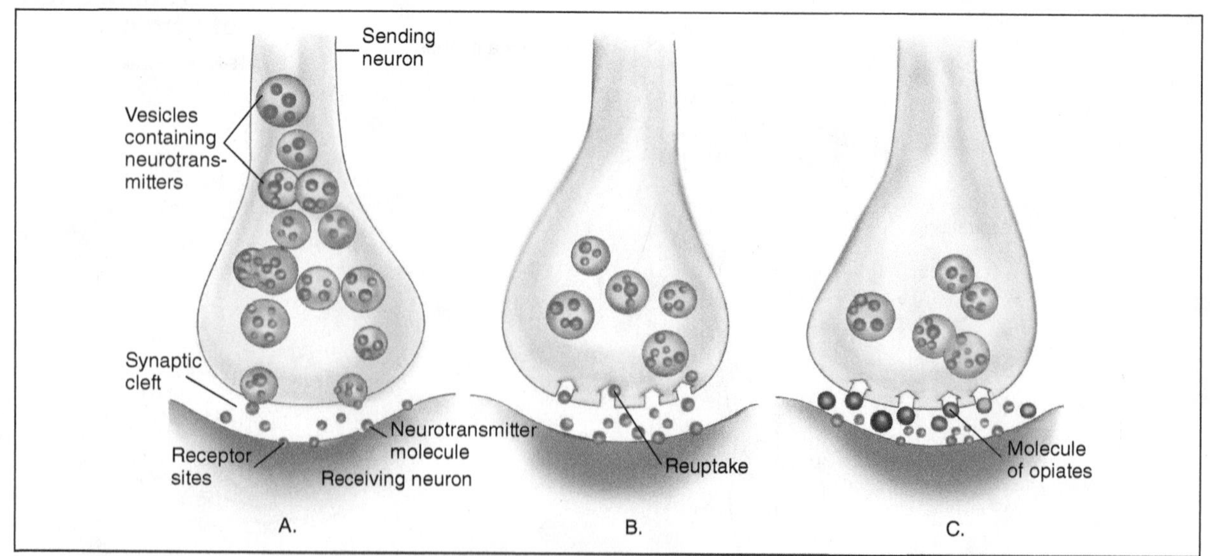

S. Rathus, S. Maheu, & S. Veenvliet. *PSYCH, 1e.* © 2012 Nelson Education Ltd. Reproduced by permission. www.cengage.com/permissions

If naloxone is given to someone who then takes heroin, the heroin has no effect. Obviously naloxone has practical applications in the treatment of opiate overdose, but it also has theoretical implications. Because naloxone's chemical structure is similar to morphine, researchers thought that the two drugs might be acting at some common brain receptor site and that the naloxone is blocking the morphine's action at that site.

FIGURE 11.3 The effect of opiates on our brain and nervous system

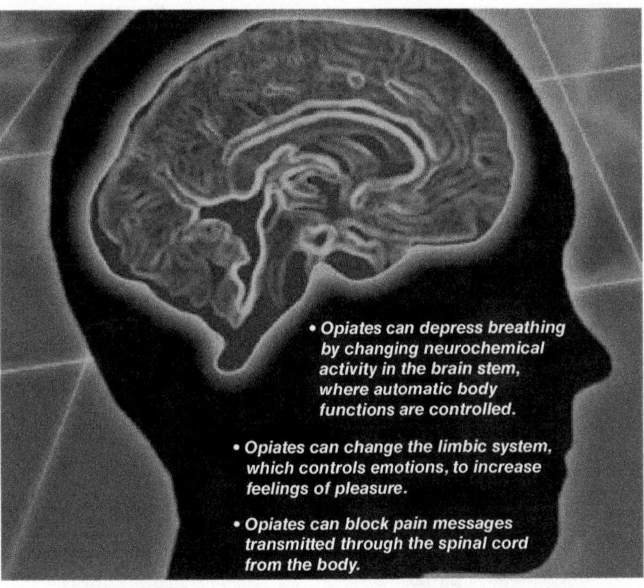

• Opiates can depress breathing by changing neurochemical activity in the brain stem, where automatic body functions are controlled.
• Opiates can change the limbic system, which controls emotions, to increase feelings of pleasure.
• Opiates can block pain messages transmitted through the spinal cord from the body.

Soucre: NIDA

What Do Endorphins Do?

The scientific questions that arose from the discovery of the endorphins have focused on just why the brain is endowed with its own morphine: What do endorphins do? Ongoing research started with the premise that, because opiate drugs apparently mimic endorphin activity by stimulating the opiate or endorphin receptor sites in the brain, endorphins might share many properties with opiate drugs, such as pain relief and production of pleasure. One idea is that endorphins are part of a natural pain-relief system. It has been argued that endorphins are released and produce analgesia or pain relief after certain kinds of pain or stress (Goldstein, 2001). This may help explain why, under certain circumstances such as on the battlefield or in athletic events, a person may sustain severe injury but not feel pain, at least for a time. Pain relief produced by acupuncture may be related to endorphin release because naloxone can reverse acupuncture-induced analgesia (Han & Terenius, 1982). Because the major action of naloxone is to block the endorphin receptors, naloxone-reversible analgesia is strong evidence that the acupuncture needles are triggering the release of endorphins and relieving pain through this system. Other evidence shows that pain relief induced by placebo can activate endorphin receptors in several brain regions (Zubieta & Stohler, 2009). This suggests an endorphinergic basis for at least some cases in which simply "expecting" that you have taken a pain-relieving drug is sufficient to relieve pain. Furthermore, a PET study compared brain activity in individuals who experienced pain relief produced by placebo and by opiate drugs and found similar patterns in the brain regions that were activated (Petrovic et al., 2002). So there is good evidence that endorphin systems are involved in some of the brain's natural pain-control mechanisms. Over the years, many other claims have been made about the endorphins, but this literature has conflicting results, and other functions of the endorphins remain unclear.

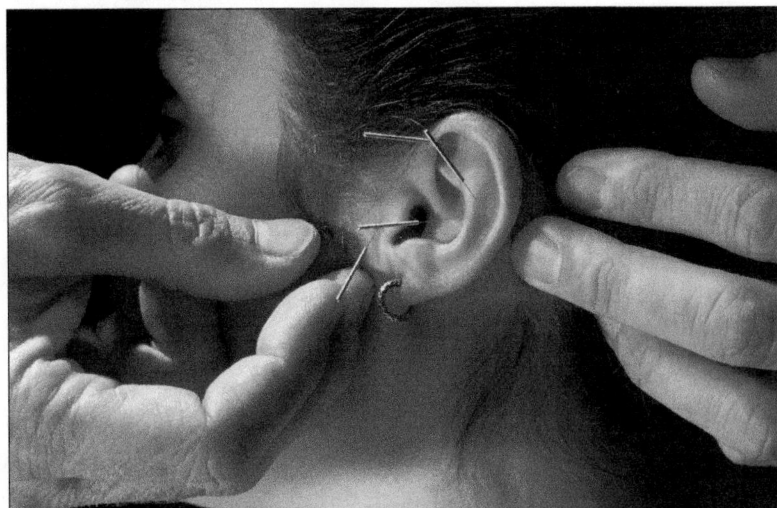

Corbis

Acupuncture may relieve pain by releasing endorphins.

Medical Use of Opiate Drugs

The major medical use of opiate drugs is for their analgesic or pain-relieving effects. As noted, opiates have been used for this purpose for centuries and remain the most potent and selective pain relievers known to medicine. Unlike the depressant-type anesthetic drugs discussed earlier, opiate analgesics relieve pain without causing unconsciousness. After receiving moderate doses of opiates, patients remain conscious and are able to report painful sensations but do not suffer from the pain.

The other major drugs that possess such analgesic properties are the over-the-counter painkillers: aspirin, acetaminophen, and ibuprofen, but none of these are as effective at relieving pain as the opiates (see Chapter 14). Table 11.2 lists some of the major opiate drugs used as analgesics along with their potency and their duration of action. Recall that *potency* refers to the dose required for a drug to produce a given effect. In Table 11.2, potency is given relative to an effective dose of morphine, which is given a value of one. For example, heroin has a value of two in Table 11.2 because heroin is approximately twice as potent as morphine. This means that if 10 milligrams of morphine were required to relieve pain in a given patient, then only five milligrams of heroin would be required.

Morphine is the prototype opiate analgesic and is the standard by which others are measured. It is used primarily for severe pain.

Morphine is the prototype opiate analgesic and is the standard by which others are measured. It is used primarily for severe pain. As we have noted, although heroin is more potent than morphine, it is not used medically in North America. Addiction is also a risk in using opiate drugs for pain relief. Within the last decade, the addictive qualities of opiates have come to the forefront in medical care and research. We know that opiates activate the reward circuit, just as many other drugs do, creating a pleasurable effect (e.g., Laviolette, Nader, & van der Kooy, 2002). In fact, opioids affect our brain by acting on three classes of receptors: kappa, delta, and mu (e.g., Dhawan et al., 1996). Each receptor class affects us in a unique way. Specifically, the

TABLE 11.2 Comparison of the Major Opiate Drugs

Generic Name	Brand Name	Potency	Duration of Action (Hours)
Morphine		1	4–5
Heroin		2	3–4
Hydrocodone	Vicodin	1	5–7
Hydromorphone	Dilaudid	5	4–5
Codeine		0.1	4–6
Oxycodone	Percodan, OxyContin	1.5	4–5
Methadone	Dolophine	1	12–24
Meperidine	Demerol	0.1	2–4
Propoxyphene	Darvon	0.05	6
Fentanyl	Sublimaze	100	1–3
Pentazocine	Talwin	0.2	2–3

Note: Potency estimates are presented relative to an effective dose of morphine (1).
Source: Based in part on Jaffe and Martin (1990) and Zacny (1995).

mu receptor appears to be the main class involved in opiate addiction. Researchers (e.g., Kieffer, 1999) have found that mice who lacked this receptor no longer found morphine rewarding, and morphine withdrawal symptoms were not seen in these animals. Experiments using positron emission tomography (e.g., Zubieta et al., 2000) *have* found an increase in the mu receptor levels in the anterior cingulate of humans addicted to opiates.

The roles of the kappa and delta opiate receptors appear to be ones of reducing dopamine function in the nucleus accumbens, and reinforcement of drug use, respectively. Naltrexone is a long-acting opiate antagonist. Its use in opiate addiction is based on its ability to antagonise any effects of opiates (Lingford-Hughes & Nutt, 2003). Withdrawal from opiates can lead to nausea, gastrointestinal disturbances, chills, and a general flu-like state in humans (e.g., Jaffe, 1980) and ptosis (drooping eyelid), teeth chattering, jumping, irritability, wet dog shakes, and diarrhea in animals (e.g., Wei et al., 1973). To reduce the risk of addiction less potent opiates are used whenever possible, and treatment is as brief as possible. When pain is severe and chronic, however, as with terminal cancer patients, tolerance inevitably develops, and higher doses of more potent drugs must follow to relieve the patient's pain. Ultimately, high doses of morphine may be the only way to relieve the suffering, and eventually, even this may not be enough.

Should physicians in the Canada be permitted to administer heroin? One argument against heroin is that heroin is more addicting than morphine because of its potency. Yet, in the treatment of severe pain of terminally ill patients, addiction seems irrelevant. Besides, patients are normally receiving high and frequent doses of morphine, so they certainly are addicted to morphine by the time heroin treatment is begun. Heroin is converted to morphine in the brain, and thus morphine is the active chemical in producing pain relief in both cases (heroin is more potent because it penetrates the blood–brain barrier more efficiently). One could accomplish the same degree of pain relief by giving larger and larger doses of morphine, but terminal cancer patients often become very thin and may lose tone in their veins with repeated injections. Thus, it may become difficult to administer enough morphine solution to be effective. Here is where the more potent heroin can be of value, because less solution is required.

Alternatively, an additional solution may come with the development of more potent opiate drugs that have not acquired the stigma associated with heroin. For example, fentanyl, a synthetic opiate drug, is at least 50 times more potent than heroin and is used primarily to produce anesthesia. However, the potent and long-acting drug OxyContin was designed and marketed for patients with severe chronic pain, and as we noted above, it has already been associated with a wave of abuse and addiction. Figure 11.4 shows the effects of OxyContin on our brain and nervous system.

Unless pain is very severe, prescription opiate preparations are used that are less potent or given in lower doses than morphine. Thus codeine, hydrocodone (Vicodin), propoxyphene (Darvon), lower doses of oxycodone (OxyContin, Percodan), and pentazocine (Talwin) often are prescribed for pain (see Table 11.2). In general, opiate drugs are the most potent and effective drugs available to medicine in the treatment of pain. The limitations of their use as analgesics are primarily their abuse liability: their tendency to produce tolerance and dependence. Tolerance and dependence develop for all these drugs, although some, such as pentazocine (Talwin), for example, are thought to be less liable for abuse than others. It is hoped that safer analgesic drugs will be developed as we learn more about endorphins and their ability to produce natural analgesia.

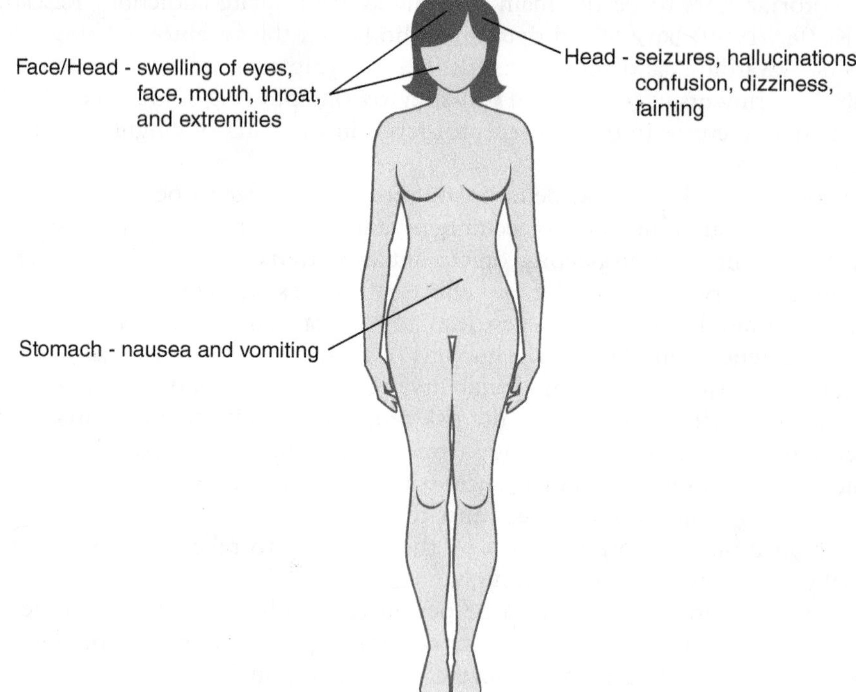

FIGURE 11.4
Effects of OxyContin on the brain and nervous system

Source: Zubada/Shutterstock

Opiate drugs have other medical uses. Opiates have a constipating effect that can be a problem for addicts but is of value in treating diarrhea. Opiates still are used to treat coughs. The drug most commonly used for this purpose is dextromethorphan, which is a synthetic opiate that has no analgesic or addictive properties but is an effective cough suppressant (Jaffe & Martin, 1990). A final medical

CONTEMPORARY ISSUE BOX 11.3

Ultralow-Dose Naltrexone and NMDA Antagonists: New Approaches to Make Prescription Opiates Safer

Opiate drugs remain the most valuable medications available for the relief of severe pain, but we have noted the many problems associated with their use and misuse. New strategies are being developed to help reduce some of these problems that involve the combination of the prescription opiate painkiller with some other drug. One such strategy involves the combination of an ultralow dose of the opiate antagonist naltrexone with the opiate agonist. Apparently, if the naltrexone dose is sufficiently low, it can actually enhance the pain-relieving effects of the opiate agonist but may still block the rewarding effects of the drug, retard the development of tolerance, and lessen withdrawal severity. These results have mainly been reported from nonhuman experiments (e.g., Largent-Milnes et al., 2008), but early trials in human patients with pain using a combination of oxycodone (OxyContin) and ultralow-dose naltrexone (Oxytrex) have been promising (Webster, 2007). Similarly, combinations of drugs that block n-methyl d-aspartate (NMDA) receptors and opiate agonists have been reported to enhance pain relief and block tolerance development and may have therapeutic potential (Craft & Lee, 2005; Fischer et al., 2008). Hopefully, the development of new compounds such as these will increase the safety of pain medication and lessen the problem of diversion and abuse of prescription opiate drugs.

DRUGS AND CULTURE BOX 11.4

Canada's Methadone Maintenance Program

In Canada, opiate dependency is most often treated using methadone, a long-acting synthetic opioid agonist. A methadone maintenance program can be used to treat all forms of opioid dependence, regardless of the route of administration (oral or injection), and includes a number of components (which may vary in delivery and intensity):

- methadone dose;
- medical care;
- treatment for other substance use;
- counselling and support;
- mental health services;
- health promotion, disease prevention, and education;
- linkages with other community-based supports and services; and
- outreach and advocacy.

Methadone works by alleviating the symptoms of opiate withdrawal and diminishing the euphoric effects of other opioids, so that self-administered illicit opioids will not lead to euphoria and therefore are less likely to be used. These effects are long lasting, up to 24 hours. Individuals take their medication (methadone) orally once daily, usually mixed into an orange drink. Tolerance to the effects of methadone develops very slowly, so individuals can often be maintained on the same dose of methadone safely for many years. When appropriately prescribed and dispensed, methadone is considered a medically safe medication (Health Canada, 2008).

use for opiates such as methadone is in the treatment of heroin addicts in withdrawal and in maintenance programs designed to help addicts stay off heroin (see Drugs and Culture Box 11.4).

Given the longstanding and widespread medical use of opiate drugs for the treatment of pain, the recent epidemic of prescription opiate use noted previously took substance abuse professionals by surprise. Conventional wisdom was that these drugs were relatively low in abuse liability when used as directed for pain, and the basis for the sudden increase in illicit use is not completely understood. Nora Volkow, director of the National Institute on Drug Abuse, noted three potential reasons for the increases (Compton & Volkow, 2006). First, the number of prescriptions written for opiate painkillers increased, and the increase in illicit use may be a by-product of the increased availability that resulted. A second reason may involve the ready availability of prescription opiates via the Internet. The emergence of Internet access to prescription drugs has made them available without physician supervision. Third, changes in prescribing practices with more prescriptions by primary care physicians who are not necessarily expert in pain management may be related to increased diversion and abuse (Compton & Volkow, 2006). Although diversion of prescription opiate drugs has clearly become a significant national problem, leading to legislative proposals to ban some of these drugs (Tolman, 2005), it is important to remember that they are of critical importance in the medical treatment of pain and are thus of significant societal value. As Cicero, Inciardi, and Munoz (2005) put it: "Steps need to be taken to reduce prescription drug abuse, but very great care needs to be exercised in the nature of these actions so that legitimate and appropriate use of these drugs in the treatment of pain is not compromised as a result" (p. 662).

The emergence of Internet access to prescription drugs has made them available without physician supervision.

Acute Psychological and Physiological Effects of Opiates

Opiate drugs have acute effects in addition to analgesia. Subjective reports of the euphoria produced by opiates mention drowsiness, body warmth, and a heavy feeling of the limbs (Jaffe & Martin, 1990). William S. Burroughs (1953) describes the feeling in his autobiographical novel *Junky:* "Morphine hits the backs of the legs first, then the back of the neck, a spreading wave of relaxation slackening the muscles away from the bones so that you seem to float without outlines, like lying in warm salt water" (p. 7). Both the naturally occurring and synthetic opiates are capable of producing these pleasurable effects in most individuals; however, in laboratory studies, opiate abusers appear to generally report more positive effects and liking than non-abusers (see Comer & Zacny, 2005, for a review), but the basis for this is unclear. The pleasure experienced under the influence of opiates seems to interfere with the user's other interests. Burroughs described it as follows: "Junk shortcircuits sex. The drive to nonsexual sociability comes from the same place sex comes from, so when I have an H(eroin) or M(orphine) shooting habit I am non-sociable. If someone wants to talk, OK. But there is no drive to get acquainted" (p. 124). In fact, there is good evidence that opiate drugs reduce sexual drive or interest and often produce impotence in men (Quaglio et al., 2008). Consistent with Burroughs's anecdotal reports, laboratory studies show that opiates impair social interactions (Meyer & Mirin, 1979). People who smoke opium or take other opiate drugs often report vivid dreamlike experiences. These are the basis for the expression "pipe dreams." Opiates may also interfere with cognitive function. Animal studies indicate impairments in learning and memory (e.g., Galizio et al., 2003), and research with clients on methadone maintenance suggests that some methadone doses may produce cognitive impairment as well (Mintzer, Copersino, & Stitzer, 2005).

The acute physiological effects of opiate drugs resemble those of depressant drugs, with some differences. Like depressants, opiates cause respiratory depression and lowered body temperature (Grilly, 2002; see Table 11.3). Nausea and vomiting often occur immediately after taking opiates. Perhaps the most visible sign of opiate drug use is constriction of the pupils. This effect is so pronounced in overdose that "pinpoint pupils" are a diagnostic sign of opiate poisoning. When a high dose of heroin is fatal, the immediate cause is usually respiratory failure. The lethal dose

TABLE 11.3 Effects of Administration and Withdrawal of Opiate Drugs

Administration	Withdrawal
Decreased body temperature	Increased body temperature
Decreased blood pressure	Increased blood pressure
Pupil constriction	Pupil dilation
Drying of secretions	Tearing, runny nose
Constipation	Diarrhea
Decreased sex drive, impotence	Spontaneous ejaculation/orgasm
Respiratory depression	Yawning
Analgesia	Pain
Euphoria	Depression/anxiety

of heroin is surprisingly high, however. As Brecher (1972) noted, many overdose victims on the street are found on autopsy to have injected less than would be expected to be lethal. These cases involve not simply an overdose of heroin but also a lethal drug interaction between heroin and alcohol or another depressant drug. Opiates and depressant drugs potentiate one another (Ho & Allen, 1981). This synergy can often be lethal, and many of the most publicized "heroin" overdoses actually involve synergy, such as the death of Janis Joplin in 1970, as reported in *Time*:

> The quart bottle of Southern Comfort (whiskey) that she held aloft onstage was at once a symbol of her load, and her way of lightening it. As she emptied the bottle, she grew happier, more radiant and more freaked out.... Last week on a day that superficially at least seemed to be less lonely than most, Janis Joplin died on the lowest and saddest of notes. Returning to her Hollywood motel room after a late-night recording session and some hard drinking with friends at a nearby bar, she apparently filled a hypodermic needle with heroin and shot it into her left arm. The injection killed her. (Brecher, 1972, p. 113)

Marcel Hartmann/Sygma/Corbis

Actor Heath Ledger died from the synergy produced by a combination of prescription opiates and depressant drugs.

We now recognize that the alcohol was as responsible for her death as the heroin. Synergy between depressant drugs and prescription opiates is also a dangerous possibility when these drugs are combined. The recent death of actor Heath Ledger (from a combination of prescription opiate OxyContin and benzodiazepine depressants) illustrates such synergy.

Chronic Effects of Opiates

Tolerance

The effects of opiate drugs are somewhat different when they are taken chronically. As we noted, tolerance develops to opiates, so their effects are generally diminished unless the user escalates the dose, which often occurs. Figure 11.5 shows the pattern of opiate intake in both a human and a rhesus monkey of continuous drug availability studied under laboratory conditions. Each graph shows the drug intake plotted over consecutive days in the experiment. The human data come from an experiment in which a volunteer with a history of extensive drug abuse was studied under laboratory conditions in which he could regulate his daily intravenous morphine dose. Note the gradual increase in dose he chooses over time. For the first month, the participant never administered more than 500 milligrams per day. By the fourth month, however, he frequently took more than 1000 milligrams. Also note the bottom panel of Figure 11.5, which reveals a similar pattern of heroin self-administration by monkeys that could obtain intravenous heroin by pressing a lever. Clearly, the emergence of tolerance to the rewarding consequences of opiate drugs is a phenomenon of great generality.

Withdrawal and Dependence

The motives for the continued use of opiates over time may change. Although repeated use is initially motivated by a desire to reexperience the pleasant rush

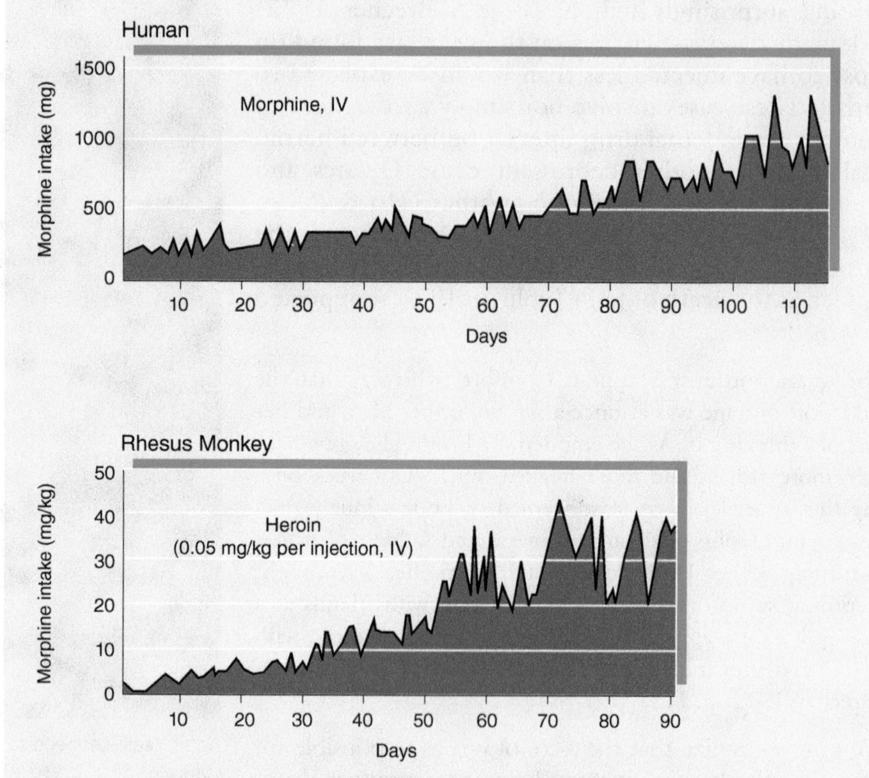

FIGURE 11.5
Patterns of opioid intake in a human and a rhesus monkey under conditions of continuous drug availability

Source: This article was published in *Behavioral Analysis of Drug Dependence* by Henningfield, Lukas, and Bigelow, eds. Goldberg and Stoleman. © Elsevier 1986.

associated with taking the drug, addicts report that continued use of a drug does not make them nearly as high as before. They continue to use the drug to avoid the unpleasant symptoms of abstinence. Thus, the processes that maintain heroin use change from positive to negative reinforcement. The withdrawal symptoms associated with opiate dependence may appear after only one to two weeks of chronic use of heroin, morphine, or a synthetic opiate drug. The symptoms become more severe with longer-term use of higher doses. Early indications of withdrawal begin eight to 12 hours after the last dose and include flu-like symptoms such as runny nose, tearing, sweating, irritability, and tremor. As time passes, these symptoms become more severe and others appear, including pupil dilation, anorexia, and piloerection (goose bumps). This last symptom leaves an addict looking a bit like a plucked turkey and may be the basis for the expression "cold turkey." These symptoms continue to worsen and reach a peak after 48 to 72 hours. At this time, heart rate and blood pressure are elevated, and the addict experiences severe flu-like symptoms such as nausea, diarrhea, sneezing, excessive sweating, and pain in the bones. In addition, an addict may show spastic movements of the arms and legs that may appear similar to kicking. This is thought to be the basis for the expression "kicking the habit." Other somewhat bizarre symptoms, which apparently indicate a rebound of the addict's sexual system, include spontaneous erection and ejaculation in men and orgasm in women. The loss of fluids and failure of addicts to eat or drink much during withdrawal can leave addicts physically and emotionally drained and occasionally can be fatal (Jaffe & Martin, 1990).

It is worth noting that a suitable dose of any opiate drug (but not depressant drugs) will reverse the abstinence symptoms and restore a feeling of well-being to addicts. Hospital detoxification procedures take advantage of this fact by treating addicts in withdrawal with low doses of a synthetic opiate drug such as methadone. The dose of methadone given is sufficient to reduce the severity of the addicts' withdrawal symptoms but not enough to produce much of a high. Gradually over a period of several weeks, the dose of methadone is tapered off until finally addicts show no further signs of physical dependence. If physical withdrawal symptoms were the only factors maintaining heroin addiction, detoxification would be a cure. However, after detoxification procedures, an estimated 90 percent relapse within two years after leaving the hospital, and most of these relapses occur during the first six months after detoxification. Thus, returning addicts to the environment in which they became addicted is most likely to result in relapse, even in the absence of physical withdrawal symptoms.

That heroin (and other drug) addiction depends on more than just physical withdrawal symptoms is illustrated nicely by the heroin addiction epidemic that failed to occur. During the early 1970s, as the Vietnam War was drawing to a close, heroin addiction rates were high among returning American soldiers, with some estimates reaching 21 percent. These soldiers were required to go through a detoxification before their return to the United States, but given a 90 percent relapse rate, one would have expected most would return to heroin use at home. Thus, an epidemic of heroin addiction in the United States was expected. Follow-up studies showed that very few soldiers did relapse (less than 15 percent), however, which illustrates clearly that environmental and psychosocial factors associated with Vietnam were apparently responsible for the development of the dependence. Upon returning to the United States, Vietnam veterans found heroin far less available. That, added to the changes in lifestyle and social environment in the United States, apparently eased the pressures that led to their initial dependence (Robins, Helzer, & Davis, 1975). The radical change in environment from Vietnam to the United States cannot be duplicated in the typical treatment setting. This is one reason that treating heroin addiction is so difficult, although a number of different types of treatment have been developed.

More recently, the role of culture in opiate use has surfaced as a new challenge in Canada. Doda, also known as poor-man's heroin, is an opium-derived drug that is gaining popularity among Canada's South Asian community. Doda is made by crushing the opium poppy pod and mixing it with liquid, such as tea, or used as meat seasoning. The drug is especially popular among individuals who need to stay awake for long periods or need sustained energy, such as taxi drivers or construction workers. Although doda is less potent than other opiate drugs it can still become addictive. Further, doda produces a quick high followed by feelings of relaxation and calm, but it can also cause loss of concentration, slurred speech, drowsiness, impotence, constipation, and mood swings. Doda is illegal in Canada, and drug seizures have taken place in Toronto, Calgary, Edmonton, and British Columbia (Delaney, 2010).

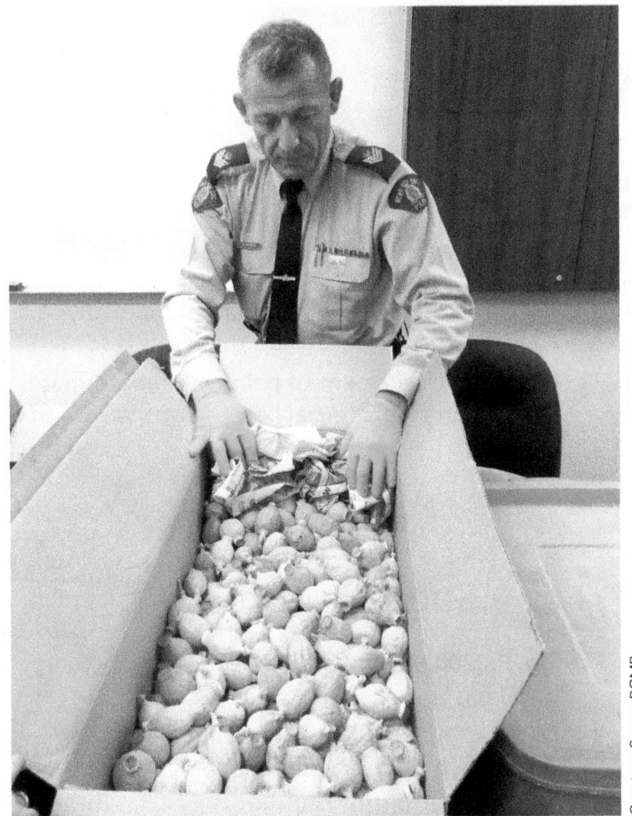

Courtesy Surrey RCMP

Doda use is a growing concern in Canada leading to increased drug seizures.

SUMMARY

- Opium is produced from the sap of the poppy plant, and it has been used for medicinal purposes for centuries.
- In the 19th century the major active agent in opium, morphine, was isolated. More potent than opium, morphine was prized for its analgesic effects but also became a major addiction problem.
- Heroin was developed as an alternative to morphine but soon became the addict's drug of choice. Although opiate drugs remained important in medicine, after the passage of the legislation in Canada and the United States, heroin became a major criminal drug.
- Opiate drugs act in the brain by mimicking endorphins, natural neurotransmitters that are involved in the regulation of pain.
- The major medical use for opiate drugs is in the treatment of severe pain.
- Opiates depress respiration, lower body temperature, and cause capillary constriction. They induce a pleasurable euphoria as well as relieve pain.
- Opiate use stimulates the reward circuit of the brain. Regular use of opiates results in tolerance and an abstinence syndrome characterized by flu-like symptoms and intense drug craving. Heroin addiction is more complex than simple avoidance of withdrawal symptoms.

Key Terms

analgesia p. 251
heroin p. 252
naloxone p. 262
opium p. 250

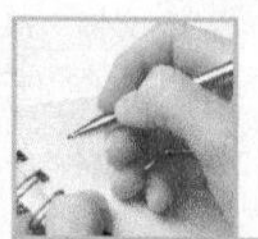

Essays/Thought Questions

1. Heroin is often considered to be the prototype addictive drug. Why do you think this is so?
2. Medical management of pain with opiates has often been controversial because of the risks of diversion and abuse. Considering the recent problems with OxyContin in this regard, what do you think about public policy, pain management, and opiate drugs?

Suggested Readings

Ashton, R. (2002). *This is heroin*. London: Sanctuary Publishing Ltd.

Inciardi, J.A. (2002). *The war on drugs III: The continuing saga of the mysteries and miseries of intoxication, addiction, crime, and public policy.* Boston: Allyn & Bacon.

CHAPTER 12

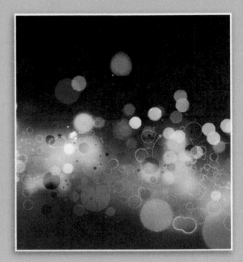

Psychotherapeutic Medications

Did You Know

?

- Twenty percent of Canadians suffer from mental illness.
- Cannabis was one of the first drugs to be used to treat mental illness.
- The prevalence of psychotherapeutic medication is twice as high among women as among men.
- The elderly are most likely to misuse psychotherapeutic drugs.
- Anxiety is the most common type of mental illness in Canada.
- If you become dependent on sleeping pills you may experience a rebound effect of insomnia.
- It is dangerous to take psychotherapeutic medication while pregnant.

More typically today, medications are intended to provide people with some relief and ideally with the opportunity to function better in their environments.

Canadians have a one in five chance of having a mental illness in their lifetime, and over 10 percent of Canadians are currently suffering from some type of mental illness (Mood Disorders Society of Canada, [MDSC] 2009). The treatment of mental illness is undoubtedly a critical issue not just in Canada, but also throughout the world.

Psychoactive substances have been used to treat mental illnesses for centuries. In fact, many of the substances described in this text, such as alcohol, cannabis, and opium, have been used as treatments for mental illness at one time or another. In some cases, the motivation to administer psychopharmacological agents to the mentally ill has been simply to subdue them. More typically today, medications are intended to provide people with some relief and ideally with the opportunity to function better in their environments.

The development, testing, and distribution of psychotherapeutic drugs, are a major worldwide industry. Fewer than a dozen countries (predominantly Canada, the United States, Italy, Japan, Germany, France, the United Kingdom, Brazil, and Spain) account for approximately 75 percent of the world's pharmaceutical sales. Canada has the greatest number of psychotherapeutic users per capita of any country in the world, the second highest number of sedative users in the world, and the fourth highest number of prescription narcotics users in the world. In 2006, 51 million prescriptions for psychotheraputic medications were dispensed by pharmacies throughout Canada (MDSC, 2009).

psychotherapeutic Exerting a special or unique action on psychological functioning.

We open this chapter with an overview of the use of psychotherapeutic drugs. Following a brief historical overview, we discuss some epidemiological features of what are called **psychotherapeutic** drugs. The term *psychotherapeutic* describes those drugs that have a special or unique effect on the mind or mental functioning. (In the field of psychiatry, these psychotherapeutic drugs are often called psychotropics.) We discuss mechanisms of drug action, and provide an overview of four major classes of psychotherapeutic drugs: antipsychotics, antidepressants, antianxiety agents, and antimanic or mood-stabilizing drugs. We supplement this material with case examples to give you a feeling for the problems or disorders these drugs are intended to relieve.

Historical Overview

The roots of psychopharmacology are based in the 19th century, when a science of chemistry was developing, and the field grew rapidly during the 20th century. The actual coining of the term *psychopharmacology* in 1920 is attributed to David Macht, an American pharmacist (Caldwell, 1970).

The Pre-Chlorpromazine Era

Nineteenth-century society had very little understanding of mental illness. Although there were several compendia of treatments and psychopharmacological agents for mental illnesses (especially in England, France, and Germany), the proposed remedies were mostly speculative and without scientific support. Many of the approaches used were actually cruel, including bloodletting, hot irons, flogging, revolving chairs, starvation, and sneezing powder (Spiegel & Aebi, 1983). Nevertheless, attempts were made to understand and treat, or in some cases, "cleanse" those with mental illness. The efforts of Emil Kraepelin, Phillip Pinel, and J.E. Esquirol were particularly noteworthy. These scientists were involved in the development of a classification system of mental illnesses. They believed that a scientific understanding and categorizing of mental illnesses were prerequisites to the identification of effective treatments.

Moreau also found that manic patients given cannabis subsequently calmed down and relaxed. Unfortunately, the effects of the cannabis tended to be temporary.

One of the more systematically studied drugs in this period was cannabis. In the 1840s, the French physician Jacques-Joseph Moreau de Tours was working at a mental hospital in Paris. He theorized that treatment should "substitute symptoms of mental illness with similar but controllable drug-induced symptoms" (Caldwell, 1978, p. 16). Moreau used cannabis and found gaiety and euphoria to be among its effects. He decided to give cannabis to two hospital patients with depression to see whether it would produce similar results in them. These patients did indeed respond to the cannabis, appearing happy and becoming talkative. Moreau also found that **manic** patients given cannabis subsequently calmed down and relaxed. Unfortunately, the effects of the cannabis tended to be temporary.

The first half of the 20th century brought further attempts to use drugs and other therapies to treat mental illness. For example, tests were conducted on the effectiveness of giving amphetamines to depressed and **narcoleptic** patients, and carbon dioxide inhalation procedures were used in the treatment of illnesses referred to as psychoses and **neuroses**. Also used in the treatment of psychoses were antihistamines, insulin shock, and **psychosurgery**. Electroshock therapy was used to treat severe depression (a procedure still used today). Finally, in 1949, an Australian physician named John Cade discovered that the alkali metal lithium successfully moderated manic conditions, although concerns about toxic reactions to it prevented its approval for use in the United States until 1970. Lithium remains a mainstay in the treatment of bipolar illnesses today.

SPL/Photo Researchers, Inc.

Early psychiatric hospitals did not have the advantages of psychotherapeutic drugs to treat mentally ill patients. This drawing depicts a mentally ill patient during the early 1800s.

Despite many efforts, the collective impact of these advances in the treatment of mental illness was modest at best. In fact, the total positive impact of this progress pales in comparison to the successes experienced in the later use of another drug, chlorpromazine. To the extent that psychopharmacology is defined as the use of psychotherapeutic medications to restore and maintain some degree of mental health, its true coming of age was in Paris in 1951.

manic
Relating to mania, a mood disturbance that typically includes hyperactivity, agitation, excessive elation, and pressured speech.

narcoleptic
A state characterized by brief but uncontrollable episodes of sleep.

neuroses
Nonpsychotic emotional disturbance, pain, or discomfort beyond what is appropriate in the conditions of one's life.

psychosurgery
Surgery that entails the cutting of fibres connecting particular parts of the brain or the removal or destruction of areas of brain tissue with the goal of modifying severe behavioural or emotional disturbances.

The Age of Chlorpromazine

Chlorpromazine was synthesized by Paul Charpentier in 1950. Its first use was as a psychotherapeutic medication in general surgery. Chlorpromazine was used as an anesthetic; it decreased patients' anxiety about surgical preparations and prevented shock during surgery. Henri Laborit primarily conducted this work in surgery, and his observation of chlorpromazine's calming effects led him to suggest its potential use in psychiatry. This application was initially tried at Val-de-Grace, a military hospital in Paris. Agitated psychotic patients appeared calm following administration of chlorpromazine. In addition, the patients' thoughts appeared to become less chaotic and the patients were less excitable. Notably, the patients did not exhibit any loss of consciousness. Instead, they showed a disinterested and detached demeanour, or what Deniker (1983) has called "the syndrome of psychomotor indifference" (p. 166).

Chlorpromazine has had a profound effect on the field of psychiatry. As described by Caldwell (1978):

> By May 1953, the atmosphere in the disturbed wards of mental hospitals in Paris was transformed: straightjackets [sic], psychohydraulic packs and noise were things of the past! Once

more, Paris psychiatrists who long ago unchained the chained, became pioneers in liberating their patients, this time from inner torments too, and with a drug: (chlorpromazine). It accomplished the pharmacologic revolution of psychiatry—then and there. (p. 30)

Word of the successful use of chlorpromazine spread rapidly. In 1953, researcher and medical physician Heinz E. Lehmann learned of this new drug and soon became a pioneer in its use. The Drugs and Culture Box 12.1 describes Lehmann's work in his own words. The use of chlorpromazine was a pivotal and profound factor leading to the decrease of hospitalized psychiatric patients in Canada, the U.S., and Europe.

DRUGS AND CULTURE BOX 12.1

In His Own Words: Heinz E. Lehmann Brings Chlorpromazine to North America

In the spring of 1953, while working as a psychiatrist at the Douglas Hospital (then Verdun Protestant Hospital) in Montreal, I came across an article in a French medical journal that reported interesting findings with a new drug. At that time, there were no drugs that were effective in the treatment of major mental illnesses such as schizophrenic psychosis or manic-depressive disorder.

For more than 10 years in my psychiatric work, I had been challenged and frustrated by hundreds of mentally ill patients for whom there were only shock treatments, that were sometimes dangerous and had only limited, temporary effects when they worked. Most mentally ill patients, once hospitalized, would remain confined for the rest of their lives.

The new drug about which I had read in the journal was chlorpromazine which had been produced by Rhône Poulenc. The scientists of this pharmaceutical company had demonstrated in important animal studies that the drug was apparently safe and capable of producing intriguing and hitherto unknown effects on the animal's behaviour. Also, two French psychiatrists, J. Delay and P. Deniker, had observed some fascinating effects of the drug in some of their patients. Neither the best dose of the drug nor the kind of diagnosis of psychiatric illness for which it was specifically indicated had as yet been established. I decided to try the drug on my patients.

It was not difficult in those days to find volunteers among my patients and their families for a new treatment. With one of my colleagues, Dr. G. Hanrahan, I started a clinical research trial on 75 patients with chlorpromazine. Rhône Poulenc provided the new drug.

Three months later, we were able to report our results in a new scientific paper. Our clinical results were so unique and surprising that they were almost incredible at that time. For the first time in history, there was now a drug that could suppress hallucinations—frightening, morbid voices and visions that did not exist in the outside world but were very real to the patients—and paranoid delusions of persecution. Our paper was the first report on a major, systematic trial with the new drug in North America. Even before it was published, the findings reported in the manuscript had so much impressed Dr. Henry Brill, an official at the New York State Department of Mental Hygiene at that time, that he introduced the treatment with chlorpromazine in the New York State mental hospitals. He soon published reports that confirmed our findings, and within a short time hundreds of articles all over the world established the drug and its derivatives as the standard antipsychotic treatment for schizophrenia.

In 1957, I received the American Albert Lasker Award, probably the most prestigious medical award after the Nobel Prize, for my work with chlorpromazine. I think I was the first Canadian researcher to receive this award.

In the years to follow, hundreds of thousands of mentally ill patients all over the world could be discharged from mental hospitals into the community and maintained there while being treated with chlorpromazine and similar antipsychotic drugs that were soon developed after chlorpromazine had shown the way. In Canada alone, from 50 000 to 80 000 persons are in need of treatment with antipsychotic drugs.

Grant support by the Medical Research Council of Canada and the U.S.-based National Institute of Mental Health—more than one million dollars from the latter, as well as grants from various pharmaceutical companies—made it possible for me and my coworkers to further develop the new psychopharmacological treatment and science that chlorpromazine had brought into being. Douglas Hospital, the old-fashioned, overcrowded, under-staffed, and under-funded mental hospital of the 1940s, harbours now less than half the former number of patients and has become one of Canada's leading research centres in the neurosciences.

Heinz E. Lehmann passed away on April 7, 1999.

Source: Canadians for Health Research. *Introduction of Chlorpromazine Treatment of Mental Illness in North America*. Found at: http://www.chrcrm.org/en/salute-excellence/introduction-chlorpromazine-treatment-mental-illness-north-america.

The decades following the introduction of chlorpromazine witnessed much growth in the field of psychopharmacology. The next major event was the appearance of reserpine in 1954. This drug, similar to chlorpromazine, was originally used in the treatment of another medical disorder (arterial hypertension), and the physicians using the drug noted symptoms of indifference in their patients. Because of this effect, reserpine was given to psychiatric patients. The drug had positive effects overall, but its action often took several weeks to be apparent (see Deniker, 1983), and patients who took the medication often appeared depressed. Thus, reserpine never achieved the popularity of chlorpromazine.

Other advances in the field were antianxiety (or anxiolytic) medications, such as meprobamate (which also was used as a muscle relaxant), and antidepressant medications, such as monoamine oxidase inhibitors (MAOIs) and tricyclic antidepressants. Another drug that received renewed attention was LSD. Because of the psychotic-like effects produced by LSD, researchers used it to create a "model psychosis" to study (with limited success, to date) possible etiological factors contributing to mental illness. They could also treat the LSD-created symptoms with psychotherapeutic drugs.

In retrospect, the 1950s were a frontier period for psychopharmacology. Much growth was experienced, and advances in the field continue to be made (although none with quite the impact and significance of chlorpromazine, which is widely used today). These advances have had a profound effect on the current treatment of mental illness. As noted, psychopharmacology contributed to decreases in the numbers of hospitalized psychiatric patients. Unfortunately, there have been downsides to this deinstitutionalization. Although psychotherapeutic medications often ameliorate the primary symptoms associated with a disorder, this does not necessarily mean that social coping skills or general "life skills" simultaneously materialize or reappear. Thus, some form of continuing care is often warranted. It had been expected that a variety of outpatient psychiatric services would be available to serve the needs of those discharged with chronic mental illness. Because that has not been the case, many patients once under psychiatric care are now without such services. It also has been argued that this lack of ongoing care contributes to the increased incidence of homeless people, many of whom suffer from psychiatric illnesses.

Epidemiology

As stated earlier, one in five Canadians will suffer from some type of mental illness in their lifetime. The most common mental illnesses are anxiety, depression, and substance abuse. In Canada, eight percent of individuals will experience clinical depression in their the lifetime and 12 percent will experience some form of anxiety disorder. One in 30 Canadians meets the criteria for substance dependence. Further, 30 percent of people diagnosed with mental illness also have substance abuse problems (MDSC, 2009). Despite the significant number of Canadians suffering from mental illness, only a minority seeks clinical services for their disorders. For example, 90 percent of Canadians suffering from depression never seek treatment. These mental health problems exact an enormous toll for individuals, employers, and Canadian society as a whole (e.g., Langlieb & Kahn, 2005). The following statistics illustrate Canada's crisis of mental illness*:

- It costs $170 820 per year to keep someone with serious mental illness in the hospital.
- The unemployment rate among people with serious mental illness is 70–90 percent.
- Between 30 and 35 percent of homeless people suffer from mental illness.

* Mood Disorder Society of Canada, *Quick Facts: Mental Illness and Addiction in Canada,* 2009.

- Depression is on a par with smoking as a predictor of mortality.
- There are 4000 suicides in Canada each year; 90 percent of Canadians who commit suicide have a diagnosable mental illness.
- Among Canadian children and youth, 1.2 million people are affected by mental illness at any given point in time; 15 percent of preschoolers will have significant levels of depression.
- In 2007 $1.16 billion was spent on antidepressants.
- Mental illness results in an annual loss of $33 billion to the Canadian economy.

In Canada, the rate of antidepressant use has increased 4.6 percent every year since 1998. (MDSC, 2009)

As previously discussed it is not uncommon for someone suffering from mental illness to also have a substance abuse problem. Comorbidity, which refers to the simultaneous occurrence of two or more mental illnesses is very common. In fact, almost half (45 percent) of the adults with one mental disorder met the criteria for at least one other disorder. The signs of mental illness often appear early, with half of those diagnosed with a mental disorder showing signs of the disease by age 14, and three-quarters showed signs by age 24. The symptoms associated with mental health disorders frequently are treated with prescription medications, most commonly prescriptions for an antidepressant or antianxiety medications. In Canada, the rate of anti-depressant use has increased 4.6 percent every year since 1998 (MDSC, 2009).

There are important trends among people who use psychotherapeutic medications. First, the prevalence of psychotherapeutic medication use is about twice as high among women as among men. Second, psychotherapeutic drug use increases with age, a trend seen more dramatically among men. Third, greater use of psychotherapeutics is found among those who live alone, those with more education, and those with higher incomes.

Although most psychotherapeutic medications are used as prescribed, the nonprescribed use and abuse of psychotherapeutic drugs are a significant problem. Abuse of prescription drugs can take many forms, ranging from patients who exceed recommended dosages to the street sale of pharmaceuticals (Weiss & Greenfield, 1986). People who abuse prescription drugs divert them from legal distribution by stealing from drugstores or pharmaceutical companies, pilfering supplies of hospitals or clinics, and altering or forging prescriptions. The consequences of prescription drug abuse are immense. For example, prescription drug abuse is implicated in significant numbers of injuries and deaths, drug-related emergency room cases, and drug-related deaths.

The drugs most often abused or misused in Western cultures are depressants and stimulants. In 2008, psychotheraputic medications were the second highest class of drugs dispensed in Canada (next to cardiovascular medications) accounting for 57 198 000 prescriptions. Unfortunately, people of all ages have been known to misuse prescription drugs. This abuse is especially notable among the elderly. For example, it is not uncommon to see the elderly misuse prescribed medications in combination with each other, with over-the-counter drugs, or with alcohol. (The use of multiple prescription drugs is not always intentional because doctors sometimes provide prescriptions to the elderly without being aware of other prescription medications they already are using.) Before leaving the discussion on prescription drug misuse and abuse, we should note that a variety of over-the-counter substances with psychoactive properties are also subject to abuse. Examples are nonprescription hypnotics that contain antihistamines, nonprescription cold and allergy products, laxatives, nonprescription stimulants, and diet pills. Over the years, both legislative and medical association groups have made efforts to monitor and control the availability of and access to prescribed medications. Most psychotherapeutic medications are under federal control and require a prescription for use. However, according to the Mood Disorders Society of Canada (2009) there are some concerns about the drug approval process in Canada. Specifically, they note the following (Mood Disorder Society of Canada, *Quick Facts: Mental Illness & Addiction in Canada*, 2009)*:

- Ninety percent of drug trials are designed and funded by the same pharmaceutical companies that intend to market them. This creates a concern for biased reporting that has resulted in a refusal of peer reviewed journals to publish these types of studies.
- The sample size and length of drug trial are limited in scope and time, which may not provide an adequate opportunity for adverse reactions to appear. A recent example is the drug Vioxx. Vioxx was originally approved by both Health Canada and the FDA in 1999 for the treatment of arthritis, pain, and migraines. However, in 2004, Vioxx was removed from the market after it was found to significantly increase the risk of cardiovascular disease (heart attack and stroke) among its users. Prior to its approval clinical trials showed a non-statistically significant increase in risk of cardiovascular events, but "pre-marketing approval trials are too small to flush out all of the risks of a drug" (CMAJ, 2005).
- There is an increase in off-label prescribing, meaning that physicians prescribe drugs for uses other than approved by Health Canada.
- If a pharmaceutical company applies for and is refused permission to market their drug for a new use, this fact is not made public.

Classes of Drugs and Their Actions

Psychotherapeutic drugs, like other drugs, can be classified along a variety of dimensions, such as chemical structure, clinical actions, and sites of action (see Chapter 1). However, the most common classification used in psychiatry, and the one we use, is by therapeutic usage. This classification yields four basic categories:

1. Antipsychotics
2. Antidepressants
3. Antianxiety agents
4. Antimanic medications.

In the following sections, we describe representative psychotherapeutics in each of these classifications.

Antipsychotics

In 2007 Canadians spent $629 million on antipsychotic medications. As you will recall, the introduction of antipsychotic medications in the 1950s was a major turning point in the treatment of severe psychiatric disorders, especially schizophrenia. *Schizophrenia* is a term that encompasses an array of thought disorders, including disturbances in areas of functioning such as language, affect, perception, and behaviour. These disturbances, depending on the type of schizophrenia, may include distortions of reality (such as delusions and hallucinations), profoundly blunted mood, and withdrawn or bizarre behaviour. It is estimated that schizophrenia affects approximately one percent of people over a lifetime, and the rate appears to be slightly higher among men than women (APA, 2000b; Lewine, 1988). Despite the low prevalence of the disorder schizophrenia has a considerable negative impact on the Canadian economy: *$2.02 billion* in direct and indirect costs and *$4.83 billion* for lost of productivity and suicide, totalling *$6.85 billion a year*.

Antipsychotic medications have been very successful in treating the symptoms of schizophrenia, such as agitation, mania, hallucinations, delusions, fury, and accelerated and disorganized thinking processes (Magliozzi & Schaffer, 1988). Let's look at the

* Mood Disorder Society of Canada, *Quick Facts: Mental Illness and Addiction in Canada*, 2009.

THIS IS YOUR BRAIN ON PSYCHOTHERAPEUTIC MEDICATIONS

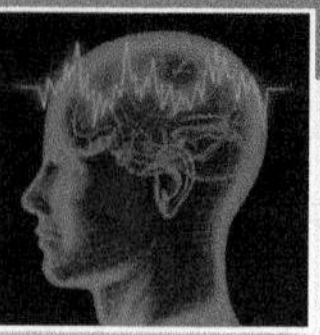

Antipsychotic Medications

First generation antipsychotic medications block dopamine from binding to receptor sites.

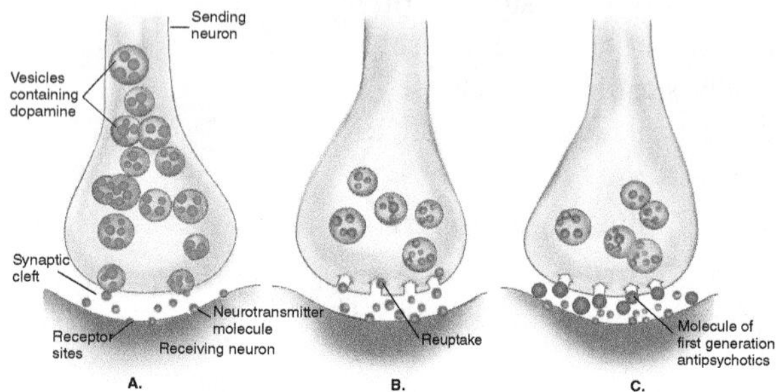

Second generation antipsychotic medications block dopamine and serotonin from binding to receptor sites.

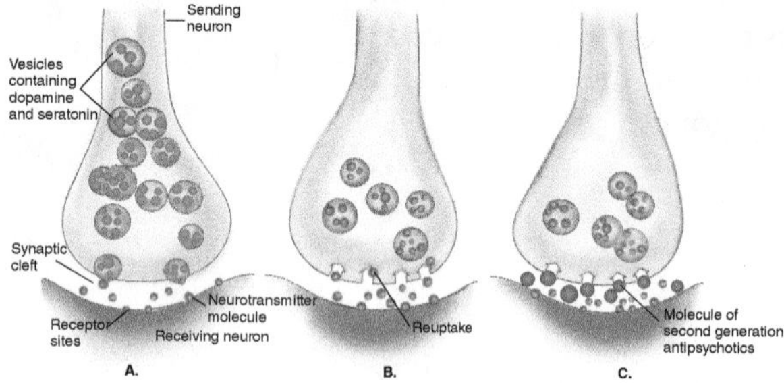

Antidepressant Medications

Tricyclic antidepressants block the uptake of serotonin and norepinephrine, thereby increasing the levels of both in the brain.

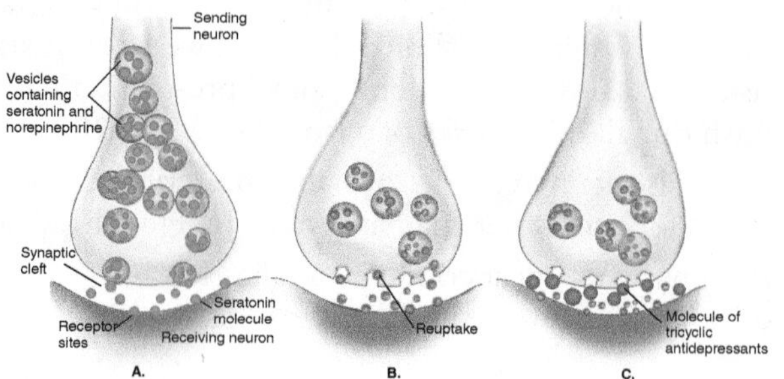

Selective serotonin reuptake inhibitors block the reuptake of serotonin, allowing serotonin to remain in the synapse and increasing its concentration in the brain.

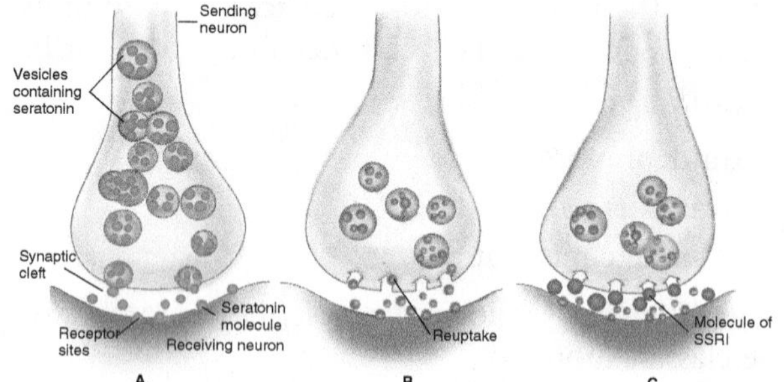

agitated depression
Depressed mood accompanied by a state of tension or restlessness. People with agitated depression show excessive motor activity, as they may, for example, be unable to sit still or may pace, wring the hands, or pull at their clothes.

box ("This is your brain on psychotheraputic medication") to see how these different psychotheraputic medications affect our brain. Sometimes an individual has previously or concurrently experienced a significant depressive or manic episode, in which case a diagnosis of schizoaffective disorder might be given to reflect the presence of symptoms of both schizophrenia and a major affective disorder. To a lesser extent, antipsychotics also have been used in the treatment of mania, **agitated depression**, toxic (such as drug-induced) psychoses, emotionally unstable personalities, and psychoses associated with old age. Antipsychotic medications are also known as **neuroleptics** or major

Monoamine oxidase inhibitor antidepressants (MAOIs) inhibit the activity of monoamine oxidase, the **enzyme** that breaks down neurotransmitters, such as norepinephrine, dopamine, and serotonin. This results in higher concentrations of these neurotransmitters in the brain.

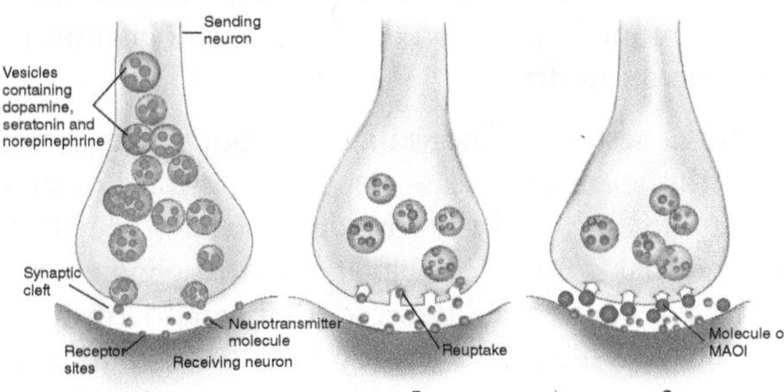

Antianxiety Medications

In addition to antidepressants, the following drug classes may also be used to treat anxiety disorders.

Barbiturates bind to GABA receptors thereby increasing the activity of GABA, an inhibitory neurotransmitter increase. They also block a specific type of glutamate receptor (called AMPA or AMPAR) thereby decreasing the activity of glutamate, an excitatory neurotransmitter. The result is an overall decrease in the CNS activity.

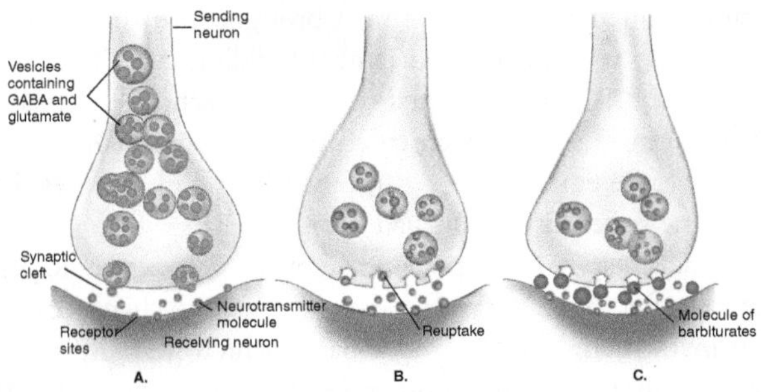

Benzodiazepines bind to benzodiazepine receptors leading to an increase in neural inhibition in the GABA system.

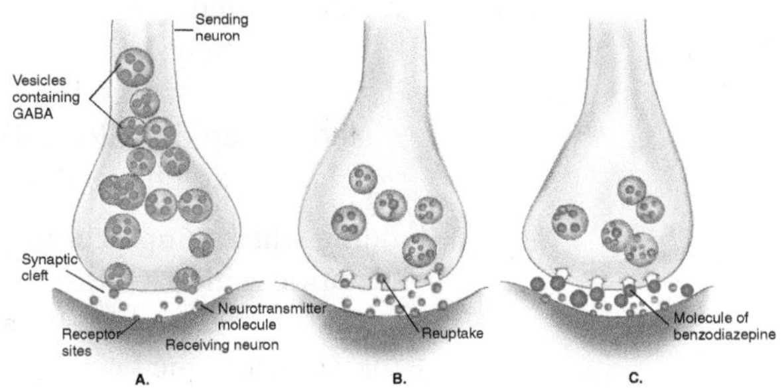

Antimanic Medications

Lithium decreases the neural activity of serotonin, norepinephrine, and dopamine. Specifically, it increases the reuptake of serotonin and norepinephrine, and it decreases the effects of dopamine and norepinephrine at postsynaptic receptors.

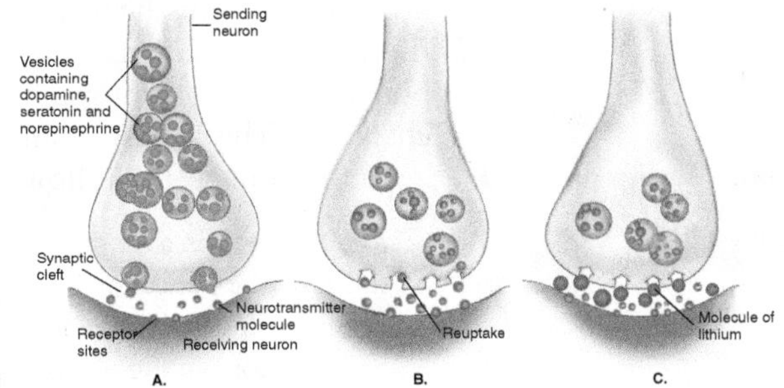

tranquilizers (the latter term is used much less frequently now). The term *neuroleptic* is derived from the Greek word that means "to clamp the neuron" (Snyder & Largent, 1989). *Antipsychotics* is the term more commonly used in North America, with *neuroleptics* used more often in Europe. The terms are used interchangeably in this discussion. Examples of antipsychotic medications are listed in Table 12.1 on page 289.

neuroleptics
Tranquilizing drugs used to treat psychoses; a synonym is *major tranquilizer.*

There are several types of medications that are used to treat mental illness. Each mental illness has its own specialized category of medications that address the specific symptoms of these disorders.

Antipsychotic Medication

According to the Centre for Addition and Mental Health (2009), antipsychotic medications are further classified as:

1. First generation (typical) drugs that block dopamine. These include chlorpromazine (once marketed as Largactil), flupenthixol (Fluanxol), fluphenazine (Modecate), haloperidol (Haldol), loxapine (Loxapac), perphenazine (Trilafon), pimozide (Orap), trifluoperazine (Stelazine), thiothixene (Navane), and zuclopenthixol (Clopixol).
2. Second generation (atypical) drugs that block dopamine and also affect serotonin levels. These include speridone (Risperdal), quetiapine (Seroquel), olanzapine (Zyprexa), ziprasidone (Zeldox), paliperidone (Invega), aripiprazole (Abilify), and clozapine (Clozaril). Some second generation drugs have milder movement-related side-effects than first generation drugs.

Finding which antipsychotic class works best for an individual takes both time and experimentation with each drug class. Within each drug class, roughly one-third of sufferers will find that it works well, another third will find that the drug helps only with some symptoms, and the final third will find that it does not help at all. Most people who take antipsychotics over a longer term are now prescribed the second generation drugs.

The basic—but oversimplified—notion regarding antipsychotic medications is that they primarily affect the reticular activating system, the limbic system, and the hypothalamus. The effects on the reticular activating system generally moderate spontaneous activity and decrease the patient's reactivity to stimuli. The action within the limbic system serves to moderate or blunt emotional arousal. These actions are thought to produce the drug's dramatic effects on schizophrenic or agitated behavioural patterns. The effects on the hypothalamus help modulate metabolism, alertness, and muscle tone. Because of these effects, antipsychotics are the major approach to the drug treatment of schizophrenia. The way antipsychotic drugs affect neural activity, in general, is illustrated in this chapter's "This is your brain on psychotheraputic medications" box on page 280.

paranoid schizophrenia A type of schizophrenia distinguished by systematic delusions or auditory hallucinations related to one theme.

Let us look at the following case example of clinical **paranoid schizophrenia***:

Mr. Simpson is a 44-year-old, single, unemployed, white man brought into the emergency room by the police for striking an elderly woman in his apartment building. Mr. Simpson had been continuously ill since the age of 22. During his first year of law school, he gradually became more and more convinced that his classmates were making fun of him. He noticed that they would snort and sneeze whenever he entered the classroom. When a girl he was dating broke off the relationship with him, he believed that she had been "replaced" by a look-alike. He called the police and asked for their help to solve the "kidnapping." His academic performance in school declined dramatically, and he was asked to leave and seek psychiatric care.

Mr. Simpson got a job as an investment counselor at a bank, which he held for seven months. However, he was getting an increasing number of distracting "signals" from coworkers, and he became more suspicious and withdrawn. It was at this time that he first reported hearing voices. He was eventually fired, and soon thereafter was hospitalized for the first time, at age 24. He has not worked since.

Mr. Simpson has been hospitalized 12 times, the longest stay being eight months. However, in the past five years he has been hospitalized only once, for three weeks. During the hospitalizations he has received various antipsychotic drugs. Although medication has been prescribed on an outpatient basis, he usually stops taking it shortly after leaving the hospital. Aside from twice-yearly lunch meetings with his uncle and his contacts with mental health workers, he is isolated socially. He lives on his own and manages his own financial affairs, including a modest inheritance. He reads the *Wall Street Journal* daily. He cooks and cleans for himself.

Mr. Simpson maintains that his apartment is the center of a large communication system that involves all three major television networks, his neighbors, and apparently hundreds of "actors" in his neighborhood. There are secret cameras in his apartment that carefully monitor all his activities. When he is watching TV, many of his minor actions, such as getting up to go to the bathroom, are soon directly commented on by the announcer. Whenever he goes outside, the "actors" have all been warned to keep him under surveillance. Everyone on the street watches him. His neighbors operate two different "machines"; one is responsible for all of his voices, except the "joker." He is not certain who controls this voice, which "visits" him only occasionally and is very funny. The other voices, which he hears many times each day, are generated by this machine, which he sometimes thinks is directly run by the neighbor whom he attacked. For example, when he is going over his investments, these "harassing" voices constantly tell him which stocks to buy. The other machine he calls "the dream machine." This machine puts erotic dreams into his head, usually of "black women."

Mr. Simpson describes other unusual experiences. For example, he recently went to a shoe store 30 miles from his house in the hope of getting some shoes that wouldn't be "altered." However, he soon found out that, like the rest of the shoes he buys, special nails had been put into the bottom of the shoes to annoy him. He was amazed that his decision concerning which shoe store to go to must have been known to his "harassers" before he himself knew it, so that they had time to get the altered shoes made up especially for him. He realizes that great effort and "millions of dollars" are involved in keeping him under surveillance. He sometimes thinks this is all part of a large experiment to discover the secret of his "superior intelligence." (Spitzer et al., 1989).

Although several theories address the action of antipsychotics, the dopamine hypothesis is generally accepted. This theory is based on the observation of amphetamine-induced psychosis, which serves as a pharmacological model of schizophrenic behaviour. The symptoms evidenced in this model of psychosis are readily ameliorated through the use of neuroleptic drugs. Furthermore, it appears that most amphetamine-induced psychotic behaviour is mediated through increased release of dopamine in the brain.

Thus, the dopamine theory has two core components:

1. psychosis is induced by increased levels of dopaminergic activity, and
2. most antipsychotic drugs block postsynaptic dopamine receptors (Baldessarini, 1985; Bishara & Taylor, 2008; Gardner, Baldessarini, & Waraich, 2005).

Unfortunately, it is not certain what leads to this dopaminergic overactivity in the first place It is believed that although antipsychotic medications block norepinephrine, serotonin, and acetylcholine, their primary action is as central dopamine antagonists (Galenberg, 1991; Meyer & Quenzer, 2005). That is, these drugs block central dopamine receptors, particularly the D_2 subtype, and thus inhibit dopaminergic neurotransmission in the brain. The postsynaptic receptor blockade in the limbic system is thought to reduce the schizophrenic symptoms.

The preceding discussion presents the predominant beliefs about the general actions of antipsychotic medications. Much research is ongoing, however, to identify the precise mechanisms of action that account for their effects. Although the precise mechanisms underlying the actions of neuroleptics remain to be isolated, current knowledge does point to at least some role for dopamine in the modulation of psychotic behaviours.

Although the antipsychotics have produced many positive effects in the treatment of mental disorders, their use comes with significant side effects. Antipsychotics

extrapyramidal
Outside the pyramidal tracts, with origin in the basal ganglia. These cell bodies are involved with starting, stopping, and smoothing out movements.

dyskinesia
Disordered movements.

akinesia
Slowness of movement and underactivity.

tardive dyskinesia
An extrapyramidal complication characterized by involuntary movements of the mouth and tongue, trunk, and extremities; a side effect of long-term (two or more years) use of antipsychotic drugs.

also affect the **extrapyramidal** tract by blocking postsynaptic receptors in the basal ganglia, and these actions produce some of the most profound side effects associated with antipsychotics. Chief among the acute side effects are motor disturbances, which, taken together, give the appearance of a Parkinsonian syndrome. People who have Parkinson's disease are characterized by tremor, blank rigidity, gait and posture changes, and excessive salivation. Extrapyramidal symptoms are the most apparent motor disturbances, primarily **dyskinesia** (disordered movements) and **akinesia** (slowness of movement and underactivity). These are experienced acutely by at least 50 percent of patients who take antipsychotics (Bhana et al., 2001; Chakos et al., 1992; Mackay, 1982). The side effects of antipsychotics tend to be dose related: Stronger side effects are associated with higher doses of the antipsychotic medication.

The most common side effect associated with the long-term use of antipsychotics is another extrapyramidal complication known as **tardive dyskinesia**. Tardive dyskinesia, which typically can be seen after two years or more of antipsychotic drug use, is characterized most often by repetitive involuntary movements of the mouth and tongue (often in the form of lip smacking), trunk, and extremities. Most cases of tardive dyskinesia are preceded by the Parkinson-like symptoms described earlier. The current estimates are that tardive dyskinesia occurs among about one-third of treated patients (Fait et al., 2002; Gitlin, 1990), and many if not most of the tardive dyskinesia symptoms are permanent. The effects are seen more among women than men. Efforts to control or eliminate these effects include reducing the dose of the drug, which sometimes reduces the side effect and still provides some relief from the psychotic symptoms; administering medications designed to treat the side effects symptomatically (for example, benztropine [trade name Cogentin] or trihexyphenidyl [Artane]); and instituting what are called "drug holidays," during which the patient is off medication to have a physiological break from the use of the drug.

Although great strides have been made in the pharmacological treatment of psychotic disorders, concerted efforts in this area are continuing. One focus is on developing neuroleptics that provide symptom relief but act through different mechanisms. The hope is to avoid or minimize the side effects (especially tardive dyskinesia) of current antipsychotic medications. A second emphasis is on developing neuroleptics that not only diminish the obvious symptoms such as hallucinations but also alleviate some less visible symptoms, such as emotional withdrawal. One excellent example in this regard is clozapine (trade name Clozaril), which is used in the treatment of psychotic and schizophrenic disorders. Clozapine was the first of a new class of antipsychotics collectively referred to as atypical or second-generation antipsychotics (Bonham & Abbott, 2008). Most of the subsequent antipsychotics in this class seek to emulate the pharmacological properties believed to be responsible for clozapine's particular clinical profile (Grunder, Hippius, & Carlsson, 2009). The major attractive feature of clozapine is that it has yielded antipsychotic efficacy among patients who have not responded to other antipsychotics, such as haloperidol. In addition, clozapine appears to produce a minimum of acute extrapyramidal side effects and is a rare antipsychotic that does not appear to produce tardive dyskinesia. Like all medications, however, clozapine has side effects. The most significant concern with clozapine is the occasional side effect of agranulocytosis, a destructive condition in which the bone marrow stops producing white blood cells, thus opening the door to infection. If undetected, agranulocytosis results in death, so close monitoring of the patient is required. Close monitoring of heart functioning also is needed, especially early in the course of treatment, based on recent reports of fatal myocarditis, an inflammation of the heart lining. Though initially not available to large numbers of clients because of the high costs of the drug and the associated blood-test monitoring, the subsequent availability of generics of clozapine is allowing more patients to benefit from the use of this medication.

Another area of recent attention has been evaluation of the relative effectiveness of antipsychotic medications. The general clinical experience is that no one antipsychotic medication is the "magic pill" for all patients with schizophrenia. Instead, treatment providers have sometimes needed to shift patients from one medication to another until finding the medication with the best individual effect. In one study, for example, five medications (olanzapine [trade name Zyprexa], perphenazine [Trilafon], quetiapine [Seroquel], risperidone [Risperdal], and ziprasidone [Zeldox]) used to treat schizophrenia were compared (Lieberman et al., 2005). It was found that all five medications blunted the symptoms of schizophrenia, but that nearly 75 percent of the patients stopped taking the drugs they were on because of discomfort or specific side effects. One of the drugs—olanzapine (Zyprexa)—appeared to help more patients control symptoms for a longer period of time, although with a higher risk of side effects that in turn increased risk of diabetes.

The general clinical experience is that no one antipsychotic medication is the "magic pill" for all patients with schizophrenia.

DRUGS AND CULTURE BOX 12.2

The Right to Refuse Psychotherapeutic Medications

As you are aware, countries and cultures vary considerably in the extent to which they tolerate freedom of speech and other forms of behavioural expression. Not surprisingly, this often predicts the extent to which patients with mental illness (however defined) have any say in how they are treated. In some cultures, the response to behaviours viewed as "different" or "mentally ill" is to subdue people through incarceration, restraints, drugs, or some combination of these interventions. In other cultures, treatment might include a more collaborative approach in which patients discuss their problems with a counsellor or work with a psychiatrist in trying different drugs to see how they work.

But how far should the rights of individuals extend? For example, should a person who is voluntarily or involuntarily admitted to a psychiatric facility have the opportunity to refuse psychotherapeutic drugs? For many years, people hospitalized for psychiatric treatment had little if any say in whether drugs would be administered, based in part on the assumption that they had no expertise in the area of psychotherapeutic medications and that being hospitalized to begin with suggested impaired functioning and thus the inability to make decisions.

This issue has been addressed in court cases over the years. In one case, in the U.S., seven Boston State Hospital patients filed suit to stop the (nonemergency) administration of medications without their informed consent. Relatedly, the patients claimed the right to refuse medication. The psychiatrists faced a dilemma. On the one hand, they knew by experience that certain drugs were able to significantly relieve emotional distress. On the other hand, some of these drugs had unpleasant side effects and patients understandably might want to avoid these. The court decided in favour of the patients. It ruled that patients (whether voluntarily or involuntarily admitted to the hospital) should be presumed competent to accept or refuse psychotherapeutic medications. The court added that when a patient was not deemed competent, a court-appointed guardian needed to make the decision whether to use medications.

In Canada, similar cases have been brought forward. For example, in 2003 Scott Starson won the right to refuse antipsychotic medications. Starson suffers from schiz-affective disorder but is also a physics genius. He told the Supreme Court of Canada that he would rather stay hospitalized than be medicated as he believes the medication "dull[s] his mind to the physics research that is his life's passion." The Supreme Court of Canada ruled six to three in his favour (Bailey, 2003).

Is this the final word? No, probably not. New cases arise and can yield different rulings. However, the practical implication of these cases may not arise very often for the simple reason that hospitalized psychiatric patients do not frequently raise the issue of refusing their medications.

What do you think? Should Canadians suffering from mental illness have the right to refuse treatment?

dundanim/Shutterstock.com

Common symptoms of depression are dysphoric mood, loss of interest, sleep disturbance, withdrawal, and difficulties in concentration.

Finally, it should be noted before closing that other pharmacological treatments for schizophrenic or psychotic disorders continue to be evaluated and distributed for use in clinical settings. Among the latest is risperidone (trade name Risperdal), which provides many of the benefits associated with clozapine without the agranulocytosis risk. Unfortunately, risperidone appears to present an increased risk of diabetes (as indicated in the aforementioned Lieberman et al. 2005 study). Further, patients taking risperidone (along with quetiapine, olanzapine, and clozapine) may have an increased risk of sudden death from cardiac arrhythmias and other cardiac causes than patients not taking these medications (Ray et al., 2009). A second promising treatment is aripiprazole (Abilify), which seeks to stabilize the dopamine system. Both medications have shown very positive outcomes and many fewer and less severe side effects. Finally, another opening frontier in the advance of antipsychotics medications revolves around glutamate (as opposed to the more traditional focus on dopamine). Glutamate is central to brain processes involving perception, memory, and learning. Experimental work is underway with ketamine (often used in pediatric anesthesia) that targets glutamate receptors, with some preliminary positive indications.

Antidepressants

Depression is among the most common psychiatric disorders in Canada, with eight percent of the population suffering from depression at some time in their life (MDSC, 2009). Depressions vary in severity, duration, and frequency of occurrence; the most common symptoms that contribute to what has been characterized as a depressive syndrome (as opposed to cases where a person might feel sad or blue) include dysphoric mood, loss of interest, disturbances in appetite and weight, sleep disturbance, fatigue, withdrawal, thoughts of suicide, and difficulties in concentration. Depressions frequently are classified as either **endogenous**, in which symptoms tend to be chronic and associated with genetic constitutional factors, or **exogenous**, in which symptoms are thought to be in response to some situation or event (Cooperrider, 1988). The average age for onset of a first depressive episode traditionally has been in the late 30s or early 40s, although depressions are being seen more frequently among younger people and even among preschool children under the age of six (Luby et al., 2009). The length of a depressive episode is also variable, although periods of six months are common. Depression is diagnosed much more frequently among women than among men (Ebmeier, Donaghey, & Steele, 2006). Around 50 percent of the people who experience a major depressive episode do not have a recurrence of the illness (Coryell & Winokur, 1982).

endogenous
Developed from within; when applied to depression, the term means that depressive symptoms seem to be due to genetic factors.

exogenous
Developed from without; when applied to depression, the term means that depressive symptoms seem to be in reaction to a particular situation or event.

The following case, excerpted from Spitzer et al. (1989), is an example of major depression rated as moderately severe*.

Connie is a 33-year-old homemaker who separated from her husband three months previously. She has a four-year-old son, Robert.

Connie left her husband, Donald, after a five-year marriage. Violent arguments between them, during which Connie was beaten by her husband, had occurred for the last four years of their marriage, beginning when she became pregnant with Robert. During their final argument, about Connie's buying an expensive tricycle for Robert, her husband had held a loaded gun to Robert's head and threatened to shoot him if she didn't agree to return the tricycle to the store. Connie obtained a court order of protection that prevented Donald from having any contact with her or their son. She took Robert to her parents' apartment, where they are still living.

Connie is an only child, and a high school and secretarial school graduate. She worked as an executive secretary for six years before her marriage and for the first two years after, until Robert's birth. Before her marriage Connie had her own apartment. She was close to her parents, visiting them weekly and speaking to them a couple of times a week. Connie had many friends whom she also saw regularly. She still had several friends from her high school years. In high school she had been a popular cheerleader and a good student. In the office where she had worked as a secretary, she was in charge of organizing office holiday parties and money collections for employee gifts.

During their first year of marriage, Donald became increasingly irritable and critical of Connie. He began to request that Connie stop calling and seeing her friends after work, and refused to allow them or his in-laws to visit their apartment. Connie convinced Donald to try marital therapy, but he refused to continue after the initial two sessions.

Despite her misgivings about Donald's behavior toward her, Connie decided to become pregnant. During the seventh month of the pregnancy, she developed thrombophlebitis and had to stay home in bed. Donald began complaining that their apartment was not clean enough and that Connie was not able to shop for groceries. He never helped Connie with the housework. He refused to allow his mother-in-law to come to the apartment to help. One morning when he couldn't find a clean shirt, he became angry and yelled at Connie. When she suggested that he pick some up from the laundry, he began hitting her with his fists. She left him and went to live with her parents for a week. He expressed remorse for hitting her and agreed to resume marital therapy.

At her parents' and Donald's urging, Connie returned to her apartment. No further violence occurred until after Robert's birth. At that time, Donald began using cocaine every weekend and often became violent when he was high.

In the three months since she left Donald, Connie has become increasingly depressed. Her appetite has been poor, and she has lost ten pounds. She cries a lot and often wakes up at five in the morning, unable to get back to sleep. Ever since she left Donald, he has been calling her at her parents' home and begging her to return to him. One week before her psychiatric evaluation, Connie's parents took her to their general practitioner. Her physical examination was normal, and he referred her for psychiatric treatment.

When seen by a psychiatrist in the outpatient clinic, Connie is pale and thin, dressed in worn-out jeans and dark blue sweater. Her haircut is unstylish, and she appears older than she is. She speaks slowly, describing her depressed mood and lack of energy. She says that her only pleasure is in being with her son. She is able to take care of him physically, but feels guilty because her preoccupation with her own bad feelings prevents her from being able to play with him. She now has no social contacts other than with her parents and her son. She feels worthless and blames herself for her marital problems, saying that if she had been a better wife, maybe Donald would have been able to give up the cocaine. When asked why she stayed with him so long, she explains that her family disapproved of divorce and kept telling her that she should try harder to make her marriage a success. She also thought about what her life would be like trying to take care of her son while working full-time and didn't think she could make it.

Although stimulants once were used as a treatment for depression, their effectiveness was limited, especially among people with severe depressions. Today, stimulants are rarely used for depression. Instead, several classes of antidepressant medications are prescribed, each acting in a manner different from stimulants, which produce a euphoria that does not generally occur with the antidepressants (Cooperrider, 1988). The ways in which each class of antidepressant affects neural activity is illustrated in the "This is your brain on psychotheraputic medications" box on page 280.

The first class includes the cyclic antidepressants. Historically, these were referred to as tricyclic antidepressants because of their three-ring chemical structure nucleus. Some more recent antidepressants have more varied chemical structures, however, and have been identified as heterocyclic antidepressants. Included among these are antidepressant medications called selective serotonin reuptake inhibitors (SSRIs), which often treat the symptoms of depression more effectively than the tricyclics and are associated with fewer side effects for many users. The most common SSRIs are fluvoxamine (trade name Luvox), paroxetine (Paxil), fluoxetine (Prozac), and sertraline (Zoloft). We use the term cyclic when referring to these antidepressants generally and the term tricyclics when referring to that specific group of antidepressants. The second class of antidepressants includes MAOIs (recall that this acronym refers to the monoamine oxidase inhibitors), which are used less frequently than the cyclic antidepressants. Finally, in the third class are newer antidepressant medications that either have mechanisms of action that are not yet well understood or have specific therapeutic effects that mirror those of both the tricyclics and the SSRIs. Representative antidepressant medications in these three categories are listed in Table 12.1.

Both the tricyclics and MAOIs were available in the late 1950s. As with other psychotherapeutic medications, their potential antidepressant effects were discovered serendipitously. The tricyclics initially were being investigated as antipsychotic agents, whereas the MAOIs initially were used in the treatment of tuberculosis. In both cases, investigators noted antidepressant effects—for example, some tuberculosis patients treated with an MAOI showed an energized state. Before discussing the cyclics and MAOIs in more detail, we need to present the postulated biochemical hypotheses for depression

It is believed that depression results from a deficiency in biogenic amines, specifically catecholamines and serotonin, which act as central nervous system neurotransmitters (see Chapter 3). According to the catecholamine hypothesis, depression results from a deficiency in catecholamines (particularly norepinephrine) at varied neuron receptor sites in the brain. The cyclics are believed to block the reuptake of norepinephrine from the synaptic cleft. Thus, the result is a greater concentration of norepinephrine in the synaptic cleft, alleviating the hypothesized neurotransmitter

TABLE 12.1 Representative Antidepressant Medications

Generic Name	Trade Name
Cyclic antidepressants	
Fluoxetine	Prozac
Imipramine	Tofranil, Imavate, Antipress
Amitriptyline	Amitril, Elavil
Desipramine	Norpramine
Doxepin	Sinequan
Nortriptyline	Aventyl, Pamelor
Protriptyline	Vivactil
Amoxapine	Asendin
Clomipramine	Anafranil
Maprotiline	Ludiomil
Sertraline	Zoloft
Paroxetine	Paxil
Fluvoxamine	Luvox
MAOIs	
Tranylcypromine	Parnate
Isocaroxazid	Marplan
Phenelzine	Nardil
Newer medications	
Trazodone	Desyrel
Venlafaxine	Effexor
Mirtazapine	Remeron
Nefazodone	Serzone
Bupropion	Wellbutrin
Reboxetine	Edronax
Citalopram	Celexa
Escitalopram	Lexapro
Duloxetine	Cynbalta
Milnacipran	Pristiq
Desvenlafaxine	Ixel, Savella

Note: The most frequently prescribed antidepressant drugs include sertraline (Zoloft), escitalopram (Lexapro), fluoxetine (Prozac), and bupropion (Wellbutrin).

deficiency. This cyclic-mediated process is thought to occur in the amygdala and reticular formation areas of the brain.

The catecholamine theory is derived in large part from observations of the effects of the antipsychotic agent reserpine, discussed earlier in the historical overview. Patients given reserpine often exhibit a depressed appearance. Furthermore, reserpine was found to deplete brain concentrations of norepinephrine. Thus, there was the suggestion that such depletions were causally related to depression.

The serotonin hypothesis, the other central theory of antidepressant action, postulates that depression is the result of a deficiency of the neurotransmitter serotonin in the brain stem (Galenberg & Schoonover, 1991; Kalus, Asnis, & van Praag, 1989). People who are depressed have reduced levels of serotonin and chemicals involved in its metabolism in their cerebrospinal fluid. Like the catecholamine norepinephrine, the cyclics have been found to prevent the uptake of serotonin (Cooperrider, 1988).

The findings suggest that increased cell proliferation and increased neuronal numbers may be mechanisms by which antidepressant treatment overcomes the atrophy and loss of hippocampal neurons associated with depression.

Although the cyclics block the uptake of amines, MAOIs prevent the breakdown of the neurotransmitters (Cohen, 1997; Cooperrider, 1988; Meyer & Quenzer, 2005). The enzyme monoamine oxidase metabolizes a variety of neurotransmitters, including norepinephrine and serotonin. MAOIs inhibit this degradation process and thus enhance the availability of the transmitter within the neuron. Thus, the actions of the cyclics and MAOIs each are consistent with the hypothesis that decreased brain catecholamine activity causes depression and that these antidepressants (using different mechanisms) reverse this process by increasing catecholamine activity in the brain.

Taken together, the cyclics and MAOIs each appear to enhance the functional activity of one or more neurotransmitters, but our understanding of the mechanisms remains clouded. One finding that contributes to our lack of understanding is that the effects noted occur within hours, although the therapeutic antidepressant action can take days or weeks for the patient to experience.

Although current theories about the actions of antidepressants are best viewed as tentative, recent work on the neurobiology of depression has provided some exciting new insights. A link has been known to exist between depression (and also chronic stress and anxiety) and atrophy and cell loss in the hippocampus. Research by several researchers (e.g., Duman, 2004; Duman, Nakagawa, & Malberg, 2001; Malberg et al., 2000; Santarelli et al., 2003) has demonstrated that antidepressant treatment increases neurogenesis, or new cell growth, in the hippocampus. This neurogenesis may block or reverse the effects of depression on hippocampal neurons. Further, the new cell growth appears to take several weeks to occur, and this may account for the fact that antidepressant medications typically take several weeks to exert their action. The findings suggest that increased cell proliferation and increased neuronal numbers may be mechanisms by which antidepressant treatment overcomes the atrophy and loss of hippocampal neurons associated with depression.

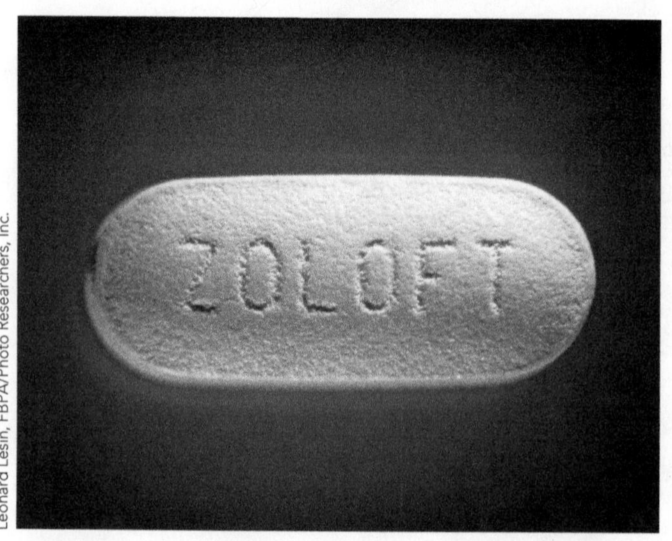

Leonard Lesin, FBPA/Photo Researchers, Inc.

Zoloft is among the most commonly prescribed antidepressant medications.

The cyclics and MAOIs are absorbed readily through the gastrointestinal tract (Fait et al., 2002).

The cyclics are administered only rarely through injection, and MAOIs always are taken orally. Following absorption, relatively high concentrations of the drugs develop in the brain especially but also in other organs. Then the antidepressant pharmacokinetics resemble those of the antipsychotics, especially chlorpromazine (Baldessarini, 1985). More is known of the absorption and distribution of the cyclics than of the MAOIs, in part because of the difficulty in isolating MAOI metabolites (Tyrer, 1982b). Metabolism for each occurs primarily in the liver, with most excreted through the urine.

Despite the rapid absorption of antidepressant medications, one disadvantage in their use (noted previously) is that clinical action frequently takes two to three weeks to be apparent in the patient's functioning. Unfortunately, patients experience most of the undesired side effects of antidepressants during this initial period of use, and many patients terminate their use because they experience the side effects in the absence of rapid symptom relief. The most common side effects of the cyclics are drowsiness; a variety of anticholinergic effects such as dry mouth, constipation, and difficulty in urinating; blurred vision; orthostasis (dizziness upon standing up); decreased libido; weight gain; and tachycardia (Andrews & Nemeroff, 1994). In addition, use of some of the newer SSRI antidepressant medications may be associated with a greater risk of bone breaks (Richards et al., 2007) and, among older women, an increased rate of bone loss at the hip (Diem et al., 2007). The most common side effects of the MAOIs are drowsiness, dry mouth, dizziness, weight gain, insomnia, constipation, and fatigue. In addition, MAOI use is associated with two other unwanted effects. The first is temporary low blood pressure when changing position (such as from sitting to standing), and the second is impaired sexual functioning. Men may experience impotence and difficulty in ejaculating, and women may report orgasmic inhibition. The use of MAOIs also requires dietary restrictions. Most significant among these is avoiding substances that contain tyramine, such as most cheeses and some alcoholic beverages (especially Chianti wine). MAOIs and tyramine interact to cause potentially severe hypertensive reactions. Finally, a concern in the use of antidepressants is their potential for lethal use. Overdosing on cyclics can result in coma, respiratory difficulties, and a variety of cardiac problems. Accordingly, the patient's potential for suicide has to be assessed before most of the cyclics are prescribed. MAOIs do not produce intoxicating effects, and overdosing on them is not common.

An area of recent concern regarding some antidepressants, primarily SSRIs, is the possibility of suicide, especially among children. This concern prompted Health Canada and the U.S. Food and Drug Administration (FDA) to issue a warning that people taking antidepressants can become suicidal and should be closely monitored, especially when patients start using an antidepressant or when the dose is increased or decreased. Manufacturers of 10 popular antidepressants (trade names Prozac, Zoloft, Wellbutrin, Zyban, Paxil, Celexa, Effexor, Serzone, Luvox, and Remeron) were urged to issue revised warning labels for the medications identifying these concerns. These concerns also led Great Britain to markedly increase restrictions on the prescribing of antidepressants for children. In 2003 the British Medicines and Healthcare Products Regulatory Agency declared Celexa, Effexor, Lexapro, Luvox, Paxil (called Seroxat in Britain), and Zoloft as too risky for children under the age of 18. Physicians, and also patients and parents, will need to incorporate these considerations into decisions on whether and which antidepressants to use, and on balancing the risks of using antidepressants against leaving the illness untreated pharmacologically.

CONTEMPORARY ISSUE BOX 12.3

Antidepressant Medications: Drug versus Placebo Effects

An issue often discussed in the context of psychotherapeutic medications is whether receiving a medication provides more relief than receiving a placebo (a patient receives an inactive pill but believes it is an active medication). Part of the reason for comparing those who receive the active medication with those who receive a placebo is to account for the therapeutic effects associated with receiving a medication, such as the expectation of improvement, independent of the medication's active ingredients.

In a review of many studies comparing the effects of antidepressant medications with placebo, Kirsch and Sapirstein (1999) concluded that only about 25 percent of the "response" to medication treatment was due to the pharmacological effect of the medication. Fully 50 percent of the effect was due to the psychological impact of administering the medication (the placebo effect). The remaining 25 percent of the treatment response was attributed to "nonspecific factors," such as the therapeutic relationship between the doctor and the patient. According to Dr. Sapirstein, "People benefiting from drugs are benefiting because they think that taking the antidepressant medicine is working. If we take these results and say that improvement is due to what the patients think, then how people think and its effect on how they feel are more powerful than the chemical substance."

More recently, Dr. Andrew Leuchter and his colleagues (Leuchter et al., 2002) have demonstrated that placebo medications can actually induce changes in brain functioning for individuals with major depression. These alterations are different from the brain changes caused by antidepressant medications. Patients who responded to the placebo showed increased activity in the prefrontal cortex of the brain, whereas those who responded to the medication showed suppressed activity in that area. According to the authors of this study, the finding raises questions about two commonly held beliefs. The first is that administration of an inert pill appears to be an active treatment rather than no treatment, as previously thought. And second, the placebo response is not equivalent to an active drug response because the two groups' brain physiology was altered differently. They caution, though, that their data do not indicate a causal link between brain changes and the effects of a placebo or medication. Further research is needed to assess causal links and longer-term outcomes for these two groups of patients.

The therapeutic effects of antidepressants for many patients are impressive once the lag time has passed. The cyclics in particular markedly alleviate depressive symptoms. MAOIs also have strong supportive treatment effectiveness rates when compared with placebos, although the positive outcomes are not as dramatic as with the cyclics. Also, MAOIs, when compared directly with cyclics, tend to be less effective. Research continues on the development of more effective medications as well as alternatives to medication (including the use of electroconvulsive therapy, or ECT, in the most severe cases of depression that do not respond to medication). Nondrug therapies, aside from psychotherapy, include herbs, dietary supplements, light therapy (daily exposure to a box providing artificial light), and exercise. Another recent development is transcranial magnetic stimulation (TMS), a noninvasive procedure that activates the brain's emotive centres. This may be especially helpful for patients with depression who have not responded to other treatment interventions and have been classified as having "treatment-resistant depression" (Matthew, 2008).

Antianxiety Agents

Anxiety disorders are the most common mental illness in Canada, affecting nine percent of men and 16 percent of women in any given year (MDSC, 2009). In 2007,

$247 million was spent on antianxiety medications in Canada. These medications act to depress central nervous system activity thereby calming someone down and decreasing their "anxiety" level. Before describing anxiety and today's approaches to its treatment, we first need to understand depressant drugs in general. We should note, first of all, that although alcohol is the prototype depressant drug, many other drugs can depress the CNS and behaviour. These include a variety of different chemical agents but especially the **barbiturates**, the benzodiazepines, nonbarbiturate sedatives, and the general anesthetics (see Tables 12.2 and 12.3). These drugs are often classified according to their most common medical uses, but such a classification can be misleading. On the one hand, benzodiazepines such as diazepam (trade name Valium) and chlordiazepoxide (Librium) are often labelled as **anxiolytic** (anti-anxiety) drugs. Although moderate doses of these compounds do indeed relieve anxiety and are widely used for this purpose, in larger doses, benzodiazepines produce **sedative-hypnotic effects** (that is, they induce sleep) and are now prescribed widely as sleeping pills. Barbiturates, on the other hand, often are called sleeping pills and can certainly be effective in this regard. In lower doses, barbiturates are also anxiolytic, and if the dose is high enough, these and other depressants can produce surgical anesthesia. All depressant drugs (including alcohol) can relieve anxiety at low-dose levels, produce intoxication at moderate levels, induce sedation and sleep

barbiturates
Depressant drugs formerly used as sleeping pills; currently used in anesthesia and treatment for epilepsy.

anxiolytic
Anxiety-reducing.

sedative-hypnotic effects
The calming and sleep-inducing effects of some drugs.

TABLE 12.2 Representative Depressant Drugs

Generic Name	Brand Name	Slang Name
Hypnotics		
Barbiturates		
Pentobarbital	Nembutal	yellow jackets, nembies
Secobarbital	Seconal	reds
Amobarbital	Amytal	blues, Amys, blue Angels
Phenobarbital	Luminal	
Methohexital	Brevital	
Thiopental	Pentothal	
Aprobarbital	Alurate	
Mephobarbital	Mebaral	
Chloral hydrate		
Methaqualone	Quaaludes	ludes
Ethchlorvynol	Placidyl	
Zolpidem	Ambien	
General anesthetics		
Halothane	Fluothene	
Propofol	Diprivan	
Nitrous oxide		

TABLE 12.3 Representative Antianxiety Agents

Generic Name	Trade Name
Benzodiazepines	
Chlordiazepoxide	Librium
Diazepam	Valium
Flurazepam	Dalmane
Alprazolam	Xanax
Lorazepam	Ativan
Oxazepam	Serax
Temazepam	Restoril
Clorazepate	Tranxene
Triazolam	Halcion
Flunitrazepam	Rohypnol
Midazolam	Versed
Estazolam	ProSom
Clonazepam	Klonopin
Prazepam	Centrax
Halazepam	Paxipam
Nonbarbiturates, nonbenzodiazepines	
Meprobamate	Equanil
Hydroxyzine	Vistaril, Atarax
Ethinamate	Valmid
Buspirone	BuSpar

Note: The most frequently prescribed antianxiety drugs incude alprazolam (Xanax), lorazepam (Ativan), clonazepam (Klonopin), and diazepam (Valium).

general anesthesia
The reduction of pain by rendering the subject unconscious.

at still higher levels, produce **general anesthesia** at very high-dose levels, and eventually lead to coma and death (see Figure 12.1). Due to differing potency, duration of action, and safety, some depressants are used for specific purposes more often than others (for example, nitrous oxide is used almost exclusively for anesthesia). The benzodiazepines are currently the most important class of drugs for treating anxiety and sleeping disorders. Figure 12.2 illustrates the potential side effects of the antianxiety medication alprazolam.

Early History

Perhaps the first depressant compound other than alcohol to be used was the gas nitrous oxide, discovered by Joseph Priestley and synthesized by Humphry Davy in 1776. These English scientists were the first to note that inhalation of nitrous oxide produced a short period of intoxication similar to drunkenness. Because the euphoric

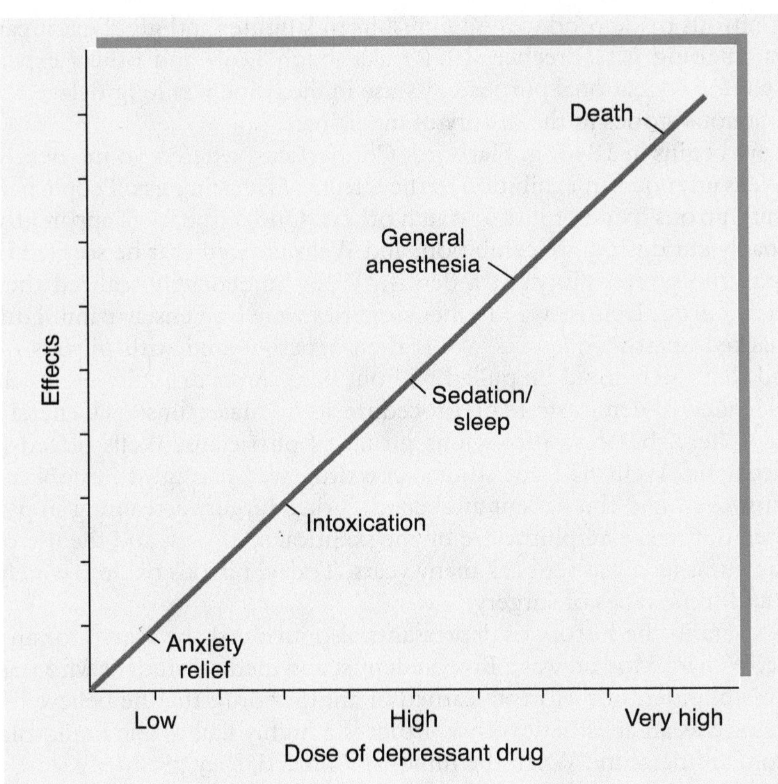

FIGURE 12.1
Effects per dose of a depressant drug

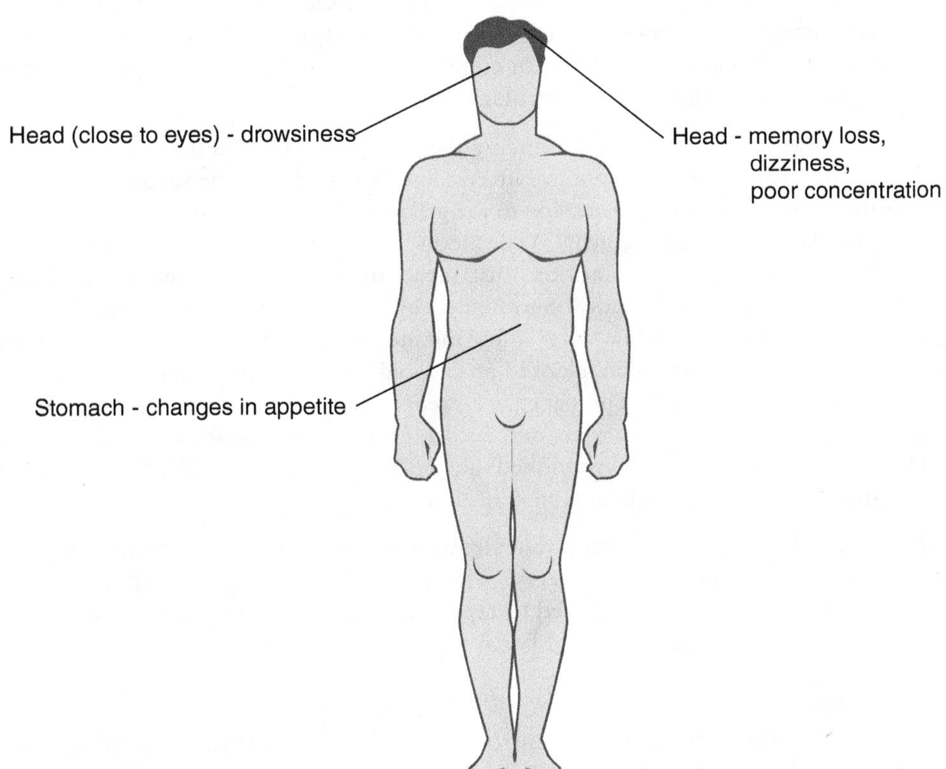

FIGURE 12.2
Potential side effects of alprazolam

Source: Zubada/Shutterstock

state that nitrous oxide produces often results in laughter and giggling, it came to be known as laughing gas (Brecher, 1972). Although Davy and others experimented with the gas for recreational purposes, its use in medicine was long delayed by one of the most famous stories in the history of medicine.

The story begins in 1845, in Hartford, Connecticut, where a young dentist named Horace Wells attended an exhibition of the effects of laughing gas. People paid admission to sniff nitrous oxide or just to watch others. One of the users apparently tripped and was badly cut during the exhibition, and Wells noticed that he seemed to feel no pain despite the severe injury. As a dentist, Wells immediately realized the possible uses of such a drug. Dentistry and other surgeries were immensely painful during this era that lacked anesthetic agents. Wells then experimented with nitrous oxide and discovered that teeth could be pulled without pain. After proclaiming his discovery, Wells was invited to demonstrate his procedure at the Massachusetts General Hospital in Boston. There, before a prestigious group of physicians, Wells placed a patient under anesthesia. Wells had not studied the drug well enough to establish dosages reliably, however, and the patient awakened during surgery screaming in pain. Wells was laughed out of the amphitheatre by the skeptical scientists, and the use of nitrous oxide as an anesthesia was set back many years. Today, nitrous oxide is widely used in dentistry and some types of surgery.

The next era in the history of depressants also involved the search for an effective anesthetic. William Morton was a Boston dentist and medical student who was familiar with Wells's blunder, but Morton learned of another drug that he believed might be a better choice as an anesthetic: ether. Ether is a highly flammable liquid that vaporizes at room temperature. When the fumes are inhaled, they produce a state of intoxication. After conducting some initial experiments with ether, Morton asked permission to demonstrate its use as a general anesthetic. In 1846, just a year after Wells's failure, Morton gave his demonstration at Massachusetts General Hospital. A large crowd gathered to observe and possibly to laugh at the brash young student who claimed to have developed a method for eliminating surgical pain. Smith, Cooperman, and Wollman (1980) describe the events:

> Everyone was ready and waiting, including the strong men to hold down the struggling patient, but Morton did not appear. Fifteen minutes passed, and the surgeon, becoming impatient, took his scalpel and turning to the gallery said, "As Dr. Morton has not arrived I presume he is otherwise engaged." While the audience smiled and the patient cringed, the surgeon turned to make his incision. Just then Morton entered...[the surgeon] said, "Well, sir, your patient is ready." Surrounded by a silent and unsympathetic audience, Morton went quietly to work. After a few minutes of ether inhalation, the patient was unconscious, whereupon Morton looked up and said, "Dr. Warren, your patient is ready." The operation was begun. The patient showed no sign of pain, yet he was alive and breathing. The strong men were not needed. When the operation was completed, Dr. Warren turned to the astonished audience and made the famous statement, "Gentlemen, this is no humbug." (pp. 258–259)

Morton had just given the first public demonstration of surgical anesthesia and had revolutionized the practice of surgery. The use of ether as an anesthetic quickly became widespread, and it is still used today occasionally along with newer anesthetics such as halothane, related gases, and barbiturates.

Barbiturates

A number of depressant drugs were introduced in the 19th century, including chloroform, chloral hydrate, and paraldehyde, but the next truly significant development was the introduction of the barbiturates in 1862. The first barbiturate was developed in that year in the Bayer laboratories in Munich, Germany. Barbiturate compounds are synthesized using, among other things, chemicals found in urine, and some say Bayer gave the drugs their name to honour a woman named Barbara who provided the urine samples (Barbara's urates?). Others claim the name was to honour St. Barbara, and there are other stories as well (Perrine, 1996). We may never know, but regardless of how they were named, the class of depressant drugs called barbiturates now includes more than 2000 different compounds. Because so many barbiturates have been developed, custom dictates that both generic and brand names of these drugs end with the suffix "-al." A few representative barbiturates are listed in Table 12.2.

The effects of these various barbiturates are generally similar, differing primarily in potency and duration of action (see "This is your brain on psychotheraputic medications" box on page 281). Thus, pentobarbital and secobarbital are considered potent and short acting (duration of action two to four hours), amobarbital is intermediate (six to eight hours), and phenobarbital longer acting (eight to 10 hours). Barbiturates, like benzodiazepines, are thought to act by influencing inhibitory neurotransmission, a mechanism of action we discuss later in this chapter. In general, barbiturates that have a rapid onset and short duration of action are used as anesthetics today (for example, pentobarbital), whereas those with slower onset and longer duration of action are preferred for the treatment of epilepsy (phenobarbital).

Barbiturates were introduced into general medical practice in 1903, when barbital was marketed under the brand name Veronal. They soon became popular as a treatment for anxiety and as the first "sleeping pills" (Brecher, 1972). Use of barbiturates continued to increase until the 1960s, but has declined markedly in the years since.

Bettmann/Corbis

William Morton successfully used ether inhalation to render a patient unconscious in the first public demonstration of surgical anesthesia.

Peter Turnley/Turnley/CORBIS

The toxicology results carried out on the blood of singer Michael Jackson showed that he died of an overdose of propofol (trade name Diprivan), a powerful sedative/anesthetic sometimes prescribed for insomnia. On the day Jackson died, his doctor had also given Jackson diazepam (Valium), lorazepam (Ativan), and midazolam (Versed).

Several reasons account for the rise and fall of barbiturate use. Of the various afflictions people experienced in the 20th century and currently, sleeping disorders and anxiety problems are among the most common. Thus, any drug that offers relief from anxiety or promises sleep to insomniacs has potential for tremendous popularity and commercial success. The barbiturates do have the capacity to induce sleep and to relieve anxiety, and this accounts for their ascendance. However, consumers and physicians did not at first know a number of the problems associated with barbiturate use (discussed next). These led to the decline of barbiturate use in the past 25 years.

All the barbiturates possess the properties of CNS depressants. Thus, in moderate doses, they produce a drunken euphoric state. Similar to alcohol, barbiturates may produce a loss of motor coordination, a staggering gait, and slurred speech. Loss of emotional control and behavioural disinhibition are also characteristic effects. Sedation and sleep are produced by increased doses, and higher doses produce surgical anesthesia. Physiological effects include respiratory depression, which is responsible for most of the overdose deaths associated with barbiturates. In addition, some depression of heart rate, blood pressure, and gastrointestinal activity is noted at higher doses.

As noted, the barbiturates once were used extensively as sedative-hypnotic drugs, but except for certain specialized uses, they now have been replaced by the safer benzodiazepines. Short-acting barbiturates still are used to produce anesthesia. Other current uses include emergency treatment of convulsions and prevention of seizures in people with certain types of epilepsy (Perrine, 1996).

Tolerance develops fairly rapidly to many effects of the barbiturates.

One major reason for the movement away from the medical use of barbiturates involves tolerance and dependence. Tolerance develops fairly rapidly to many effects of the barbiturates. Whereas a given dose may be effective at inducing sleep for a while, the patient soon may require a higher dose to sleep if the drug is used regularly. If doses escalate too much and regular use persists, patients will experience an abstinence syndrome when they attempt to withdraw from barbiturates. The symptoms of the barbiturate withdrawal syndrome are similar to those of alcohol—shakes, perspiration, confusion, and full-blown delirium tremens (DTs) in some cases (see Chapter 9)—but convulsions and seizures are more likely to occur in barbiturate withdrawal; they are seen in five percent to 20% of the cases (Schuckit, 1995). As with alcohol, the severity of barbiturate withdrawal depends upon the extent of use. Mild symptoms such as **rebound insomnia** (discussed next) and anxiety may occur after a brief use of barbiturates, whereas life-threatening convulsions occur only after heavier use.

rebound insomnia
Inability to sleep produced as a withdrawal symptom associated with some depressant drugs.

Many people became dependent on barbiturates even though the drugs were used only under medical supervision. Suppose someone is in crisis—say, after the death of a spouse or other loved one. A physician may prescribe a sleeping pill to help the person rest during the crisis. After a few weeks, the patient may feel emotionally ready to sleep without the drug—and indeed may be. But the first night the patient attempts to sleep without the barbiturate, the person may have a great deal of trouble because of rebound insomnia, one of the features of barbiturate withdrawal (Mendelson, 1980). That is, after the chronic use of barbiturates, abstinence produces insomnia even in someone who was untroubled with insomnia previously.

A related problem involves the type of sleep experienced while under the influence of barbiturates and after heavy use of sleeping pills. Barbiturates do induce sleep, but like alcohol, they reduce the amount of time spent in the rapid eye movement or REM stage of sleep. This may account in part for the "hungover" feeling some people report after sleeping with the aid of a drug. Although they get enough hours of sleep, it may not be "high-quality" sleep. Further, when subjects try to sleep without a pill after taking drugs for several nights, they may experience **REM rebound**; that is, they spend more time than normal in REM. Often accompanying REM rebound are vivid dreams and nightmares with nocturnal awakening.

REM rebound
An increase in the rapid eye movement or REM stage of sleep when withdrawing from drugs that suppress REM time.

So even if the tired patients are able to sleep without drugs during barbiturate withdrawal, they may awaken early in the morning and not be able to get back to sleep. Other factors may be involved, but it is clear that once dependence on sleeping pills has developed, considerable time must pass before normal sleep patterns return (Mendelson, 1980). All of these factors make it easy to understand why dependence on drugs such as barbiturates for sleeping so often develops. Dependence certainly limits the usefulness of these and other depressants as a treatment of sleep disorders.

An additional problem with the barbiturates is the risk of fatal drug overdose. The lethal dose of many barbiturates is fairly low compared to the effective dose in inducing sleep, and accidental overdoses have been a problem. This is particularly evident when barbiturates are taken in combination with alcohol or other depressant drugs, because these drugs potentiate one another (Schuckit, 1995). Barbiturates often were prescribed to people suffering from depression because sleeping disorders are a common symptom of clinical depression. Because there is a risk that severely depressed patients may attempt suicide, having a prescription for barbiturates could make them more likely to succeed in their attempt. Barbiturates have been the lethal drug in many suicides, including celebrated cases such as that of Marilyn Monroe.

Barbiturates (particularly the short-acting barbiturates) produce a euphoric state similar to alcohol intoxication. In fact, a recent laboratory study compared the behavioural and subjective effects of alcohol with those of the barbiturate pentobarbital and concluded that they were virtually identical, with the exception that the barbiturate was somewhat more sedating and more likely to be abused than alcohol (Mintzer et al., 1997). As a result, barbiturates became significant recreational drugs on the street during the 1950s and 1960s. An estimated five billion doses of barbiturates entered the illicit market in 1969 alone (Brecher, 1972). Clearly, barbiturates were causing some major societal problems, and the quest was on for safer drugs to relieve anxiety and induce sleep.

Quaaludes and Other Nonbarbiturate Sedatives

Several nonbarbiturate sedatives were introduced in the 1950s and 1960s, as possible alternatives in the treatment of anxiety and sleep disorders. Meprobamate (trade name Equanil), ethchlorvynol (Placidyl), and glutethimide (Doriden) have all been used in this way, but each seemed to possess the same undesirable properties as the barbiturates. One important candidate as an alternative to barbiturates was methaqualone, first marketed under the brand names Quaalude and Sopor in 1965. Although some thought methaqualone would be much safer because it was not a barbiturate, this did not prove to be true. It quickly became evident that methaqualone was toxic at high doses, especially when taken in combination with alcohol. In addition, dependence develops rapidly to methaqualone, with abstinence symptoms similar to those produced by alcohol and barbiturates. Thus, medical enthusiasm for methaqualone was quickly dampened. Because it produces a pronounced state of "drunkenness" and developed a reputation as a sexual enhancer, however, methaqualone became a major street drug in the 1970s, and was sometimes known as "disco biscuits" or "ludes." Very little research is available about the true effects of methaqualone on sexuality. Anecdotal data are mixed: Some users report a disinhibition they find enhances sexual experience, but others report it interferes with sexual behaviour (Abel, 1985). Actually, given the similarity in pharmacology between methaqualone and other depressants such as alcohol, it would be surprising if there were any major differences in the way these drugs affect sexual behaviour.

The problems of abuse with methaqualone and other nonbarbiturate sedatives far outweigh their medical benefits, and currently these drugs are rarely used for the management of sleep problems or anxiety. In fact, methaqualone has become a Schedule I drug and is no longer produced for medical use. A major reason these drugs and the barbiturates have lost favour is the widespread acceptance of the benzodiazepines as the treatment of choice in these disorders.

The Problem of Anxiety

At this point, it makes sense to define anxiety and to provide some background and perspective on its treatment today. (A list of the most commonly prescribed antianxiety drugs is provided in Table 12.3.) Anxiety is frequently experienced as some or all of four categories of symptoms: (1) motor tension (for example, shakiness, muscle tension, restlessness), (2) autonomic hyperactivity (sweating, pounding heart, stomach tightness, flushing), (3) apprehensive expectation (anxiety, fear, rumination), and (4) vigilance (impatience, hyperattentiveness, insomnia) (APA, 2000a). Figure 12.3 shows the physical effects of anxiety disorders.

Clinicians frequently speak of two types of anxiety. The first is a trait or characterological anxiety, in that people seem to experience their anxiety practically all

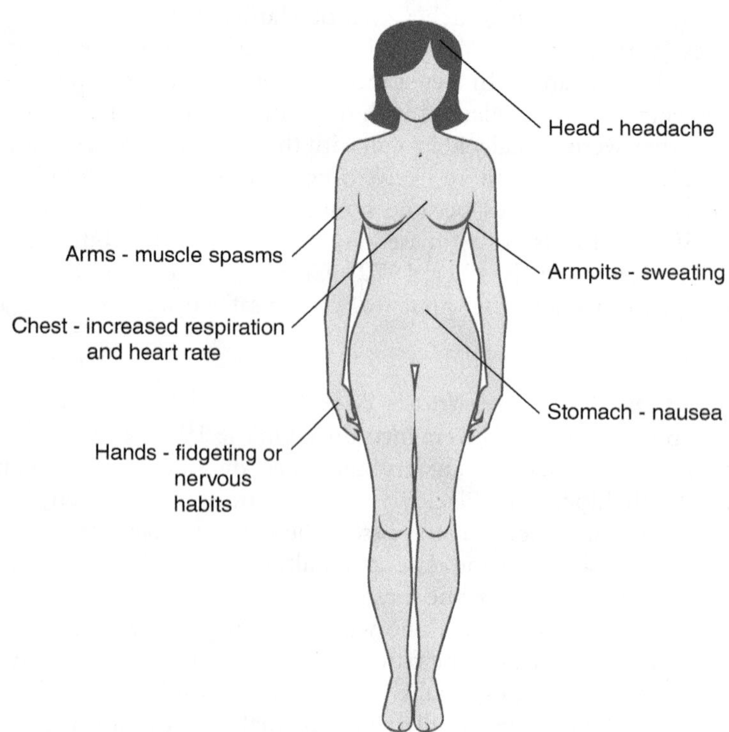

FIGURE 12.3
Physical effects of anxiety disorders

Source: Zubada/Shutterstock

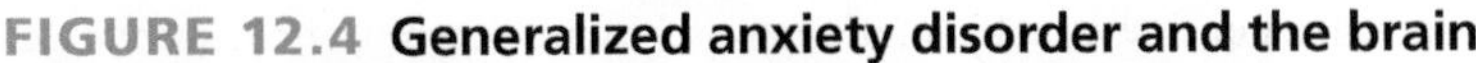

FIGURE 12.4 Generalized anxiety disorder and the brain

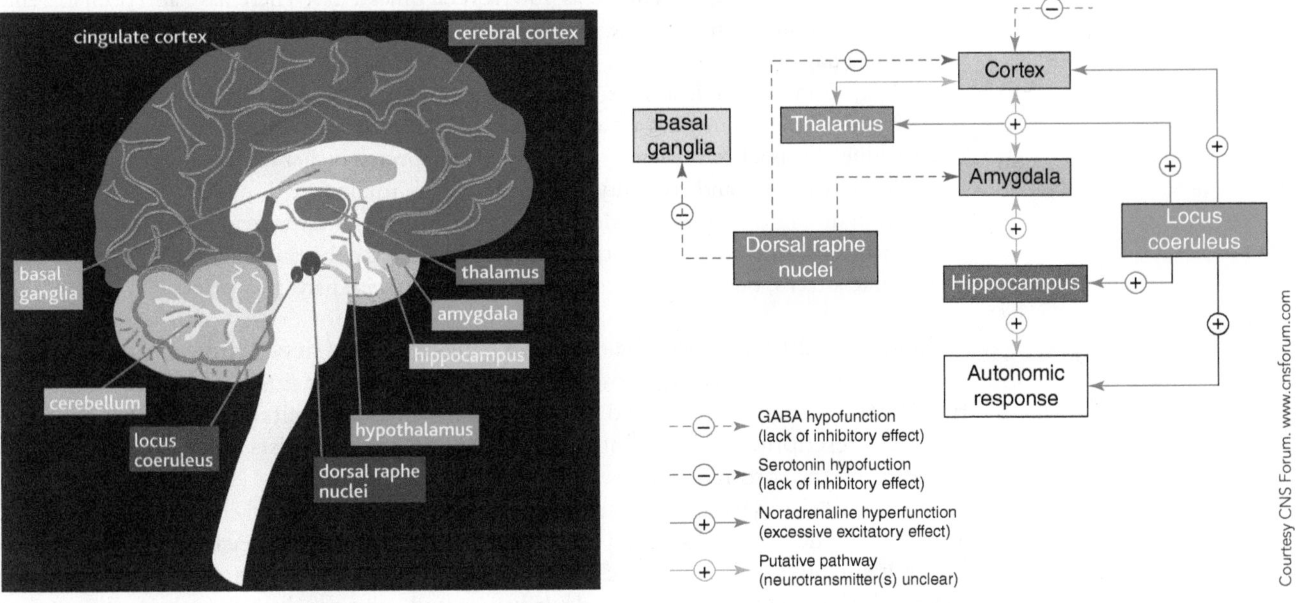

Courtesy CNS Forum. www.cnsforum.com

the time. This generalized anxiety affects 1.1 percent of Canadians (MDSC, 2009). Figure 12.4 shows the parts of the brain that are affected by generalized anxiety disorder. The second is a more transient state, called situational anxiety, wherein the anxiety is much greater at some times than at others, when the person may not even feel anxious at all. Examples of this type of anxiety are specific phobia, which affects 6.2–8.0 percent of Canadians and social phobia, which affects 6.7 percent of Canadians (MDSC, 2009). A related type of anxiety is panic attacks, which are recurrent and unpredictable periods of intense fear and impending doom (ibid.). These attacks frequently include sweating, palpitations, dizziness, and difficulty in breathing. Less than one percent of Canadians suffer from panic attacks. A case illustration of panic attacks from Spitzer et al. (1989) follows*:

> Mindy is a stylishly dressed, 25-year-old art director who is seeking treatment for "panic attacks" that have occurred with increasing frequency over the past year, often two or three times a day. These attacks begin with a sudden intense wave of "horrible fear" that seems to come out of nowhere, sometimes during the day, sometimes waking her from sleep. She begins to tremble, is nauseated, sweats profusely, feels as though she is gagging, and fears that she will lose control and do something crazy, like run screaming into the street.
>
> Mindy remembers first having attacks like this when she was in high school. She was dating a boy her parents disapproved of, and had to do a lot of "sneaking around" to avoid confrontations with them. At the same time, she was under a lot of pressure as the principal designer of her high school yearbook, and was applying to Ivy League colleges. She remembers that her first panic attack occurred just after the yearbook went to press and she was accepted by Harvard, Yale, and Brown. The attacks lasted only a few minutes, and she would just "sit through them." She was worried enough to mention them to her mother; but because she was otherwise perfectly healthy, she did not seek treatment.

* Reprinted with permission from *DSM-IV TR Casebook: A Learning Companion to the Diagnostic and Statistical Manual of Mental Disorders,* Fourth Edition, Text Revision, (Copyright 2002). American Psychiatric Association.

Over the eight years since her first attack, Mindy has had them intermittently, sometimes not for many months, sometimes, as now, several times a day. There have also been extreme variations in the intensity of the attacks, some being so severe and debilitating that she had to take a day off from work.

Apart from her panic attacks and a brief period of depression at 19, when she broke up with a boyfriend, Mindy has always functioned extremely well, in school, at work, and in her social life. She is a lively, friendly person who is respected by her friends and colleagues both for her intelligence and creativity and for her ability to mediate disputes.

Even during the times that she was having frequent, severe attacks, Mindy never limited her activities. She might stay home from work for a day because she was exhausted from multiple attacks, but she never associated the attacks with particular places.

Before the 20th century, the common palliative for anxiety symptoms was drinking alcohol, perhaps the oldest known means of sedation. For much of this century, into the 1950s, anxiety was treated primarily with bromide salts (which were available without prescription) and barbiturates. By the 1930s, scientists were discovering that the use of the bromides had many dangerous side effects (Feldman, Meyer, & Quenzer, 1997). Barbiturates, such as phenobarbital, were used then more frequently as an anxiolytic agent. As noted earlier, however, it gradually became clear that these drugs were physically addictive because users developed tolerance and exhibited a severe withdrawal reaction when drug use ceased. As a result, efforts were directed at developing an anxiolytic medication that would effectively treat the anxiety but not be physically addicting. The first in the desired group of nonbarbiturate sedatives was meprobamate, but again, it was found that a severe withdrawal syndrome was associated with discontinuing its use after some period of time on the drug. The world was still looking for a safer anxiolytic.

CONTEMPORARY ISSUE BOX 12.4

Internet Pharmacies: Rx for Disaster?

Prescription drugs have become easier than ever to obtain, thanks to the proliferation of Internet-based pharmacies. Literally thousands of such sites, both foreign and domestic, have appeared in recent years. In many cases, people may obtain drugs without speaking to a doctor and/or without having a prescription.

Many view the marketing of prescription drugs over the Internet as a dangerous trend. They cite concerns about three different types of online providers. First, and of greatest concern, are sites that sell products like GHB, a "date rape" drug. Second are sites, predominantly foreign, that sell misbranded, counterfeit, or out-of-date drugs. And third are sites that sell drugs to individuals who do not hold a prescription obtained through a qualified health professional.

The near boundary-less nature of the Internet has made it difficult for regulators trying to get a handle on Internet drug sales. At minimum, the sheer number of online pharmacies in operation overwhelms regulators. They are hoping that ongoing efforts to craft Internet licensing criteria will provide much-needed relief. In addition, a host of legislative efforts are underway. One example is the Ryan Haight Online Pharmacy Consumer Protection Act of 2008, which addresses the purchase or dispensing of controlled substances via the Internet. The act is named for a teenager whose death resulted in part from the ease with which he obtained a narcotic drug over the Internet without a valid prescription. The act amends the Controlled Substances Act to prohibit the delivery, distribution, or dispensing of a controlled substance over the Internet without a valid prescription. The act also requires that a face-to-face physician contact occur prior to the issuance of a prescription for a controlled substance.

Benzodiazepines

benzodiazepines Currently the most widely prescribed anxiolytic drugs.

In the late 1950s, scientists at Roche Laboratories synthesized a new group of compounds known as the **benzodiazepines**. Animal tests with these drugs showed sedative, anticonvulsant, and muscle-relaxant effects similar to those of the barbiturates. An additional feature was that they produced a "taming" effect in monkeys. Even more intriguing, these drugs showed very low toxicity; that is, the lethal dose is sufficiently high that it is difficult to attain. The first of the benzodiazepines, chlordiazepoxide (trade name Librium), was first marketed in 1960, closely followed by the introduction of its more potent cousin, diazepam (Valium) in 1963 (Sternbach, 1983). These two drugs quickly came to dominate the market as treatments for anxiety and insomnia. By the 1970s, they were among the best-selling drugs in America, with 100 million prescriptions written for benzodiazepines in 1975 alone (Harvey, 1980). More recently, because of widespread concern about dependence and other side effects, the use of these drugs is down, but they are still frequently prescribed. The way benzodiazapines affect neural activity, in general, is illustrated in this chapter's "This is your brain on psychotheraputic medications" box on page 281.

Depressant drugs share many traits. Alcohol, barbiturates, nonbarbiturate sedatives, and of course benzodiazepines all have similar effects when equated for dose. In addition, cross-tolerance occurs between these drugs, and they potentiate one another. Cross-dependence also occurs because an appropriate dose of any depressant can be used to reduce the withdrawal symptoms produced by any other. In fact, benzodiazepines are commonly used to withdraw alcoholics from alcohol. Thus, substantial evidence indicates a common mechanism of action for depressant drugs (Julien, 2001).

In fact, benzodiazepines are commonly used to withdraw alcoholics from alcohol.

By the 1970s, evidence had begun to accumulate that GABA, the brain's major inhibitory neurotransmitter, might provide the common link (Costa, Guidotti, & Mao, 1975; Ticku, Burch, & Davis, 1983). The problem was that no direct evidence was found that any of the depressant drugs bound to the GABA receptor site. Then, in 1977, two independent laboratories reported the discovery of binding sites for benzodiazepines (Möhler & Okada, 1977; Squires & Braestrup, 1977), and it was subsequently shown that, although specific to benzodiazepines, these receptors are part of what is now called the GABA/benzodiazepine receptor complex (Feldman, Meyer, & Quenzer, 1997). Apparently the normal neural inhibition produced by GABA is greatly enhanced when there is activity at the benzodiazepine receptor. Benzodiazepines act by enhancing neural inhibition in the GABA system.

When taken orally, benzodiazepines generally are absorbed slowly and have a long duration of action. Considerable variability exists in duration of action, however, which accounts for the different uses for and effects of the different benzodiazepines. Table 12.4 shows the half-lives for some of the widely used benzodiazepines (the time required for half of the drug to be metabolized). The longer-acting benzodiazepines such as Valium are considered most useful when it is desirable to maintain the patient at a constant level of drug over an extended period—for example, when an individual is suffering from an anxiety reaction. The short- and intermediate-duration benzodiazepines are more useful for treating insomnia when it is desirable to have the drug effects wear off by morning.

A number of reasons exist for the commercial success of the benzodiazepines. First, they are effective at relieving anxiety and inducing sleep. In fact, benzodiazepines are sometimes claimed to be uniquely effective as anxiolytic agents. It is true they relieve anxiety in animal studies and in humans at doses that do not produce motor impairment (ataxia) or pronounced sedation. In animals, anxiolytic action is tested by determining the ability of a drug to increase rates of a punishment response (see Chapter 5). Animals, typically rats, are trained to press a lever to produce food or water reinforcement. Then, during some periods, lever pressing is punished by electric shock; during

TABLE 12.4 Kinetic Classification of Representative Benzodiazepines

Type	Half-life (hours)
Long half-life	
Flurazepam (Dalmane)	75
Diazepam (Valium)	50
Intermediate half-life	
Alprazolam (Xanax)	15
Lorazepam (Ativan)	15
Short half-life	
Triazolam (Halcion)	4
Midazolam (Versed)	1

other periods, no shock is delivered. Normally, rats will show decreased rates of lever pressing in the punishment component. When benzodiazepines are given to animals trained with such procedures, the rates of lever pressing in the punishment component go up almost to baseline levels at doses that do not affect the unpunished component. The clinical efficacy of various benzodiazepines measured in humans is correlated closely with these antipunishment actions, and for this reason, the facilitation of a punishment response is viewed as an excellent animal model of human anxiety. In fact, novel anxiolytic drugs have been discovered on the basis of antipunishment effects on this animal model. Although other depressant drugs also show antipunishment effects, none is as selective in this regard as benzodiazepines. This is one reason for considering benzodiazepines as possessing some unique anxiolytic actions.

The potent anxiolytic actions of benzodiazepines occur at doses that produce fewer serious side effects than barbiturates. Although drowsiness may occur when taking benzodiazepines, it is less of a problem than with other depressant drugs. Because the lethal dose is so high, suicide and accidental overdose are far less of a risk with benzodiazepines than with other depressant drugs. Benzodiazepines do interact to potentiate alcohol and other depressant drugs, however, and fatal overdoses are not uncommon with such drug combinations. So benzodiazepines, though not nearly so toxic as depressants such as barbiturates or methaqualone, are not without overdose risk.

In addition to use in anxiety disorders, benzodiazepines are often prescribed for insomnia. These drugs are effective at reducing both the amount of time required to fall asleep and the amount of awake time in cases where the person wakes up after the initial sleep onset. As we noted for the barbiturates, though, benzodiazepines also change the pattern of sleep. Benzodiazepines suppress the amount of REM sleep and change the EEG patterns observed during non-REM sleep. Unlike barbiturates, the short- or intermediate-duration benzodiazepines—sleeping pills such as the popular and controversial triazolam (trade name Halcion) or temazepam (Restoril)—do not often produce "hangover" or day-after effects. Rebound insomnia is a problem with all of the benzodiazepines but to a lesser extent than it was with the barbiturates (Parrino & Terzano, 1996). Finally, other side effects have been reported, particularly depression and paranoia with Halcion.

Rebound insomnia is a problem with all of the benzodiazepines but to a lesser extent than it was with the barbiturates.

Benzodiazepines also are used for purposes other than anxiety and insomnia management. For example, benzodiazepines have muscle-relaxant and anticonvulsant actions and are often used as a treatment for muscle spasms and seizures. Short-acting benzodiazepines such as midazolam (trade name Versed) are used as anesthetics in some surgical procedures.

Finally, benzodiazepines are frequently used to medically manage withdrawal from alcohol. Because alcohol shows cross-dependence with benzodiazepines and other depressants, tapering off from alcohol use is made easier through the use of benzodiazepines. The general practice, often referred to as *detoxification*, involves providing an initial dose of the benzodiazepine that is sufficient to suppress potentially dangerous alcohol withdrawal symptoms. Then, over a period of weeks, the dose is gradually reduced. There is great concern that an individual with a history of alcohol problems may simply substitute benzodiazepine abuse for alcohol, so the goal of most detoxification programs is to taper the client off benzodiazepines as rapidly as possible.

Tolerance develops to benzodiazepines, and there is cross-tolerance between them and other depressants. Tolerance to benzodiazepines develops slowly, however, and fairly high doses are needed for tolerance to develop. There is some controversy about the frequency of withdrawal symptoms following benzodiazepine use. It has been argued that withdrawal occurs only at very high doses, but more recent studies find withdrawal affects between five percent and 35 percent of patients who have taken benzodiazepines for one month or longer (Miller & Greenblatt, 1996). When withdrawal syndromes do occur, they are similar to those associated with alcohol and barbiturates but generally not so severe. Abstinence symptoms may not appear for several days or even more than a week and may persist for up to four weeks. The main symptoms are rebound insomnia, anxiety, tremors, sweating, and occasionally more serious problems such as seizures (Schuckit, 1995). One of the problems in interpreting benzodiazepine withdrawal is differentiating abstinence symptoms from the symptoms the drug was suppressing.

The issues of abuse of and dependence on benzodiazepines have been controversial. Benzodiazepines do turn up on the street but far less frequently than barbiturates or Quaaludes did in their day. In general, the potential for abuse of benzodiazepines is considered to be fairly moderate in comparison with most other depressants (Cappell, Sellers, & Busto, 1986). There are still reports of abuse and dependence, and they appear to be most common in individuals who abuse other drugs (King, 1994). The risk of abuse is higher for people who have a history of drug or alcohol problems than for those without such a history. For example, one laboratory study compared the effects of alprazolam (trade name Xanax) in a group of men with alcoholism who had abstained from alcohol for up to 72 hours with a group of men without alcoholism. The pharmacokinetics (absorption and metabolism) of the drug did not differ in the two groups, but those with alcoholism reported that they "liked" the effects of the drug more. "Liking" the drug was measured on a questionnaire that correlates with drug-abuse liability (Ciraulo et al., 1988). Griffiths et al. (1980) also have investigated benzodiazepine self-administration in human volunteers who have histories of sedative abuse. In double-blind laboratory studies, these researchers have shown that humans will self-administer benzodiazepines and prefer them to placebo but, like nonhumans, prefer barbiturates (Griffiths et al., 1980). When different benzodiazepines were compared, the more potent drugs with a rapid onset of action, such as Valium and Xanax, were preferred to the less potent compounds with slower onset of action, such as oxazepam (Griffiths, McLeod, Bigelow, Liebson, Roache, & Nowowieski, 1984; Griffiths, McLeod, Bigelow, Liebson, & Roache, 1984; Mumford, Rush, & Griffiths, 1995). This observation may explain the recent rash of reports of abuse of the potent benzodiazepine Rohypnol (flunitrazepam), or "roofies" as they are referred to on the street (see Contemporary Issue Box 12.5).

CONTEMPORARY ISSUE BOX 12.5

Roofies: A Story of Sedative Abuse

Benzodiazepines are generally thought to possess relatively modest potential for abuse, but alarms have been ringing for some time about "roofies," "rope," or "roach." This drug turns out to be flunitrazepam, a benzodiazepine marketed as a sleeping pill in Europe and Latin under the brand name Rohypnol. Flunitrazepam is a short-acting benzodiazepine that appears to be more potent than other drugs in this class in producing intoxication, sedation, and behavioural disruption (Farre, Teran, & Cami, 1996). The effects of roofies are basically the same as those of the other benzodiazepines discussed (Woods & Winger, 1997), but because the drug is more potent, it may be more likely to be abused and produce adverse effects.

Of particular concern is the link between roofies and memory loss or blackouts. This effect has resulted in roofies' apparent association with date rape. Cases have surfaced that involved men slipping the drug into a woman's drink without her knowledge and, after the drug "knocked her out," raping her (Seligman & King, 1996). Prosecution of these cases can be difficult because the women are often unable to remember much about the crime. In addition, there is concern about the potential of roofies to produce dependence and dangerous drug interactions. A synergistic combination of flunitrazepam and alcohol put rock star Kurt Cobain into a coma just a month before his suicide.

Tolerance, dependence, and abuse are associated with the benzodiazepines, but the problems produced are far milder than those connected with other depressant drugs. Over the years, however, a number of other problems associated with benzodiazepine use have emerged. As with other depressants, the significant side effects of benzodiazepines are drowsiness and motor impairment. Although even these side effects are rare with benzodiazepines alone (see Cappell, Sellers, & Busto, 1986, for a review), they may become particularly problematic when benzodiazepines are taken, as they often are, in combination with alcohol or other depressant drugs (see Contemporary Issue Box 12.6).

anterograde amnesia Loss or limitation of the ability to form new memories.

A more recently recognized problem is that benzodiazepines may interfere with the storage of memories, a phenomenon called **anterograde amnesia**. Thus, when individuals are awakened by a phone call from sleep induced by benzodiazepines, they may fail to remember the phone conversation. The drug may be present in sufficient dose the next morning so that the patients forget what they had for breakfast or what was read in the morning paper. These are examples of benzodiazepine-induced amnesia, and evidence is mounting that it is a common problem, particularly with some of the popular benzodiazepines such as triazolam (trade name Halcion) and alprazolam (Xanax) (Perrine, 1996; Salzman, 1992). This type of effect is not unique to benzodiazepines. After all, alcohol is known to produce the more dramatic memory loss of the blackout (see Chapter 6). Barbiturates and methaqualone also produce blackouts, which suggests that some type of memory deficit may be characteristic of any depressant drug.

Nonbenzodiazepine Treatment

Because of the problems reviewed in the preceding sections, considerable interest has focused on the development of new drugs for the treatment of anxiety problems and sleep disorders. One example is a drug called zolpidem (trade name Ambien). Zolpidem's chemical structure is different from the benzodiazepine drugs, but it is still

CONTEMPORARY ISSUE BOX 12.6

Depressant Drugs and Potentiation

All the depressant drugs reviewed to this point tend to potentiate one another; that is, the effects of the drugs when combined are greater than would be expected from the individual doses considered alone. Potentiation is among the most dangerous aspects of drug use. The vast majority of deaths from drug overdose are due not to overdose of a single drug but rather to smaller doses of more than one drug taken in lethal combination. Alcohol, barbiturates, nonbarbiturate sedatives (Quaaludes, meprobamate), and benzodiazepines all interact to produce additive effects. They interact with heroin and other opiate drugs to produce additive effects as well. Many deaths attributed to heroin overdose actually involve heroin taken in combination with alcohol or other depressant drugs. Such a combination of depressants killed Elvis Presley, and it kills thousands of others every year.

Another problem with additive effects involves cases in which lower doses are consumed. Consider a young woman who is given a prescription for Valium to help her weather a family crisis. Suppose after taking her Valium, she goes out with some friends for dinner and has a couple of beers. Perhaps she could tolerate this much alcohol without impairment under normal conditions, but by drinking in combination with the Valium, she may find herself quite intoxicated. If she attempts to drive home after such a drug combination, the loss of motor coordination may prove fatal. Combinations of alcohol with another depressant are thought to be responsible for many highway deaths above and beyond those caused by alcohol alone (O'Hanlon & De Gier, 1986). Never combine depressant drugs with alcohol or one another.

Michael Ochs Archives/Getty Images

Elvis Presley died from a combination of depressant drugs.

thought to act as an agonist of the same "benzodiazepine" receptors. Thus, zolpidem produces more or less the same array of depressant drug effects that are associated with the benzodiazepines. However, zolpidem is effective at inducing sleep at doses that interfere very little with the "natural" sleep structure. That is, zolpidem induces sleep with less suppression of the REM stage than benzodiazepines, and it appears less likely to produce "hangover" effects or rebound insomnia (Parrino & Terzano, 1996). As a result, Ambien has become one of the most widely prescribed drugs for the treatment of insomnia. However, it should be noted that, depending on the dose, zolpidem can produce the same side effects as the benzodiazepines (Rush & Griffiths, 1996).

Another nonbenzodiazepine anxiolytic drug is buspirone (trade name BuSpar). Buspirone's chemical structure and activities are very different from any of the traditional depressant drugs. It appears to affect the serotonin neurotransmitter system, not the GABA/benzodiazepine receptor complex. Perhaps because of its different mechanism of action, buspirone has been shown to be effective in the treatment of anxiety with fewer side effects than the alternatives. For example, no withdrawal symptoms have been reported following chronic use of buspirone, and it is considered to have no significant abuse potential. Animals will not self-administer buspirone, and humans report no intoxication or euphoria after using it (Rush & Griffiths, 1997; Tunnicliff, Eison, & Taylor, 1991). Little sedation or motor impairment is seen during buspirone treatment, and it interacts less with alcohol than other depressant drugs (Rush & Griffiths, 1997). Simply put, buspirone seems to relieve anxiety without producing many of the undesirable effects of the other anxiolytic drugs. One difference is that buspirone's anxiolytic effects are delayed. It often requires three to four weeks of treatment before benefits appear. In contrast, the benzodiazepines are immediate. Also, buspirone appears less effective in the treatment of panic disorder and does not relieve insomnia (Coplan, Wolk, & Klein, 1995). Despite these limitations, buspirone is a valuable alternative for the treatment of anxiety and raises the hope that developments in psychopharmacology may lead to safer treatments for psychological problems.

Simply put, buspirone seems to relieve anxiety without producing many of the undesirable effects of the other anxiolytic drugs.

Beyond these issues, it should be noted that antidepressant medications also are used in the treatment of anxiety disorders. Tricyclic antidepressants and SSRIs both have been used in the treatment of such anxiety disorders as panic disorder, obsessive-compulsive disorder, and posttraumatic stress disorder.

Mood-Stabilizing Drugs

The most specific treatment for the mood disorders of mania and bipolar disorder is lithium. Mania is a state with pronounced elevations in mood and increased activity. Symptoms of a manic episode typically include increased talkativeness, flights of ideas or racing thoughts, grandiosity, decreased need for sleep, and excessive involvement in behaviours that can produce negative consequences (such as buying sprees or sexual indiscretions) (APA, 2000a). Although these symptoms seem to describe someone who is "happy-go-lucky" or "pleasantly high," their occurrence and severity generally are profound and significantly disrupt the person's functioning. For people with this disorder, the first manic episode generally occurs in their 20s or 30s, although there are exceptions in both directions. The natural course of an untreated manic episode is generally a couple of months.

Manic attacks are usually a component of what is called bipolar, or manic-depressive, disorder; these individuals often experience periodic episodes of depression as well. The following case (Spitzer et al., 1989) illustrates the manic component of bipolar disorder. It is an example of the development of manic symptoms late in life*:

> A wealthy, 72-year-old widow is referred by her children, against her will, as they think she has become "senile" since the death of her husband six months previously. After the initial bereavement, which was not severe, the patient had resumed an active social life and become a volunteer at local hospitals. The family encouraged this, but over the past three months, has become concerned about her going to local bars with some of the hospital staff. The referral was precipitated by her announcing her engagement to a 25-year-old male nurse, to whom she planned to turn over her house and a large amount of money. The patient's three sons, by threat and intimidation, have made her accompany them to this psychiatric evaluation.
>
> Initially in the interview the patient is extremely angry at her sons and the psychiatrist, insisting that they don't understand that for the first time in her life she is doing something for herself. She then suddenly drapes herself over the couch and asks the psychiatrist if she is attractive enough to capture a 25-year-old man. She proceeds to elaborate on her fiancé's physique and sexual abilities and describes her life as exciting and fulfilling

* R. L. Spitzer, M. Gibbon, A. E. Skodol, J. B. W. Williams (2002). *DSM-IV-TR Casebook*. Washington DC: American Psychiatric Association. Reprinted with permission from the Diagnostic and Statistical Manual of Mental Disorders. © 2002.)

for the first time. She is overtalkative and repeatedly refuses to allow the psychiatrist to interrupt her with questions. She says that she goes out nightly with her fiancé to clubs and bars and that although she does not drink, she thoroughly enjoys the atmosphere. They often go on to an after-hours place and end up breakfasting, going to bed, and making love. After only three or four hours' sleep, she gets up, feeling refreshed, and then goes shopping. She spends about $700 a week on herself and gives her fiancé about $500 a week, all of which she can easily afford.

Lithium is an alkaline metal readily available throughout nature and is found in the form of silicate in such rocks as petalite, lepidolite, and spodumene (Tyrer & Shaw, 1982). Lithium's mood-stabilizing properties were discovered in the 1940s. An Australian physician, John Cade, was giving research animals lithium in an attempt to decrease uric acid-induced kidney damage. In the course of his work, he observed a calming effect on the animals and speculated that lithium might be useful in humans as a mood attenuator (Baldessarini, 1985; Sack & DeFraites, 1977). Cade administered lithium to a sample of manic patients and observed positive responses. Subsequent research eventually led to the approval of lithium for clinical use in the United States in 1970, although it was in clinical use in Europe several years earlier. There is strong evidence that lithium is effective with these two indications. Lithium probably is, incidentally, the only drug in psychiatry for which there is effective prophylaxis against disease recurrence (Fieve, 1976; Sack & DeFraites, 1977).

As with the antidepressants discussed earlier, the major biological theory regarding mania concerns the monoamine neurotransmitters. In depression, underactivity of neurotransmitters is hypothesized, and the hypothesis for mania is increased functional activity of the neurotransmitters. Within these hypotheses, the central focus is on catecholamines and serotonin. The way lithium affects neural activity, in general, is illustrated in the "This is your brain on psychotheraputic medications" box on page 281. At the presynaptic level, lithium appears to enhance reuptake of serotonin and norepinephrine. Lithium also appears to decrease dopamine and norepinephrine effects at the postsynaptic receptors (Gitlin, 1990). Importantly, lithium serves to normalize the mood of manic patients, not just offset mania through sedation.

The most common preparations of lithium salts are carbonates (lithium carbonate, or Li_2CO_3), which are prepared in tablet form. In terms of pharmacokinetics, lithium, which is taken orally, is absorbed completely from the gastrointestinal tract (primarily the small intestine) and distributed throughout the system. The lithium is distributed in the body water and is not metabolized. Excretion occurs almost entirely by the kidneys, with between 90–95 percent eliminated through urine.

Despite its success in the treatment of mania, cautions must be taken into account prior to and during lithium use. Several of these considerations pertain to lithium's therapeutic index, or safety margin. In this regard, the difference between the therapeutic and toxic levels is small. When the therapeutic range is exceeded, at least several of the following symptoms might be observed: drowsiness, blurred vision, ataxia, confusion, cardiac irregularities, and even seizures and coma. Some deaths have been reported. Thus, lithium use requires close medical supervision. Also, pretreatment medical work-ups are specifically geared toward ruling out cardiovascular problems or renal disease. Cardiac problems are a concern because toxic effects can cause cardiac irregularities, which could then exacerbate preexisting cardiovascular problems. Renal functioning must be satisfactory so that the lithium is efficiently excreted. If it is not, lithium will accumulate in the body. Finally, several side effects are associated with lithium use, including gastrointestinal problems such as nausea, diarrhea, fine hand tremor, urinary frequency, and dry mouth. These side effects often decrease within a period of weeks, however.

Although lithium remains the major drug used in the treatment of mania, other drugs are available when the patient does not tolerate lithium or when the patient does not respond to the lithium. The most frequently used alternative is carbamazepine (trade name Tegretol), better recognized as an antiepileptic drug. Chemically related to the tricyclic antidepressants, carbamazepine has been shown to be effective with patients who have rapid-cycling manic-depressive episodes. Other alternatives to lithium that are available are clonazepam (trade name Klonopin), topiramate (Topamax), tiagabine (Gabitril), and valproic acid (Depakote), another anticonvulsant drug. There also has been recent interest in the use of several of the atypical antipsychotic medications because of their mood-stabilizing properties (in particular olanzapine [Zyprexa], aripiprazole [Abilify], and quetiapine [Seroquel]) (Alda et al., 2009).

Psychotherapeutic Drugs and Pregnancy

No psychotherapeutic medication is totally safe for use during pregnancy, and all carry warnings regarding use when a patient is pregnant. As a result, a judgment needs to be made between the health of the mother on the one hand and the risks to the unborn child on the other. The approach most recommended is that psychotherapeutics not be used during pregnancy unless absolutely necessary and then only after nondrug interventions, such as counselling, have been tried first.

Psychotherapeutic drug use during pregnancy is potentially unsafe for several reasons. Certainly, on one level, the risks to the mother are at least the same as when she is not pregnant. However, the risks are increased when one considers the variety of physical changes that occur during pregnancy, including alterations in metabolism and endocrine, renal, and cardiac changes (Kerns & Davis, 1986). These and other changes create an environment in which absorption, distribution, and excretion of the drug can occur. One effect of antipsychotic medication on the mother is lowered blood pressure, which can compromise the placental blood flow to the fetus.

teratogenic
Producing abnormalities in the fetus.

The fetus also faces risks, particularly **teratogenic** effects, long-term effects on neurobehavioural functioning, and direct toxic effects of the drug. This is especially the case during the first trimester of pregnancy, when particularly critical fetal development (including organ and limb development) occurs (Howland, 2009). Three points should be kept in mind (Kerns & Davis, 1986). First, all classes of psychotherapeutic drugs cross the placenta. Second, drug effects can change the blood flow within the placenta and thus influence the transport and nutritive functions of the placenta. Third, the fetus, compared to an adult, has greater cardiac output and a greater proportion of blood flow to the brain. This results in a greater exposure of the drug to the brain. Comparable considerations, to a lesser extent, come into play in the context of breast-feeding. Concentrations of some psychotherapeutic medications are detectable in the breast milk of mothers taking such medications (Field, 2008).

The effects of psychotherapeutic drugs on the fetus are not well established. Most of the research has been conducted, for obvious reasons, on animals rather than humans. And the work involving humans, usually follow-up studies on women who used these drugs during pregnancy and their offspring, is hard to interpret. For example, many of the pregnant women who use psychotherapeutic medications have used more than one drug, and many have used other substances as well, such as alcohol or cigarettes. Nevertheless, there are indications, with varying levels of risk, that various teratogenic, neurobehavioural, and toxic consequences can occur when psychotherapeutics are used during pregnancy. Perhaps the most widely recognized effect is the association of lithium used during the first trimester of pregnancy with a significant teratogenic risk of cardiovascular system impairment (Fait et al., 2002).

SUMMARY

- Psychotherapeutic medications are prescribed in hopes of providing mentally ill people some relief and ideally the opportunity to function better in their environments.
- Early efforts to deal with mental illness included a variety of speculative approaches, many of which were cruel. These included bloodletting, hot irons, flogging, and starvation.
- Later on, in the mid-1800s, cannabis was studied as a treatment for depression and mania.
- During the first half of the 1900s, amphetamines were used in the treatment of depression and narcolepsy, and carbon dioxide in the treatment of various psychotic and neurotic conditions.
- In 1949, the Australian physician John Cade discovered the benefits of lithium in the treatment of mania, and lithium remains a mainstay in the treatment of that disorder today.
- The greatest advance in psychopharmacology was the use, starting around 1950, of the drug chlorpromazine as an antipsychotic medication. A host of other drugs were introduced in the years following, including antianxiety medications (including meprobamate, a muscle relaxant) and antidepressant medications (including the cyclic antidepressants and monoamine oxidase inhibitors).
- Twenty percent of Canadians will experience some form of mental disorder in their lifetime. Most have symptoms associated with anxiety, depression, or alcohol abuse.
- Psychotherapeutic drug use is more likely among women, older people, people living alone, the more educated, and those with higher incomes.
- The illicit use of prescription medications is a serious problem. Prescription drugs are a factor in a large number of drug-related emergency room cases and drug-related deaths.
- Psychotherapeutic drugs can affect the neurotransmitter/receptor system. The prominent processes are binding directly to the receptor site, serving as a receptor agonist or antagonist; causing the release of more neurotransmitters; blocking the reuptake of neurotransmitters back into the presynaptic neuron; changing the number of receptor sites or the sensitivity of the receptors; altering the metabolism of the neurotransmitter; and altering the enzymatic degradation of the neurotransmitter.
- Like other drugs, psychotherapeutic drugs can be classified in different ways. The most common way is by therapeutic use, and the four major categories are antipsychotics, antidepressants, antianxiety agents, and mood-stabilizing drugs.
- Antipsychotic medications, also known as neuroleptics or major tranquilizers, are used to treat schizophrenia and other disorders, such as mania, agitated depression, toxic psychoses, emotionally unstable personalities, and psychoses associated with old age. These medications affect primarily the reticular activating system, the limbic system, and the hypothalamus.
- The dopamine hypothesis is the most accepted explanation of the action of antipsychotic medications. Two core elements of the dopamine hypothesis are that increased levels of dopaminergic activity induce psychoses, and most antipsychotic drugs block postsynaptic dopamine receptors.
- Tardive dyskinesia is a major side effect of long-term use of antipsychotic drugs. It is characterized by repetitive, involuntary movements of the mouth and tongue, trunk, and extremities.
- Depression is one of the most common psychiatric disorders in Canada, and throughout the world. Depression often is classified as one of two major types: endogenous or exogenous.

- Two major classes—cyclic antidepressants and monoamine oxidase inhibitors (MAOIs)—of antidepressant medications now are prescribed.
- Antidepressant-medication treatment of depression follows from the biochemical hypothesis of the disorder. The hypothesis is that depression results from a deficiency in two biogenic amines—catecholamines and serotonin—that act as CNS neurotransmitters.
- All depressant drugs (including alcohol) produce similar effects. At low doses, they relieve anxiety; at moderate doses, they induce sleep; and at higher doses, they produce general anesthesia and eventually coma and death.
- The first depressants discovered were drugs used for general anesthesia, such as nitrous oxide and ether. Modern surgery would not be possible without this development.
- The development of the barbiturate drugs led to the use of depressants as sleeping pills and as treatment of anxiety symptoms and epilepsy.
- The use of barbiturates was limited when adverse effects were discovered. These include rapid development of tolerance, severe withdrawal symptoms, high risk of overdose, and high abuse potential.
- A number of barbiturate-like compounds have been developed (such as methaqualone, or Quaaludes), but they have the same undesirable effects as the barbiturates.
- The discovery of benzodiazepines revolutionized the medical use of depressant drugs because they relieve anxiety with fewer side effects than previous depressants.
- Benzodiazepines and other depressant drugs are believed to act at the GABA receptor site in the central nervous system.
- The anxiolytic effects of benzodiazepines are more selective than those of other depressants because they relieve anxiety at doses that produce minimal sedation and motor impairment.
- Although less problematic than barbiturates, benzodiazepines may produce tolerance and dependence, and withdrawal symptoms may occur.
- Lithium is the major drug used to treat the mood disorders of mania and manic-depressive illness. Lithium is the only psychotherapeutic drug that is an effective prophylaxis against disease recurrence.
- Use of lithium is based in the biological theory that bipolar disorder results from an overactivity of the neurotransmitters in the brain. Lithium appears to enhance reuptake of serotonin and norepinephrine at the presynaptic level and to decrease dopamine and norepinephrine effects at the postsynaptic receptors.
- No psychotherapeutic drug is totally safe for use during pregnancy. The best approach is that psychotherapeutic drugs be given to a pregnant woman only when necessary and when nondrug therapies, such as counselling, have been tried and have failed.
- Psychotherapeutic drug use during pregnancy can pose a health risk to both the mother and the fetus. Although the experimental evidence is not solid, the fetus may face various teratogenic, neurobehavioural, and toxic consequences of its mother's use of psychotherapeutic medications during pregnancy.

Key Terms

agitated depression p. 280
akinesia p. 284
anterograde amnesia p. 306
anxiolytic p. 293
barbiturates p. 293
benzodiazepines p. 303
dyskinesia p. 284
endogenous p. 286
exogenous p. 286
extrapyramidal p. 284
general anesthesia p. 294
manic p. 275
narcoleptic p. 275
neuroleptics p. 281
neuroses p. 275
paranoid schizophrenia p. 282
psychosurgery p. 275
psychotherapeutic p. 274
rebound insomnia p. 298
REM rebound p. 299
sedative-hypnotic effects p. 293
tardive dyskinesia p. 284
teratogenic p. 310

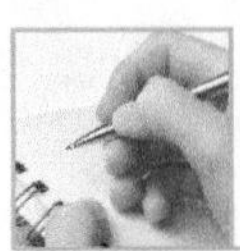

Essays/Thought Questions

1. Should herbal remedies such as St. John's wort be available to consumers without a prescription? What guidelines, if any, should be in place to ensure the safe use of such remedies and to establish that the remedy acts as advertised?
2. What are the advantages and disadvantages of a pregnant woman's use of psychotherapeutic medications?

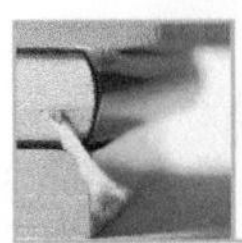

Suggested Readings

Gordon, B. (1979). *I'm dancing as fast as I can*. New York: Bantam Books Inc.

Russo, E. (2001). *Handbook of psychotropic herbs: A scientific analysis of herbal remedies for psychiatric conditions*. Binghamton, NY: Haworth Herbal Press.

Silverman, H. M. (2008). *The pill book* (13th ed.). New York: Bantam Books Inc.

Spitzer, R.L., Gibbon, M., Skodol, A.E., Williams, J.B.W., & First, M.B. (1989). *DSM-III-R casebook*. Washington, DC: American Psychiatric Press Inc.

Styron, W. (1992). *Darkness visible: A memoir of madness*. New York: Vintage Books.

CHAPTER 13

Other Prescription and Over-the-Counter Drugs

Did You Know

?

- Birth control pills contain synthetic forms of one or both of the female sex hormones.
- Anabolic steroids are synthetic forms of testosterone.
- Acne, baldness, and liver damage are all side effects associated with steroid use.
- Many over-the-counter diet pills contain epinephrine and caffeine.
- Many natural health products (NHP) do not have sufficient evidence that they provide 'healthy' benefits to the body and mind.
- GHB is a naturally occurring neurotransmitter in the brain that acts as a depressant.
- Inhalant abuse is most common among First Nation youth on reserves, and street and inner city youth in Canada.
- Volatile solvents inhibit and depress the central nervous system, much like other depressants. They are regarded as dangerous because of their availability and perception as safe.
- Amyl nitrite is clinically used in treating angina pain in cardiac patients.

Overview

We have discussed the major traditional classes of psychoactive drugs. Other drugs of importance did not fit neatly into the earlier chapters, however, and some of them will be reviewed here. We first discuss common prescription drugs, including birth control pills and anabolic steroids. Next we consider psychoactive drugs that, although regulated by Health Canada through the Food and Drugs Act (FDA), can be legally purchased without a prescription; that is, the over-the-counter drugs. These include primarily analgesics (such as aspirin), antihistamines and other cold and allergy medications, diet pills, and sleeping aids. Then we review an array of herbal remedies, hormones, and dietary supplements that have psychoactive properties. These products are legally available but are not regulated by the FDA. Finally, we discuss a group of legal chemicals that produce volatile fumes with psychoactive effects: the inhalants.

Prescription Drugs

In Canada, drugs that are approved for use are classified according to Canada's National Drug Scheduling System, under the National Association of Pharmacy Regulatory Authorities (NAPRA). Developed in 1995, these schedules created a consistent condition for the sale of drugs across Canada, as well as clarified how drugs are categorized according to their pharmacological and toxicity effects. Table 13.1 provides the schedules and criteria.

Birth Control Drugs

The first birth control pill became legalized in Canada in 1969, and since that time, "the pill" has had a profound impact on our culture. It is no accident that the so-called sexual revolution of the late 1960s coincided with the widespread availability of the pill.

The most common form of the birth control pill is the **combination pill**, which consists of synthetic forms of two female sex hormones: **progesterone** and **estrogen**. In some forms of the combination pill (multiphasic), the amount of synthetic progesterone or estrogen varies depending on where the woman is in the menstrual cycle. The combination birth control pill works by suppressing ovulation (release of a mature egg from the ovary). It is taken daily for 21 days and then removed for seven days, during which a period of menstruation should occur. Most birth control pill packages contain placebo or vitamin pills to be taken during the seven off-days to help the woman stay in the habit of taking a pill each day.

combination pill
Birth control pill that contains synthetic forms of both female sex hormones: progesterone and estrogen.

progesterone
One of the female sex hormones involved in the regulation of ovulation and the menstrual cycle.

estrogen
One of the female sex hormones involved in the regulation of ovulation and the menstrual cycle.

TABLE 13.1 NAPRA Drug Schedules

Schedule	Category	Examples
Schedule I	Drugs that can only be sold by prescription	Oxycontin Birth control pills Tylenol #3
Schedule II	Drugs that can be sold without a prescription but must be kept behind the counter	Nicorette (quit smoking aid) Some diet pills EpiPens
Schedule III	Drugs that can be sold without a prescription and can be displayed in the pharmacy; also known at Over-the-Counter (OTC) drugs	Tylenol, Advil Dimetapp Gravol

TABLE 13.2 Comparison of Contraceptive Methods

Method	Failure Rate in Typical Users (%)
Vasectomy	<0.2
Patch	<1
Ring	<1
Combination birth control pill	3
IUD	6
Condom	15
Diaphragm plus spermicide	16
Withdrawal	25
Rhythm, body temperature	25
Chance	90
Abstinence	?

Basically, the pill works by "tricking" a woman's brain into responding as if she were already pregnant. When a woman is pregnant, she no longer ovulates. The hypothalamus and pituitary gland are responsible for regulating ovulation. When circulating levels of estrogen and progesterone are high (as in the case of pregnancy or use of the birth control pill), these structures do not release the hormones that are necessary to prepare the ovaries to release an egg, and thus ovulation is prevented.

To keep circulating levels of estrogen and progesterone continually high enough to inhibit ovulation, the woman must faithfully remember to take a birth control pill every day, at approximately the same time of day. If she misses a pill, she must take it as soon as possible. If she misses more than one pill, her levels of circulating estrogen and progesterone may have dropped sufficiently low to allow ovulation to occur. Used properly, the combination pill is one of the most reliable forms of birth control available, with a failure rate of 0.5–8.0 percent, much lower than most alternatives (Hyde & DeLamater, 2006) (see Table 13.2 and Drugs and Culture Box 13.1). The pill has other advantages over other contraception methods as well. Because it does not require taking precautions just before or after intercourse, it permits more spontaneity in sexual activity than other approaches. A disadvantage of the pill compared to condoms, of course, is that the pill does not prevent the spread of sexually transmitted disease. In addition, the pill has a number of side effects.

One of the more serious concerns is the increased risk of blood clots in users of the combination pill. Blood clots can produce strokes or heart attacks, and indeed women older than 40 show an increased risk of heart attack when they take the combination pill. This risk is greatly increased if the woman is also a cigarette smoker. Mood changes, including severe depression, are often reported by women on the pill (ibid.).

In an effort to minimize the side effects of estrogen, an alternative form of birth control pill has been developed that contains only small amounts of synthetic progesterone (progestin). The **progestin pill** is sometimes called the minipill. It is thought to work somewhat differently from the combination pill in that it may not always block ovulation. Rather, the major effect of progestin is to alter the cervical mucus medium in such a way as to block sperm entry. A limitation of the progestin pill is that it is less effective than the combination pill, although it is still more reliable than other reversible methods (see Table 13.2).

progestin pill
Birth control pill (sometimes called the minipill) that contains only progestin, a synthetic progesterone.

DRUGS AND CULTURE BOX 13.1

What Kind of Birth Control Is Best?

Perhaps the question most college and university women have when reading about the pill is whether it is the best method of contraception. It is impossible to evaluate the pill without considering the other available methods. Table 13.2 lists the failure rates for various methods of birth control in typical users. The difference between these techniques often amounts to error in their proper use. Failure is minimized with surgical procedures such as vasectomy but, in addition to the possible complications of surgery, the procedure may be irreversible. Thus, surgical procedures are uncommon among young people. Notice that the hormonal treatments (the pill, the ring, the patch) are the most effective techniques not requiring surgery. Their main drawbacks are the side effects noted in the text. The intrauterine device (IUD) is also highly effective and is a very popular technique, but the IUD also can produce side effects. The most common are irregular bleeding and pelvic pain. More serious complications are less common but may include greater risk of pelvic inflammatory disease, uterine perforation, and complications if pregnancy should occur when the IUD is in place. Women also use a variety of "barrier" techniques, including the diaphragm and the contraceptive sponge. These devices block the cervical opening and, when used with a spermicide, produce acceptable failure rates. A disadvantage of these methods is the repeated insertion and removal of the device, which some women find problematic.

The condom has gained favour as a method of birth control because it may protect users from sexually transmitted disease. With the current concern about AIDS, condoms should be recommended to most couples. Unless used properly (and reliably), however, condoms have a high failure rate, as Table 13.2 shows. As you will also note in Table 13.2, techniques such as withdrawal and rhythm have a common side effect: pregnancy! Then, of course, there is abstinence....

A more recent development in contraception is the continuous birth control pill (e.g., Seasonale). These are combination estrogen/progestin pills like those discussed previously, but they differ in formulation. With the standard combination pill regimen, a woman takes estrogen/progestin pills for three weeks, followed by inactive pills for one week accompanied by a menstrual period (a 28-day cycle). With continuous birth control pills, a woman takes hormonally active pills for three consecutive months followed by inactive pills for one week so that she has only four, one-week menstrual periods each year.

As we noted, a major limitation in the effectiveness of the pill is that users must remember to take it every day. Newer developments in birth control, such as the vaginal ring and the contraceptive patch, provide longer-lasting methods of delivering estrogen and progestin that require less frequent administration by users:

- The *vaginal ring* is a doughnut-shaped device that is placed in the vagina where it slowly releases progestin, estrogen, or both. The vaginal ring functions much like the pill in preventing ovulation. The ring is kept in place for three weeks and is then removed for the fourth week to permit menstrual flow.
- The *contraceptive patch* is a thin strip of plastic material that attaches to the skin like a bandage. The side that makes contact with the skin releases the same hormones as the pill and the ring, in appropriate doses over a one-week period. The woman replaces a patch every seven days for three weeks and then goes for seven days without a patch.

The obvious advantage of both the ring and the patch is that a woman does not need to remember to take daily pills throughout the month. Methods like the vaginal ring and patch thus have lower failure rates than the pill (estimated at one percent) and may eventually replace the birth control pill as the most popular means of contraception (Hyde & DeLamater, 2006).

An option for women who have had unprotected intercourse is to take emergency contraception, the 'morning-after' pill (e.g., Plan B). Generally, emergency contraceptives deliver high doses of progestin and are most effective if taken within 12 to 24 hours after intercourse, with some effectiveness continuing for up to five days after intercourse. Emergency contraception may work by preventing ovulation, fertilization, or implantation—it is not thought to cause abortion. The 'morning-after' pill is available in Canada as a Schedule II drug, under the NAPRA system. A more controversial emergency pill is the progesterone antagonist mifepristone (RU-486). If this drug is taken during the first 49 days of pregnancy, it causes the embryo to be aborted. Because it induces abortion, mifepristone has generated considerable protest, but it is in widespread use in Europe and has now been approved for use in the United States (Hyde & DeLamater, 2006). Mifepristone remains illegal for use in Canada.

When considering contraception controversies and, in particular, the potential side effects of birth control pills and other methods of contraception, one must keep things in perspective. Although risks are associated with use of the pill, they are lower than the risks involved in pregnancy and delivery.

Anabolic Steroids

Background

On a sunny day in September 1988 in Seoul, Korea the world of sports was changed forever. Ben Johnson ran the 100-metre dash in 9.79 seconds to win the Olympic gold medal and break the world record. Johnson had become the world's fastest human. Then, just two days later, after traces of the **anabolic steroid** stanozolol were found in Johnson's urine sample, he was stripped of his record and his medal, and he left the games in disgrace. The reverberations in the sports world are still being felt; perhaps more significantly, Johnson's scandal opened the eyes of the public to the problem of steroid abuse.

anabolic steroids
Tissue-building drugs that produce masculinizing effects as well.

testosterone
The male sex hormone; anabolic steroids are basically synthetic versions of testosterone.

Anabolic steroids are synthetic drugs that resemble the male sex hormone **testosterone**. In addition to its role in determining male sexual characteristics such as facial and chest hair (androgenic or masculinizing effects), testosterone helps build body tissues and repair damaged tissue. Such bodily construction processes are called anabolic effects. People can also obtain anabolic effects by taking synthetic testosterone for certain medical problems or for improved athletic performance or bodybuilding. The clinical uses of anabolic steroids include treatments for testosterone deficiency, some types of anemia, breast cancer, osteoporosis, and arthritis. Anabolic steroids are often obtained illicitly, however, and are used for bodybuilding or otherwise enhancing athletic performance.

Anabolic steroids were first developed in Nazi Germany in the 1930s, allegedly to help create an army of supermen (Marshall, 1988). The first known use of anabolic steroids in athletics is reported to have been by Russian weight lifters and some female athletes in the early 1950s. By the 1968 Olympics, steroids were in widespread use.

Not until 1976 did the International Olympic Committee (IOC) rule that athletes could not use steroids. Urine testing was used to enforce this policy. Since that time, a great many athletes have tested positive and have been banned from the games, but the Ben Johnson case was certainly the most notorious. At the 2008 Beijing Olympic Games, numerous athletes were disqualified or sent home because of drug violations, and many more were dropped from their teams before the games.

Steroid use by athletes, particularly major league baseball players, has made regular headlines, largely stemming from repercussions from the BALCO scandal and leaks of positive steroid results from supposedly confidential urine tests conducted years ago (see Drugs and Culture Box 13.2).

DRUGS AND CULTURE BOX 13.2

The Canadian Centre for Ethics in Sport

The Canadian Centre for Ethics in Sport publishes an annual Substance Classification booklet that lists Canadian brand-name medication and their ingredients. In addition, they report on the threats to sport with respect to 'doping,' which has significant health risks for athletes, children, and youth.

In response to the numerous positive results of urine and blood doping testing conducted on CIS football players in the spring of 2010, the Canadian Centre for Ethics in Sport convened a Task Force to examine the issue of performance-enhancing drug use in football. The Task Force recommended several key issues to be addressed:

- anti-doping and ethical decision-making education should be incorporated in the provincial and territorial curriculum to target young athletes in and out of the sport of football;
- health education that focuses on body image and performance-enhancing drug use should be included for all students;
- performance-enhancing drug education should be mandatory for coaches, strength and conditioning personnel, and other administrators;
- significantly increase testing from the current level of two to three percent to 30 percent of the total number of football players;
- establish a 'report doping in sport' hotline and associated web-based reporting tool supported by an effective communications plan to promote the resource;
- further consequences, beyond player ineligibility (CADP Sanctions) should be applied to teams and institutions; and
- development of transparent cost sharing agreements between anti-doping organizations, government, corporate sponsors, institutions, sport organizations, and professional football should be considered.

Source: Canadian Centre for Ethics in Sport. *Performance Enhancing Drugs Pose a Significant Health Risk for Athletes, Children and Youth: Final Report of the Task Force on the Use of Performance Enhancing Drugs in Football.* Pg. 11. 2011.

Concern about steroids also increased as it became evident that their use had become widespread not just among elite athletes but also for cosmetic purposes by men (and to a lesser extent, women) who simply wanted to enhance their physical appearance. Apparently "getting big" has become so important that many young people are willing to risk using steroids to achieve the larger muscles and better definition they believe are associated with these drugs.

Possession of steroids without a prescription is illegal in Canada and is regulated by the Controlled Drugs and Substances Act as a Schedule IV controlled substance. Rates of steroid use in Canada are not readily available; however, there is concern that the prevalence of any use among high school athletes is unacceptable. Rates in the U.S. range around two to three percent of high school athletes (Johnston, O'Malley, Bachman, & Schulenberg, 2009a). The rate may be substantially higher than this among older adults, particularly those who are weight lifters or bodybuilders but, as with any illicit drug, it is difficult to assess the actual prevalence. Rates obtained through mandatory drug testing by the NCAA, NFL, and Olympic committees have generally found less than three percent positive tests, but these data appear at odds with the reports of journalistic and governmental investigations as well as survey data (McCloskey & Bailes, 2005; Yesalis et al., 2000). The problem is that users can circumvent the drug tests. When testing occurs only at particular competitive events, like the Olympics, users can avoid a positive test by discontinuing use for a time prior to testing. Random testing is more difficult to beat, but low doses, designer steroids, use of natural compounds like testosterone and human growth hormone (HGH), and use of masking drugs are all strategies that may be effective.

CONTEMPORARY ISSUE BOX 13.3

BALCO, Bonds, and Baseball

In June 2003, a track coach named Trevor Graham came into possession of an unknown drug that was being distributed by BALCO, a San Francisco outfit that provided training programs and "supplements" to many of the country's elite athletes. Graham gave the U.S. Anti-Doping Agency a syringe of the drug, which turned out to be a designer steroid, tetrahydrogestrinone (THG), which was undetectable by any of the standard drug testing screens at the time. Federal grand jury and Senate investigations in 2003 and 2004 of BALCO and its chief executive, Victor Conte, then launched what some have called "the biggest doping scandal in sports history" (McCloskey & Bailes, 2005, p. 61). Many of the nation's top athletes were named as BALCO clients and linked with use of THG, other steroids, and a host of other performance-enhancing drugs. These included many track and field athletes, among them gold medalist Marion Jones and football players like Bill Romanowski, but the sport most affected by the BALCO investigations was major league baseball. Top stars like Mark McGwire, Rafael Palmeiro, and Jason Giambi were all linked to steroid use, but the spotlight really focused on Barry Bonds.

Bonds shattered baseball's record for most home runs in a season (previously held by McGwire) with 73 in 2001, and in 2007 broke Hank Aaron's career record of 755. Faced with unassailable evidence that he received steroids from BALCO, Bonds admitted taking both the "clear," a liquid absorbed under the tongue, and the "cream," which was applied directly to the muscles. Both the cream and the clear were undetectable designer steroids, but Bonds denied knowing they were steroids. However, two journalists (Fainaru-Wada & Williams, 2006) provided evidence that Bonds had full knowledge of his program for use of steroids and other performing-enhancing drugs, and in 2007 Bonds was indicted for perjury on the basis of his grand jury testimony. In 2008, major league baseball implemented a new steroid-testing policy with escalating penalties for positive tests. But many say it is too little, too late. Some of the most cherished records in the sport are held by Bonds (or soon will be). Will major league baseball place a "steroid asterisk" by Bonds' home-run records?

Andy Lyons/Getty Images Sport/Getty Images

So, actual use of anabolic steroids may be higher than our estimates indicate. But how high? The BALCO investigations and the claims of two former baseball stars (Ken Caminiti and Jose Canseco) that 50 percent to 85 percent of all major league baseball players use steroids launched a major scandal, but the accuracy of such allegations cannot be verified. In any case, the focused attention on steroid use in the past decade has led to considerable research, and we are beginning to get a better idea of just how steroids work and what side effects may follow their use.

Actions of Anabolic Steroids

The anabolic steroids include danazol, methyltestosterone, ethylestrenol, methandrostenolone, nandrolone, oxandrolone, oxymetholone, stanozolol, and tetrahydrogestrinone (brand names include Anadrol, Anavar, Danocrine, Dianabol, Metandren,

TABLE 13.3 Anabolic Steroids

Drug	Trade Name	Route of Administration
Danazol	Danocrine	Oral
Ethylestrenol	Maxibolin	Oral
Methandrostenolone	Dianabol	Oral
Methyltestosterone	Metandren	Oral
Oxandrolone	Anavar	Oral
Stanozolol	Winstrol	Oral
Nandrolone	Androlone, Durabolin, Nandrolin	Injection
Methandriol	Anabol, Durabolic, Methabolic, Steribolic	Injection

and Winstrol). Although some may be taken orally or topically, others must be injected to be effective (see Table 13.3). The metabolism and elimination of steroids are variable. Steroids can be detected reliably in urine for four to 14 days after use, but there are reports of positive urine tests as long as 13 months after the use of nandrolone (Marshall, 1988).

A related compound, androstenedione is a precursor to testosterone and was marketed over the counter as an alternative to the illegal steroids to enhance strength and performance. Mark McGwire made "Andro" famous when he admitted to using it during his record-breaking home-run streak in 1998. Because androstenedione was associated with many of the side effects of anabolic steroids, the FDA made it an illegal substance in 2004.

One ironic feature of the widespread use of steroids by athletes is that medical researchers have had great difficulty determining whether they really enhance performance. It is clear that at puberty male testes increase testosterone output to result in the increased muscle mass and strength characteristic of males at that age. This does not necessarily mean that supplemental testosterone will cause further gains in a normal man, however. Many studies of the effects of anabolic steroids on weight gain, strength, and performance have been conducted. Although most of these have shown improvement in participants who took steroids, some have not. Overall, the consensus in the scientific community is that steroids do produce gains in size and strength (Friedl, 2000a).

Side Effects of Anabolic Steroids

Physical side effects are associated with anabolic steroid use. Perhaps the most commonly reported are acne, balding, and reduced sexual desire. Men often experience atrophy of the testes and a related decline in sperm count and enlargement of the breasts. It seems ironic that many male steroid users have to take special drugs to prevent breast growth! These effects are usually reversible. Women may experience pronounced masculinizing effects from steroid use, and many of these effects are irreversible. They include growth of facial and chest hair, baldness, deepening of the voice, breast shrinkage, clitoral enlargement, and menstrual irregularities. Another cause for concern is that steroid use often changes cholesterol levels that may increase the risk of heart disease. Damage to liver function is also common and can include an increased risk of liver cancer (Langenbucher,

Csakisti/Dreamstime LLC

Bodybuilders are among a group of 'dopers' often under scrutiny for the negative effects of anabolic steroid use during competitions.

Hildebrandt, & Carr, 2008). The late NFL All-Pro Lyle Alzado attributed his inoperable brain cancer to heavy steroid use. Whether steroids play a causal role in this and other types of cancer is controversial, however (Friedl, 2000b). Additional problems, such as premature bone fusion causing stunted growth, can occur when children and adolescents use steroids. Alteration of normal pubertal development is also a risk in young people.

In addition to the physical side effects of steroids, there are psychological effects. Most users report a mild euphoria when they use steroids, and increased energy levels also are noted. Less desirable are reports of increased irritability and aggressiveness, sometimes leading to violent behaviour. Mood swings and even psychotic reactions have been reported. Pope and Katz (1988) reported on a study of 41 bodybuilders and football players who had used steroids. Nine of the subjects (22 percent) experienced emotional disturbance, and five (12 percent) developed psychotic reactions during their steroid regimens. One of the subjects deliberately drove a car into a tree at 40 mph (64 km/h). Another described becoming irritated at a driver in front of him who had left his blinker on. At the first stoplight, he jumped out of his car and punched out the other car's windshield! Of course, these case studies do not establish that steroids alone were responsible for these effects, but several double-blind studies have also reported increased aggression and mood swings in subjects who received steroids, albeit with less dramatic outcomes than those described here (see Kanayama, Hudson, & Pope, 2008, for a review). Users of anabolic steroids also had higher-than-expected rates of violent death (Petersson et al., 2006). As well, steroid use has also been associated with withdrawal symptoms and dependence in as many as 30 percent of overall users in some studies (Kanayama, Hudson, & Pope, 2009).

> *"Steroids make the athlete more aggressive and in some sports that is seen as an advantage."*
>
> Al Oerter, four-time Olympic gold medalist in discus

Athletes will continue to use steroids as long as they believe their competition is using them. Better testing methods are needed, but perhaps more important would be *regular* tests. Many current procedures allow athletes to discontinue the drugs prior to an important event to avoid a positive urine test. Regular random tests are more likely to reduce cheating. But what of the thousands of young men (and women) who are not Olympic-calibre athletes who are taking steroids to improve their performance at the high school or college/university level or just to "get big"?

Steroids can cause major problems, and many drug education programs do not even discuss them. Clearly there is a need to make the public aware of the potential dangers of steroid abuse. See Figure 13.1.

Over-the-Counter Drugs

In order for a drug to be marketed and sold as Over-The-Counter (OTC) in Canada, the manufacturer of the drug must complete a Notice of Compliance (NOC) from Health Canada. The standards by which OTC are approved for sale are guided by the criteria for effectiveness and margin of safety (as discussed in Chapter 3).

FIGURE 13.1 Side effects of anabolic steroids

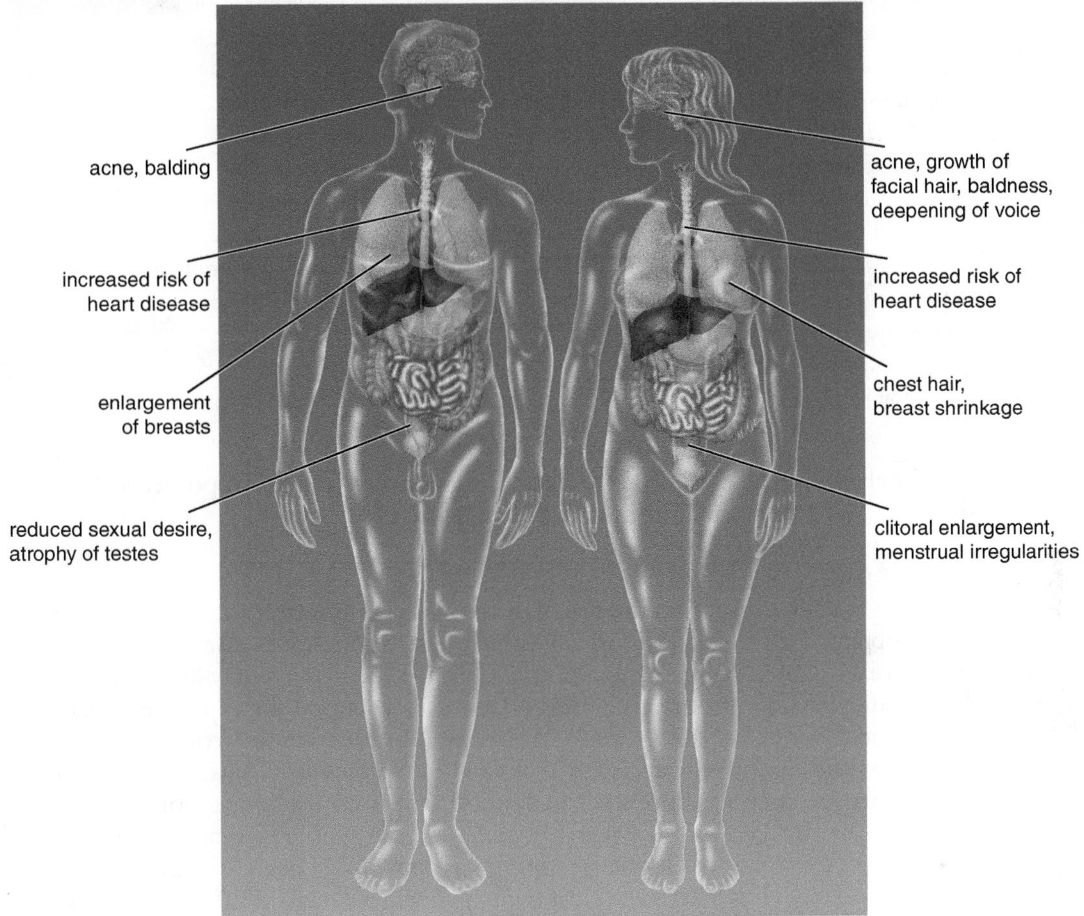

Source: BSIP/Photo Researchers, Inc.

NAPRA Classification

As mentioned earlier in the chapter, NAPRA divides drugs into three categories: those that require a prescription from a physician to purchase (such as the psychiatric drugs discussed in Chapter 12 and the birth control pills and anabolic steroids described previously); those that are available without a prescription but placed behind the pharmacy dispensary; and those considered safe enough to dispense without a prescription, which are called over-the-counter drugs. Today, NAPRA is charged with regulating and reviewing OTC drugs—no small task when you consider more than 300 000 products were on the market!

Rather than focusing on specific brands, NAPRA has organized the ingredients found in these products and divided them into categories generally. These categories are listed in Table 13.4. As you can see, OTC drugs treat a wide range of ailments. The major goals of considering drugs for OTC scheduling focus on two major criteria: safety and efficacy. Drugs authorized as OTC drugs must meet the standard of "generally recognized as safe" (GRAS) and "generally recognized as effective" (GRAE). Drugs that do not meet these criteria are removed from OTC products. Note, however, that *safety* and *efficacy* are relative terms. Some OTC drugs can be hazardous, and some are of very limited efficacy.

TABLE 13.4 General Classification of OTC Drugs

1. Antacids	13. Analgesics
2. Antidiarrheal products	14. Antitussives
3. Sunscreens	15. Eye products
4. Dandruff products	16. Dental products
5. Bronchodilators	17. Emetics
6. Stimulants	18. Antiperspirants
7. Cold remedies	19. Antimicrobials
8. Skin preparations	20. Hemorrhoidal products
9. Laxatives	21. Sedatives and sleep aids
10. Antiemetics	22. Allergy drugs
11. Vitamin and mineral products	23. Contraceptive products
12. Oral hygiene products	24. Weight-control products

This chapter focuses on three categories that have psychoactive properties: analgesics, cold and allergy medications, and sedatives.

Analgesics

In Chapter 11, we discussed the use of opiate drugs in the treatment of pain. But the use of opiates for pain relief is usually reserved for severe cases. Many effective painkillers are available over the counter, and aspirin is the most widely known and used. **Acetylsalicylic acid** (aspirin) is closely related to a chemical found in the bark of the willow and other trees (salicylic acid). Willow bark was used in the treatment of painful conditions and fever by the ancient Greeks and by Native Americans. Salicylic acid was isolated and used as a pain reliever in Europe, but it causes severe stomach distress. Not until the late 19th century was acetylsalicylic acid synthesized and named *aspirin* by the Bayer Company of Germany. Aspirin has come to be one of the most important drugs in medicine. It is marketed under the brand names Anacin, Bufferin, and Excedrin, to name just a few.

acetylsalicylic acid Chemical name for aspirin.

Fred Goldstein/Dreamstime LLC

Over-the-counter drugs are considered safe enough to dispense without prescription.

Aspirin is analgesic (produces pain relief without unconsciousness), antipyretic (reduces fever), and anti-inflammatory (reduces swelling). It is thought to work by means of a mechanism quite different from opiate analgesia. Aspirin (and other OTC painkillers) act by blocking the production and release of **prostaglandins**, chemicals released by the body at sites of pain. These chemicals are thought to enhance certain kinds of pain—dull pain and aches, such as headache—and to produce inflammation. Indeed aspirin is not very effective at treating sharp pains or stomach pain. It is, however, very effective with muscle aches, headaches, and soreness due to inflammation such as arthritis (Grogan, 1987).

prostaglandins
Naturally occurring chemicals blocked by aspirin and related analgesics.

Aspirin has some adverse effects. It frequently causes stomach irritation and bleeding and is contraindicated in people who have stomach problems. Aspirin may be related to a rare and dangerous disease called Reye's syndrome. Reye's syndrome occurs only in children treated with aspirin for flu or chicken pox and involves severe vomiting, disorientation, and sometimes coma, brain damage, or death. Thus, aspirin should be avoided by children who have these diseases. Aspirin is also an anticoagulant and may prolong bleeding under certain circumstances. However, this same mechanism may be useful in the prevention of strokes and heart attacks (Julien, Advokat, & Comaty, 2008).

An effective analgesic drug useful for people with stomach problems is **acetaminophen**. This drug, marketed under brand names such as Datril (U.S.) and Tylenol, reduces fever and produces analgesic effects but does not cause stomach irritation. Acetaminophen is not a potent anti-inflammatory drug, however, and may cause liver problems in high doses. The U.S. reports that acetaminophen-related overdoses are fairly common and account for over 56 000 emergency room visits and nearly 500 deaths every year. It should be noted that many of these occur because people take multiple products containing acetaminophen without knowing it, often in products that combine acetaminophen with another painkiller. It is worth noting that overdoses on OTC analgesic drugs are leading causes of poisonings in children. As few as 10 Extra-Strength Tylenol can be lethal to a child (Grogan, 1987). It is important to keep these and all drugs out of the reach of children.

acetaminophen
Aspirin-like analgesic.

Other widely used OTC painkillers are **ibuprofen** and **naproxen**. Ibuprofen was exclusively a prescription drug until the 1980s, but now it is marketed under brand names such as Advil and Nuprin (U.S.) and has captured a large share of the OTC painkiller market. Naproxen is marketed under the brand names of Naprosyn and Aleve and was approved as an OTC drug in 1994. These drugs have analgesic and anti-inflammatory effects that are similar to aspirin but are generally better tolerated. Like other OTC pain relievers, however, ibuprofen and naproxen can produce side effects, including stomach irritation and liver and kidney damage in high doses (Julien, Advokat, & Comaty, 2008).

ibuprofen
Aspirin-like analgesic.

naproxen
Aspirin-like analgesic.

Cold and Allergy Medications

The common cold is common enough that its victims spend over $1.3 billion on OTC cold remedies in Canada and the United States every year. OTC cold and allergy medications contain a variety of different ingredients, including analgesics such as aspirin or acetaminophen, which are of value in reducing aches, pain, and fever. In addition, many OTC cold preparations contain a decongestant such as **pseudoephedrine** (Sudafed). Because pseudoephedrine is one ingredient used to produce illicit methamphetamine, such products are now sold behind the counter (see Chapter 5). Cold remedies also may include expectorants, which help to break up phlegm so that it may be coughed up. **Antitussive** agents actually suppress coughing and are often included in cold and cough formulations (dextromethorphan is an example).

pseudoephedrine
An over-the-counter decongestant.

antitussives
Cough-suppressant drugs.

antihistamines
Common over-the-counter drugs with decongestant effects.

Other common ingredients in OTC cold and allergy preparations are **antihistamines**. These compounds actually are more effective in the treatment of hay fever and related allergic reactions. Many allergic symptoms are caused by the release of a naturally occurring chemical called histamine. As the name suggests, antihistamines act by blocking histamine. Commonly used antihistamines include diphenhydramine, chlorpheniramine maleate, and loratadine (Claritin). Several side effects limit the usefulness of antihistamines, however. Drowsiness and fatigue are probably the most significant. It can be hard to stay awake after taking antihistamines, and in fact, diphenhydramine is the major ingredient in most OTC sleeping aids. Other side effects include thickening of mucus secretions, blurred vision, dizziness, dry mouth and nose, and sweating (Grogan, 1987).

Over-the-Counter Sedatives

As noted previously, the major ingredient in OTC sleeping aids is an antihistamine, diphenhydramine. Because fatigue is a common side effect of antihistamines, they sometimes can help people who are suffering from insomnia. However, other side effects associated with antihistamines (for instance, dry mouth, dizziness, and nausea) may limit their use as sleeping aids. In addition, the problems associated with using prescription sleeping pills may apply to these drugs, too, as discussed in Chapter 12.

Natural Health Products and Dietary Supplements

In 1994, the Natural Health Products Dictoriate (NHPD) defined and regulated all natural products according to the following:

- the diagnosis, treatment, mitigation, or prevention of a disease, disorder, or abnormal physical state or its symptoms;
- restoring or correcting organic functions; or
- modifying organic functions that maintains or promotes health.

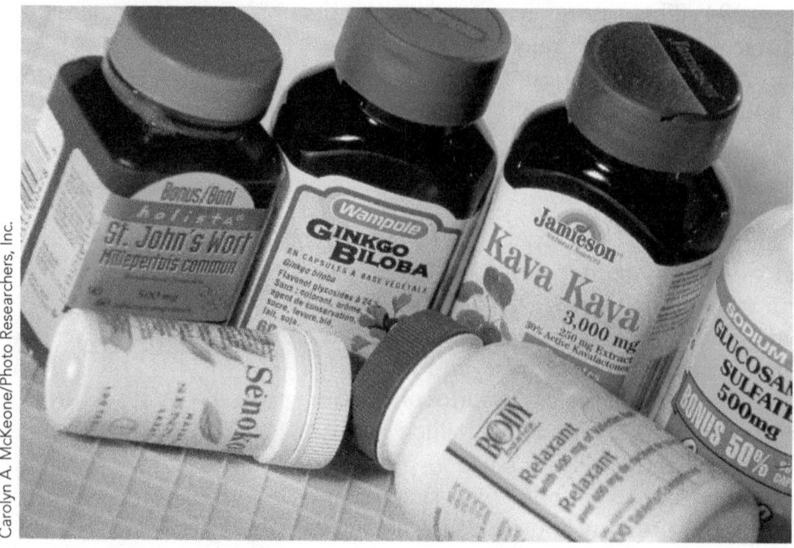

Carolyn A. McKeone/Photo Researchers, Inc.

Herbal/natural health supplements.

A product and site licence is required to be sold as OTC. The licence requires manufacturers to list the products active ingredients, source, potency, non-medicinal ingredients, and recommended use. These must all be present on the label and/or packaging. The most commonly used NHPs are vitamins, Echinacea, herbal remedies, and homeopathic medicine (Health Canada, 2005). This chapter reviews the most common NHPs here.

DHEA

Dehydroepiandrosterone (DHEA) is a hormone naturally secreted by the adrenal glands. It is offered as a miracle drug in health food stores with claims that it prevents heart disease, cancer, obesity, and diabetes. It is said to be an "antiaging" hormone as well. The bad news is that virtually no evidence supports any of these claims, although the hormone may have some mood-enhancing effects. DHEA is a precursor of testosterone in the body, and many DHEA effects may be related to the androgenic effects noted earlier in this chapter. So, although DHEA may not prevent aging, it may produce acne, premature baldness, and other side effects noted earlier for anabolic steroids (Julien, Advokat, & Comaty, 2008).

Ephedra/Ma Huang

A number of plant species from the genus *Ephedra* have been used for many years for their stimulant effects. *Ephedra sinica* is native to Asia and is frequently sold under its Chinese name, *ma huang*. Another species, *E. nevadensis*, grows in the American West and is known as Mormon tea. The main psychoactive compound in ephedra is ephedrine. Ephedrine is a potent stimulant with effects much like those reviewed in Chapter 5. It is sympathomimetic and produces behavioural effects similar to those of other stimulants (Karch, 2000). Until 2004, ephedrine products were marketed through stores or by mail order to increase energy, prevent drowsiness, suppress appetite, and in high-dose formulations, as an "herbal" alternative to ecstasy (see Chapter 10). These products contained a wide variety of plant products and drugs, including caffeine, theophylline, pseudoephedrine, and ephedrine. Many side effects and some deaths due to heart attack and stroke were associated with ephedra products, particularly those with high doses of ephedrine (Spinella, 2001). The February 2003 death of Baltimore Orioles pitcher Steve Bechler—which was linked to his use of ephedra—prompted an expedited review of ephedra preparations, and in 2004, the FDA (U.S.) and the NHPD in Canada banned products containing ephedrine from over-the-counter sales.

Ginkgo Biloba

Extracts from the leaves of the ginkgo tree have been touted as a "smart drug," a drug that enhances memory and concentration. In fact, a number of studies have provided evidence that ginkgo extract improved memory and information processing in patients who have Alzheimer's disease, perhaps by improving blood flow to the brain (Spinella, 2001). However, these improvements are small, at best, and results from different studies have been mixed (Julien, Advokat, & Comaty, 2008). Ginkgo extract contains many different chemicals, and it is unclear which are responsible for the benefits seen in Alzheimer's patients, so more research is clearly indicated on this interesting plant.

Close-up shot of the leaves of a Gingko tree *(Gingko biloba)*.

Kava

The kava plant (*Piper methysticum*) is cultivated on South Pacific islands, where it has been used for religious and cultural ceremonies for hundreds of years. The roots of the plant are crushed and generally prepared in a tea. Kava appears to produce a sedating or relaxing effect similar to alcohol or other depressant drugs, and the supplement preparations sold in North America imply that it can relieve stress and anxiety. Kava is becoming increasingly popular in North America. In the U.S. Kava bars have sprung up, and kava is frequently advertised and sold on the Internet as a legal high (Dennehy, Tsourounis, & Miller, 2005).

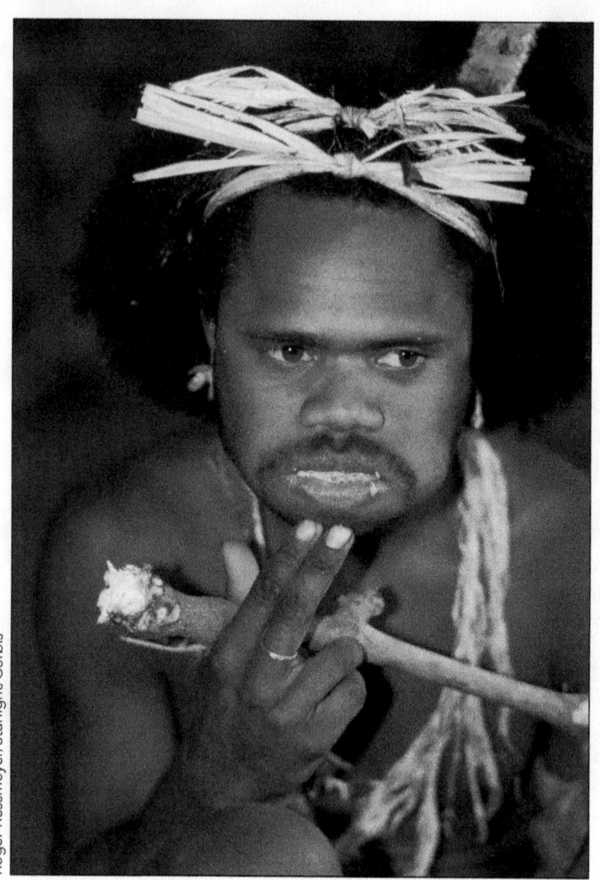
Roger Ressmeyer/Starlight/Corbis

A man in Yakel Village chews a mouthful of kava root.

Side effects from kava may include drowsiness and blurred vision, and there have also been reports of liver toxicity. These have been problematic enough that kava has been banned in Canada and other countries (e.g., France, Germany), although it remains legal in the United States (Julien, Advokat, & Comaty, 2008).

Like the depressant drugs, the active compounds in kava, a group of chemicals called kavalactones, appear to enhance the actions of the neurotransmitter GABA. Several controlled studies of kava preparations or kavalactones have supported the claims that kava produces relaxing or anxiolytic effects (Malsch & Kieser, 2001). Few side effects have been documented, but kava can produce an alcohol-like intoxication in higher doses, and abuse problems have been reported in the South Pacific.

Melatonin

Melatonin is a naturally occurring hormone produced by the pineal gland. It is thought to regulate biological rhythms and sleep. Numerous brands of synthetic and natural melatonin (from animal pineal gland) are available in stores, and they are recommended to consumers to treat everything from heart disease to cancer. A number of controlled studies suggest that melatonin is superior to placebo as a sleeping pill and in preventing "jet lag." Melatonin can reduce the time it takes for people to fall asleep and can lengthen sleep time (Zhdanova & Friedman, 2002). Other claims associated with melatonin have not been confirmed, however. In addition, some side effects are irritability, altered menstrual cycles, and vasoconstriction that may reduce blood flow to the brain and heart.

S-Adenosy-Methionine

S-Adenosy-methionine (SAM or SAMe) is a compound found naturally in the body that is marketed as a supplement with the formal claim that it promotes "emotional well-being." It was tested in Italy as an antidepressant, which found that SAMe was more effective than a placebo, but these claims lack empirical support, at least with respect to the dosage forms available in North America (Julien, Advokat, & Comaty, 2008).

St. John's Wort

St. John's wort (*Hypericum performatum*) is often known as the 'master' of the herbal alternatives movement because of its improvement of memory and other cognitive functions. It is also regarded for its antidepressant effects. It is a perennial plant that has been cultivated in Europe for centuries. Extracts of hypericum contain a wide variety of active chemicals, including hypericin and pseudohypericin. Whether St. John's wort is really a significant antidepressant remains controversial. Some studies have found hypericum to be superior to placebo, but others have found no effects or even that patients treated with St. John's wort showed less improvement than those on placebo. Hypericum may produce side effects as well, including photosensitivity and lethargy, and it may alter the metabolization of numerous other drugs with potential for dangerous interactions, thus making St. John's wort of questionable safety (see Julien, Advokat, & Comaty, 2008 for a review).

Gamma Hydroxybutyrate

Gamma hydroxybutyrate (GHB) is a substance found in the brain that is thought to be a natural neurotransmitter or neurohormone. Its effects are generally those of depressant drugs. It is structurally related to GABA and, like many depressant drugs discussed already, influences GABA transmission. There are also specific brain receptors for GHB that may confer unique properties to GHB, but little is known about their function (Maitre et al., 2000).

GHB was originally used as an anesthetic in Europe, but in North America, it was marketed as a supplement for an odd combination of claimed benefits: to enhance athletic performance and sexual activity, and to induce sleep. GHB became a widely abused drug in the 1990s, and was linked with so many problems that it now declared a Schedule III drug. Although GHB is no longer legally available in Canada, it is still widely used. It is frequently smuggled into the country, and because it is easy to synthesize, much GHB is "home brewed."

Often considered among the "club drugs," GHB is usually taken orally in a salty-tasting liquid solution. Users report that the drug produces a euphoric intoxication; however, GHB is a potent depressant, and unconsciousness and coma have been frequently reported. Generally, these symptoms resolve within a few hours, but a number of deaths have been linked to GHB (Galloway et al., 2000). GHB toxicity and coma appears more likely when it is taken in combination with alcohol or other drugs (Liechti et al., 2006). This is consistent with findings from animal research that GHB is synergistic with alcohol and other depressants (Beardsley, Balster, & Harris, 1996). Also in keeping with the pattern of effects of most depressant drugs, tolerance and dependence to GHB have been reported. GHB is one of several drugs (for example, Rohypnol or roofies) that have been used to commit "date rape" by rendering a target unconscious (Galloway et al., 2000).

Inhalants

Inhalants are the kinds of psychoactive drugs that can be found under the sink, in the bathroom cupboards, or in the garage. For many of us, these household products are used daily to clean our house, run our cars, and cut our grass. However, ordinary household products have the potential for inappropriate abuse through being inhaled or sniffed. The harmful ingredients in these products have become a major concern for Canadians as the consequences of their abuse are particularly threatening. Inhalant products are more recently regarded as dangerous recreational drugs. This section begins with a historical overview of inhalant use and describes the general categories of inhalants, how they interact with our brain and body, potential for abuse and their acute and chronic effects.

iStockphoto

Common household products, such as cleaners, hairspray and gasoline are being abuse by adolescents for their chemical euphoria from sniffing, or huffing the chemical. Table 13.5 lists some of these products of concern for abuse.

ethylene
A sweet-smelling gaseous compound that produces euphoria when inhaled.

ether
A gaseous compound that was used for its analgesic effects in dentistry, historically.

whippets
Small containers of pressurized nitrous oxide, most commonly used in household and kitchen products in pressurized cans.

History of Inhalants

Inhaling of incense, oils, perfumes, and spices, especially for religious purposes, has been practised in most parts of the ancient world. In both Egyptian worship and Babylonian rituals, inhaling exotic perfumes was common practice for both spiritual and healing powers. Inhaling gas vapours to alter one's state of consciousness was practised by priestesses to note the rites of the Oracle of Delphi in ancient Greece (Broad, 2002). The gas vapours—likely **ethylene**—produced an out-of-body sense of euphoria.

It wasn't until the late 1800s that nitrous oxide and ether were documented as anesthetic drugs. Used as surgical analgesics, these gases became used as intoxicants. In fact, nitrous oxide was considered a substitute for alcohol. Throughout the 19th century these gases were used both as anesthetics and for recreational purposes. Here is a brief history of nitrous oxide and **ether**.

Nitrous Oxide

Nitrous oxide was popularized by the British chemist Sir Humphrey Davy in 1798. He regarded nitrous oxide's effects as pleasant and hilarious, calling it 'laughing gas' and hosting parties where he and his literary friends inhaled it for fun at these parties. By the early 1800s, recreational use of nitrous oxide became popular in England and the Americas as an alternative to alcohol. In the 1840s public exhibitions were held to promote 'gallons of gas' for inhalation as entertainment and as a tactic to market the drug. During this time in the mid-1840s Horace Wells, a dentist, completed his own tooth extraction using 'laughing gas. Feeling no pain during the extraction, this began its use as an analgesic gas in dentistry.

It was in the 1960s that the recreational use of nitrous oxide reappeared in the form of **whippets**—small containers of pressurized nitrous oxide used to dispense whipped cream in restaurants. Soon, tanks of nitrous oxide were sold illicitly and used at parties and on college campuses. Typically, college students would fill a balloon with the gas, then inhale the gaseous fumes from the balloon, providing them with an immediate euphoric state that lasted a few minutes.

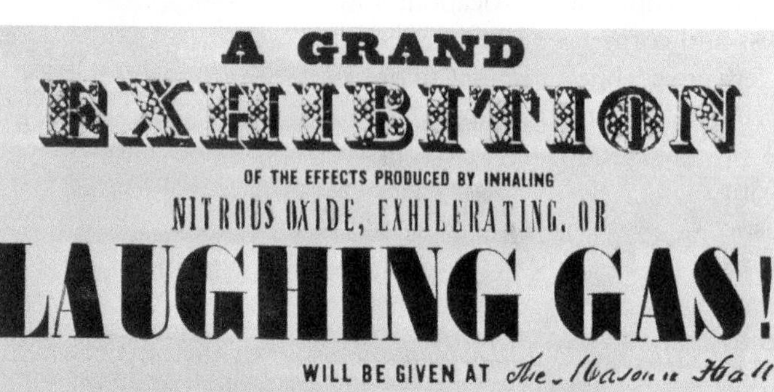

The promotion of the recreational use (and for entertainment) of nitrous oxide to demonstrate its merry and harmonious effects. This led to using nitrous oxide as an anesthetic in dentistry.

Ether

Similar to nitrous oxide, ether was introduced to dentistry due to its analgesic effects during dental surgery. Realizing its medical significance after performing minor surgeries using sulfuric ether, Dr. Crawford Long, in 1842 published the results of his surgery, but it wasn't until William Morton, in 1846, that ether was hailed as a surgical breakthrough in dentistry (Smith, 1927).

It wasn't until the Temperance Movements and during prohibition in the 1920s that ether became quite popular as an alternative to alcohol in the U.S. and other parts of the prohibition world. It was also used in Germany during World War II by soldiers as an adjunct to alcohol. Although nitrous oxide and ether have an early history as surgical anesthetics, it was in the 1950s that reports of inhalation and abuse of other chemicals, including glue appeared.

There is no doubt that the practice of inhaling gases has been beneficial throughout medical history. As medical science emerged during the early 1950s in North America and the world, attention to such gases shifted to new recreational practices using other chemicals—solvents, aerosols, glue, and nitrites. We turn our discussion now to the common categories of inhalants and to the concerns regarding potential abuse.

Categories of Inhalants

Although it is difficult to classify all substances which can be inhaled, let's take a look at some of the major categories that tend to best represent the types of inhalant use in our society today: volatile solvents and nitrites. Many of these substances are found in common household products, which are readily available to purchase and to potentially abuse (see Table 13.5).

Volatile Solvents

Volatile solvents include household and industrial products that contain chemical compounds that have the potential to be hazardous if inhaled. Some of these products include glue, paint thinners, and nail polish removers. A solvent is a chemical in a liquid that dissolves other substances. Volatile means the rapid evaporation of a chemical when released to the air. Products such as hair spray, spray paint, computer duster, and

TABLE 13.5 Common Household Products Used as Inhalants and Their Chemical Ingredients

Paint and paint thinners	esters, acetone, benzene
Nail polish remover	acetone, ethyl acetate
Glues and cements	toluene, ethyl acetate, hexane, acetone, methyl ethyl ketone
Varnish and removers	toluene, methylene chloride, methanol, acetone
Spot removers	carbon tetrachloride, petroleum products, trichloroethylene, carbon tetrachloride
Hair spray	butane, propane
Permanent marker ink	trichloroethylene
Lighters	butane, isopropane
Freon	benzene, hexane, toluene
Spray paint	acetone, toluene, ether
Gasoline	butane, propane
Whipped cream	nitrous oxide
Disinfectants	acetone, toluene, carbon tetrachloride
Computer cleaner duster	acetone, toluene, chloride

other contents that 'spray' contain a liquefied-gas propellant that acts as a solvent allowing it to spray when released.

The potential abuse of volatile solvents (and aerosols) is simple. Because they are inhaled into the lungs, intoxication occurs very rapidly, and feelings of a euphoric 'high' are almost instant. These products are readily available at grocery stores, hardware stores, and pharmacies, which makes them easy to purchase and quite inexpensive compared to many other drugs.

The most common ways that volatile solvents are inhaled include:

Huffing: Users soak the solvent in a fabric (usually a shirt sleeve or sock) and place it over their nose and mouth to inhale the fumes.

Bagging: Users inhale the fumes from a bag that is placed over the nose and mouth or over the head. Aerosol propellants can be sprayed into a balloon or bag and then inhaled.

Sniffing: Users inhale a solvent directly from a container through their nose or mouth.

The fumes from volatile solvents can also be inhaled in a small room, such as a closet, or vehicle.

Pharmacological Effects of Volatile Solvents

Most inhalants produce their euphoric effects by depressing the CNS. This action is similar to the mechanism of action of both alcohol and benzodiazepines (also depressants). The chemical compounds found in volatile solvents have a variety of effects on the neurotransmitters in the brain and therefore present specific dangers to the body's system. Table 13.6 explains some of the effects of the main chemical ingredients listed in Table 13.5.

Rates of abuse of volatile solvents have been reported in the 2004 Canadian Addiction Survey. For example, among males 15 years and older, the rate of reported inhalant use in their lifetime is 1.9 percent; among females of the same age the rate is 0.7 percent. These rates are much lower than the U.S. where 4.5 percent of students reported using an inhalant, and nine percent of grade 8 students reported use within the last year (Beauvais et al., 2002). General conclusions from the Canadian survey suggest that inhalant abuse is most common among young students as well as street youth, inner city youth, and some First Nations youth living in rural areas of Canada (Adlaf, Begin, & Sawka, 2005).

The rates of abuse among First Nations living on the reserves are much more concerning. Reports from the 2003 Pauingassi First Nation (Manitoba) provided that

TABLE 13.6 Effects of Chemical Ingredients in Inhalants

Acetone	Damage to the mucus membrane of the respiratory tract
Hexane	Damage to peripheral nerves leading to muscle weakness and **atrophy**
Toluene	Reduction in short-term memory, damage to the inner ear (causing hearing loss), dysfunction of the cerebellum resulting in coordination and movement difficulties
Benzene	Leads to cancer-related disorders, such as leukemia and anemia
Gasoline	Usually contains additives (for example, triorthocessyl phosphate [TCP]) which is linked to CNS degeneration, and muscle disorders (gasoline also often contains other chemicals, such as toluene, and hexane)
Carbon tetrachloride	Damage to kidneys, potentially causing failure; build up of fat in the liver causing damage

atrophy
A decrease in muscle mass, which causes the muscle to become weak,

DRUGS AND CULTURE BOX 13.4

First Nations Youth and Inhalant Abuse

In 1993, the National Youth Solvent Abuse Program (NYSAP) opened a number of Youth Solvent Addictions Centres across Canada. The Program is monitored by Health Canada and is managed through a national committee of addiction treatment experts who promote a **continuing of care** approach for youths who are struggling with inhalant abuse.

The NYSAP's goal is to improve the functional abilities of individuals addicted to inhalants and minimize the effects and risks associated with this type of abuse. In-centre education and prevention programs exist within the continuing of care practice, which generally lasts approximately 18 months. In addition, outreach programs are available for families and the centre's clients for followup and additional education.

Through research and practice, reports to the high inhalant abuse reports among First Nations youth and other street or inner city youth has pointed to several factors that are linked to solvent abuse and play an important role in the increase of inhalant abuse among these groups (Kaweionnehta Human Resources Group, 1993). Some of these factors include high rates of poverty, boredom, loss of self-respect, unemployment, family breakdown, poor social and economic structures, and the systemic racism and discrimination of land, language, and cultural identity faced by First Nations communities.

Consider some other reasons that youth, in general, would be more attracted to inhalant use and abuse outside of the factors linked to specific target groups discussed here.

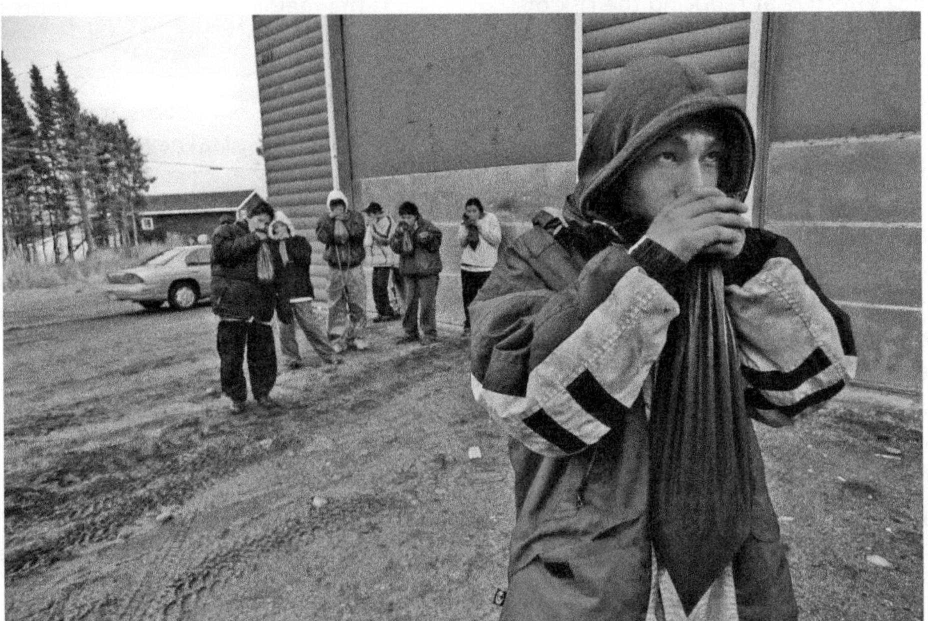

CP PHOTO/Ted Ostrowski

Youths huffing gas.

50 percent of children under 18 years of age and living on the reserve abused solvents. Drugs and Culture Box 13.4 discusses several of the factors that contribute to the high rate of solvent abuse on First Nations reserves.

continuing of care
A treatment approach that is comprised of pre-treatment and post-treatment care in which the client is actively involved, usually by reporting to the treatment centre/program.

Nitrites

Historically, amyl nitrite and butyl nitrate were used in the 19th century for their observed effects of decreasing blood pressure and a relaxation of muscles. Amyl nitrite has been used medically since the late 19th century for the treatment of angina and as a treatment for cyanide poisoning.

Use of nitrites recreationally became recognized in the 1970s as a drug of choice among the gay communities to enhance the pleasure of sex. The chemicals in nitrites cause a rapid dilation of the arteries and reduce blood pressure to the brain, producing a euphoric high and the relaxation of muscles, ultimately enhancing sexual pleasure.

Amyl nitrite is often called 'poppers' or 'snappers' to reflect the popping sound that is made when the capsule is broken. Once opened, the vapours of the nitrite are inhaled into the air. Effects are immediate (within 30 seconds) and cause light-headedness, a flushing sensation, and euphoria; the effects only last about five minutes.

Butyl nitrite is a bad-smelling nitrite that is known recreationally as "Locker Room" or "Oz." These terms reflect the popularity of use among males. Similar effects result from sniffing butyl nitrite as amyl nitrite.

SUMMARY

- The combination birth control pill contains synthetic versions of the two female sex hormones: estrogen and progesterone.
- Though highly effective at reducing the risk of pregnancy, the birth control pill has been linked to such side effects as increased risk of heart attack and stroke.
- Anabolic steroids are generally synthetic versions of the male sex hormone testosterone and are used to promote the development of muscle mass and to enhance athletic performance.
- Side effects associated with anabolic steroids include masculinizing effects in women, liver damage, acne, hair loss, and emotional disturbance.
- Three major analgesic drugs are available without prescription: aspirin, acetaminophen, and ibuprofen.
- Aspirin relieves pain, reduces fever, and is anti-inflammatory. Its side effects include stomach irritation and bleeding. The effects of ibuprofen are similar.
- Acetaminophen is a potent analgesic drug, but it lacks the anti-inflammatory effects of aspirin. It also is less likely to cause stomach irritation.
- The antihistamine compound diphenhydramine is the major ingredient in nonprescription sleeping pills.
- There are many herbal drugs marketed in Canada as dietary supplements, memory boosters, and antidepressants. They include DHEA, ephedra, ginkgo biloba, kava, melatonin, SAMe, and St. John's wort
- GHB is a naturally occurring neurotransmitter that has the properties of a depressant drug. It is often referred to as a 'club drug' because of its popularity among youths at raves.
- Inhalants are a large group of volatile compounds that can alter consciousness when taken into the lungs. Many of them are organic solvents that can damage the brain.
- Volatile solvents are mostly household and commercial products sold in pharmacies, hardware stores, and grocery stores.
- Nitrites produce bad-smelling vapours when 'popped' and are used to enhance sexual pleasure, and euphoria.

Key Terms

acetaminophen p. 325
acetylsalicylic acid p. 324
anabolic steroids p. 318
antihistamines p. 326
antitussives p. 325
atrophy p. 332
combination pill p. 315
continuing of care p. 333
estrogen p. 315

ether **p. 330**
ethylene **p. 330**
ibuprofen **p. 325**
naproxen **p. 325**
progesterone **p. 315**
progestin pill **p. 316**
prostaglandins **p. 325**
pseudoephedrine **p. 325**
testosterone **p. 318**
whippets **p. 330**

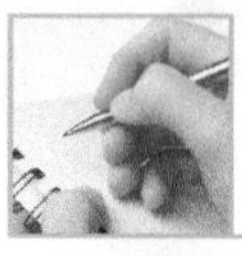

Essays/Thought Questions

1. How should athletic competitions deal with the problem of anabolic steroid use?
2. Herbal medications can be advertised and sold without NHPD regulation as long as the product is not specifically represented as a treatment for a disease. What are the pros and cons of this decision?

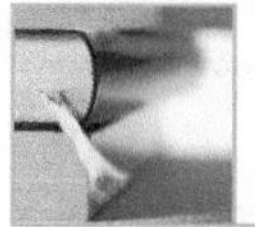

Suggested Readings

Julien, R.M., Advokat, C.D., & Comaty, J.E. (2008). *A primer of drug action* (11th ed.). New York: W.H. Freeman & Company.

Spinella, M. (2001). *The psychopharmacology of herbal medicine*. Cambridge, MA: MIT Press.

Yesalis, C.E. (2000). *Anabolic steroids in sport and exercise* (2nd ed.). Champaign, IL: Human Kinetics Press.

CHAPTER 14

Treatment of Substance-Use Disorders

Did You Know

?

- It is possible to experience spontaneous remission of substance-use disorders.
- Alcoholics Anonymous has groups all over the world.
- The biopsychosocial model may best explain the causes of drug use.
- Methadone maintenance is an effective treatment for heroin dependence.
- Many individuals who are mentally ill also have substance-use problems.
- Canadian youth, women, and the Aboriginal community require more specialized treatments that address their unique challenges for drug recovery.

Now that we have covered the most commonly used psychoactive substances, we are ready to address the question: What is done for people whose use becomes abuse or dependence? The question pertains to **treatment**, or planned activities designed to change some pattern of behaviour(s) of individuals or their families. In this chapter, we are concerned with patterns of substance use. Both psychological and behavioural treatments and pharmacological treatments are discussed.

treatment
Planned activities designed to change some pattern of behaviour(s) of individuals or their families.

Because the information about treatment is large in both volume and variety, it is useful to have a model to guide us through this chapter. Figure 14.1 is a model of what might occur during the course of treatment, from the time an alcohol or drug problem is recognized to the outcome, or the result that is attributed to treatment. In this case, the essential outcome of interest is change in alcohol or other drug use patterns.

You should read Figure 14.1 from left to right. For any treatment to happen, a problem must first be recognized. That recognition may come from the individual, or it may come first from other sources (family, friends, legal system, employer) in the individual's environment. Even with external feedback about a problem, individuals still may not be convinced that they actually do have a problem and need to change. This complex decision point typically is described by terms such as a person's *motivation* to change or *commitment* to change. With problem recognition, if change is initiated it typically happens in one of three ways. People may decide to change their substance use without any kind of help. For example, many ex-smokers stopped without help, and this is also the case for some people with alcohol or other drug problems. However, it may take a few tries to be successful (Sobell et al., 1993). This phenomenon has been called **spontaneous remission**. Another option that individuals may choose is self-help groups, such as Alcoholics Anonymous. And a third possibility is that individuals go into some kind of professional treatment. Frequently, individuals may combine self-help group attendance with professional treatment activities.

For any treatment to happen, a problem must first be recognized.

spontaneous remission
Resolution of a problem without the help of formal treatment.

If individuals initiate professional treatment, some type of assessment of their problems usually occurs first. Assessment leads to the specification of treatment goals, which contribute to placement in a specific treatment setting or activity. The content and structure of treatments are influenced by models and theories of alcohol and drug problems, reflected by the broken line in Figure 14.1.

FIGURE 14.1 **A model of events that occur in the course of treatment of substance-use disorders**

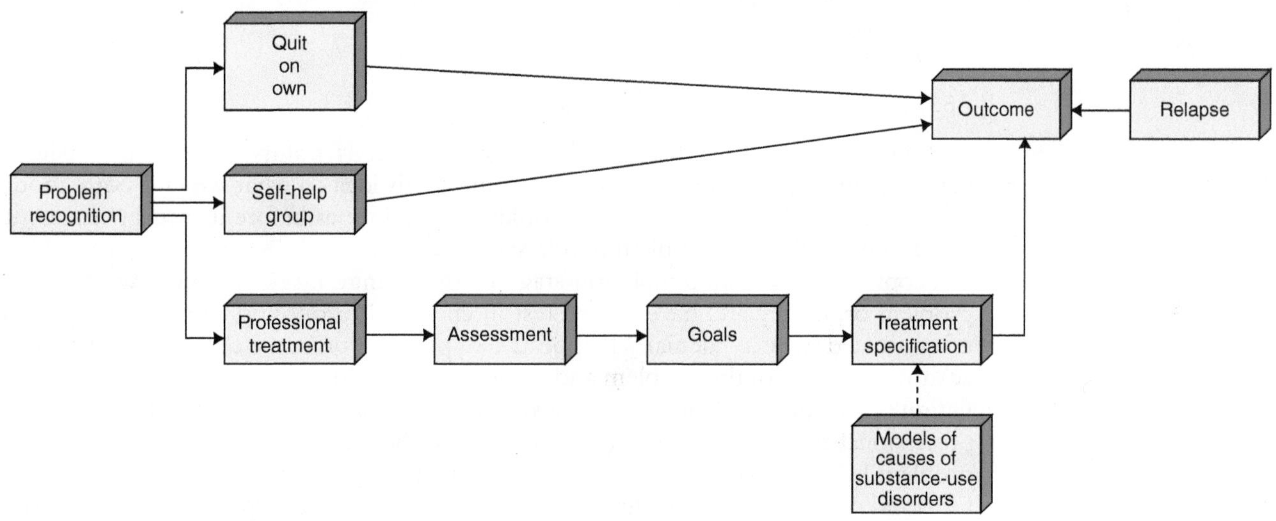

The result, or outcome, of these change options is of primary interest. Outcomes can take a variety of forms, especially over a long period of time. Following treatment for alcohol and other drug use, individuals may relapse after some time of substance-use problem reduction or resolution. If that happens, the person "goes back" to any of the preceding points in Figure 14.1, including back to the step of considering whether the person has a commitment to change.

With this framework, we can begin our presentation on treatment of the substance-use disorders. Like Figure 14.1, we start with a discussion of problem recognition and motivation to change.

Motivation to Change

Denial may persist even with evidence of a problem that is blatant to everybody but the person who has the problem.

Terms like *motivation* have been around as long as human behaviour has been observed and interpreted. Motivation to change has been considered essential if individuals have any hope that treatment of a behavioural or psychological problem will be effective. In the context of substance-use disorders, motivation to change is discussed often and sometimes heatedly. For example, it frequently is asserted that the major barrier to change is a person's denial of a problem with alcohol or drugs. Denial may persist even with evidence of a problem that is blatant to everybody but the person who has the problem.

Despite all the discussion of motivation, it has not been as fruitful as we might expect in helping us to understand change in behaviour like alcohol and drug use. Part of the problem is the many different ways to define a motivation to change and to measure it when conducting research or in clinical practice. One solution to this problem that has proved productive in addictions (smoking, alcohol, and other drug use) research is to look at "readiness" (or commitment) to change instead of grappling with the abstract idea of motivation. There have been several attempts to do this, but the one that has the greatest influence is the stages of change model (Prochaska, DiClemente, & Norcross, 1992). This model is thought to apply to people who change on their own or who use outside resources to change. The model has five stages:

1. Precontemplation
2. Contemplation
3. Preparation
4. Action
5. Maintenance

A person may cycle through the stages to various points several times before reaching problem resolution. You can connect this idea to what we said both about self-quitters "quitting" smoking or drinking several times before it seems permanent and about the difficult problem of relapse.

People in the precontemplation stage of the change model are not aware of the problem or, if they are, have no interest in change. Precontemplators are those who often are said to be in "denial." It appears that progression in the change cycle requires acknowledgment of the problem and its negative consequences, and an accurate evaluation of change possibilities and how they might occur (for example, with or without professional treatment). Contemplators vacillate between the pros and cons of their problem behaviour and between the pros and cons of making changes in it. So, they are deciding whether to change, but they have taken no steps to do so. People in the preparation stage are on the edge of taking action to change and may have made a try in the recent past. To progress, a commitment to take action and to set goals is needed. Individuals in the action stage already are engaged in explicit activities to change.

Maintenance, the last stage, involves the continued use of behaviour-change activities for as long as three years after the action stage began. After that time, the problem might be considered resolved. People are thought to progress through each of these stages in the process of change. The rate of progression and the amount of recycling differ from person to person and from problem to problem for a given person, but going through the stages applies generally. We should add here that identification of a person's stage is problem specific. For example, a person's stage of change for his or her drinking may not be indicative of that person's stage of change for smoking.

What this all means for us is that the stage of change helps us to identify a person's perception of the problem and readiness to change it. These factors may help us to determine the timing and content of treatment, or whether self-help groups or professional treatment is needed at all (Connors, Donovan, & DiClemente, 2001). Moreover, the stage may tell us what needs to be done to move the change process forward. For example, although coming to one's own conclusion that change is needed is the most effective foundation of long-term changes, external (to the individual) pushes to change (for example, from a spouse or employer) may help the person to progress from the precontemplation stage to a later stage that is characterized by a more internally based desire to change (Ryan, Plant, & O'Malley, 1995).

With problem recognition and a source of motivation to change, the next step is a decision about how change will occur.

With problem recognition and a source of motivation to change, the next step is a decision about how change will occur. In turn, we consider problem resolution on one's own, the use of self-help groups, and the use of professional treatment services.

Change without Formal Treatment

We do not have sufficient space to discuss the research on spontaneous remission of alcohol and other drug-use problems, but suffice it to say that it happens. In fact, it is generally agreed that more people with such problems resolve them on their own than by using self-help groups or professional treatment. How such changes are initiated is of interest and has been studied most extensively with alcohol problems. Sobell et al. (1993) reported the best study methodologically of this question to date. Most of the people these researchers studied (57 percent) said their change resulted from weighing the benefits and costs of continuing their current alcohol-use pattern. When the disadvantages seemed to grow in number and importance, change occurred. Notice how similar this is to what people in the contemplation stage are thought to do. Another 29 percent of the study participants reported that change was immediate, and they either could not recall what triggered the change or said it was a major event, such as a serious alcohol-related health problem.

It is worth saying more about the 29 percent of Sobell et al.'s (1993) research participants who reported that change was immediate. This group is poorly represented in current ideas and theories about behaviour change and its maintenance. Yet, as the Sobell et al. study suggests, immediate change is far from rare; we see this theme in fiction (Charles Dickens's Scrooge) and often in our own experiences or those of family members and friends. William Miller and Janet C'de Baca published a book called *Quantum Change* in 2001 about sudden-change experiences. The book describes the "quantum change" experiences of people from all walks of life and what happened to them in the years afterward. Miller and C'de Baca offer some ideas and questions to stimulate the scientific study of how sudden change occurs, in the hope of beginning to close an important gap in our knowledge of behaviour change.

The most important point to take from this brief discussion is that spontaneous remission occurs and apparently occurs often. How often has not been determined; to specify the prevalence would be extremely costly and complex. Nevertheless, even with our limited knowledge of it, the phenomenon of change without treatment has taught us a lot about change processes in general, including change that occurs with the use of treatment resources. Many individuals with a diagnosis of substance-use disorder do eventually seek help from treatment resources (Kessler et al., 2001). We turn next to one of those resources: self-help groups.

Self-Help Groups

Peer self-help groups are a major part of the treatment of substance-use disorders. According to Emrick, Lassen, and Edwards (1977), members of peer self-help groups perform therapeutic functions without professional credentials. A member of a peer self-help group might have training pertinent to conducting therapy, but such credentials are not used in performing group functions. Members of these groups all have some identified problem that is the focus of the group's therapeutic activity. The term *peer self-help* distinguishes these groups from those in which therapeutic agents (the group leader, for example) are not identified as having the same problems as the clients. Therefore, through the peer self-help group, participants both give and receive help with their problems.

Although the peer self-help movement does not use professionally defined methods to help participants with their problems, professionals are not shunned. In fact, the professional community is welcome to join the peer self-help group in achieving common goals of helping people alleviate their problems (for example, Alcoholics Anonymous, 1972). Professionals and the self-help group have complementary functions. In practice, professionals who work in the treatment of alcohol and drug problems often use relevant self-help groups (such as Alcoholics Anonymous for alcohol problems and Narcotics Anonymous for other drug problems) in a professionally run rehabilitation program and as part of aftercare planning. Indeed, many alcohol and drug treatment programs are organized around principles of peer self-help groups.

In discussing treatment of the substance-use disorders, we must review peer self-help groups because of their popularity and influence. Peer self-help also has been a popular treatment of choice for other addictive behaviours, such as Weight Watchers and TOPS (Taking Off Pounds Sensibly) for treatment of obesity, Smokers Anonymous for treatment of cigarette smoking, and Gamblers Anonymous for treatment of compulsive gambling.

Alcoholics Anonymous

In this section, we briefly describe the peer self-help movement organized for helping individuals identified as alcoholics—Alcoholics Anonymous (AA). In 2010, there were 4887 AA groups across Canada with 94 164 members. In total, there were 115 773 AA groups and 2 103 033 members across the world, as of 2010 (Alcoholics Anonymous, 2011). Because of space limitations, we cannot describe in detail the major self-help groups for the treatment of drug problems, called Narcotics Anonymous (NA). NA is analogous to AA, however, and what we know about AA can be applied readily to NA.

Emrick, Lassen, and Edwards (1977) called AA the prototype self-help group because it is the oldest group, established in 1935. It has been the basis for the development of other self-help movements for treatments in other problem areas. The AA movement began when an alcoholic surgeon (Dr. Bob) and an alcoholic stockbroker (Bill W.) helped each other to maintain sobriety. From Ohio, they spread their idea that alcoholics need to help each other. Today, AA is an international organization. A few alcohol self-help groups, such as Alateen and Al-Anon, have been derived from AA. Alateen's purpose is to help teenagers who have an alcoholic parent; Al-Anon generally is aimed at spouses and others close to those with alcoholism.

The bases of the AA "program" are self-help recovery through following the Twelve Steps and group participation. The core of AA is the model of recovery outlined in the Twelve Steps, which are listed in Table 14.1. In the first step, AA absolutely dismisses the notion that people with alcoholism can control their drinking or can ever reach that position. The beginning of recovery occurs when those with alcoholism admit to themselves as being powerless over alcohol, that without alcohol a return to health is possible, and that with it, the downward spiral to self-destruction continues. One cause of controversy is the frequent reference to God in the Twelve Steps. An immediate reaction to this is that AA is only for those with alcoholism who accept Western religious beliefs. However, AA takes pains to accent the phrase

TABLE 14.1 The Twelve Steps of Alcoholics Anonymous

1. We admitted we were powerless over alcohol—that our lives had become unmanageable.
2. Came to believe that a Power greater than ourselves could restore us to sanity.
3. Made a decision to turn our will and our lives over to the care of God as we understood Him.
4. Made a searching and fearless moral inventory of ourselves.
5. Admitted to God, to ourselves, and to another human being the exact nature of our wrongs.
6. Were entirely ready to have God remove all these defects of character.
7. Humbly asked Him to remove our shortcomings.
8. Made a list of all persons we had harmed, and became willing to make amends to them all.
9. Made direct amends to such people wherever possible, except when to do so would injure them or others.
10. Continued to take personal inventory and when we were wrong promptly admitted it.
11. Sought through prayer and meditation to improve our conscious contact with God as we understood Him, praying only for knowledge of His will for us and the power to carry that out.
12. Having had a spiritual awakening as the result of these Steps, we tried to carry this message to alcoholics, and to practice these principles in all our affairs.

Source: The Twelve Steps are reprinted with permission of Alcoholics Anonymous World Services, Inc. ("AAWS") Permission to reprint the Twelve Steps does not mean that AAWS has reviewed or approved the contents of this publication, or that AAWS necessarily agrees with the views expressed herein. A.A. is a program of recovery from alcoholism only—use of the Twelve Steps in connection with programs and activities which are patterned after A.A., but which address other problems, or in any other non-A.A. context, does not imply otherwise.

"God as we understood Him," which means people may interpret "God" or "Higher Power" as they wish. The importance of referring to a Supreme Being is to emphasize that people with alcoholism have lost control over alcohol and their lives and must enlist the assistance of a greater power in recovery. A final point is that the Twelve Steps recovery program is oriented toward action, both in self-examination and change and in behaviour toward others.

recovery
In the addictions field, changes back to health in physical, psychological, spiritual, and social functioning. It generally is believed that recovery is a lifetime process that requires total abstinence from alcohol and nonprescribed drugs.

The Twelve Steps are a guide designed for people to follow largely by themselves on the road to **recovery**. In addition to the bases of the steps, there are other parts to the AA program. One of these is group participation. Two major types are discussion meetings and speakers' meetings. In a discussion meeting, the chairperson of the group tells his or her personal history of alcoholism and recovery from it, and then the meeting is opened for members' discussion of alcoholism and related matters. In a speakers' meeting, a couple of members recite their personal histories of alcoholism and recovery. In open speakers' meetings, anyone who is interested may attend; closed meetings are for alcoholics only.

One purpose of group meetings is to aid recovery through peer identification and learning from the experience of others. Building social relationships that do not revolve around alcohol represents an entirely new social life. The importance of forming sober social relationships may be seen in various AA functions such as "Sober Anniversaries" (the first day of a member's current episode of continuous sobriety) and "Sober Dances" (dances without alcohol or drugs).

Other major activities in the AA program are "Twelfth Stepping" and sponsorship. Twelfth Stepping refers to the twelfth of the Twelve Steps, which involves members reaching out to other alcoholics in a time of need. A member may help active alcoholics begin the AA program or help current AA members return to sobriety after they have begun drinking again. Sponsorship is similar to Twelfth Stepping, but there are important differences. First, sponsorship involves a stable one-to-one relationship

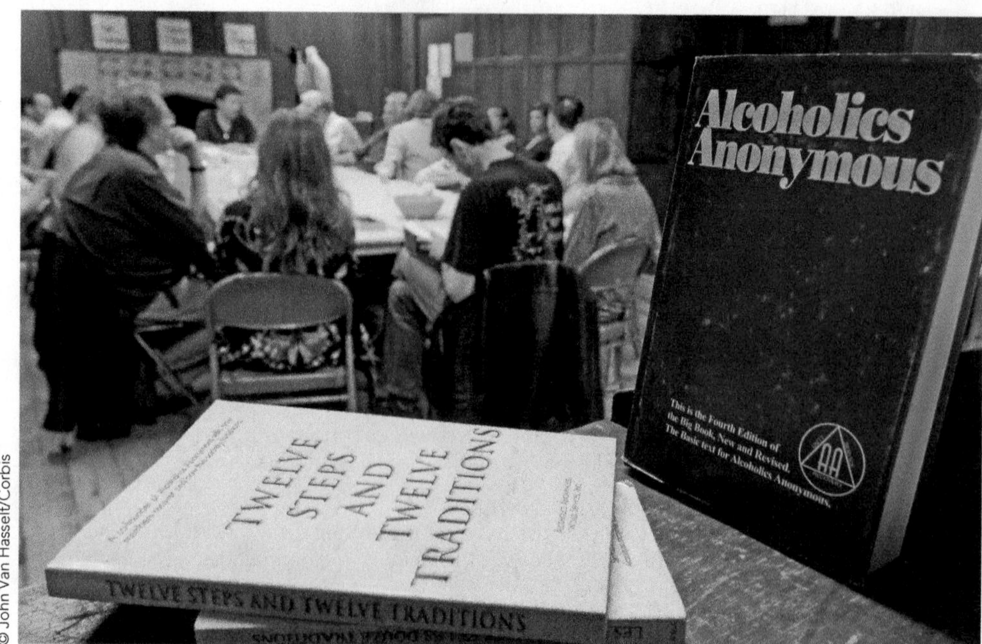

Attendance at Alcoholics Anonymous meetings is the most popular self-help method for changing drinking behaviours in the United States.

between a member with more sobriety (the sponsor) and one with less (the sponsee). To quote, "[T]he process of sponsorship is this: An alcoholic who has made some progress in the recovery program shares that experience on a continuous, individual basis with another alcoholic who is attempting to attain or maintain sobriety through AA" (Alcoholics Anonymous, 1983, p. 5). Another important difference is that the sponsor helps the sponsee in ways such as taking the newer member's "inventory" (looking at what is behind a person's behaviour) when asked; guiding an individual to AA literature, such as the *Big Book* and *Twelve Steps and Twelve Traditions*; and explaining the AA program to family and others close to the sponsee. The sponsor–sponsee relationship is more varied and more enduring than that involved in Twelfth Stepping. AA members view both types of activities as essential to their continued sobriety. What has been described for AA is directly applicable to Narcotics Anonymous (NA). NA's organization and program of recovery are derived directly from AA's, including the use of the Steps to Recovery Program, group meetings, and the sponsor–sponsee relationship. As the name implies, NA evolved to help people addicted to opiate drugs, usually heroin. However, people who identify their primary problem as addiction to drugs of any type other than alcohol use NA instead of AA.

In summary, the AA program of recovery has been the cornerstone of a self-help movement that has been of value to many and that is reaching increasing numbers of people. It is worth mentioning again that both AA and NA may be, and are, used alone as programs of treatment, but many members of these organizations began treatment or concurrently are receiving treatment from professional sources.

Other Self-Help Groups

We have spent so much space on AA and its "relatives" because they are by far the most prevalent, influential self-help treatments for alcohol- and drug-use disorders. Perhaps stimulated by AA's success, other types of self-help groups for alcohol and drug problems have been organized. One important example is Women for Sobriety (WFS), which began in 1975 (Women for Sobriety, 1985). WFS groups are now available throughout the United States, Canada, and other countries.

WFS agrees with AA that alcohol- and drug-use disorders are progressive illnesses. Complete abstinence from these substances is required to arrest the illnesses, but they cannot be cured. Also similar to AA, WFS members meet in groups (weekly) that a moderator leads. The WFS "New Life Acceptance Program" consists of the following 13 statements*:

1. I have a life-threatening problem that once had me. I now take charge of my life and my disease. I accept the responsibility.
2. Negative thoughts destroy only myself. My first conscious sober act must be to remove negativity from my life.
3. Happiness is a habit I will develop. Happiness is created, not waited for.
4. Problems bother me only to the degree I permit them to. I now better understand my problems and do not permit problems to overwhelm me.
5. I am what I think. I am a capable, competent, caring, compassionate woman.
6. Life can be ordinary or it can be great. Greatness is mine by a conscious effort.
7. Love can change the course of my world. Caring becomes all important.
8. The fundamental object of life is emotional and spiritual growth. Daily I put my life into a proper order, knowing which are the priorities.

* Women for Sobriety

9. The past is gone forever. No longer will I be victimized by the past. I am a new person.
10. All love given returns. I will learn to know that others love me.
11. Enthusiasm is my daily exercise. I treasure all moments of my new life
12. I am a competent woman and have much to give life. This is what I am and I shall know it always.
13. I am responsible for myself and for my actions. I am in charge of my mind, my thoughts, and my life.

So far, it is not clear why WFS required a new name, because it seems like a slight variant of AA. The focus of WFS is the special psychological and social needs and concerns that women face in achieving and maintaining sobriety. However, AA in general does not share this focus. WFS suggests that its program may be used alone to maintain sobriety, in conjunction with professional services, or in conjunction with AA.

A self-help group that claims to be based on methods that are scientifically validated is Self-Management and Recovery Training (SMART) (Rajacic, 1997). There are SMART groups located throughout Canada, the U.S., the U.K., and Australia. SMART groups usually have four to 12 members and are led by a "coordinator," someone who has maintained sobriety for an appreciable amount of time and who believes in SMART principles. Coordinators also may be individuals who have never had an alcohol problem (Fletcher, 2001). Meetings are traditionally in person, but more recently they have begun to use online support methods as well. SMART groups offer support and practical tools that address four key areas of recovery (SMART Recovery, 2011):

1. Enhancing and Maintaining Motivation
2. Coping with Urges
3. Managing Thoughts, Feelings, and Behaviours
4. Living a Balanced Life

SMART helps people combat irrational beliefs that are obstacles in quitting drinking; this is modelled after Albert Ellis's system of psychotherapy called rational emotive behaviour therapy. Then SMART helps people cope with feelings like fear and anger without drinking. Work on thoughts and feelings must be followed by changes in behaviour for success in addressing an alcohol problem. Behaviour change is said to occur by engaging in activities that are enjoyable that do not involve alcohol use.

SMART had been aligned with a former self-help movement called Rational Recovery (Trimpey, 1992). On January 1, 1999, however, Rational Recovery stopped holding self-help group meetings and, in fact, now condemns the self-help group movement. Rational Recovery considers itself an educational movement based on cognitive-behavioural principles (similar to rational emotive behaviour therapy) and the addictive voice recognition technique (AVRT). AVRT is said to be a way to stop and take control of the "inner voice" that tells people to drink. Rational Recovery principles are disseminated via the Internet, videotapes and CDs, and books.

The last self-help group we discuss is SOS, which stands for Secular Organizations for Sobriety or, as an alternative, Save Our Selves. This self-help support group began in 1986 as an alternative to AA. As in SMART, the SOS alternative has no emphasis on spirituality or higher powers in staying sober. Instead, individuals are viewed as being in charge of making rational decisions about their use of alcohol and drugs. SOS's popularity is increasing rapidly and, as of 1990, had more than 200 sites in the United States where groups meet. SOS also has groups in Europe and Canada (specifically in Toronto and Ottawa). Like AA, SOS uses peer support group meetings as the vehicle for staying sober. Groups generally have 10 to 12 members and meet weekly for one to one-and-a-half hours, but other procedures are possible, as the parent organization is flexible regarding the schedule and format of individual support group meetings. These meetings have a rotating leader, who is a group member. Groups are free, but members may make donations to sustain the group financially.

The core principle of SOS is that sobriety—abstinence from alcohol and drugs—is maintained "one day at a time," an expression well known to AA members. The "Sobriety Priority" program is the philosophy that underlies SOS, with these major points:

1. acknowledgment of one's addiction as a disease and a habit;
2. acceptance of one's problem; and
3. placement of sobriety as the number-one priority, separate from other problems or concerns in life.

These three points may be viewed as analogous to AA's Twelve Steps. In SOS, groups are seen as safe places where members can discuss their concerns and ways that they stay sober. No limit is placed on how long people may stay in a group or on the number of meetings they attend.

Self-help groups are an extremely important resource that people use to change their patterns of alcohol or other drug use. Self-help groups may be used alone or in conjunction with professional treatment services, which is our next topic. Before we go into our discussion of what happens in such treatment, however, it is important for you to know something about the ideas (models and theories) behind it. You have seen in our review of self-help groups how beliefs about the causes of alcohol and drug problems greatly influenced the content of the self-help group and what participation in it involved. The same is true for professional treatments.

Models of Substance-Use Disorders

There are many different models and theories that have been championed to explain the causes of alcohol dependence. These conceptual views have spanned biological, psychological, and social/environmental domains of variables; tended to be heavy on one of the three variable domains and light or silent on the other two; and often explained something about the development of alcohol dependence, but not everything (Miller & Hester, 1995).

To make learning about these models and theories easier, we have organized them into five major categories (with specific variations within the categories):

1. Moral model
2. American disease model
3. Biological model
4. Social learning model
5. Sociocultural model

Each model has implications for designing treatment of the substance-use disorders. Our discussion is based heavily on chapters by Miller and Hester (1989, 2002).

Five Model Categories

The first category is the moral model, in which individuals are seen as personally responsible for problems they may incur from their use of drugs and alcohol. That is, the development of a substance-use disorder is seen as the product of a series of personal decisions or choices to use those substances in a way that is harmful. This perspective implies that choices other than to use alcohol and drugs were available to the person but were not taken. Depending on the variation of the model, treatment consists of either spiritual or legal intervention.

The American disease model is especially important because of its widespread prevalence and prominence in the United States. It also is the foundation of Alcoholics Anonymous and other self-help groups. In the American disease model (it is called American because it is not nearly so popular in other countries) dependence on alcohol and drugs is viewed as the product of a progressive, irreversible disease. The disease is described as a merging of physical, psychological, and spiritual causes. The treatment that follows from the disease model is to identify people who have the disease, confront them with it, help them to accept that they have it, and persuade them to abstain from alcohol and other drugs.

In the biological model, dependence on alcohol or other drugs is viewed as the result of genetic or physiological processes. Theories about how the pharmacological action of drugs themselves in the brain can lead to dependence also fall under the biological umbrella. The treatment most clearly implied from biological models is to advise biologically at-risk people of their risk for developing a disorder, and perhaps to counsel those who are at risk to avoid alcohol and other drugs altogether.

Social learning theory is the position that alcohol and drug disorders are the result of complex learning from an interaction of individuals with their environments. Situations and psychological processes are most important. For example, harmful substance-use patterns may develop from direct experiences in using alcohol and drugs, from modelling the behaviour of other individuals when they drink or use drugs in a harmful way, from false beliefs about the powers of alcohol and drugs in helping to get through difficult times, or from a failure to learn ways to cope with stress without alcohol or drug use. Treatment follows straightforwardly from this conception: Arrange the person's environment so that nonabuse of psychoactive substances is reinforced and abuse is not, or is punished (Higgins et al., 1991); display individuals ("models") engaging in desirable alcohol-use patterns (use of psychoactive drugs other than for medical purposes never is viewed positively by the greater society); teach facts about the actions of alcohol and drugs on the body and how humans experience their effects; and teach nondrug ways to cope with stress.

According to the sociocultural model, subcultures and societies shape alcohol- and drug-use patterns and consequences. Examples are norms and rules that a subculture has for alcohol use (such as when it is appropriate, as at adult dinner parties, and when it is not, as at work) and laws about substance use (such as what drugs are legal and what drugs are not). The treatment that follows from this perspective is interventions that affect large groups of people or society in general. For example, taxing sales of alcoholic beverages is an effort in part to control their availability and accessibility. Another example of a sociocultural intervention is the classification of drugs by "schedule" status.

You can see that the five major models and theories of substance-use disorder reflect a wide array of perspectives. You also might notice that, in general, the models do not overlap much. A summary of the five models and their implications for treatment is presented in Table 14.2.

TABLE 14.2 The Five Major Models of the Causes of Substance-Use Disorders and Their Implications for Treatment

Model	Cause(s)	Treatment
Moral	The making of personal choices to use alcohol and drugs in a harmful way, when other choices could have been made	Punish legally or intervene spiritually
American disease	Progressive, irreversible diseases that are the products of a mix of physical, psychological, and spiritual causes	Identify those with the disease, confront them with it, and persuade them to abstain from drugs and alcohol
Biological	Genetic or physiological processes	Advise people at risk for problems of their risk status, and counsel them to avoid alcohol and drugs
Social learning	Complex learning based on the interaction of the individuals with their environments	Arrange the environment to reinforce nonabuse of substances; do not reinforce, or punish, abuse; provide models of appropriate substance use; debunk myths about alcohol and drugs; teach nondrug alternatives for coping with stress
Sociocultural	Practices and rules of subcultures and societies	Intervene in ways that affect large groups or society in general (e.g., drug-use laws and alcohol taxes)

Source: R. K. Hester and W. R. Miller, *Handbook of Alcoholism Treatment Approaches: Effective Alternatives, 2nd ed.*, ©1995. Adapted by permission of Pearson Education, Inc., Upper Saddle River, NJ.

Biopsychosocial Model

If no one model or theory of causes of substance-use disorders proves adequate, as is the case, then there must be some way of proceeding with treatment design. We could be atheoretical in our efforts, but that approach tends not to be too productive. Instead, we can combine the disciplines (biological/medical–psychological–social/environmental) into one perspective. As you saw in Chapter 9, the term *biopsychosocial* reflects an attempt to simultaneously take into account three major variable domains that are known to influence human health and behaviour. You will recognize again that this combined perspective follows from the theme of the drug experience and its determinants that we have articulated and developed since the first chapter of this text.

It is no secret that taking a biopsychosocial perspective of the causes of the substance-use disorders leads us to a new level of complexity. But drugs and human behaviour is a complex subject that requires complex analysis for its understanding. Because of its complexity and recency, the biopsychosocial viewpoint is just that, a viewpoint, at this time—it is not precise or developed enough to be called a theory. Our premise is that this perspective has been providing and will continue to provide a guide for the kind of research that will find explanations of the causes of substance-use disorders.

It is no secret that taking a biopsychosocial perspective of the causes of the substance-use disorders leads us to a new level of complexity. But drugs and human behaviour is a complex subject that requires complex analysis for its understanding.

Professional Treatment: Assessment and Goals

When individuals go to professionals for help to change their substance use, a process of assessment and treatment goal setting typically is initiated. Actually, models of etiology influence this part of the treatment experience as they do the treatment content. We also should note that discussing assessment and goals here is not meant to imply they are not relevant for self-change or self-help groups. Although no systematic, formally structured assessment occurs in those contexts, there has been some type of appraisal, however unsystematic or subtle, that a problem exists. Furthermore, goals are set that define the desired end of the change process. Again, such goals may not be explicitly documented or articulated, but they direct change. Note how this general concept of the need to set goals to direct change is incorporated in the stages of change model.

An overarching assumption in professional settings is that good assessment underlies good treatment. When we say *assessment* in this context, we mean the use of mostly formal (e.g., standard psychological tests) but sometimes informal (e.g., casual observation of a patient's behaviour on a treatment unit) procedures to measure some aspect of a person's functioning. Assessment of people who appear for drug and alcohol treatment may include several different procedures.

Measuring qualities or characteristics of a person to design treatment means that treatment is tailored to the person. This is the same as matching the treatment to the individual. Matching concerns decisions about what treatment choices are preferred for different individuals to produce the best results. Along these lines, a major task of assessment and matching is to help define or specify treatment goals. Treatment goals refer to the purposes or aims of a treatment, which in general are to "get better"; however, that is too general to be of much use in guiding a treatment. We can be more specific. For example, in drug and alcohol treatment, everybody agrees that the person's use of drugs and alcohol must change. In many countries, that typically means a change to complete abstinence from these substances, although we will see that there has been some controversy over whether all people require a goal of total abstinence from alcohol.

There may be goals of alcohol and drug treatment besides a person's substance use. It may be important for changes to occur in an individual's family, work, and social functioning. This is because in virtually all people who appear for substance-abuse treatment, their use of alcohol or other drugs has affected other parts of their lives. Those changes in turn may affect a person's use of alcohol and drugs. It is important to see that the influences of substance use on different areas of life, and the reverse, are consistent with a biopsychosocial model. Substance use may be affected by multiple and varied factors, and the use of alcohol or other drugs may have multiple and varied consequences. These consequences may in turn affect future substance use.

How these multiple influences work in the development, maintenance, and change in substance use tends to differ for each person. As a result, a person's goals for treatment must be tailored to that person's specific, unique circumstances. Professionals working in drug and alcohol treatment call this "individualizing" treatment goals.

Abstinence or Moderation?

Before we leave the topic of treatment goals, it is important to discuss a specific question about goals relating to alcohol use. Traditionally, and still predominantly in Canada and the United States, the assumption is that the goal of treatment for alcohol problems is abstinence from alcohol. This applies to self-help treatments as well as to professional treatment services; indeed, AA and other self-help groups are adamant that abstinence is essential to a person's long-term improved functioning. However, a number of reports in the literature both on self-change and on treatment have stated that individuals identified as alcohol abusers or alcohol dependent can modify their alcohol use to a stable, moderate level.

These findings have created and still create heated controversy. The controversy stems from the disease model of alcohol problems, which implies that lifelong abstinence is the only safe course toward amelioration of alcohol problems. The need for abstinence typically is not questioned in the treatment of other drug problems, however. It is likely that abstinence from nonprescribed use of drugs is the only acceptable goal because the drugs are illegal, and society has a strong reaction against illicit drug use.

The question of moderation as a drinking goal is of more than academic importance. Knowledge about different drinking outcomes would increase our understanding of the causes and course of alcohol problems and improve the results of our treatment efforts through better individualization of treatment goals. We do know that moderate drinking outcomes happen, but knowledge beyond that is sketchier. It seems to make the most sense to frame this question the same way we framed treatment goals in general: They should reflect the individual's specific, unique circumstances.

Research does help somewhat in telling us what are the best "circumstances" for a goal of moderate drinking. Overall, it seems that less severe alcohol dependence (in DSM-IV terms, or in terms of physical dependence on alcohol), an individual's belief that moderate drinking is possible, younger age, employment, and psychological and social stability provide the "backdrop" for the feasibility of a moderate drinking outcome (Rosenberg, 1993). Some of these factors are not static (such as beliefs about moderate drinking), however, and it would be essential to monitor them closely over time to make sustained moderate drinking most likely.

Moderate drinking outcomes will continue to stimulate debate and research for years to come. The best result of this activity would be a better understanding of the course of alcohol problems and the creation of better treatment service delivery. This result is assuming greater practical importance as programs that support moderate drinking outcome goals become more common and accessible. For example, there is now considerable information about moderate drinking programs available online. These programs are usually designed for an individual to complete the program (literature, training, and so on) on their own for a fee. Examples include the "Sensible Drinking System" and "Moderation Management."

Harm Reduction

Harm reduction refers to an emphasis on reducing the negative consequences of using a substance rather than on reducing the quantity or frequency of its consumption. In practice, harm-reduction programs may encourage lighter consumption, but the focus is on reducing the harmful consequences that may ensue from substance use (Single, 1995). Common examples of applying the harm-reduction idea to substance use among the general public are using a designated driver when social occasions involve alcohol consumption and training bartenders to recognize signs of intoxication in their patrons and to stop serving them alcohol accordingly.

Harm reduction is an idea that originally was applied in the treatment of illicit drug users. For example, offering addicts clean syringes to avoid the transmission of HIV or other viruses follows directly from a harm-reduction approach. This idea also is relevant to alcohol treatment and stands in contrast to zero-tolerance or abstinence-only approaches. Harm reduction in some cases offers advantages over an abstinence-only goal. For instance, a harm-reduction approach may be valuable in encouraging college and university students or other young adults to consider modifying the circumstances or quantity of their alcohol consumption, whereas an abstinence-only approach would be far less likely to have that result (Baer et al., 2001). Similarly, harm-reduction approaches are useful for bringing into treatment drug addicts who claim they do not want to stop using drugs entirely but who may be interested in reducing the problems that their drug use causes them.

However, there is often resistance to the application of the harm-reduction model to the treatment of the substance-use disorders. As you might have guessed, the resistance is based at least in part in the reluctance to "condone" the use of alcohol or other drugs, even in individuals who show no signs of physical dependence on them. It is essential to recognize that the harm-reduction model neither condones nor censures substance use. Rather, it takes the pragmatic view that some individuals in a society will use alcohol or other drugs, and the most important goal for these individuals and the society they live in is to reduce the frequency and severity of any negative consequences that may follow from such use.

After assessment and specification of treatment goals, the next step in professional treatment is to make the best use of that information to place individuals in the best treatment environment to meet their needs. Two levels of such matching may be considered: the treatment setting and the services that are delivered within a setting. We turn now to review both of these, first for alcohol treatment and then for other drug treatment. We also comment on how effective alcohol and drug treatments are. When we say drug treatment, we mean treatment for drugs of abuse, such as the opiates, stimulants, and depressant drugs.

Harm reduction has been a part of Canada's Drug Strategy since 1987, and, although controversial, the need for this type of treatment is paramount.

Harm reduction has been a part of Canada's Drug Strategy since 1987 and, although controversial, the need for this type of treatment is paramount. For example, in 2005 alone, 350 to 650 Canadians contracted HIV through injection drug use. Further, each year there are approximately 5000 new cases of Hepatitis C, with 70 percent of sufferers having current or past injection drug use (Canadian Harm Reduction Network [CHRN], 2011). In Canada, the main types of harm-reduction strategies include needle distribution and methadone maintenance programs. Canada has other harm-reduction strategies but they are not broadly practised across the country, such as crack pipe distribution, user empowerment projects, safer drug use sites, heroin prescription, social justice projects, overdose prevention programs, and survival guides produced by and for drug users (CHRN, 2011).

The CHRN partnered with the Canadian AIDS Society to examine harm-reduction programs and practices across Canada. Specifically, they examined programs in Yukon Territory; Victoria, British Columbia; Edmonton Alberta; Winnipeg, Manitoba; Rouyn-Noranda, Quebec; Ottawa, Ontario; Québec City, Quebec; Halifax, Nova Scotia; and St. John's, Newfoundland. Their goal was to document and disseminate information on the innovative and useful ways that harm-reduction programs are being offered in Canada, and such programs have successfully addressed the challenges of drug rehabilitation (CHRN, 2011). In their report they identify the challenges of drug rehabilitation, such as

- marginalization and discrimination of drug users, which impedes the recovery process,
- lack of peer involvement,
- unique challenges of remote and rural areas,
- threats to sustainability due to lack of funding or community support, and
- potential staff burnout.

Also, in their report they provide a comprehensive list of how to successfully address these challenges. The Drugs and Culture Box 14.1 provides this detailed content.

DRUGS AND CULTURE BOX 14.1

Ways to Address Challenges That Face Reduction Programs

In their final report, entitled "Learning From Each Other: Enhancing Community-Based Harm Reduction Programs and Practices in Canada" (2011), the Canadian Harm Reduction Network and the Canadian AIDS Society present several solutions that address the challenges that face harm-reduction programs in Canada. The following table summarizes some of their suggestions.

Challenge	Possible Solution or Strategy for Success
Lack of Community Support	Join forces: community members, service organizations, researchers, and potential partner organizations Use the media effectively and educate them about the program Establish good working relationships with the police, politicians, etc. Anticipate and address community concerns and consult the community before bringing a program to their neighbourhood and keep them informed Recognize community members and agencies contributions and support Organize community-building events Exhibit patience and perseverance
Lack of Peer Involvement	Members with drug-experience should be permitted to contribute to the program because they have a lot to offer Use members' firsthand knowledge and experience to support others in their recovery Include members in program planning, delivery, and evaluation Members can be advocates, spokespersons, and educators to others
Marginalization and Discrimination	Provide a welcoming, non-judgmental space Make services as accessible as possible Offer services such as food, clothing, medical care, personal and social support, activities, and referrals
Rural and Remote areas	Use mobile outreach vans
Lack of Funding	Use information from community-based research when applying for funding
Staff Burnout	Pair seasoned workers and volunteers with new ones to provide support and continuity Provide practice guidelines for outreach workers Keep informed and keep staff informed Celebrate and support dedicated staff and volunteers

Alcohol Treatment Settings and Services

Types of Settings and Services

The settings and services of treatment for alcohol problems could be classified in a number of ways. We use the classification that Armor, Polich, and Stambul published in their well-known 1976 Rand Corporation study of alcoholism treatment in the United States. The settings that Armor et al. described are still widely used (American Psychiatric Association, 2000b).

Armor, Polich, and Stambul (1976, p. 102) identified the general treatment settings of hospital setting, intermediate setting, and outpatient setting. Within each of these settings, specific treatment services are offered. Inpatients in the hospital setting live there for the duration of their treatment, and their care is similar to that given to people hospitalized for physical problems. For example, nurses play a large role in treatment, and much weight is given to the medical aspects of alcohol problems. On the other hand, many of the specific alcohol rehabilitation methods followed in hospital-based programs are **psychological treatment** in origin. The emphasis of these nonmedical treatment methods is on learning about the self and the environment we live in, how they alter the development of alcohol problems, and how people can change both their self and their environment to produce desired changes in psychoactive substance use. (Similar treatment methods are followed in inpatient "free-standing" alcohol programs. These programs do not operate within the hospital setting and typically are "for profit"; that is, they need to make a profit to stay in business.) Partial hospital care occurs in the hospital setting, but the patient* is not in the setting for 24 hours a day. Typically, treatment programs of this type are designed for four- to eight-hour schedules, usually in the daytime or evening. The last type of service in the hospital setting is detoxification, mainly involving the medical management of alcohol withdrawal symptoms. Care mostly consists of the management of medications given to treat withdrawal, although counselling is available, especially referral to additional treatment services.

psychological treatment
Treatment geared to changing emotions, thoughts, or behaviour without the use of medications or other physical or biological means.

Within the intermediate treatment setting are halfway house services. Halfway houses usually are designed as **milieu treatment** settings. (In milieu treatment, the organization and structure of a setting are designed to be therapeutic.) These settings are the patients' residence during treatment. Other treatment services usually available include **counselling**, **psychotherapy**, and a strong orientation toward the use of self-help groups, usually Alcoholics Anonymous (AA).

milieu treatment
Treatment in which the organization and structure of a setting are designed to change behaviour.

counselling
In alcohol and drug treatment, counsellors are specially trained professionals who perform a variety of treatment activities, including assessment, education, and individual, marital, and family counselling.

psychotherapy
Typically, conversation between a specially trained individual (therapist) and another person (or family) that is intended to change patterns of behaviour, thoughts, or feelings in that person (or family).

The outpatient setting is perhaps the most idiosyncratic of the three that Armor, Polich, and Stambul (1976) described. Two general distinctions of treatment services are made: individual and group. In individual treatment, patients work with a professional in a one-to-one relationship. Similarly, "individual" couples or families may work with a professional in a planned course of treatment. Hester and Delaney (1997) described an outpatient program that was designed for individuals whose drinking is relatively heavy (compared to population norms) but who are not dependent on alcohol. The intervention is called Behavioral Self-Control Program for Windows (BSCPWIN) and involves delivery of a drinking moderation program over eight weekly sessions by interaction with a personal computer program. This individual treatment program is based on both social learning theory and motivational enhancement principles; it differs from the typical outpatient program in its use of a personal computer to deliver the intervention and the consequent use of minimal therapist time. Because therapist time is greatly reduced, the potential for reducing treatment costs is considerable.

Hester and Delaney's (1997) work is an early example of how outpatient alcohol treatment is becoming more and more idiosyncratic as computer technology becomes more advanced. Prominent in this regard is the growing number of outpatient treatments being evaluated that present the content of the intervention on the Internet (Cunningham, 2009). These methods have the potential of being acceptable to people who, for various reasons, are not receptive to face-to-face, in-person (with a counsellor or therapist) treatment. Furthermore, they have the potential of reducing the costs of delivering treatment considerably.

* In the treatment of psychiatric disorders, including addictions, professionals are inconsistent in their use of the words *patient* and *client* to refer to individuals who present themselves for treatment. Underlying this disagreement are beliefs about the utility of a medical model as a guide to understanding the psychiatric disorders. In addition, often what term is chosen depends on the setting of treatment. For example, individuals in hospital inpatient settings are more likely to be referred to as patients, as compared with people who receive treatment in outpatient clinics. In this chapter, we use the terms *patient* and *client* as synonyms to refer to individuals who are in formal treatment for their alcohol or drug problems.

Group outpatient treatment usually involves five to 10 individuals meeting together in regular sessions led by a professional. Much of what helps group members to change theoretically stems from the way they interact with each other and form relationships. The leader's job is to guide this process and to keep group members on productive tracks of discussion. Groups often are organized around specific themes, which govern the types of people who join each group and what they discuss. Examples of themes are adults whose parents were alcoholic and ways to prevent a recurrence (relapse) of alcohol problems once they are treated. Other groups are general and have only the theme of maintaining abstinence from substance use. Interestingly, in this context, some Internet-based interventions also involve a "support network," not unlike a therapy group, that may or may not have a network moderator or "leader" (Cunningham, 2009).

Much of what helps group members to change theoretically stems from the way they interact with each other and form relationships.

Individual and group treatments may be conducted by workers with different types of mental health training. They may be "paraprofessionals," working in direct patient care and not possessing a formal degree, and they may be professionals, who are physicians (typically psychiatrists), clinical psychologists, social workers, clinical nurse specialists, and certified alcohol (or other drug) counsellors. Actually, people in any of the professional disciplines also may earn certification as alcohol and drug counsellors.

Outpatient care also varies in intensity; that is, some patients may have program contact only monthly or less often, with little structure in schedule, and other outpatient programs may be similar to what we described for the partial hospital setting. When such programs are not in the hospital, they typically are called day (or evening) treatment programs.

It is somewhat artificial to assign the settings for treatment of alcohol (and, for that matter, drug) abuse to discrete categories because a treatment episode for many people involves participation in more than one treatment setting. A common course of treatment includes detoxification from alcohol and later referral to an inpatient or outpatient treatment program. Or, individuals may begin treatment by completing an inpatient intensive rehabilitation program and then engage in outpatient treatment as part of an **aftercare** plan. Other combinations are possible, each suited to individual needs. At the end of this chapter, we discuss how trends in health insurance coverage have led to a major shift to the outpatient setting for treatment of alcohol-use disorders, in contrast to earlier emphasis on inpatient treatment.

aftercare
In alcohol and drug treatment, therapeutic activities following the completion of a formal treatment program.

Categories of treatment settings and services can give only an outline of the actual treatment activities that occur in alcohol programs. It is difficult to characterize alcohol programs except in the broadest terms. What is called individual or group counselling or psychotherapy may refer to many specific activities. The activities can occur in any of the treatment settings described, with some settings having greater latitude than others. For example, the smallest range of treatment activities take place in settings devoted primarily to detoxification. In contrast, outpatient or inpatient treatment programs can include many different activities that are called treatment, including medical care to a limited degree and pharmacotherapy.

Pharmacological Treatment

Although our discussion of alcohol treatment has emphasized nonmedical interventions, drugs frequently are used in the treatment of alcohol problems. This practice is known as ***pharmacotherapy***. In discussing pharmacotherapy, we distinguish between detoxification and postdetoxification treatment. Detoxification of people who are physically dependent on alcohol often involves the use of drugs in the medical management of withdrawal, although there are drug-free approaches to detoxification. These latter approaches, "social detoxification," occur when a person's withdrawal is monitored by professional staff in a treatment setting, but no drugs are administered, if at all possible. There is little controversy about using drugs in managing acute withdrawal (Mayo-Smith, 1997); however, there are some disagreements over the use of chemicals in treatment activities subsequent to detoxification.

The first type of pharmacotherapy for alcohol problems uses compounds that alter the metabolism of alcohol if it is consumed. Peachey and Annis (1985) reviewed these compounds, which they called the alcohol-sensitizing drugs. In Canada and the U.S., individuals seeking treatment for alcohol dependence may be given disulfiram (Anitbuse), carbimide (Temposil), or naltrexone. The chemical action of alcohol-sensitizing drugs results in an increase of acetaldehyde in the blood level after alcohol consumption. The consequence of the increased acetaldehyde depends on how much alcohol is drunk. For people on therapeutic doses of disulfiram or carbimide, one or two drinks will produce flushing, tachycardia (excessively rapid heartbeat, usually a pulse rate of over 100 per minute), tachypnea (excessively rapid respiration), sensations of warmth, heart palpitations, and shortness of breath. These effects usually last about 30 minutes and are not life-threatening. If larger quantities of alcohol are consumed, however, the reaction may include intense palpitations, dyspnea (difficult or laboured breathing), nausea, vomiting, and headache, all of which may last more than 90 minutes. In some people, this more severe reaction has induced shock, loss of consciousness, or death due to myocardial infarction (Peachey & Annis, 1985, p. 202).

The unpleasant effects of drinking while on a regimen of the alcohol-sensitizing drugs are the reason such drugs are used in treatment. The assumption is that fear of experiencing the unpleasant effects will deter people from drinking and will build a learned aversion to alcohol. If a person on disulfiram or carbimide tests out the effects of drinking, the same learned aversion will proceed more rapidly because of the addition of experiencing direct, as well as imagined, negative consequences. The learned aversion to alcohol underlies eventual avoidance of it. When alcohol-sensitizing drugs are used, they are applied as part of a rehabilitative program that is concerned with the physical, psychological, and social problems that tend to accompany abusive drinking patterns.

A second type of pharmacotherapy for alcohol problems is based in biological theories of etiology, which focus on abnormalities or changes in brain chemistry as causes or consequences of substance abuse. Such theories imply that a correction of the abnormal brain chemistry is essential to alleviating the substance-use problem. From a broader perspective, including a biological component to treatment is entirely compatible to the biopsychosocial approach to drug use and its modification that this text takes. Pharmacological agents also may be applied as part of programs that are not derived from any particular model of alcohol dependence, simply if it is believed that such agents are effective (Brewer, 1996).

In recent years, the major advances that have been made in understanding the biological bases of addiction have resulted in the development and evaluation of pharmacotherapies for alcohol-use disorders. Table 14.3 shows some of the drugs that are used in Canada and the U.S. for the treatment of alcohol-use disorders. You can see that the pharmacological agents have diverse biological actions, and some of the drugs are thought to act on the brain in different ways. In addition, drugs currently showing promise in clinical trials for treatment of alcohol-use disorder include topiramate, baclofen, ondansetron, olanzepine, and quetiapine (Swift & Leggio, 2009).

TABLE 14.3 Common Drugs Used to Treat Alcohol Dependence

Pharmacotherapy	Hypothesized Action
Naltrexone	Works as an opiate antagonist
Acamprosate	Indirect partial agonist of the NMDA receptor and antagonist of metabotropic glutamate receptors
Disulfiram (Antabuse)	Interferes with the metabolism of alcohol

Source: Based on Koob, Lloyd, and Mason (2009); Lingford-Hughes, Welch, and Nutt (2004), NIAAA (2000); Swift and Leggio (2009).

Effectiveness of Alcohol Treatment

After reading about a variety of settings and methods that fall into the category of alcohol treatment, you probably are wondering whether any of the effort is worth it; that is, you probably are wondering about the effectiveness of alcohol treatment. When we talk about treatment effectiveness, we refer to the relationship between participating in some treatment and achieving some treatment goal. Therefore, treatment effectiveness concerns whether and how treatment participation causes different outcomes. Evaluations of the effectiveness of treatment are called **treatment outcome research.**

treatment outcome research
Research designed to show a causal relationship between undergoing a treatment and some physical, psychological, or social change.

In this section, we do not cover detoxification services because they are not considered rehabilitation. Rather, they should be viewed as effective in managing safe alcohol withdrawal but not in providing rehabilitation beyond that. When we discuss the effectiveness of treatment aimed at rehabilitation, we must take into account the rate of spontaneous remission of alcohol problems. As you might guess, to show that a treatment is worth its cost requires a demonstration that it helps significantly beyond the rate of spontaneous remission. This reasoning is sound, but it is extremely difficult to determine the rates of spontaneous remission. People who resolve their problems without treatment are the ones with whom clinicians and researchers are least likely to have contact. Professionals instead tend to see people who are referred to a formal treatment setting. We noted earlier in this chapter that making a credible effort to determine the prevalence of spontaneous remission of alcohol problems would be complex and costly.

Despite this problem, estimates of spontaneous remission have been made for alcohol-use disorders, mostly through studies of people who entered a formal treatment program but dropped out of it prematurely and could say they received "no treatment." Another method to estimate spontaneous remission involves rates of improvement in "no treatment" or similar control groups in treatment outcome studies. The estimates of spontaneous remission of alcohol problems that have been made vary with the definition of remission, the comparison groups used, and the length of the interval during which functioning is measured. Miller and Hester (1980) suggested that the spontaneous remission (abstinence or improvement in drinking patterns) in one year for individuals not treated for their alcohol problems is 19 percent, and Emrick (1975) calculated 13 percent for abstinence and 28 percent for abstinence plus "improved." "Improved" in this case means drinking is not as severe in amount or frequency compared to before treatment, but the person is not always abstinent.

Nonpharmacological Professional Treatment

As you can tell from this discussion about spontaneous remission and treatment outcome, the main criterion considered is drinking behaviour, even though earlier you saw that other criteria could be used. Questions about the effectiveness of nonpharmacological professional treatment have been studied for many years. We can offer some general conclusions about the effectiveness of nonpharmacological treatments. First, a longstanding finding is that no single alcohol treatment type or setting is consistently better than others, but staying in any kind of treatment increases the chances of long-term improvement, even with rates of spontaneous remission taken into account (McKay, Murphy, & Longabaugh, 1991; NIAAA, 1993).

Studies have shown that the amount of money saved in, say, health care and business expenses as a result of improvements in people undergoing treatment is greater than the amount of money the treatment costs.

Some may find little positive in this overall conclusion about the effectiveness of alcohol treatment, but these findings should not be taken lightly. For example, studies have shown that the amount of money saved in, say, health care and business expenses as a result of improvements in people undergoing treatment is greater than the amount of money the treatment costs. Similarly, research that insurance companies completed suggests that substance abusers (and their families) use significantly fewer health care services after treatment than before. This shows the benefits of alcohol treatment in financial terms; the more important, but more difficult to measure, gains in human welfare are considerable.

The downside of our conclusion about alcohol treatment effectiveness is that it does not leave us with much of a guideline about placing a person in a specific treatment based on our assessment and the person's goals for change. Alcohol treatment research has advanced to emphasize patient–treatment matching, however, and this seems to be a productive direction for the field. Although our knowledge about matching is still not too sophisticated, there is some research on matching patients to some treatment settings and services. For example, inpatient or residential treatment settings may be best reserved for individuals whose alcohol problems are more severe, or who have other drug problems, or who have less social stability (for example, are not employed, not married, not living in a permanent residence), or who have psychiatric disorders. For other individuals, outpatient treatment likely will do just as well as inpatient and at far less cost. Another example is that psychotherapy works best if patients' conceptual level (defined by preference for rules, dependence on authority, and abstractness of thinking) is matched to their therapist's (McKay, Murphy, & Longabaugh, 1991). Finally, a major study of patient–treatment matching suggests that the severity of patients' psychiatric problems should be taken into account in assigning individuals to treatments implemented in the outpatient setting (Project MATCH Research Group, 1997).

It seems that the accumulation of findings such as these would take alcohol treatment to a level of more efficient service delivery. McCrady and Langenbucher (1996) substantiated this conclusion and reaffirmed in a later review of the American Psychiatric Association's practice guidelines for the treatment of substance-use disorders (McCrady & Ziedonis, 2001; McGovern & Carroll, 2003). McCrady and Langenbucher (1996) identified several specific nonpharmacological treatments for alcohol-use disorder that have been shown to be effective in well-done evaluations. The treatments that McCrady and Langenbucher identified are listed and briefly described in Table 14.4. You can see that most of the treatments listed in the table are based broadly on social learning principles. Motivational enhancement therapy also uses principles of social learning theory (also called social cognitive theory) but combines them with psychotherapy methods designed to help clients arrive at their own conclusions about the need to change rather than the therapist imposing change on clients. These promising treatment techniques and approaches would seem to be the best candidates for outcome research on patient–treatment matching.

Self-Help Treatment

What we have said so far about treatment effectiveness was pertinent to professional services. Because of its importance, self-help group treatment also should be evaluated. Almost all of the research on this question concerns AA, and we focus on that organization.

The question of how effective AA is can be difficult to answer. One reason for the difficulty is the AA emphasis on the anonymity of its members. The principle of anonymity is a major part of the "Twelve Traditions" of AA, which are a set of principles or guidelines adopted in 1950 for the operations of AA (Leach & Norris, 1977). The twelfth tradition, anonymity, "is the spiritual foundation of our traditions, ever reminding us to place principles before personalities." This tradition is strictly adhered to in AA groups and makes outcome research very difficult because it often requires identification of those receiving treatment.

Nevertheless, some research has been done. In their review of research related to AA's effectiveness, Emrick (1989) and Emrick et al. (1993) concluded:

> (a) it is not possible to predict who will affiliate with AA, except that it seems that people who have more severe alcohol problems are more likely to join;
>
> (b) among people who do join AA, it is not clear who will do well and who will not;
>
> (c) people who go to AA before, during, or after receiving other forms of treatment do as well as if not better than people who do not volunteer to go to AA;
>
> (d) AA participation is associated with relatively high abstinence rates but with average overall improvement in drinking rates;
>
> (e) people who achieve abstinence seem to participate in AA more than those who moderate their drinking or who continue to drink at a problem level. (Emrick, 1989, pp. 48–49)

People's success in AA may be related to processes such as ways to cope with stress, beliefs that one can cope effectively in different situations without alcohol, and commitment to abstinence from alcohol (Morgenstern et al., 1997).

TABLE 14.4 Effective Nonmedical Treatments for Alcohol-Use Disorders

Treatment	Brief Description
Motivational enhancement	Use of verbal psychotherapy, including feedback about the connection between alcohol use and negative consequences, to encourage individuals to "move forward" in the stages of changing their alcohol use patterns
Classical conditioning-based treatments	Application of principles of classical conditioning (see Chapter 5) either (1) to condition a negative reaction to alcohol cues such as sight, taste, or smell, or (2) to extinguish or eliminate urges to use alcohol in the presence of cues related to it
Conjoint treatments	Involvement of significant others (e.g., spouse or other family members) in a therapy approach that follows social learning principles (see Table 14.2)
Social learning-based treatments	Application of social learning principles to reduce or eliminate alcohol consumption; specific treatments include relapse prevention (discussed later in this chapter), community reinforcement, and social skills training (SST)—teaching individuals to use nonalcohol ways of coping with interpersonal situations

Source: Based on McCrady and Langenbucher (1996).

CONTEMPORARY ISSUE BOX 14.2

Brief Interventions for Alcohol Problems

Traditional ideas about alcohol treatment have been challenged by increased awareness and discussion of "brief" interventions for alcohol problems. What is called brief is relative to traditional alcohol treatment. Brief interventions average one to three sessions, and each session lasts up to 45 minutes, but much less time is often spent in a session. Traditional alcohol treatment has far more sessions that usually last about an hour. Brief interventions have been applied in several different settings, including college and university campuses, but perhaps the most important is the general medical care setting. Patients in that setting tend to have higher rates than the general population of unidentified alcohol problems of varying degrees of severity because of the correlation between heavy alcohol use and physical problems. Accordingly, if some type of intervention could be done in these settings to thwart the development of more severe alcohol problems, then there is the potential to save society billions of dollars. Fleming et al.'s (1997) study, showing that a physician-delivered brief intervention for alcohol problems detected in primary medical care settings can be effective, attracted a lot of attention among health care professionals. Since then, other studies also have shown that brief interventions are effective for treating alcohol problems (NIAAA, 1999, 2005). Furthermore, the success of brief interventions in treating alcohol problems has led more recently to evaluations of their effectiveness in treating people who have problems with other drugs, such as marijuana and amphetamines (Baker, Boggs, & Lewin, 2001; Stephens, Roffman, & Curtin, 2000).

Brief interventions can be as simple as feedback about the consequences of heavy alcohol use for a person (for example, "You have some liver problems, and we can trace it to your drinking") or advice to cut down or stop drinking. They are based on the idea that alcohol problems exist on a continuum of severity and that interventions can occur at any point along that continuum. The research has shown that, for the most part, brief interventions have been used with people who have mild to moderate alcohol problems; they are effective compared to no treatment in reducing alcohol consumption to below "risk" levels. There is some speculation about who is most helped by brief interventions and why they work. These clearly are topics for future research.

The findings about brief interventions have great practical implications for alcohol treatment providers and for saving society a lot of money and suffering. They also have implications for theories of the causes of alcohol problems. For example, what do you think disease or biological model adherents might say about brief interventions?

Emrick's (1989) review, confirmed by subsequent research (Humphreys et al., 2004), concludes that AA seems to help some but not all people. So, making blanket referrals to AA as part of a treatment plan, which is common, is not warranted. With the growth of groups such as SMART and SOS, other self-help options are available. Of course, currently we do not have clear evidence about the effectiveness of participation in these alternative groups, but studies are in progress. It is essential that matching research be aimed at discovering which individuals fit best with which self-help group participation.

As difficult as it is, well-controlled treatment outcome research on self-help groups is important. Emrick (1989) cited a few such studies on AA, but they involved individuals who were mandated by the legal system to attend treatment. This is not the best patient population for evaluation of a treatment's effectiveness because of its dubious commitment to change. Furthermore, future outcome studies of AA should include enough AA participants to make it likely that researchers will be able to detect any beneficial effects that AA might have (Tonigan, Toscova, & Miller, 1995). Controlled treatment outcome studies on self-help groups would go a long way toward helping clinicians to use such groups in ways that are best for their patients.

Effectiveness of Pharmacological Treatments

With the exception of disulfiram, pharmacotherapies for alcohol-use disorders have been developed only in recent years, and therefore we have relatively little outcome data on them. Furthermore, it is believed that all pharmacotherapies should be accompanied by psychological and social treatments if they are to have longer-term effectiveness (O'Brien, 1996). The first pharmacotherapy to consider is disulfiram. When disulfiram became available, it was thought to be the long-sought answer to alcohol treatment. Unfortunately, the results of more than 50 years of research show that disulfiram has fallen far short of this mark. One problem in interpreting the research on disulfiram is that it has not been done well. The clinical trials on disulfiram that have been well controlled show modest effects on number of drinking days, but they also have yielded inconsistent findings (Garbutt et al., 1999).

One factor to keep in mind when evaluating disulfiram is that its effects may be enhanced considerably if its use is combined with a behavioural program that in part consists of supervised administration of the disulfiram (e.g., by the patient's spouse) to the patient (Hughes & Cook, 1997). This apparently addresses a major practical problem with using disulfiram clinically: It typically requires daily administration of the prescribed dose, and patients tend to show poor compliance with such a regimen. Disulfiram implants have been tried as another way to solve the compliance problem, but their effectiveness has not been shown clearly, and the bioavailability of the implanted disulfiram has not been demonstrated in clinical trials. Additional well-controlled studies of supervised disulfiram therapy would allow us to specify the conditions under which its administration is most likely to enhance outcomes.

The approval of naltrexone was based largely on the results of two relatively small-scale clinical studies showing that naltrexone helped to reduce the craving for alcohol and the severity of any relapses to alcohol use that occurred after a period of abstinence (O'Malley et al., 1992; Volpicelli et al., 1992). As a result, the evaluation of naltrexone in the treatment of alcohol-use disorders has been an active research topic since the mid-1990s.

Kranzler and Van Kirk (2001) reviewed controlled clinical trials of naltrexone that have been conducted and compared its effects to placebo on outcomes such as percentage of days drinking alcohol and percentage of patients who "relapsed" (we discuss relapse later in this chapter). Their review showed only modest effects of naltrexone as well as inconsistency among the studies in their findings on naltrexone's effectiveness. Therefore, the promise that naltrexone showed in earlier research has been reduced somewhat by the results of later studies. On the other hand, we have learned more about what factors enhance naltrexone's effectiveness. For example, patients who report a greater degree of craving for alcohol and who have a family history of alcoholism tend to do better with naltrexone treatment (Swift & Leggio, 2009).

Kranzler and Van Kirk's (2001) review, as well as later reviews (Swift & Leggio, 2009), reveal modest results for acamprosate. As we noted earlier, this medication has received both Health Canada and the FDA approval for use and it is used and studied widely in the rest of the world. The studies of acamprosate to date show, like naltrexone, modest effectiveness overall and inconsistency in findings from different studies. Interestingly, acamprosate has shown to be most effective in clinical trials conducted in Europe, but has shown far more modest effects in trials conducted in the United States. The reason(s) for this discrepancy are yet to be specified.

All trials testing the efficacy or effectiveness of naltrexone and acamprosate have involved their use in conjunction with some type of behavioural counselling or therapy.

The question of which medication is the more effective when used with some kind of nondrug therapy—acamprosate or naltrexone—may have occurred to you. A recent study that was conducted in 11 academic treatment settings in the United States and included almost 1400 adult patients diagnosed with alcohol dependence was designed to address just this question (Anton et al., 2006). The findings were complex, and we will just briefly describe those relevant to the general question of which drug therapy was the more efficacious when used in combination with either or both of two types of behavioural treatment ("medical management" and cognitive-behaviour therapy). In this regard, patients taking naltrexone who had either medical management alone or medical management and cognitive-behaviour therapy had outcomes that were superior to patients who received medical management only and placebo. On the other hand, patients receiving acamprosate with any combination of behavioural treatments did no better than patients receiving the same behavioural treatments and placebo. It also is notable that patients who received cognitive-behaviour therapy and medical management and placebo (a nondrug treatment) did as well as the groups taking naltrexone with medical management only or with medical management and cognitive-behaviour therapy.

It also is notable that patients who received cognitive-behaviour therapy and medical management and placebo (a nondrug treatment) did as well as the groups taking naltrexone with medical management only or with medical management and cognitive-behaviour therapy.

In summary, the research on pharmacotherapy for alcohol-use disorders is still considered to be in its early stages. We already have increased our knowledge on this topic considerably, however, and have learned that the questions are complex. Future research needs not only to identify promising medications but also to determine more precisely how they work and what characterizes individuals who benefit most from different medications (notice the similarity of this conclusion to the concept of matching patients to treatment). In addition, because alcohol affects multiple neurotransmitters, simultaneous use of more than one medication may be needed to help some people. Research on this possibility is just beginning.

Other Drug Treatment Settings and Services

There is a wide array of treatment services available for those who abuse drugs. Allison and Hubbard (1985) noted:

> Treatment programs may involve outpatient, residential, or day treatment and may take place in a hospital, clinic, mental health center, prison, or group home environment. Treatment may be drug-free or use chemical aids. Counselling, job training, physical health care, and a variety of other services may or may not be part of the treatment program. The staff may be highly trained professionals or the program may be of the self-help type. (p. 1322)

The traditional classification of drug-abuse treatments includes detoxification, methadone maintenance, residential, and outpatient. Our discussion of other drug treatment will make clear that this classification combines treatment setting with treatment services. Like alcohol treatment, the primary goal of detoxification is a medically managed withdrawal from physical dependence on drugs. Managing detoxification often involves the use of medications but could be drug-free. As with alcohol withdrawal treatment, detoxification services may include some counselling directed in part at guiding the patient to additional treatment services.

A major modality of drug treatment is the therapeutic community (TC). Drug TCs are run mostly by ex-addicts, who work as peer counsellors and administrators. In recent years, however, TC staff members have included more health professionals (DeLeon, 1995). There is heavy reliance on self-help groups. The TC is a highly structured program, especially at the beginning of treatment, and clients gain more responsibilities and independence as they progress through the program by meeting certain requirements. In TCs, the emphasis is on group counselling and therapy, which often are confrontational.

The essential agent of social and psychological change in TCs is purported to be the community itself (ibid.). Earlier in this chapter, we referred to this idea as milieu treatment. One well-known example of a drug TC is the Stonehenge Therapeutic Community, established in 1971 in Guelph, Ontario. Stonehenge provides long-term, intensive treatment programs lasting four to six months for people whose lives have been destroyed by alcohol and drug dependence. Their principles of treatment state that*:

- Treatment should be modified to match the needs of clients, not the reverse.
- Individual needs are different and client treatment plans must recognize this.
- Every effort must be made to build self-esteem and incorporate opportunities for success throughout treatment.
- Clients must be partners in their treatment and include shared decision making with the entire community.
- Support continues when formal treatment ends, through Aftercare.
- Treatment must be constantly evaluated and improved upon.

The final drug-abuse treatment modality is outpatient. Almost half of the drug abusers in treatment receive their treatment in this setting (Center for Substance Abuse Treatment, 1997). The outpatient setting may or may not have a policy prohibiting pharmacotherapies. Outpatient drug treatment is the most varied of the treatment types and includes a wide range of programs and services. Typically, an outpatient program offers counselling once or twice a week with each session lasting one to three hours, and treatment can be provided on a one-on-one or group basis. In Canada, government outpatient programs usually have a minimal fee or no fee at all (Alcohol Drug Rehab Canada, 2011). Outpatient programs usually fall into one of the following categories:

- Drop-in—no appointment necessary
- Dual diagnosis—when also suffering from a mental illness
- Faith-based
- Group
- Individual
- Intensive outpatient—treatment offered several hours per day, several days (or nights) per week for several weeks
- Outreach

Treatment of Nonopiate Drug Abusers

In general, the classification of drug-abuse treatment refers to services that have been available for the treatment of heroin abuse. In this regard, the great expansion in drug-abuse treatment services over the last 40 years was largely due to public alarm over increasingly widespread use and abuse of heroin, with its highly visible and well-publicized negative social effects. For example, a sharp increase in violent crime in some urban areas, such as the later (late 1980s) experience with crack use, was attributed to heroin use. In recent years, however, there has been an increase in the number of individuals appearing for drug-abuse treatment who primarily abuse drugs other than alcohol or the opiates. For example, in 1977, 33.4 percent of the clients admitted to drug-abuse treatment programs were nonopiate abusers, and this proportion had increased to 54.9 percent by 1980 (USDHHS, 1984). This trend continued

* Courtesy of Stonehenge Therapeutic Community, 2011.

throughout the 1980s, with a high number of people presenting themselves for treatment of cocaine dependence.

Like abusers of heroin and alcohol, nonopiate abusers may appear in treatment settings other than those designed specifically to treat the substance-use disorders. These include hospital emergency rooms, physicians' offices, and general psychiatric treatment settings. They currently also appear in settings traditionally created for those who abuse heroin, such as the therapeutic community (Center for Substance Abuse Treatment, 1997). In general, little is known about any unique problems and characteristics of those who abuse nonopiate drugs that might be important for their treatment, although there has been some discussion of this question (Washton, 1990; also see Schuckit's [1994] discussion of the treatment of stimulant dependence).

Pharmacotherapy of Other Drug Problems

Lingford-Hughes, Welch, and Nutt (2004), Litten and Allen (1999), McLellan et al. (2000), and Swift and Leggio (2009) summarized the major pharmacotherapies available for the treatment of drug-use disorders other than alcohol. Table 14.5 presents a list of the pharmacotherapies that have Health Canada and FDA approval for the treatment of opioid dependence.

Methadone maintenance is the pharmacotherapy for drug-use disorders other than alcohol that has received the most attention—probably more than any other drug treatment, for that matter—from researchers and the popular press. The attention centres on the conflict in treating dependence on a chemical substance (heroin, an opiate) with an opiate agonist (methadone). Proponents of this approach say that if heroin addicts' desire for heroin is prevented by methadone, then they will be more likely to break out of the destructive lifestyle associated with drug addiction and engage in rehabilitation leading to a socially acceptable and productive way of living. The major opposition to methadone treatment is that it perpetuates individuals' dependence on an opiate drug. Interestingly, evidence against this fear has come recently from a study conducted with heroin addicts in Canada who failed in methadone treatment, but who were successful in treating their addiction if they were treated with heroin, in prescription form (Oviedo-Joekes et al., 2009). Although this approach to treating people with severe heroin addiction has been used in Europe for years, it had not been tried in North America because of the great resistance to using heroin to treat heroin addiction.

Methadone maintenance treatment typically involves administration of a daily, prescribed dose of methadone to block addicts' cravings for heroin. Usually, methadone maintenance programs are outpatient so that individuals may pursue activities that build a socially productive life. Furthermore, many programs (and provincial, state, or federal regulations) require patients to receive some kind of counselling while enrolled in methadone maintenance, and patients are required to adhere to a formal set of rules for continued participation in methadone treatment.

TABLE 14.5 Pharmacotherapies for Opioid Dependence

Methadone	Long-acting opioid
Levo-alpha-acetylmethadol (LAAM)	Opiate agonist or partial agonist
Buprenorphine	Partial agonist at different opioid receptors
Naltrexone (naloxone)	Opiate antagonist

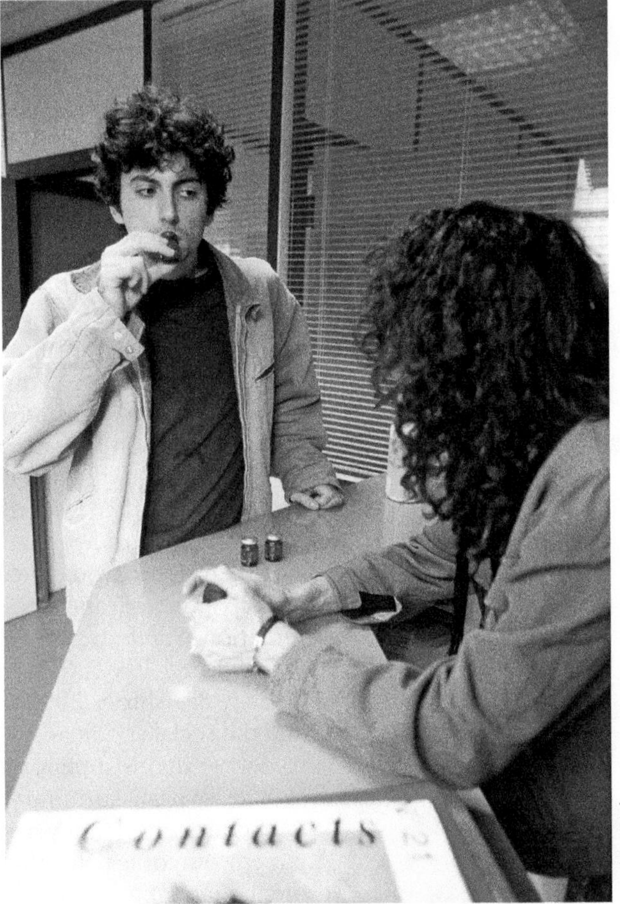

Garo/First Light

Methadone maintenance remains a controversial treatment for opiate dependence.

As you might have guessed, one problem with the use of methadone is its potential for abuse; that is, addicts may use their methadone in nonprescribed ways just as they used heroin. Methadone programs have tried to handle this problem by requiring patients to swallow the methadone dose on the program premises while observed by the medical staff. In fact, one measure of progress in this program is whether the individuals come to the clinic less often than daily to get the methadone dose. As progress is made, people may earn the privilege of taking two to several days' worth of methadone home at a time.

Another way to handle the problem of compliance is to administer **levo-alpha-acetylmethadol (LAAM)**, which is similar in pharmacological action to methadone but has longer-lasting effects. The advantage of a longer-lasting methadone substitute is that patients are more likely to comply with the regimen for taking the drug.

Methadone maintenance involves replacing one opiate, say, heroin, with another, methadone. Another pharmacotherapy for heroin use involves blockade of opiate receptors by the use of naltrexone, which we discussed in the section on alcohol treatment. Naltrexone or its shorter-acting analogue drug, naloxone, is used most commonly with patients who have been maintained for long periods on methadone and then choose to become drug-free. The naltrexone may help these patients bridge the gap between methadone maintenance and a drug-free life. Naltrexone works, theoretically, because the abused opiate cannot achieve its effect in the brain (also see the discussion earlier in this chapter on the use of naltrexone in the treatment of alcohol dependence). The result is that the individual loses a major reason for using the opiate—its psychoactive effects. Along these same lines, buprenorphine, a mixed opiate agonist–antagonist, blocks the effects of heroin and has FDA approval for use in treatment of opiate drug dependence.

levo-alpha-acetylmethadol (LAAM) A drug used in treating heroin addiction that is similar in action to methadone but has longer-lasting effects.

More recently Health Canada approved the use of Suboxone, a drug that is a combination of buprenorphine and naloxone, for the treatment of opiate dependence. Suboxone is a tablet that is dissolved under the tongue that suppresses the symptoms of opioid withdrawal and reduces the cravings for opioid drugs. The use of naloxone creates unpleasant withdrawal symptoms if the product is misused.

Effectiveness of Drug Treatment

The history of research on the effectiveness of drug treatment is not nearly as long as that for alcohol, but a number of good studies has appeared in the last few decades. Our summary of what is known about drug treatment effectiveness, like that of alcohol treatment, excludes detoxification.

The literature on drug treatment effectiveness has profited from the completion of several large, multisite (i.e., different programs), multimodal (i.e., different settings, like outpatient and methadone maintenance) studies (Ball, Meyers, & Friedman, 1988; DeLeon, 1984; Hubbard et al., 1989) and reviews of treatment research (Institute of

Medicine, 1990b). Findings from the most recent large-scale, multisite drug treatment evaluation, called the Drug Abuse Treatment Outcome Study (DATOS) (Fletcher, Tims, & Brown, 1997), provided data that were largely consistent with the results of earlier research. Compared to the literature on alcohol, less attention is given in the drug treatment evaluation literature to individual treatment techniques or services. Instead, research tends to focus on the treatment settings, as we have organized them in this chapter.

Nonpharmacological Professional Treatment

Table 14.6 presents major conclusions about the effectiveness of therapeutic community and outpatient drug treatment. Note that conclusions about treatment are based on drug use as well as on correlated events such as social productivity and criminal behaviour. The research on drug treatment reflects society's interest not only in whether a person has stopped illicit drug use but also in whether social disruption and disorder have stopped. Table 14.6 shows that, overall, two of the three major drug settings (the other is methadone maintenance) seem to be associated with improved functioning, if the person stays in treatment. Unfortunately, dropping out of drug treatment is a chronic problem that is difficult to solve. One of methadone maintenance's great advantages in this regard is that it is correlated with better treatment retention. Similarly, even though more good research is needed on this topic (French & McGeary, 1997), it seems that if people stay in drug treatment, it is cost-effective (Franey & Ashton, 2002). That is, society gets more back from the reduced drug use and the social and financial productivity that are associated with treatment than it pays to deliver the treatment services.

The overall summary of nonpharmacological drug treatment effectiveness is encouraging, but we should add there is considerable individual variation in patient outcomes. The big gap in this treatment literature pertains to patient–treatment matching research. Although several excellent studies done some time ago have matched patients to drug treatments (e.g., McLellan et al., 1983), more studies guided by the matching question would advance drug treatment (Franey & Ashton, 2002).

TABLE 14.6 Effectiveness of Therapeutic Community and Outpatient Drug Treatment

Setting	Conclusions
Therapeutic community	Drug use and criminal behaviour end while in residence; associated with a more productive life following discharge if length of stay in residence was sufficient (at least several months)
	High treatment attrition rates
	Treatment is cost-effective
Outpatient treatment	Associated with improved functioning compared to no treatment or detoxification only
	Benefits of treatment greater with longer involvement in treatment
	Treatment is cost-effective for people who stay in treatment longer than six months

Source: Adapted from Institute of Medicine. *Treating drug problems (Vol. 1)*. Washington, DC: National Academy Press.

Self-Help Treatment

We can say very little on this topic because, as we noted earlier, virtually all the research on self-help groups has concerned AA. We know essentially nothing about the effectiveness of drug self-help groups like Narcotics Anonymous or Cocaine Anonymous, because the research simply has not been done. Like AA, however, drug self-help groups are popular, and their effectiveness is an important research question. Also similar to alcohol treatment, involvement in self-help groups following an episode of drug treatment is associated with improved outcomes (Fiorentine, 1997).

Pharmacological Treatments

The review of the literature through the 1980s on methadone's effectiveness showed positive findings. First, methadone treatment is associated with reduced drug use and criminal behaviour compared to no treatment, detoxification alone, or methadone treatment terminators. Second, methadone, as we noted earlier, is effective in bringing reluctant addicts into treatment and keeping them there. Third, methadone is a cost-effective treatment of opioid dependence. These conclusions, which are based on clinical research done over almost three decades, have been supported and extended

DRUGS AND CULTURE BOX 14.3

"Special Populations" and Alcohol and Drug Treatment

As discussed earlier in this chapter, there is no single treatment method that will work for everyone. One possible reason for this may be that individuals differ in biological or, more prominently, social and cultural factors. These differences may make some treatments more practical and successful for certain subgroups, while making other treatments inappropriate or even dangerous. In Canada, we can focus on three special populations (or subgroups of the population) that face specific challenges when it comes to drug rehabilitation: adolescents, women, and Aboriginal Canadians.

Drug use among Canadian youth is a significant problem. However, the vast majority of treatments, especially medications, are based on research and clinical experiences with adults. The lack of focus on adequate treatment methods for adolescents is at best a hindrance to their successful recovery but at worse potentially life-threatening. For example, studies show that, for adolescents, assessment of social factors in substance use, such as patterns of use and attitudes about use that peers have, is critical. Similarly, social skills training to resist peer pressure to use substances may be an emphasis in treatment. Further, most drug trials use adult participants, which may result in inappropriate medications and/or dosages for teens. In addition, the stigma associated with drug dependence may prevent some adolescents from seeking treatment in the first place. What stereotype comes to mind when you think of adolescent drug use? How do you think this stereotype might hinder successful recovery?

For women, the challenges of drug treatment may include issues such as lack of childcare options, social stigma, and the fear of losing their children. In women, substance-use problems tend to develop faster than they do in men and tend to be more strongly related to psychological and familial variables. Failure to use this information precludes sensitive diagnosis and effective treatment. Can you think of any other challenges that Canadian women face when seeking drug treatment?

Canada's Aboriginal community faces a multitude of unique challenges when seeking drug treatment. These challenges include living in remote or rural areas that do not have the needed resources, psychological and family variables, and the lack of culturally appropriate treatment programs. How can we address the challenges that face Aboriginal Canadians when they seek drug treatment?

In order to fully address the challenges that face these special populations we must examine the unique factors that led to their drug use in the first place, the challenges that they face when seeking treatment, and the unique program focus and structure needed to help them succeed. Without sensitivity to these group differences, assessment and treatment will continue to be inadequate.

CONTEMPORARY ISSUE BOX 14.4

Treatment Research and Clinical Practice

Through the first half of the 20th century, treatment of the substance-use disorders was not informed by scientific research designed to identify the most effective treatment methods. Simply put, up to the 1960s, there were few treatment research studies in the substance-use disorders area that met high standards of scientific rigor so that we could have confidence in the validity of their findings. As a result, consumers had to take on faith anyone's claims that a given treatment method worked. But the picture began to change in the 1970s, and today we are fortunate to have a considerable amount of high-quality treatment research on the substance-use disorders. This means that alcohol and drug treatment that most people receive today is "empirically supported" (based on research findings of what methods are "effective" or is "evidence-based"). Right?

Unfortunately, wrong. Although research findings have had some influence on what happens in the clinical practice of alcohol and drug treatment, it is not as much influence as one might hope for or even expect. That is because it has become apparent to many that it is one thing to have built an impressive foundation of knowledge, but it is another thing to consistently apply that knowledge to enhance the quality of care that patients receive. Therefore, knowledge *diffusion* (another commonly used term is *dissemination,* and in the treatment area, *translation*) poses its own set of formidable challenges.

In this regard, we have learned in recent years that barriers of different types must often be overcome if knowledge is to be applied consistently, that is, if empirically supported methods of assessment and treatment are to become the standard of care in a given setting. These barriers may exist on multiple levels and could include factors related to the provider of the services (the clinician), to the patient who is to be the recipient of the services, or to the system in which treatment is delivered. For example, if a new treatment method is found through clinical trials (to be effective, then clinicians must learn the new methods, become skilled in their use, and perhaps abandon familiar and comfortable ways of doing things. Or, patients may resist the new service or treatment method because it is different from what they have heard others claim works best. The system itself may resist going against long-held beliefs about treatment or simply may not provide the resources needed to support its clinicians in learning and mastering the delivery of a new treatment method.

The new awareness of the knowledge–practice gap in alcohol and drug treatment has resulted in studies that concern ways of overcoming the barriers to dissemination of treatment research. Can you think of some methods directed at clinicians, their patients, or the treatment system to shrink the knowledge–practice gap that could be tested?

in more recent studies (Leshner, 1999; McLellan et al., 2000; Vocci, Acri, & Elkashef, 2005). The other pharmacotherapies for opioid dependence listed in Table 14.5 also have fared well in clinical trials.

Promising Treatment Techniques

In fact, rarely is a medication prescribed without some sort of psychological or social therapy addition, although the latter treatments may be used without the adjunct of medication.

In one sense, designating treatments as pharmacological or nonpharmacological misrepresents clinical practice because, especially in recent years, treatment for illicit drug use often combines pharmacological and psychosocial therapies. In fact, rarely is a medication prescribed without some sort of psychological or social therapy addition, although the latter treatments may be used without the adjunct of medication. In this section, we discuss nonpharmacological treatment techniques or methods that have shown some promise in clinical trials with illicit drug-use disorders. In these trials, the techniques were often used as part of a broad rehabilitation program that included pharmacotherapy or were used explicitly to complement pharmacotherapy.

Perhaps the strongest evidence for using nonmedical interventions in the treatment of illicit drug-use disorders comes from studies of structured behavioural contracting programs. These programs follow a social learning model and use explicit contingencies of consequences for, typically, maintenance of sobriety. The most effective of these programs apply positive reinforcers for desired behaviour (for example, abstinence from drugs) rather than punishment for undesired behaviour. For example, Stitzer, Iguchi, and Felch (1992) found that the privilege of receiving take-home doses of methadone by submitting drug-free urines resulted in four times as many patients reducing their illicit drug use compared to the number of patients who reduced such use when no contingencies were attached to receiving take-home methadone.

Iguchi et al. (1997) extended the idea of contracting with such a contingency by showing that contingent reinforcement of completing treatment plan tasks developed by the counsellor and patient was more effective in reducing illicit drug use among opioid-dependent men and women enrolled in a methadone maintenance clinic than was contingent reinforcement of submitting clean urine. The contribution of this study is the idea that reinforcement of abstinence (indicated by clean urine) is essential for treatment progress, but gains are more likely to be maintained if the drug-dependent individual's psychosocial problems are addressed more broadly (indicated by goals and related tasks in the treatment plan). Reinforcement of achieving goals that are not compatible with drug use also tends to support abstinence from drugs. Carroll et al. (2002) showed the value of contingency contracting procedures as a complement to naltrexone treatment of individuals dependent on opioid drugs. Contingent abstinent programs implemented through the use of vouchers also have shown promise in treating individuals for their cocaine dependence (Katz, et al., 2002).

As we discussed earlier, the broadest application of contingent reinforcement principles is represented by the community reinforcement approach, which includes the patient's social and environmental network in the contingency program. The effectiveness of this program first was demonstrated in the treatment of alcohol-use disorders (Hunt & Azrin, 1973; Sisson & Azrin, 1989). Higgins and his colleagues (1991, 1993) showed that community reinforcement procedures also are effective in treating individuals who are dependent on cocaine. Moreover, this same research group showed that adding community reinforcement to a program of opioid detoxification by use of buprenorphine-enhanced abstinence from opioid drugs (Bickel, Amass, Higgins, Badger, & Esch, 1997).

Another technique that seems to be effective in treating users of illicit drugs is couples or family treatment (Stanton & Shadish, 1997). It is notable that the community reinforcement approach includes a family/couples (conjoint) component that is based in social learning principles (see Table 14.4).

In conclusion, structured programs that are based in social learning theory, as well as conjoint treatment, are nonmedical interventions that seem to enhance outcomes in the treatment of drug-use disorders. Our earlier discussion showed that treatment of alcohol-use disorders also is improved with these interventions. This seems to warrant their continued application and study in alcohol and drug treatment programs.

Special Topics in Alcohol and Drug Treatment

In this section, we discuss three topics that we think are important and that apply to both alcohol and drug treatment. The first is treatment of polysubstance abusers, or people who use more than one drug. We then briefly review the treatment of dual-diagnosis patients and especially how such treatment involves the use of psychotropic medication. The last topic is relapse (see Figure 14.1 on page 337), which has challenged alcohol and drug treatment providers for many years.

Treatment of Polysubstance Abusers

In the traditional and common way of viewing treatment, people who have an alcohol-use disorder do not have trouble with or abuse other drugs. Similarly, the traditional view gives the impression that people who have drug-use disorders have no patterns of abusive alcohol use. However, it has been known for some time that it may be a mistake to designate programs as either alcohol treatment or drug treatment.

Sokolow et al. (1981) surveyed multiple substance use among patients arriving for treatment at New York state-funded alcoholism rehabilitation programs. The total sample of 1340 men and women selected for this study represented wide ranges in age and educational background. Most (57.3 percent) of the patients were between 31 and 50 years old. In addition to their alcohol use, which was their reason for beginning treatment, patients were asked about their licit and illicit use in the past 30 days of minor and major tranquilizers, sedatives, amphetamines, antidepressants, opiates, hallucinogens, marijuana, and cocaine.

Almost half of the patients reported using at least one drug other than alcohol during the 30 days before their treatment began. About 20 percent of these patients used combinations of drugs. The single drug class reported most frequently was the tranquilizers (12.7 percent of the patients), which is notable because tranquilizers are cross-tolerant with alcohol and are the drugs most abused by those identified as alcoholics. We should also note that people identified as drug abusers often abuse alcohol, too, according to Carroll, Malloy, and Kenrick (1977). Today, it is widely recognized among treatment personnel that their patients may use multiple substances (Etheridge et al., 1997).

Studies of multiple substance use have important implications for treatment. As we have said, treatment programs have a strong tendency to focus on alcohol treatment or drug treatment, which have major differences in practice. Furthermore, some treatment providers object to treating substance abuse other than what had been identified as the patient's primary substance of abuse. Such reactions were found especially in alcohol programs, and they restrict treatment, given the prevalence of multiple substance use. In this respect, two points quickly emerge about treatment effects. First, if treatment programs concentrate on only alcohol use, for example, then the abuse of other drugs may result in poorer, shorter-lasting **treatment effects** than if the person's substance-use patterns were treated in a more unified way. Second, people seeking alcohol or drug treatment who are multiple substance abusers may have more severe social, legal, and psychiatric difficulties than those in treatment whose patterns of abuse are limited to single drug categories (Carroll et al., 1977). Beginning treatment with more severe problems predicts poorer functioning following treatment. So, failing to address patterns of multiple substance use because of program philosophy and policy could mean inadequate treatment planning.

treatment effects
The results of experiencing a treatment, usually measured in different areas of functioning, such as substance use, family functioning, and vocational functioning.

Beginning treatment with more severe problems predicts poorer functioning following treatment. So, failing to address patterns of multiple substance use because of program philosophy and policy could mean inadequate treatment planning.

Treatment of abusers of multiple substances relates to more general questions about treatment. One of these is the need to view substance use as part of a person's total pattern of behaviour to achieve an understanding of drug and alcohol use. Those who take this approach suggest that effective treatment can be planned only if connections are made among all of a person's different problems. Similarly, some clinicians and researchers believe addictive behaviour patterns have a lot in common in what causes them, what maintains them, and how they are treated. It is thought these commonalities should underlie treatment programming instead of the traditional emphasis on single addiction patterns. According to this viewpoint, behaviours identified as addictive, including, for example, alcohol and other drug abuse, overeating, and compulsive gambling, have common factors that may be addressed in "generic" treatment programs. The DSM-IV recognizes this approach in addressing the substance-use disorders as a diagnostic class rather than addressing alcohol and other drug diagnoses in a nonintegrated way. Nonetheless, it should be remembered that the properties of the various drugs of abuse vary, as might the characteristics of the users, and there is no guarantee that a program that works well for individuals with alcohol-use disorder would be successful with people whose primary drug problem is heroin.

Treatment of Dual-Diagnosis Patients

An important topic for alcohol and drug treatment providers is patients who have major psychiatric problems to go along with their substance-use problems. Such patients have been called dual-diagnosis patients. Dual-diagnosis patients, as you might imagine, typically have more complex and extensive treatment needs than do patients without major psychiatric problems, and dual-diagnosis patients tend to do more poorly in and following treatment.

Psychotropic medication may be part of the treatment of alcohol or drug abuse when a person has an alcohol or drug problem plus another psychiatric disorder. These psychiatric disorders include depression and manic depression, especially among individuals who have alcohol-use disorder. A relationship exists between alcohol- or drug-use disorders characterized by a high degree of anxiety and the **personality disorders**, particularly what is commonly called **sociopathy**. Psychotropic agents usually are used in the treatment of alcohol or drug problems on the premise that patients use alcohol and other drugs for **self-medication**. This means the individuals act as their own physician and self-prescribe alcohol and other drugs to lessen troubling psychological symptoms such as anxiety or depression. When used, psychotropic agents generally are administered in combination with nonmedical techniques in treating the substance-use disorder (Schuckit, 1996).

personality disorders
Longstanding patterns of behaviour that frequently create distress for individuals due to their personal or social consequences; usually recognizable from adolescence or earlier.

sociopathy
Personality disorder characterized by a lack of concern for social obligations or rules, a lack of feelings for others, and a tendency toward violence.

self-medication
The idea that some people prescribe their own medication, in the form of alcohol or illicit drugs, to alleviate psychological difficulties such as anxiety or depression.

Relapse

Any discussion of alcohol and drug treatment is incomplete without including relapse. Defining and measuring relapse are not as simple as you might think, but in concept, it means the reappearance of some problem after a period of its remission. With physical diseases such as cancer, which is where the term *relapse* comes from, its measurement is more straightforward.

You have seen that arriving at a definition of alcohol and drug problems that has general consensus is no easy matter, however. This difficulty carries through to defining relapse, as reflected by the different operational definitions that have been used in research on this topic.

In spite of these complexities in definition, relapse has been studied extensively in the addictions field for the last 30 years. Actually, alcohol and drug treatment providers have grappled with the problem of relapse for much longer than 30 years, and today, many people refer to alcohol and other drug abuse and dependence as "chronic relapsing conditions" (McLellan et al., 2000). The classic paper by Hunt, Barnett, and Branch (1971) illustrates this point. Their review of the literature at that time showed that about 70 percent of individuals treated for alcohol, tobacco, or heroin abuse in abstinence-oriented programs had returned to using their primary substance by the time they were out of treatment for three months. Today the problem is the same, and much treatment research is directed at discovering ways to help individuals maintain the changes they might make as a result of completing treatment.

The research on relapse and the substance-use disorders has generated several models and theories, summarized in Table 14.7. As you can see, the six models and theories make few distinctions among different drugs in the mechanisms of relapse.

TABLE 14.7 Major Models and Theories of Relapse

Model/Theory	Mechanism(s) of Relapse
Cognitive-behavioural model (Marlatt & Gordon, 1985; Marlatt & Witkiewitz, 2005)	Interaction between "high risk" (for substance use) and the individual's self-efficacy to cope with those situations without substance use determines relapse. Expectations about the utility of drugs and alcohol in a situation also are important.
Person–situation interaction model (Litman, 1986)	Relapse is determined by an interaction among three factors: situations that the individual perceives as threatening ("high risk"), availability of an adequate repertoire of coping strategies, and the individual's perception of the effectiveness of available coping strategies.
Self-efficacy and outcome expectancies (Annis, 1986; Rollnick & Heather, 1982)	Initial substance use occurs from the mislabelling of negative effect and negative physical states as craving. After the first substance use, expectations of control over such use decrease along with self-efficacy. This process leads to a more severe relapse.
Opponent process (Solomon, 1980)	Through conditioning, formerly neutral internal and external stimuli become connected with various "A" and "B" states. Reexposure or reexperiencing these states may increase the individual's motivation to use drugs following a period of abstinence.
Craving and loss of control (Ludwig & Wikler, 1974)	Internal and external stimuli associated with drug withdrawal are labelled as craving. Drugs are sought as a way to relieve craving.
Urges and cravings (Tiffany, 1990, 1992; Wise, 1988)	Drug use and drug urges and cravings have occurred often enough to be "automatic cognitive processes." In the abstinent substance abuser, these processes can be triggered by various internal and external stimuli. Relapse may occur if an adequate "action plan" not to use drugs, a nonautomatic cognitive process, is impeded or not used. Wise adds that use of one drug may trigger urges to use another as a result of action in the brain.

Source: Adapted in part from Connors, Maisto, and Donovan (1996).

Another point is the emphasis on relapse precipitants, or the events immediately preceding the relapse. Events more removed from the immediate relapse environment are given less attention. Examples of these are the social support a person has for nonproblem substance use, the period of time a person has been unemployed, and the level of tension among members of a family. Finally, the models and theories can be divided into two general categories: psychological and biological. The psychological theories emphasize cognitions, whereas the biological theories emphasize learned motivation to use drugs and cravings.

At this point, no one theory of relapse has emerged as superior to the others, so it makes sense to look across the theories to discern what may be the important ingredients of relapse. First are the internal (e.g., mood) and external (e.g., drinking setting) stimulus conditions that precede relapse. Cravings to use drugs also are important. Two types of expectancies may be relevant to relapse. The first is a person's beliefs about the effects of a drug in a given situation, and the second is a person's self-efficacy, which is an individual's estimation that he or she can successfully enact a behaviour in a given situation. Finally, a person's coping responses or skills may be important in relapse.

Research and theory about relapse have generated treatment applications, known as relapse prevention methods (Marlatt, Bowen, & Witkiewitz, 2009; Marlatt & Witkiewitz, 2005). Relapse prevention methods first have focused on assessing "high-risk" situations, or those situations associated with abuse of alcohol or drugs in the past. High-risk situations may be negative moods such as anxiety or depression, positive moods, the presence of people the patient used to drink with, or some combination of internal and external precipitants. After high-risk situations have been identified, the next step is to look at the person's ways to cope with the situation without resorting to undesired levels of substance use, and the person's self-efficacy to do so. Coupled with this is an examination of the person's beliefs about how alcohol or drug use would help in different situations. For example, people may believe that drinking at a party would help them to talk with the other people present. Assessment of these elements then determines what might be done in treatment: teaching alternative coping skills to substance use (for example, using communication skills instead of alcohol to help a person enjoy a party), improving self-efficacy, or educating the person about the actual effects of alcohol and drugs. In practice, all of these elements typically are covered, and there is a correlation among them. For example, teaching people coping skills may elevate their self-efficacy about using that skill.

Corbis

Settings such as taverns that are associated with a person's heavy use of alcohol in the past may pose a risk of that person relapsing or drinking heavily after a period of abstinence from or moderate use of alcohol.

You can see that much of what is done in relapse prevention work follows from psychological models of relapse. The major method from the biological models is cue exposure. This method essentially involves presenting (exposing) the person with cues (for example, a bottle of a favourite brand of whiskey or drug-use paraphernalia like a syringe) that might elicit cravings to use a substance, without allowing its actual use. With repeated exposure, the cravings theoretically reduce in number and intensity. So, as a person's repeated association of these "stimulus conditions" with drug use resulted in the stimuli eliciting a strong desire to use drugs or alcohol, repeated pairing of the stimuli with nonuse of substances will decrease the power of the stimuli to elicit cravings.

The work on relapse has stimulated substantial advances in alcohol and drug treatment (Carroll, 1996; Stephens, Roffman, & Simpson, 1994). However, it also brings up an important point about relapse research and prevention, and about treatment more generally. What has been absent to a large degree in theories of relapse is more serious study of conditions in the "broader backdrop" of relapse, such as the person's social environment (family functioning, job satisfaction) or general level of stress (recent job change, recent divorce). Immediate relapse precipitants obviously are important, but so are these more remote factors. In fact, we know this from research on the long-term effects of alcohol and drug treatment, which seems highly relevant to relapse. Perhaps it would help to understand this more easily if you do not think of alcohol or drug treatment as a specific entity that "acts on" a person to produce some lasting outcome. Instead, treatment is one event in the life of people who are trying to change the way they use alcohol or drugs. Furthermore, individuals and the treatment interact in a social context that strongly contributes to the course of change. Fortunately, more recent extensions of models of relapse, such as those of Witkiewitz and Marlatt (2004), have attempted to integrate immediate and more distal relapse determinants.

Models of Causes and Treatment Methods

Placing substance-abuse treatment programs in the hospital setting—a common practice—is broadly based in a disease model of thought.

So far we have presented a lot of information about alcohol and drug treatment, although space limitations prevented us from going into great detail. You may have noticed the influence of each of the models of causes that we reviewed at the beginning of this chapter. We can cite several instances. Placing substance-abuse treatment programs in the hospital setting—a common practice—is broadly based in a disease model of thought. Indeed, the great achievement that came years ago with wide acceptance of the disease model was to take the treatment of alcohol and drug problems out of the legal system (moral model) and into the hands of physicians and medical settings—an apparently more useful means of rehabilitating people with addictions.

Another example is Alcoholics Anonymous, rooted in both the disease and moral models. Pharmacological treatments, like methadone maintenance, are most clearly linked to the biological model. Within most treatment settings, psychological and social interventions are consistent with the social learning and sociocultural models. The most explicit example of this merging of models is the community reinforcement approach (Budney & Higgins, 1998; Higgins et al., 1991; Hunt & Azrin, 1973), which centres on modifying the person's environment to reinforce nonabuse of substances and not to reinforce substance abuse.

We can trace individual parts of alcohol and drug treatment to a particular model of etiology, but virtually all treatment programs combine practices that are derived from two or more of the causes models. This is the result in part of the many clinical, social, political, and economic forces that influence substance-abuse treatment programs and that affect their evolution. Another force is the current scientifically based thought that the substance-use disorders are multifaceted problems, so treatment must relate to the person's biological, psychological, and social makeup. This thinking is implemented in the collection of activities that constitute many treatment programs.

So far, we have discussed treatment freely—that is, free from concerns about how available or accessible it is. We conclude this chapter by discussing this all-important question, especially as it pertains to economic forces and alcohol and drug treatment.

Economic Factors in Alcohol and Drug Treatment

In Canada many government-established drug treatment programs are fully funded or subsidized. In other countries, such as the U.S., this is not the case. For Americans and many others around the world, the issue of cost is a controversial one and the question of whether a person gets treatment if they cannot afford it is of paramount concern. A brief history of the role of finances and insurance will help you to appreciate the current controversy (Rawson, 1990–1991).

In the early 1970s, alcohol and drug treatment was not considered in the mainstream of psychiatry, clinical psychology, and social work. By 1990, however, alcohol and drug treatment was a central concern. The change was due mostly to cocaine, AIDS, and adjustments in health care financing.

In the middle to late 1970s, interest in drug treatment had been quelled considerably because the heroin scare of the 1960s and early 1970s had quieted down. At the same time, 28-day inpatient programs became the standard alcohol treatment because of agreements among care providers, typically hospitals and health insurance companies. These 28-day programs proliferated during the 1980s, with legislation passed in many states that required insurers to cover alcohol and drug treatment. The cost to the insurance company was high; the price of completing an inpatient program varied, but it always was in the thousands of dollars. The term *chemical dependence treatment* was spawned in the 1980s, because the 28-day programs were also accommodating large numbers of individuals who abused drugs other than alcohol, especially cocaine. Treatment availability and accessibility (with an expanding economy) were rising rapidly. Another force in the treatment expansion was a social-political climate that encouraged people with alcohol and drug problems to get into treatment.

Therefore, by the late 1980s, treatment was accessible in an unprecedented way, at least for those who had health insurance or independent wealth. Typically, this trend is viewed as good, but a counterforce was operating. With increased expansion of and expectations for alcohol and drug treatment, employers' health insurance premiums were rising quickly. Quietly at first in the unbounded economy of the mid-1980s, then loudly as the economy recessed, came "managed" mental health and alcohol and drug treatment services. Managed care is a movement based on the goal of controlling the costs of health care, including alcohol and drug treatment. The term *cost-effectiveness* became popular: Is the benefit of a treatment worth what it costs?

Cost consciousness has led to a far more restricted use of inpatient alcohol and drug treatments, at least those that are paid for by health insurers. When inpatient stays are covered, they are often much shorter than 28 days. Instead, outpatient treatment is the insurer's preference. This policy is based on research that suggests that, on average, inpatient treatment is no more effective than the much cheaper outpatient treatment (Miller & Hester, 1986).

It seems that the trend to less inpatient and more outpatient care is here to stay. Many treatment providers, however, are concerned that this prescription for care is based too much on money and not enough on proven differences (or lack thereof) in treatment benefits. Some treatment providers ask: What does a lack of difference in benefits overall tell us? What is outpatient treatment anyway? (We saw earlier in this chapter that what constitutes outpatient alcohol and drug treatment is highly variable.) Is the finding of no difference true for everybody? When is the more structured, more intense inpatient treatment indicated, and when is it not?

These and similar questions became more salient for alcohol treatment in the report of a study by Walsh et al. (1991). A total of 227 individuals who were newly identified as alcohol abusers were randomly assigned to one of three treatments through their employee assistance program (thus all these people had jobs). The treatments were compulsory inpatient treatment, compulsory AA attendance, and choice of treatment option. Two years after treatment, the three groups did not differ in measures of job performance. However, a major finding was that, overall, the cost of treatment for the compulsory inpatient group was only 10 percent more than it was for the AA and choice groups (remember that AA is free in that any financial

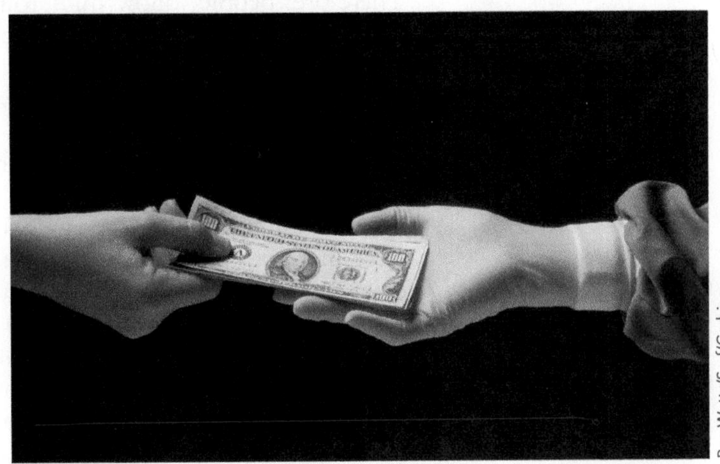

Ron Watts/Surf/Corbis

In countries such as the U.S., economics is a driving force in the treatment of the substance-use disorders.

contribution is voluntary). The small cost difference was particularly true for study participants who had used cocaine in the six months before they began treatment. The overall cost results occurred because the choice and AA groups had a much higher inpatient treatment admission rate during the two-year follow-up period than did the group who initially received compulsory inpatient care. One implication of the small cost difference that was confirmed during the follow-up assessments was that, at least for some of the time after treatment, the compulsory inpatient group used less alcohol and drugs than did the other two groups.

In summary, finances and insurance have played and do play a major role in the accessibility of alcohol and drug treatment and in what treatment options are available. In this regard, as the Walsh et al. (1991) study suggests, it may be that more intense treatments are less costly in the long run for some people, especially those who have more severe psychiatric or social difficulties (Washton, 1995). Therefore, we have a lot to learn about the effects of the strong current trend toward less intense, less expensive treatment. And we have focused in this discussion on people who rely on health insurance to pay for part or all of their health care. A serious concern is individuals who do not have health insurance—a major problem in the United States, and one that the United States must face squarely in its current push for health care reform legislation. Because of the current decreased availability of publicly funded treatment, those without insurance may find it impossible to get any professional care. This is a significant point when you remember that, overall, completing alcohol and drug treatment is associated with improved functioning in multiple areas.

The Stepped Care Approach

Our discussion in this chapter has focused on changes in patterns of alcohol and drug use and how they happen. Several main points have emerged from the discussion. Change may occur in many different ways and may or may not involve the use of professional treatment resources. Treatment itself consists of several different ways to help people reach different goals that relate to how they function in different parts of their lives, and it occurs in several different settings. Some treatment approaches or techniques have a stronger scientific base to support their effectiveness than do others. Therefore, people follow numerous pathways to change; some pathways involving professional treatment have more scientific support than others, and some seem better suited to the needs and goals of any given person. Finally, we have learned that, when we discuss professional treatment, what is accessible to individuals depends partly on their personal income and insurance coverage. Economics has been a major factor driving the pronounced trend toward briefer and less intense treatments conducted in outpatient settings.

This summary reflects major recent changes in alcohol and drug treatment services in North America. Until the middle to late 1980s, professional alcohol and drug treatment was delivered with a "one-size-fits-all" approach. That era is over, but what is next? Is there a general approach to follow that offers the most effective and efficient treatment to people at any given time that they seek it? When individuals seek professional treatment, one model to follow in finding the services needed is called the "stepped care approach," which has been an effective heuristic in guiding the treatment of other medical disorders such as hypertension (Sobell & Sobell, 2000).

According to Sobell and Sobell (2000, pp. 573–574), in the stepped care approach, the selection of any treatment is guided by three principles*:

1. treatment should be individualized with regard to the client's needs and problems;
2. the treatment selected should be consistent with the current knowledge about effectiveness; and
3. the treatment that is chosen should be the least restrictive (considering the physical effects of treatment on the client and the client's lifestyle and resources). A consequence of the third principle is that more intensive treatments are reserved for more severe problems.

These three principles apply to the selection of both initial treatment and subsequent treatments. What happens after the initial treatment is selected and begun is based on monitoring the clients' progress toward achieving their goals. If clients show improvement, then a treatment may be continued, decreased in frequency or intensity, or stopped. If there is no change or the clients show a decreased level of functioning, then a treatment may be changed in frequency or intensity, or a new treatment may be tried. Decisions about treatment are based mainly on clients' performances relevant to their treatment goals.

The stepped care approach seems simple in principle but may be complex in application. To use this approach in real clinical settings, several questions have to be considered. Are any scientifically supported treatments available for an individual's needs at a given time? Will an individual accept the treatment indicated by the stepped care approach? Will the individual be able to afford it? What is "improvement"? When is behaviour "stable"?

Despite these and other difficult questions, the stepped care approach fits well with our current knowledge about change in patterns of alcohol and drug use and about the economics of treatment delivery. Stepped care fits what we know because it fosters a scientifically based, individualized delivery of effective treatment in the most efficient, least restrictive, and least expensive way.

* (Sobell and Sobell, 2000.)

SUMMARY

- Readiness or commitment to change is an important consideration in treatment. One model of this process is the stages of change model.
- People with substance-use disorders change these problem behaviours on their own quite frequently. This is known as spontaneous remission of the substance-use patterns.
- The self-help groups Alcoholics Anonymous and Narcotics Anonymous are major resources in helping people who have alcohol- and drug-use disorders, respectively.
- Other self-help groups, presented as alternatives to AA, also are becoming more popular. Two examples are SMART and Secular Organizations for Sobriety (SOS).
- The model of etiology of alcohol- and drug-use disorder that a treatment is based on affects its design. We review five models in this chapter: moral, American disease, biological, social learning, and sociocultural.
- The biopsychosocial model of etiology addresses the inadequacy of single-factor models by combining the major types of factors that seem to influence the development of alcohol- and drug-use disorders.
- Treatments have aims or goals. In alcohol and drug treatment, goals typically follow from a thorough assessment and refer to a person's use of alcohol and drugs and to other areas of life functioning.

- It has been standard practice to specify abstinence from alcohol or other drugs as the major outcome goal for a treatment. However, some argue that moderate, nonproblem use of alcohol is a reasonable outcome goal for some patients.
- Alcohol treatment can be classified broadly into three categories of settings: hospital, intermediate, and outpatient. Within each setting, a wide variety of services may be offered.
- Approved pharmacological treatment of alcohol problems includes medication to manage withdrawal from alcohol, alcohol-sensitizing drugs, drugs that alter the reinforcing properties of alcohol, and drugs that manage alcohol craving.
- Overall, no one treatment for alcohol problems seems to be superior to others, but staying in treatment is associated with better outcomes. Individual treatments may be more effective if they are matched to patients' characteristics.
- It has proved difficult to conduct controlled outcome research on self-help groups. What research has been done suggests that AA helps some people but not everybody.
- Settings of drug treatment traditionally have been defined by treatment of heroin abuse, but abusers of other drugs now also appear in most of these settings. Traditionally, drug treatment settings include detoxification, methadone maintenance, residential, and outpatient. As with alcohol treatment, a wide variety of treatment services may be offered in a given setting.
- Approved pharmacotherapy of dependence on opiate drugs includes managing drug withdrawal, replacing one opiate (e.g., heroin) with another one that is less addictive (methadone), and using antagonist drugs (e.g., naltrexone for opioids).
- Research shows that staying in residential or non-methadone outpatient drug treatment is associated with reduced substance use and a more socially productive lifestyle. Drug treatment research would benefit from more studies of patient–treatment matching.
- Structured contingency reinforcement programs, including community reinforcement, are promising nonpharmacological treatments of illicit drug-use disorders. Conjoint therapies also seem to be effective.
- Drug and alcohol treatment providers have found that a large percentage of their patients abuse multiple substance. This has caused a change in the thinking that drug and alcohol treatment are independent efforts. Rather, there is wide recognition of the need for settings that can accommodate users of multiple substances and for understanding common aspects of the addictive behaviours.
- There has been a major increase in recognition that individuals who show up for alcohol or drug treatment may have major psychiatric disorders. One approach to treating these individuals uses psychotropic medications.
- The challenging problem of relapse has received a lot of research attention in the last 30 years. This work has resulted in treatment applications called relapse prevention.
- Stepped care is one approach to professional treatment selection that integrates current knowledge about alcohol and drug treatment effectiveness and the conditions under which it is delivered.

Key Terms

aftercare p. 353
counselling p. 352
levo-alpha-acetylmethadol (LAAM) p. 363
milieu treatment p. 352
personality disorders p. 369
psychological treatment p. 352
psychotherapy p. 352
recovery p. 342
self-medication p. 369
sociopathy p. 369
spontaneous remission p. 337
treatment p. 337
treatment effects p. 368
treatment outcome research p. 355

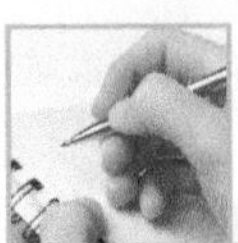

Essays/Thought Questions

1. What implications does the phenomenon of spontaneous remission of alcohol-use disorders have for designing formal treatments for them?
2. What do you think are some of the reasons that self-help groups might aid some people in their efforts to change their alcohol or other drug use?
3. Why do you think some people have argued that harm-reduction approaches to changing alcohol and drug use might be especially applicable to adolescents and young adults?
4. If no one treatment for alcohol- or other drug-use disorders has been found to be effective for everyone, do the available formal treatments for these disorders have any value?

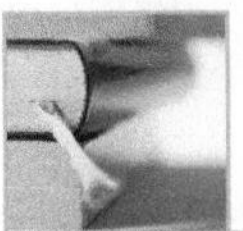

Suggested Readings

Fletcher, A.M. (2001). *Sober for good*. Boston: Houghton Mifflin Co.

Leshner, A.I. (1999). Science-based views of drug addiction and its treatment. *Journal of the American Medical Association, 282*, 1314–1318.

Miller, W.R., & C'de Baca, J. (2001). *Quantum change*. New York: Guilford Press.

Rogers, E.M. (2003). *Diffusion of information* (5th ed.). New York: Free Press.

Wagner, E.F., & Waldron, H.B. (Eds.). (2001). *Innovations in adolescent substance abuse interventions*. New York: Pergamon.

CHAPTER 15

Prevention of Substance Abuse

Did You Know

?

- There are many tertiary prevention programs that include interventions to treat people who are beyond the early stages of substance abuse or dependence.
- The sociocultural framework to understanding prevention posits that social norms directly influence the use and abuse of psychoactive substances.
- Canada's Anti-Drug Strategy is part of a five-year plan that will fund $232 million towards targeted prevention for youths, First Nations, and other high-risk areas across the country.
- Research evidence indicates that mass media prevention strategies do not result in significant changes in patterns of alcohol or drug use.
- The primary goal of affective prevention programs is to help individuals be aware of their own feelings and attitudes towards drug use as a means for prevention.

The preceding chapters included a great amount of information on alcohol and drugs, their actions, and their use and abuse. The previous chapter concerned the treatment of problems associated with substance use. This brings us to our final chapter, which focuses on the prevention of substance-use problems.

Unfortunately, professionals and funding sources historically have not made prevention a high priority. The reasons for this are not certain, but two possibilities stand out. First is that past prevention efforts have tended to yield only modest influences in changing patterns of drug use. Second is that current, ongoing substance abuse is dramatically visible and thus receives a more rapid response in personnel and financial resources. Whether this approach is shortsighted is a question that is often and strongly debated.

Although prevention traditionally has received less attention than treatment, we nevertheless are now in a period when prevention research and development are on the rise. One of the leading reasons for this increased focus on prevention is that substance use has contributed to the spread of HIV/AIDS. Intravenous drug users are one of the largest groups to have contracted HIV/AIDS in Canada (and in other countries such as the United States and Europe). Furthermore, being under the influence of alcohol or other drugs in some cases may lead users to engage in unsafe sexual practices, increasing the risk of HIV transmission. Accordingly, federal and provincial resources have been increasingly used over the past decade to fund projects designed to prevent substance use, including harm reduction strategies.

Most people agree that prevention efforts should—indeed must—be an important component of any comprehensive approach to treating substance abuse. In this chapter, we first provide an overview of definitions of prevention. The major models of prevention and their implications are then discussed. We also provide examples of several types of prevention projects and their outcomes. The chapter closes with some comments on the prospects for future work in prevention.

Defining Prevention

Prevention in this context pertains broadly to the avoidance or lessening of problems associated with substance use. This relatively straightforward definition opens the door to a variety of potential goals for prevention efforts. For example, the goal of prevention efforts aimed at illegal drug use generally is to stop its occurrence. An alternative or additional goal of such activities might be to minimize the effects of any illegal drug use that does occur (a harm reduction approach; see Drugs and Culture Box 15.1). Then the approaches chosen for implementation probably would be different. Therefore, when we speak of prevention, it is important to identify what is being prevented, whether it is onset of use, continued use, negative effects on society, health problems, or something else.

Prevention of substance abuse traditionally has been divided into three types of intervention: primary, secondary, and tertiary.

- **Primary prevention** pertains to the avoidance of substance abuse before it has a chance to occur. One goal of primary prevention is to encourage abstinence and is usually targeted at youth prior to (or just after) the initial use of a substance. For example, the "Just Say No" advertising effort used to encourage young people to turn down invitations to use drugs. Another goal of primary prevention for some substances is the development of responsible attitudes and substance-use behaviours, such as responsible drinking behaviours. A number of posters and television spots have emphasized, for example, the need not to drive after drinking or not to let friends drive drunk.

primary prevention
A prevention strategy that attempts to encourage avoidance of substance use or abuse before it has a chance to occur.

DRUGS AND CULTURE BOX 15.1

Harm-Reduction Social Policies

Countries vary widely in their social policies regarding substance use. You have read elsewhere in this book about the "war on drugs" and "zero-tolerance" policies in Canada and the United States. This stance is in striking contrast to another social policy strategy—called harm reduction or harm minimization—being implemented in other countries, particularly the United Kingdom and the Netherlands. Harm-reduction policies focus on decreasing the negative consequences of drug use for individuals and the community, even if they endorse continued but safer drug use in the interim. According to Diane Riley at the Canadian Centre on Substance Abuse, "Harm reduction establishes a hierarchy of goals, with the more immediate and realistic ones to be achieved as first steps toward risk-free use or abstinence. It is a pragmatic approach, which recognizes that abstinence may be neither a realistic nor a desired goal for some, especially in the short term."

Riley describes two examples of harm-reduction policies. The first was in Merseyside in Great Britain. Health clinics collaborated with pharmacists and police officials to establish a "comprehensive approach [to drug abuse] involving prescription of drugs, provision of clean syringes and helping rather than criminalizing drug users." Among the reported benefits of the Merseyside collaboration were low incidence of HIV in drug users, continued employment for many drug abusers, and a decrease in thefts and robberies.

A second example is from Amsterdam, which sought to reduce drug-use harm by providing medical and social services to people who were continuing to use drugs. Among the strategies used were decreased police attention to marijuana possession and use and mobile methadone distribution stations. Prison terms apply only to dealers of hard drugs. An appreciation of the potential benefits of a harm-reduction orientation has been shown more recently in its use in school-based interventions to reduce harm associated with alcohol use (McBride et al., 2004) and smoking (Hamilton et al., 2005). In both cases, the use of a harm-reduction approach was superior to standard education/abstinence-based programs.

Harm-reduction programs have been in place in Canada through the introduction of methadone maintenance programs. These programs were implemented in part to reduce crime rates among heroin users. A second strategy, more recently implemented, is needle-exchange programs designed to reduce the risk of HIV transmission among drug abusers. Both of these strategies have had their vocal opponents, however. There has been serious opposition to needle-exchange programs, despite research indicating that intravenous drug users who participate in such programs do not show an increase in the number of injections and that there has been no associated increase in the number of addictions. Nevertheless, a broad-based harm-reduction approach to the problems of drug use in both Canada and the United States is emerging.

secondary prevention Interventions designed to prevent substance-use problems just as the early signs of abuse begin to appear.

- **Secondary prevention** refers to interventions applied when substance-use problems already have begun to appear. This type of prevention is analogous to early treatment in that interventions are used when problems are first surfacing. Secondary prevention frequently is used in the legal response to substance misuse. For example, people arrested for driving under the influence of alcohol often are referred to alcohol education courses designed to decrease the likelihood of the people drinking and driving again. Similarly, educational programs are used with youthful offenders first arrested for drug possession. In each case, the emphasis is on nipping the problem in the bud, as it first appears. Central to such efforts, of course, is the early identification of these drug problems. (See Table 15.1 for early signs of potential drug problems.)

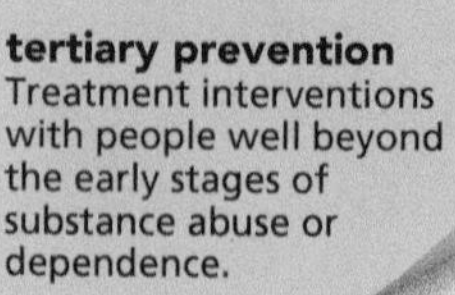

tertiary prevention Treatment interventions with people well beyond the early stages of substance abuse or dependence.

- **Tertiary prevention** includes interventions used in treating people who are beyond the early stages of substance abuse or dependence. The goals of tertiary prevention essentially are to terminate use of the substance and thus avoid further deterioration in the person's functioning. Tertiary prevention and substance-abuse treatment (see Chapter 14) are comparable activities, and prevention efforts are more appropriately viewed as being either primary or secondary in nature.

TABLE 15.1 Early Signs of Potential Drug Problems

	Potential Signs
Physical	Sleepiness or change in energy Dilated pupils Shaking hands, fidgety demeanour
Social/ Psychological	Changes in friends Changes in conversations with friends (i.e., 'coded' language) Increased secrecy about activities or personal possessions
Other	Negative changes in schoolwork, missing school. or declining grades Use of incense, room deodorizer. or perfume to hide smoke or chemical odours Evidence of drug paraphernalia (e.g., pipes, etc.)

Source: Government of Canada (2011). *National Anti-Drug Strategy, Signs and Symptoms of Drug Use.* Found at: http://www.nationalantidrugstrategy.gc.ca/prevention/parents/sign.html.

Sociocultural Model of Prevention

The sociocultural, or social science, framework to understanding prevention posits that social norms directly influence the use and abuse of psychoactive substances. This model has been used primarily in efforts to prevent alcohol and tobacco abuse, although the model also has implications for the prevention of other substance abuse, which we describe later in this section. When applied to drinking behaviour, the model consists of three basic components (Blane, 1976):

1. an emphasis on the culture's normative structure,
2. a need to integrate drinking into socially meaningful activities, and
3. a focus on providing for the gradual socialization of drinking behaviour.

As you can see, prevention efforts derived from this model strive to influence the entire climate of drinking within the culture.

One of the strongest proponents of the sociocultural model is Rupert Wilkinson (1970), who argues that alcohol use can be affected by planned policy measures. Wilkinson notes identifiable patterns of alcohol consumption that correspond to low rates of problematic drinking, and he thinks these patterns can be used as guides for ingraining altered drinking patterns in the culture.

In his 1970 seminal work, which remains applicable today, Wilkinson identified five proposals for modifying drinking patterns culturally:

- First is the need to have within the culture a low level of **emotionalism** about drinking and at the same time a lack of ambivalence about alcohol use. Emotionalism surrounding drinking, according to Wilkinson, merely creates tension and produces an environment in which discussion and change in drinking behaviour cannot occur. A more measured and nonreactive approach will have the added benefit of reducing societal ambivalence about drinking and thus provide more clarity about drinking norms.
- Second is that there must be a distinction between drinking per se and drunkenness. The notion here is that acceptable drinking and unacceptable drinking (drunkenness) both should be clearly defined. Unfortunately, arriving at such definitions is not easy.

emotionalism
Focusing on and responding to emotions, and relying on emotional connections to our world.

taboos
A custom that prohibits or restricts a practice of openly addressing an issue, event, person, or object.

- Third is that after identifying what drunkenness is, there should be firm **taboos** on its occurrence.
- Fourth, and the central proposal, is that drinking should be integrated into a broader social context; that is, alcohol consumption should not be the focus of activity at any given gathering but instead should be dependent on other activities. For example, acceptable usage to 'toast' a bride and groom at their wedding, but not drinking as the focus of the evening.
- Fifth is that society should allow the serving of alcohol only when food is also available. The belief here is that when food is available, alcohol consumption will not necessarily be the sole focus of activity. Furthermore, food slows the body's absorption of alcohol and potentially reduces the rate of drunkenness.

Taken together, these proposals designate acceptable and unacceptable forms of drinking and thus clearly identify desired patterns of responsible drinking. These patterns of drinking then should be integrated into routine family and other social activities. It is noteworthy that the goal of the sociocultural approach is not the cessation (or stoppage) of drinking but rather changes in social norms regarding drinking. Therefore, the approach is not a prohibitionist strategy, and some have argued that a fault of the sociocultural approach is that it may encourage drinking.

A major criticism of the sociocultural model is that it may not be widely applicable. Many countries, such as Canada and the United States, have diverse cultures and subcultures, customs, and values that fit one culture may not be amenable to or accepted by another. A second criticism is that the sociocultural approach, while emphasizing moderate consumption, fails to account for the value and pleasure many people attach to heavier drinking. A third concern with the model is that it assumes attitudinal

iStockphoto

One of Wilkinson's proposals for modifying drinking patterns culturally is to allow the serving of alcohol only when food is also available. The idea is that this might change our social norms regarding drinking.

changes in the culture will result in the desired behavioural changes. However, past research has provided no strong indication that attitudinal change leads to behavioural change. Finally, it is argued that the sociocultural model does not adequately consider physical problems associated with alcohol consumption (e.g., cancers and liver and stomach ailments). In fact, some think that use of the sociocultural model may result in a greater prevalence of such physical problems, even if social problems are eliminated, simply by virtue of the widespread use of alcohol (Blane, 1976; Nirenberg & Miller, 1984; Skirrow & Sawka, 1987).

The sociocultural model has been applied predominantly in the context of alcohol-use and tobacco problems, but it also has been a cornerstone to many prevention efforts geared toward problems associated with other drug use. As noted earlier, an example is the "Just Say No" campaign in the United States, which encourages people nationwide, but particularly young people, to refuse offers or temptations to use drugs. Another example is the advertising efforts of the Partnership for a Drug-Free America. The partnership's campaign, which focuses especially on marijuana, cocaine, and crack, seeks to decrease the social acceptance of drug use among young people and alert users or potential users to the risks of using drugs. In Canada, the National Anti-Drug Prevention Strategy Not4Me campaign targets youths to stand up to peer pressure toward the use of drugs through offering alternative ways to say 'no.'

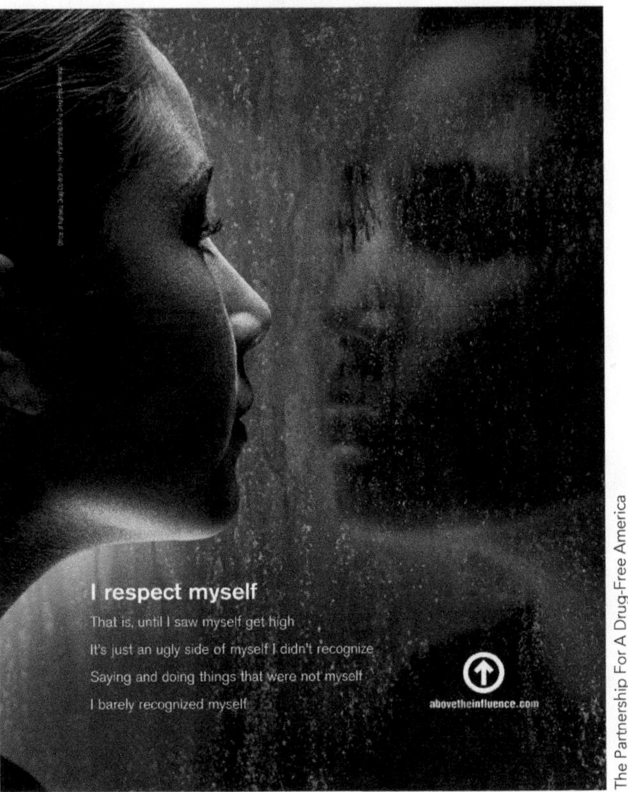

I respect myself
That is, until I saw myself get high
It's just an ugly side of myself I didn't recognize
Saying and doing things that were not myself
I barely recognized myself
abovetheinfluence.com

The Partnership For A Drug-Free America

This poster is part of a U.S. series distributed through the AboveTheInfluence.com website, a program of the Office of National Drug Control Policy. According to the website, "Our goal is to help you stay above the influence. The more aware you are of the influences around you, the better prepared you will be to stand up to the pressures that keep you down."

Principles of Drug Abuse Prevention

The National Institute on Drug Abuse (NIDA) in the United States has developed a series of "prevention principles" relevant to the implementation of prevention programs for children and adolescents. The 16 principles, which are outlined in Table 15.2, were based on numerous research studies on the origins of drug-abuse behaviours and the common elements found in effective prevention programs. NIDA issued these principles for parents, educators, and community leaders to use in their thinking, planning, selection, and delivery of drug-abuse prevention programs.

As can be seen in Table 15.2, the principles fall under several broad domains. The first domain focuses on risk factors and protective factors, the second on the planning of prevention programs (including family programs, school-based programs, or broader community programs), and the third on the actual delivery of prevention programs.

These prevention principles have overwhelming support from the science world in depicting the nature of substance use and abuse and how to prevent it. As such, these principles have been influential in the development and implementation of a variety of prevention interventions.

"There is still a misguided notion that people can experiment with drugs with impunity. But we can't predict who will go on to develop dependence, and neither can the individual. It's essential that we get a consistent message across to young people that experimentation has its great risks."

Dr. Charles Schuster, National Institute on Drug Abuse Addiction Research Center (*The Journal*, October 1993)

TABLE 15.2 Principles of Drug Abuse Prevention

Risk Factors and Protective Factors	
Principle 1:	Prevention programs should enhance protective factors and reverse or reduce risk factors.
Principle 2:	Prevention programs should address all forms of drug abuse, alone or in combination, including the underage use of legal drugs (e.g., tobacco or alcohol); the use of illegal drugs (e.g., marijuana or heroin); and the inappropriate use of legally obtained substances (e.g., inhalants), prescription medications, or over-the-counter drugs.
Principle 3:	Prevention programs should address the type of drug-abuse problem in the local community, target modifiable risk factors, and strengthen identified protective factors.
Principle 4:	Prevention programs should be tailored to address risks specific to population or audience characteristics, such as age, gender, and ethnicity, to improve program effectiveness.
Prevention Planning	
Family Programs	
Principle 5:	Family-based prevention programs should enhance family bonding and relationships and include parenting skills; practice in developing, discussing, and enforcing family policies on substance abuse; and training in drug education and information.
School Programs	
Principle 6:	Prevention programs can be designed to intervene as early as *preschool* to address risk factors for drug abuse, such as aggressive behaviour, poor social skills, and academic difficulties.
Principle 7:	Prevention programs for *elementary school children* should target improving academic and social-emotional learning to address risk factors for drug abuse, such as early aggression, academic failure, and school dropout. Education should focus on the following skills: self-control, emotional awareness, communication, social problem solving, and academic support, especially in reading.
Principle 8:	Prevention programs for *middle or junior high and high school students* should increase academic and social competence with the following skills: study habits and academic support, communication, peer relationships, self-efficacy and assertiveness, drug-resistance skills, reinforcement of antidrug attitudes, and strengthening of personal commitments against drug abuse.
Community Programs	
Principle 9:	Prevention programs aimed at general populations at key transition points, such as the transition to middle school, can produce beneficial effects even among high-risk families and children. Such interventions do not single out risk populations and therefore reduce labelling and promote bonding to school and community.
Principle 10:	Community prevention programs that combine two or more effective programs, such as family-based and school-based programs, can be more effective than a single program alone.
Principle 11:	Community prevention programs reaching populations in multiple settings—for example, schools, clubs, faith-based organizations, and the media—are most effective when they present consistent, communitywide messages in each setting.
Prevention Program Delivery	
Principle 12:	When communities adapt programs to match their needs, community norms, or differing cultural requirements, they should retain core elements of the original research-based intervention, which include: *structure* (how the program is organized and constructed), *content* (the information, skills, and strategies of the program), and *delivery* (how the program is adapted, implemented, and evaluated).
Principle 13:	Prevention programs should be long-term with repeated interventions (e.g., booster programs) to reinforce the original prevention goals. Research shows that the benefits from middle school prevention programs diminish without follow-up programs in high school.

Principle 14:	Prevention programs should include teacher training on good classroom management practices, such as rewarding appropriate student behaviour. Such techniques help foster students' positive behaviour, achievement, academic motivation, and school bonding.
Principle 15:	Prevention programs are most effective when they employ interactive techniques, such as peer discussion groups and parent role-playing, which allow for active involvement in learning about drug abuse and reinforcing skills.
Principle 16:	Research-based prevention programs can be cost-effective. Similar to earlier research, recent research shows that each dollar invested in prevention will bring about a savings of up to $10 in treatment for alcohol or other substance abuse.

Source: NIDA (2003).

CONTEMPORARY ISSUE BOX 15.2

The Amethyst Initiative: Lowering the Legal Drinking Age to Decrease Alcohol Problems?

The Amethyst Initiative, launched in 2008, represents a movement by over 100 U.S. college presidents across the country to foster "an informed and dispassionate debate" (The Amethyst Initiative, www.amethystinitiative.org) on lowering the drinking age in the U.S. from 21 to 18 years of age as a strategy for reducing binge drinking on college campuses. The Initiative also invites "new ideas about the best ways to prepare young adults to make responsible decisions about alcohol." (The word *amethyst*, by the way, is derived from the ancient Greek words meaning "not" [a-] and "intoxicated" [methustos]. According to legend, amethysts protected their owners from drunkenness.)

The foundation of the Amethyst Initiative is the argument that the minimum drinking age of 21, established in the mid-1980s by the National Minimum Drinking Age Act, has not served to decrease drinking- or alcohol-related problems among U.S. college students. According to their statement, the following were offered as premises:

- A culture of dangerous, clandestine "binge-drinking"—often conducted off-campus—has developed.
- Alcohol education that mandates abstinence as the only legal option has not resulted in significant constructive behavioural change among our students.
- Adults under 21 are deemed capable of voting, signing contracts, serving on juries, and enlisting in the military, but are told they are not mature enough to have a beer.
- By choosing to use fake IDs, students make ethical compromises that erode respect for the law. (The Amethyst Initiative, www.amethystinitiative.org)

A number of organizations and individuals are strongly opposed to the Amethyst Initiative, including Mothers Against Drunk Driving (MADD), the Governors Highway Safety Association, and several college presidents. The primary point they argue is that lowering the drinking age will result in greater alcohol consumption, more alcohol-related injuries, and more alcohol-related fatalities among those aged between 18 and 21.

There is no question, of course, that binge drinking on college campuses is a significant public health concern, and there should be focused debate on strategies for decreasing binge drinking. The specific proposal to lower the drinking age from 21 to 18 is understandably controversial. In pondering this issue, consider the following questions and issues.

First, raising the drinking age from 18 to 21 has been associated with significant decreases in alcohol-related motor vehicle accidents and fatalities in this age group (Fell et al., 2009; Wagenaar & Toomey, 2002). It is likely that lowering the drinking age from 21 to 18 will be associated with an increase in such accidents and fatalities. Relevant to this prediction, a study from New Zealand found that alcohol-related crashes rose 12 percent among 18- to 19-year-olds and 14 percent among 15- to 17-year-olds when the drinking age was lowered to 18 (Kypri et al., 2006).

Second, it is not clear that lowering the drinking age will decrease binge drinking among college students. In fact, there is the possibility that binge drinking will increase. For example, one potential scenario is that the rate of binge drinking remains unchanged among those who already are drinkers. At the same time, those currently between 18 and 20 who are not binge drinking might show an initiation of drinking, and of binge drinking, as a function of alcohol consumption becoming legal for their age group.

Third, it is likely that many college students who engage in binge drinking arrived at college with a previously established pattern of binge drinking. Changing the drinking age will not impact those individuals, who would have established this pattern prior to age 18.

Fourth, the debate would need to consider the impact of lowering the minimum drinking age on youth under the age of 18. A minimum drinking age of 18 would mean that high school seniors, who typically turn 18 during their senior year, would be able to purchase and consume alcohol (and illegally purchase it for younger high school students). This could have the unintended effect of facilitating alcohol consumption by younger adolescents. This has implications for the development of alcohol dependence, as research indicates that individuals who begin drinking prior to the age of 15 are four times more likely to meet the criteria for alcohol dependence at some point in their lives than are those who initiate drinking at an older age (Grant & Dawson, 1998).

Taken together, there should be strong encouragement of debate on strategies that have the potential for reducing binge drinking (and more generally facilitating responsible drinking decisions). It is not clear that lowering the drinking age will reduce binge drinking. Further, lowering the drinking age likely will result in an increase in alcohol-related motor vehicle accidents and fatalities and overall alcohol consumption in the 18- to 20-year-old age group.

In Canada, the legal drinking age is 19 in all provinces, with the exception of Quebec, Alberta, and Manitoba, which is 18 years. What issues would you consider important for considering given that Canada's legal drinking age is lower than that of the U.S.?

Current Topics in Prevention

Prevention efforts are a focused strategy in Canada. In this section, we provide an overview of several contemporary topics and programs in primary and secondary prevention. One prevention strategy worth noting is a 'continuum of care' model, which crosses both primary and secondary prevention strategies by looking at prevention, treatment, and intervention (Institute of Medicine, 1997). Prevention strategies in this model target specific sub-populations (e.g., youths, First Nations) and focuses on specific drug use patterns for these groups of users. One example, as noted in Chapter 13, is the the National Youth Solvent Abuse Program (NYSAP) which was established for targeting youth inhalant abuse.

We preface this section by highlighting the most noteworthy trends in prevention activities today, which include

- an increasing focus on having family (especially parental) involvement in prevention programs;
- the inclusion of attention to resistance-skills development, specifically strategies to use in avoiding pressures to use drugs;
- the development of programs in conjunction with more broad-based communitywide strategies—for example, a school-based intervention presented in conjunction with messages communicated through mass media outlets;
- the identification of subgroups of individuals most at risk for alcohol and other drug misuse and developing programs specifically for them—for example, inner-city youths, Native American youths, minority youths, and college and university students;
- a focused attention on the "gateway" drugs. Almost all programs emphasize abstinence from all illegal substances, but some programs focus on not initiating the use of tobacco, alcohol, and marijuana in particular. These are viewed as "gateway" drugs, in that their use typically precedes the use of the so-called harder drugs such as cocaine, heroin, and LSD;
- an increase in the attention to programs designed to minimize risk or negative consequences associated with any substance use that does occur. These risk-reduction programs do not sanction drug use but instead seek to minimize the negatives associated with such use for the individual and for society; and

"Drug users must be seen as human beings and not as criminals."

Dr. Pat Erickson, criminologist with the Toronto Addiction Research Foundation (*The Journal*, October 1993)

- a decrease in advertising geared toward (or readily accessible to) children and teenagers. Associated with this are efforts to reduce the positive portrayal of substance use (including smoking) in television shows and movies.

You will observe these trends in many of the programs described next.

Information for parents from Health Canada's Not4Me campaign.

Prevention in Education (School-Based Programs)

Traditionally, education programs have been aimed at adolescents and young adults, two of the more visible groups at-risk for substance abuse. More recently, efforts have been made to extend these interventions to children.

The school system has been touted as an ideal setting for providing educational materials on substance use and misuse. Indeed, Canada's education standards require education about alcohol and other drugs in the school curricula, and have been included systematicly into comprehensive instructional programs. In the past, drug education programs were hampered by teachers who had not been sufficiently trained in alcohol and drug education materials. During this time scare tactics and horror stories of drug addiction were often depicted. These programs—called the Knowledge–Attitudes–Behaviour Model in the 1970s and 1980s—functioned on the assumptions that providing information about drugs and their effects would increase students knowledge about drugs and drug use, that the increased knowledge would lead to changes in attitudes about drug use, and that these attitudes would be reflected in decreased drug using behaviour (Goodstadt, 1986).

The general outcome with respect to this model is that students presented with educational materials do increase their knowledge about the topics covered; however, there has not been much indication that patterns of substance use change (Bangert-Drowns, 1988; Botvin, 1999; Botvin & Griffin, 2003; Cellucci, 1984; Larimer & Cronce, 2007; Tobler, 1986). Indeed, in some cases (see Kinder, Pape, & Walfish, 1980; Stuart, 1974), students who were exposed to the education program were actually found in the short run to escalate their drug use! These findings represent the difficulties in prevention of drug use among children and adolescents and caution educators to be aware of other models for drug prevention. Tentatively, though, increased knowledge about alcohol and other drugs does not necessarily translate into modifications in their use.

Several factors may contribute to the unfounded change in behaviours associated with knowledge about drug use. One such factor may be related to the age at which youths are exposed to the intervention. As a result of data indicating that young children have already begun to form ideas about intoxication, drinking behaviour, and alcohol effects (Dunn & Goldman, 1996; Jahoda & Cramond, 1972; Zucker et al., 1996), more attention is being placed on educational materials geared toward children

Paul Almasy/Corbis

Billboards are an example of mass media prevention efforts. This roadside sign in France reminds motorists of the dangers of drinking and driving.

in early elementary school. Presenting materials for that level of development may be more successful than trying to modify beliefs at a later age when they are more firmly established. An example is research on smoking beliefs and behaviour. Chen and Winder (1986) wanted to determine the best time to apply a smoking intervention program. They surveyed more than 500 students in grades six, nine, and 12 in a Massachusetts school system. The results showed that students are likely to respond best to a smoking education program in grade six for several reasons. One is that fewer grade six students (6.5 percent) described themselves as occasional or regular smokers than did those in grade nine (21 percent) or those in grade 12 (32 percent). Grade six students also reported much less peer pressure to smoke than the grade nine or 12 students, less knowledge about smoking and its effects, and less familiarity with their parents' attitudes about smoking. In addition, there were indications that many of the grade six students surveyed were planning to smoke within the next five years. Consequently, aiming an education program at this age group appears to hold the most promise for engendering attitudes against personal smoking.

A related trend in the area of prevention education, starting in the 1980s, has been the use of parents serving as teachers of their children. Much of this growing emphasis on parents during the last decade derives from the view that substance use is a family concern. These parent-focused programs seek to enhance family communication about alcohol and other drugs, to have parents model or foster either abstinence or responsible use of accepted substances (generally alcohol), and to encourage abstinence from other substances (Botvin & Botvin, 1992; Kimmel, 1976). One such program, called "The Power of Positive Parenting," includes a curriculum designed to make parents aware of the profound influence their behaviour has on their children's behaviour (Richmond, 1977). Children, especially in their preschool years, turn primarily to their parents when looking for models of appropriate behaviour. The program aims to make parents aware of the ways they influence their children's beliefs about drugs and to help them determine what constitutes "responsible modeling" of, for example, drinking or smoking behaviour.

Prevention in Mass Media

By far, mass media approaches to prevention and intervention have the opportunity to be the most pervasive due to their broader audience and access to information about drug use and abuse. Mass media in this context refers to the widespread distribution of communications using such vehicles as television, radio, billboards, films, and printed material (including magazines). The most frequently used media are television and radio, typically through Health Canada or associations such as MADD Canada, which are called public service announcements (PSAs). Because mass media campaigns often involve frequent presentations of a relatively brief message (for example, a 15-second television spot), developers of these campaigns generally create a slogan that unites the material in the various spots. Slogans of some recent campaigns are "Just Say No" "Not4Me" and "Friends Don't Let Friends Drive Drunk." Most of the campaigns in recent years regarding alcohol abuse have focused on decreasing the incidence of driving under the influence, but also now focus on children's knowledge about other drugs for parents to know what to pay attention to.

Although research on mass media campaigns has not yielded a clear picture of their effects, the programs do succeed in raising knowledge levels and increasing awareness about the use of drugs (Blane, 1988; Botvin & Botvin, 1992; Gorman, 1995; Palmgreen & Donohew, 2003). Of particular note is the finding that campaigns on drunk driving consistently change the knowledge level (for example, knowing the legal definition of intoxication). As with other prevention approaches, attitude change has been found less consistently. There is no evidence, however, that general patterns of alcohol or drug use change significantly as a function of these mass media strategies. These approaches will more likely be successful if they are directed at particular substance-using groups. One example is the Montana Meth Project, designed to reduce methamphetamine use among children aged 12 to 17 (Montana Meth Project, 2008). Using graphic radio, television, and print/billboard advertisements, backed by increased enforcement and treatment availability, the state of Montana witnessed a dramatic decrease in meth use. In addition, Montana teenagers as a group had become much more wary of meth, relative to teens nationwide. The advertisement that was found to have greatest impact was a close-up picture of rotting teeth ("meth mouth"), often exhibited by chronic meth users.

Taken together, education and mass media prevention approaches continue to command the majority of resources available for prevention. Their benefits appear to be primarily in the areas of knowledge and, to a lesser extent, attitude change. Their effectiveness is likely to increase as they tailor the campaign messages and efforts to target these campaigns to particular populations of drug users. And, of course, more work is needed to increase the likelihood that these approaches will result in actual changes in substance use.

DRUGS AND CULTURE BOX 15.3

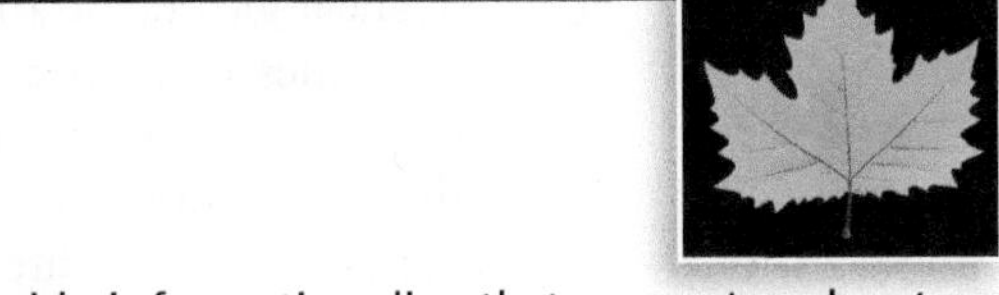

Canada's National Anti-Drug Strategy: Prevention, Treatment, and Enforcement

Canada's Anti-Drug Strategy was launched in 2008 to focus on prevention, treatment, and enforcement related to illicit drug use among young people. The campaign provides information to those most affected by drug use, including parents, young people, educators, law enforcement authorities, and communities. These campaigns each have specific goals of focus for the prevention, treatment and enforcement of illicit drug use. On their website, the Government of Canada provides the following information regarding their action plans:

The Prevention Action Plan will:

- refocus existing community-based drug-use prevention strategies, programs, and services for youth;
- provide information directly to parents, educators, and health professionals;
- develop materials for school-based awareness and prevention strategies for elementary and secondary school students;
- discourage illicit drug use through a new, national public awareness campaign; and
- provide financial help to communities for local projects to tackle the growing challenge of illicit drug use among young people.

The Treatment Action Plan will:

- enhance treatment and support for First Nations and Inuit people;

- provide treatment programs for young offenders with drug-related problems;
- enable the RCMP to refer youth with drug-related problems to treatment programs; and
- support research on new treatment models.

The Enforcement Action Plan will:

- provide funding to the RCMP so they can expand their dedicated anti-drug teams to help locate, investigate, and shut down organizations involved in the production and distribution of illicit drugs;
- provide resources to the Public Prosecution Service of Canada to provide legal advice to law enforcement at the investigative stage and to effectively prosecute those involved with the production and distribution of illicit drugs;
- increase the number of Health Canada inspectors and investigators to ensure accurate and timely analysis of suspected illicit drugs seized by law enforcement;
- increase the capacity of Canada Border Service Agency to inhibit the cross-border movement of precursor chemicals and illicit drugs;
- help law enforcement stop the flow of money that organized crime makes from the illicit drug trade;
- improve the ability of Canadian law enforcement officials to conduct joint investigations with their United States counterparts; and
- ensure that serious penalties are in place for serious drug crimes. (Health Canada, 2008)

In launching these campaigns, the Government of Canada has committed $232 million in new funding over five years to support these action plans. Progress with campaign funding has resulted in several major distributions which have focused on Canada's most drug prevalent areas, including

1. Canada's Cross Border Services Agency to decrease cross-border flow of illicit drugs,
2. Aboriginal youth treatment intervention programs,
3. Prince Edward Island addiction support programs,
4. First Nations and Inuit addiction services across Canada, and
5. Vancouver's Downtown Eastside treatment services.

Source: Backgrounder: National Anti-Drug Strategy 2008 URL: http://www.nationalantidrugstrategy.gc.ca/back-fich/doc2008_11_17b.html. National Anti-Drug Strategy. Reproduced with the permission of the Minister of Public Works and Government Services, 2012.

values clarification
A common component of affect-oriented prevention programs, which typically involves exploration of one's own needs and beliefs regarding drugs.

Affective Education Programs

Many prevention programs, particularly those geared toward youths, incorporate what is called an "affective" component. This affective feature typically involves **values clarification** and decision making. Values clarification activities include self-exploration, life values assessment, and strategies for fulfilling needs that are part of those values (Hewitt, 1982). These programs provide students with general strategies for making life choices and for applying these techniques to situations that involve alcohol or other drugs. The overall goal of the affect-oriented material is to have participants be aware of their own feelings and attitudes regarding drugs, so they can deal effectively with drug-use situations according to their individual value structures.

The logic behind the use of an affective component is that thoughts, feelings, attitudes, and values regarding alcohol and drugs play an important role in drug-use situations. Affective education programs function to increase self-esteem as a way to improve both education and positive decision-making choices. The research that has been conducted suggests that such interventions help to clarify personal views on substance use. The affective approach is intertwined with character building approaches and are incorporated in many school-board curriculums across Canada. These focus on several key values and character traits thought important for building self-esteem and self-confidence, which increases problem-solving and decision-making skills. For example, students learn alternative ways to deal with peer pressure other than saying 'no.'

Alternative Behaviours and Resistance-Skills Training

In recent years, there has been a significant growth in prevention programs that focus on developing alternatives to drug use or on developing skills to recognize and resist drug-use pressures. In developing alternatives to drug use, the objective is to provide people with the opportunity to engage in various productive activities (for example, sports, vocational training, and hobbies) that have the same or more appeal than drug use. Although this strategy makes sense in theory, evaluations of these programs have not revealed particular benefits in terms of substance-use behaviour (Botvin & Botvin, 1992; Botvin & Griffin, 2003).

Resistance-skills training interventions, on the other hand, have shown more promise. As described by Flay (1985), these interventions often include some combination of the following informational and skill-building strategies*:

- developing problem-solving and decision-making skills,
- developing cognitive skills for resisting interpersonal and media-based (e.g., pro-drinking or pro-smoking) drug-use messages,
- increasing self-awareness and self-esteem,
- learning nondrug-use skills for dealing with anxiety and stress,
- enhancing interpersonal skills such as the ability to initiate a conversation,
- developing assertiveness skills such as the ability to express displeasure and anger and to communicate needs, and
- understanding the relationship between drug use and health concerns.

Typically in these programs participants learn to be aware of social influences that lead to drug use and to use skills to resist these influences. For example, participants are exposed to strategies for refusing drugs when peers offer them. Often the programs include peers and peer leaders or coleaders. In summarizing the evaluation of resistance-skills training, Botvin and colleagues (Botvin, 1999; Botvin & Botvin, 1992; Botvin & Griffin, 2003) note some positive indications for several substances, including alcohol, marijuana, and especially cigarette smoking.

The most widely used resistance-oriented program today is DARE (Drug Abuse Resistance Education), which originated in the United States. The DARE curriculum, historically targeted at grade five and six students before they enter junior high school,

The best-known resistance-oriented program in drug-use prevention is DARE (Drug Abuse Resistance Education). The program, traditionally targeted at students in grades five and six, has been modified for use with a wider range of students.

* B. R. Flay, "What we know about the social influences to smoking prevention: Review and recommendations." C. Bell & R. Battjes (eds.), *Prevention research: Deterring drug abuse among children and adolescents,* Pg. 67–112, 1985. Rockville, MD: National Institute on Drug Abuse.

has been modified for use with a wider range of students. The program is based on the assumption that students must be educated to recognize the dangers of substance use and to resist subtle as well as direct pressures to use drugs. Accordingly, the program is designed to train students to recognize and resist peer and other influences to experiment with drugs. The curriculum includes 15 to 20 modules, each led by a law enforcement officer and lasting 45 to 60 minutes. Modules focus on topics such as refusal skills, risk assessment, decision making, interpersonal and communication skills, critical thinking, and alternatives to substance use. Despite its widespread use, the DARE program has not fared well in research evaluations (see review by Botvin & Griffin, 2003). In response, the DARE organization has been modifying the program to include components that may be more successful in curtailing drug use among students exposed to the program (see Contemporary Issue Box 15.4).

Closing Comments on Prevention

Prevention of alcohol and drug abuse is a topic that almost everyone acknowledges as being central to any coherent response to alcohol and drug problems in this country. Unfortunately, the area has been allocated few resources, at least in comparison to the monies spent annually on the treatment of alcohol and drug abuse. Although past efforts at prevention—especially education and mass media approaches—have increased relevant knowledge, they have had much less effect on alcohol and drug use. Especially critical in future research on prevention will be the design and evaluation of programs for specific cultural subgroups, the creation of programs geared toward the specific developmental levels of children and teenagers, parental involvement programs, and programs aimed at providing alternatives to alcohol and drug use.

CONTEMPORARY ISSUE BOX 15.4

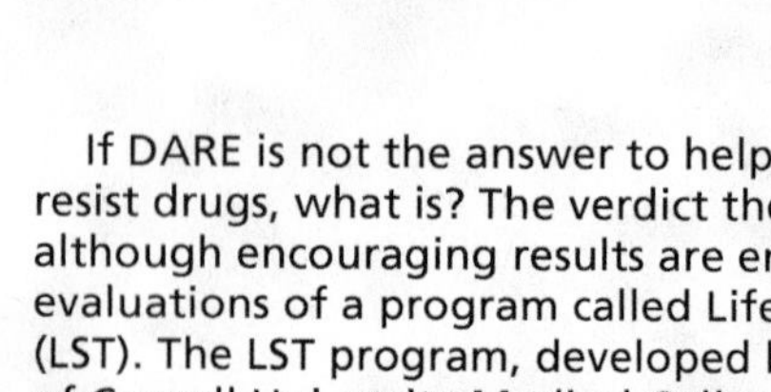

Dare We Question DARE?

Approximately three-quarters of the school systems in Canada and the United States have embraced the Drug Abuse Resistance Education (DARE) program, making it by far the most popular program in North America. Currently, there are approximately 75 000 students being taught the DARE program in 1600 Canadian schools. It has been endorsed by school officials, law enforcement agencies, and parents alike.

But is DARE getting the job done? Evaluations of the program over the past decade suggest probably not. The first strong indication appeared in 1994, when Ennett et al. published their summary of several DARE evaluation studies. Their conclusion: "DARE's short-term effectiveness for reducing or preventing drug use behaviors is small." Subsequent reports have provided a similar indication (Botvin & Griffin, 2003; West & O'Neal, 2004). In a 1999 study by Lynam et al., at a 10-year follow-up, it was found that students who had participated in DARE while in grade six did not have more successful outcomes than students not exposed to DARE.

If DARE is not the answer to helping students resist drugs, what is? The verdict there is still out, although encouraging results are emerging from evaluations of a program called Life Skills Training (LST). The LST program, developed by Gilbert Botvin of Cornell University Medical College, focuses on building students' drug-resistance abilities by helping them cope better with life's pressures. It focuses on skills for being independent, gaining personal control, communicating effectively, relieving anxiety, overcoming shyness, and developing healthy friendships. The program has been found to curtail students' use of a variety of substances, including alcohol, cigarettes, and marijuana (e.g., Spoth et al., 2008).

It remains to be seen, as the current enthusiasm for DARE begins to wane, if the program ultimately is markedly revamped or replaced by programs that have research support.

SUMMARY

- Most people agree that prevention efforts should be an important component of any comprehensive approach to substance abuse, but professionals and funding sources have not made prevention efforts a high priority.
- Prevention traditionally has been divided into three types of intervention: primary, secondary, and tertiary.
- Primary prevention refers to efforts that focus on avoiding substance use or abuse before it occurs.
- Secondary prevention involves early interventions designed to address substance abuse just as problems are beginning to appear.
- Tertiary prevention, which actually is more treatment than prevention, includes intervention used to treat people beyond the early stages of substance abuse.
- The sociocultural model of prevention posits that social norms directly influence substance use. Prevention efforts derived from this model try to influence the entire climate of drinking within a culture.
- The most common substance-abuse prevention interventions have been education and the use of mass media. Education curriculum in Canada requires alcohol and drug education in school curricula.
- Alcohol and drug education courses generally have been shown to increase knowledge levels but have not been so successful in changing substance-use patterns.
- In recent years, there has been an increasing use of parents in prevention programs, especially in programs that focus on children.
- Canada's Anti-Drug Strategy was launched in 2008 to focus on prevention, treatment, and enforcement related to illicit drug use among young people. The campaign provides information to those most affected by drug use, including parents, young people, educators, law enforcement authorities, and communities.
- Mass media campaigns appear to succeed in raising levels of knowledge and awareness about drugs. Changes in attitudes and actual drug-use behaviour have not been found consistently. Canada focuses on targeting parents as a means to promote prevention and recognizing the signs of drug abuse.
- Prevention programs with a resistance-training approach focus on training young people to recognize and resist pressures to use drugs. They offer alternative ways of responding to peer pressure and problem-solving solutions.
- The potential of prevention interventions have remained skewed by the inconsistent research findings.

Key Terms

emotionalism p. 381
primary prevention p. 379
secondary prevention p. 380
taboos p. 382
tertiary prevention p. 380
values clarification p. 390

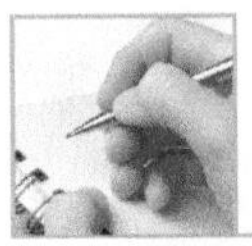

Essays/Thought Questions

1. Why do many prevention programs have modest, if any, effect on decisions by youths to use or not use drugs?
2. There has been increasing concern about "binge" drinking among college and university students. If you were designing a program to prevent or reduce binge drinking, what would be the most important elements you would include?

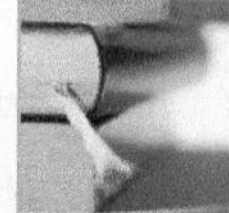

Suggested Readings

Ennet, S.T., Tobler, N.S., Ringwalt, C.L., & Flewelling, R.L. (1994). How effective is drug abuse resistance education? A meta-analysis of Project DARE outcome. *American Journal of Public Health, 84*, 1394–1401.

Government of Canada. (2011). National Anti-Drug Strategy. *Backgrounder*. Available at http://www.nationalantidrugstrategy.gc.ca/back-fich/doc2008_11_17b.html; accessed October 9, 2011.

Larimer, M.E., & Cronce, J.M. (2007). Identification, prevention, and treatment revisited: Individual-focused college drinking prevention strategies 1999–2006. *Addictive Behaviors, 32*, 2439–2468.

National Advisory Council on Alcohol Abuse and Alcoholism. (2002). *A call to action: Changing the culture of drinking at U.S. colleges.* Bethesda, MD: National Institute on Alcohol Abuse and Alcoholism (NIH Publication No. 02-5010).

National Institute on Drug Abuse (NIDA). (2003). *Preventing drug abuse among children and adolescents: A research-based guide for parents, educators, and community leaders* (2nd ed.). NIDA: Bethesda, MD.

GLOSSARY

A

absorbed When drugs have entered the bloodstream (Chapter 4). p. 62

acetaminophen Aspirin-like analgesic (Chapter 13). p. 325

acetylcholine A neurotransmitter linked with cognitive processes and memory that is found both in the brain and in the parasympathetic branch of the autonomic nervous system (Chapter 3). p. 44

acetylsalicylic acid Chemical name for aspirin (Chapter 13). p. 324

action potential The electrical impulse along the axon that occurs when a neuron fires (Chapter 3). p. 41

addiction In reference to drugs, overwhelming involvement with using a drug, in which the person feels a need to have it, develops a tolerance to it and has a strong tendency to resume use of it after stopping for a period (Chapter 1). p. 10

addictive personality The hypothesis that particular personality characteristics are common to all people with substance abuse disorders (Chapter 1). p. 8

aftercare In alcohol and drug treatment, therapeutic activities following the completion of a formal treatment program (Chapter 14). p. 353

agitated depression Depressed mood accompanied by a state of tension or restlessness. People with agitated depression show excessive motor activity, as they may, for example, be unable to sit still or may pace, wring the hands, or pull at their clothes (Chapter 12). p. 280

agonist A substance that occupies a neural receptor and causes some change in the conductance of the neuron (Chapter 3). 44

akinesia Slowness of movement and underactivity (Chapter 12). p. 284

Alzheimer's disease The most common type of dementia leading to the progressive loss of thinking and memory functions and affecting primarily individuals over the age of 65 (Chapter 3). p. 46

amotivational syndrome Loss of effectiveness and reduced capacity to accomplish conventional goals as a result of chronic marijuana use (Chapter 9). p. 214

amphetamine-type stimulants (ATSs) Refer to a group of drugs which commonly include amphetamine, methamphetamine and methcathinone. There are others, such as MDMA or "Ecstasy"—an amphetamine-type derivative with hallucinogenic properties (Chapter 5). p. 93

anabolic steroids Tissue-building drugs that produce masculinizing effects as well (Chapter 13). p. 318

analgesia Pain relief produced without a loss of consciousness (Chapter 11). p. 251

anandamide A lipid neurotransmitter mimicked by marijuana (Chapter 3). p. 50

anorectic effects Causing one to lose appetite; suppression of eating (Chapter 5). p. 95

antagonism The diminished or reduced effect of a drug when another drug is present (Chapter 4). p. 80

antagonist A substance that occupies a neural receptor and blocks normal synaptic transmission (Chapter 3). p. 44

anterograde amnesia Loss or limitation of the ability to form new memories (Chapter 12). p. 306

anticholinergic hallucinogens A class of drugs including atropine and scopolamine (Chapter 10). p. 224

antihistamines Common over-the-counter drugs with decongestant effects (Chapter 13). p. 326

antitussives Cough-suppressant drugs (Chapter 13). p. 325

anxiolytic Anxiety-reducing (Chapter 12). p. 293

apothecary A pharmacist (Chapter 9). p. 196

atrophy A decrease in muscle mass, which causes the muscle to become weak (Chapter 13). p. 332

atropine An anticholinergic hallucinogen found in certain plants (Chapter 10). p. 243

attention-deficit hyperactivity disorder (ADHD) It is a behavioural disorder, more commonly diagnosed in children, characterized by an individual's inattention, disorganized thinking and failure to complete tasks (Chapter 5). p. 91

autonomic nervous system (ANS) Part of the PNS; it has two branches, the sympathetic and the parasympathetic (Chapter 3). p. 52

axon A long cylindrical extension of the cell body of the neuron that conducts an electrical charge from the cell body to the axon terminals (Chapter 3). p. 41

axon terminals (or terminal buttons) Enlarged button-like structures at the ends of axon branches (Chapter 3). p. 42

B

barbiturates Depressant drugs formerly used as sleeping pills; currently used in anesthesia and treatment for epilepsy (Chapter 12). p. 293

basal ganglia Forebrain structures important for motor control, including the caudate nucleus, the putamen, and the globus pallidus (Chapter 3). p. 56

benzodiazepines Currently the most widely prescribed anxiolytic drugs (Chapter 12). p. 303

beta-blockers Drugs that block beta-adrenergic receptors of the sympathetic system and thus act to relieve high blood pressure (Chapter 3). p. 52

bioavailability The portion of the original drug dose that reaches its site of action or that reaches a fluid in the body that gives it access to its site of action (Chapter 4). p. 69

blackout Failure to recall events that occurred while drinking even though there is no loss of consciousness (Chapter 6). p. 120

blood alcohol concentration (BAC) A measure of the concentration of alcohol in the blood expressed in grams per 100 mL (Chapter 6). p. 114

blood–brain barrier The system that "filters" the blood before it can enter the brain (Chapter 3). p. 48

C

caffeinism Caffeine intoxication that may occur after the consumption of more than 600 mg of caffeine in a given day. It can cause symptoms such as muscle twitching, disordered thought and speech, and cardiac arrhythmia (Chapter 8). p. 187

Canadian Intense Method A technique that uses a laboratory machine to test levels of compounds in cigarettes. It is more realistic because it takes larger puffs of cigarette smoke more frequently than other methods (Chapter 7). p. 158

cannabinoids The more than 60 chemical compounds present in cannabis. One is delta-9-tetrahydrocannabinol (better known as THC) (Chapter 9). p. 202

cannabis sativa The Indian hemp plant popularly known as marijuana; its resin, flowering tops, leaves, and stem contain the plant's psychoactive substances (Chapter 2). p. 23

central nervous system (CNS) The brain and the spinal cord (Chapter 3). p. 51

cerebellum Hindbrain structure important in motor control and coordination (Chapter 3). p. 53

combination pill Birth control pill that contains synthetic forms of both female sex hormones: progesterone and estrogen (Chapter 13). p. 315

computerized axial tomography (CT) Technique that produces a three-dimensional X-ray image of the brain (Chapter 3). p. 57

confabulation A fabrication of events, when asked questions concerning them, because of an inability to recall (Chapter 6). p. 129

continuing of care A treatment approach that is comprised of pre-treatment and post-treatment care in which the client is actively involved, usually by reporting to the treatment centre/program (Chapter 13). p. 333

cortex The outermost and largest part of the human brain (Chapter 3). p. 56

counselling In alcohol and drug treatment, counsellors are specially trained professionals who perform a variety of treatment activities, including assessment, education, and individual, marital, and family counselling (Chapter 14). p. 352

crack A freebase cocaine produced by mixing cocaine salt with baking soda and water. The solution is then heated, resulting in brittle sheets of cocaine that are "cracked" into small smokable chunks or "rocks" (Chapter 5). p. 87

cradle-to-grave drug A term used to denote a drug's popularity and use throughout the lifespan (Chapter 8). p. 174

craving A term that has been variously defined in reference to drug use; typically a strong or intense desire to use a drug (Chapter 1). p. 4

cross-tolerance Tolerance to a drug (or drugs) never taken, which results from protracted tolerance to another drug (or drugs) (Chapter 1). p. 6

D

delta-9-tetrahydrocannabinol The principal active cannabinoid in marijuana responsible for the psychoactive effects (Chapter 9). p. 202

dendrites Spiny, branch-like structures that extend from the cell body of a neuron and typically contain numerous receptor sites, thus making them important in neural transmission (Chapter 3). p. 41

dependence A strong compulsion or urge; in this case to continue taking a particular drug (Chapter 1). p. 4

diffusibility A more diffusible substance is more easily entered into or "receptive" of another (Chapter 4). p. 69

disinhibition theory A theory that states that social inhibitions that act in opposition to the depressant action on the brain (in this case, through alcohol), causes a lack of anxiety or awareness towards inhibitive behaviour (i.e., aggression) (Chapter 6). p. 124

dissociative anesthetic A class of drugs including PCP and ketamine (Chapter 10). p. 224

dissolved When a drug changes from solid to liquid by mixing it with a liquid (Chapter 4). p. 64

distillation The process by which the heating of a fermented mixture increases its alcohol content (Chapter 6). p. 105

distribution The transport of drugs by the blood to their site(s) of action in the body (Chapter 4). p. 62

dopamine A neurotransmitter in the brain that is involved with movement and reward (Chapter 3). p. 47

drug Broadly defined as any chemical entity or mixture of entities not required for the maintenance of health but that alters biological function or structure when administered (Chapter 1). p. 2

drug abuse Any use of drugs that causes physical, psychological, legal, or social harm to the individual user or to others affected by the drug user's behaviour (Chapter 1). p. 2

drug dosage A measure of the quantity of a drug consumed (Chapter 1). p. 7

drug effects The action of a drug on the body. Drug effects are measured in different ways (Chapter 1). p. 3

drug efficacy The most intense, or peak, level of a drug effect (Chapter 4). p. 75

drug expectancy A person's anticipation of or belief about what he or she will experience upon taking a drug (Chapter 1). p. 9

drug potency The minimum effective dose of a drug (Chapter 4). p. 75

dyskinesia Disordered movements (Chapter 12). p. 284

E

effective dose The dose at which a given percentage of individuals show a particular effect of a drug (Chapter 4). p. 76

electroencephalography (EEG) Technique used to measure electrical activity in the brain (Chapter 3). p. 57

elimination half-life The amount of time that must pass for the amount of drug in the body to be reduced by half (50 percent) (Chapter 4). p. 71

emotionalism Focusing on and responding to emotions, and relying on emotional connections to our world (Chapter 15). p. 381

emphysema Disease of the lung characterized by abnormal dilution of its air spaces and distension of its walls. Frequently, heart action is impaired (Chapter 7). p. 169

endogenous Developed from within; when applied to depression, the term means that depressive symptoms seem to be due to genetic factors (Chapter 12). p. 286

endorphins Neurotransmitters in the brain that are mimicked by opiate drugs (Chapter 3). p. 50

energy drinks Beverages that contain large doses of caffeine, and other ingredients such as sugar, vitamins, herbal stimulants, and amino acids (Chapter 8). p. 185

enzyme breakdown One process by which neurotransmitters are inactivated. Chemicals called enzymes interact with the transmitter molecule and change its structure so that it no longer is capable of occupying receptor sites (Chapter 3). p. 44

estrogen One of the female sex hormones involved in the regulation of ovulation and the menstrual cycle (Chapter 13). p. 315

ether A gaseous compound that was used for its analgesic effects in dentistry, historically (Chapter 13). p. 330

ethylene A sweet-smelling gaseous compound that produces euphoria when inhaled (Chapter 13). p. 330

exogenous Developed from without; when applied to depression, the term means that depressive symptoms seem to be in reaction to a particular situation or event (Chapter 12). p. 286

extrapyramidal Outside the pyramidal tracts, with origin in the basal ganglia. These cell bodies are involved with starting, stopping, and smoothing out movements (Chapter 12). p. 284

F

feedback In this context, in a series of events, what happens in a later event alters events that preceded it (Chapter 4). p. 62

flashback A sudden recurrence of an LSD-like experience (Chapter 10). p. 237

forebrain The largest part of the human brain; includes the cerebral cortex, thalamus, hypothalamus, and limbic system (Chapter 3). p. 53

freebasing The term used to describe the practice of smoking cocaine by heating it until it vapourizes (Chapter 5). p. 87

G

GABA Short for gamma-aminobutyric acid; the most abundant inhibitory neurotransmitter in the brain (Chapter 3). p. 50

general anesthesia The reduction of pain by rendering the subject unconscious (Chapter 12). p. 294

glutamate An excitatory amino acid neurotransmitter (Chapter 3). p. 50

H

hash oil A potent distillate of marijuana or hashish. It first appeared in the United States in 1971 and can contain up to 60 percent THC (Chapter 9). p. 203

hashish A drug produced from the resin that covers the flowers of the cannabis hemp plant. The resin generally contains a greater concentration of the drug's psychoactive properties (Chapter 2). p. 23

heroin A drug produced by chemically processing morphine. It is more potent than morphine and has become the major opiate drug of abuse (Chapter 11). p. 252

hindbrain The lower part of the brain, including the medulla, pons, and cerebellum (Chapter 3). p. 53

hippocampus A structure of the limbic system thought to be important in the formation of memories (Chapter 3). p. 56

hypothalamus Forebrain structure that regulates eating, drinking, and other basic biological drives (Chapter 3). p. 54

I

ibuprofen Aspirin-like analgesic (Chapter 13). p. 325

indictable offence A more serious offence under the Criminal Code of Canada, punishable under the CDSA, which will result in a criminal record (Chapter 2). p. 35

inferior colliculi Midbrain structures that control sound localization (Chapter 3). p. 53

initial sensitivity The effect of a drug on a first-time user (Chapter 1). p. 7

interact When the effects of one drug are modified by the presence of another drug (Chapter 4). p. 79

intoxication A transient state of physical and psychological disruption caused by the presence of a toxic substance, such as alcohol, in the CNS (Chapter 6). p. 120

J

joint A hand-rolled marijuana cigarette (Chapter 9). p. 202

K

ketamine A dissociative anesthetic (Chapter 10). p. 244

L

L-dopa A chemical precursor of dopamine used in the treatment of Parkinson's disease (Chapter 3). p. 47

lethal dose The dose of a drug at which a given percentage of individuals die within a specified time (Chapter 4). p. 76

levo-alpha-acetylmethadol (LAAM) A drug used in treating heroin addiction that is similar in action to methadone but has longer-lasting effects (Chapter 14). p. 363

limbic system Forebrain structures including the amygdala and hippocampus (Chapter 3). p. 56

long-term memory Memory for remote events. According to one theory of memory, information enters long-term memory through short-term memory (Chapter 6). p. 121

M

magnetic resonance imaging (MRI) Technique that creates a high-resolution, three-dimensional image of the brain (Chapter 3). p. 58

manic Relating to mania, a mood disturbance that typically includes hyperactivity, agitation, excessive elation, and pressured speech (Chapter 12). p. 275

margin of safety The difference between the maximum effective dose and the minimum lethal dose (Chapter 4). p. 78

medulla oblongata The lowest hindbrain structure of the brain; important in the regulation of breathing, heart rate, and other basic life functions (Chapter 3). p. 53

mescaline An LSD-like hallucinogen found in the peyote cactus (Chapter 10). p. 224

mesolimbic dopaminergic pathway Pathway that is rewarding when stimulated (Chapter 3). p. 54

metabolism The process by which the body breaks down matter into more simple components and waste (Chapter 4). p. 62

methylated amphetamines A class of drugs including MDA and MDMA (ecstasy) (Chapter 10). p. 224

midbrain Part of the brain that includes the inferior and superior colliculi and the substantia nigra (Chapter 3). p. 53

milieu treatment Treatment in which the organization and structure of a setting are designed to change behaviour (Chapter 14). p. 352

monoamine oxidase (MAO) inhibitors Drugs used to treat depressions that inhibit the activity of the enzyme monoamine oxidase, which degrades the neurotransmitters of norepinephrine and serotonin (Chapter 6). p. 121

monoamines A class of chemicals characterized by a single amine group; includes the neurotransmitters norepinephrine, dopamine, and serotonin (Chapter 3). p. 47

myelin A fatty white substance that covers the axons of some neurons (Chapter 3). p. 41

N

naloxone A short-acting opiate antagonist (Chapter 11). p. 262

naproxen Aspirin-like analgesic (Chapter 13). p. 325

narcoleptic A state characterized by brief but uncontrollable episodes of sleep (Chapter 12). p. 275

narcotic A central nervous system depressant that contains sedative and pain-relieving compounds (Chapter 2). p. 30

neuroleptics Tranquilizing drugs used to treat psychoses; a synonym is *major tranquilizer* (Chapter 12). p. 281

neuromuscular junction Junction between neuron and muscle fibres where release of acetylcholine by neurons causes muscles to contract (Chapter 3). p. 45

neurons Individual nerve cells that are basic building blocks of the nervous system (Chapter 3). p. 41

neuropsychological tests Formal ways of measuring behavioural functions that may be impaired by brain lesions (Chapter 6). p. 129

neuroses Nonpsychotic emotional disturbance, pain, or discomfort beyond what is appropriate in the conditions of one's life (Chapter 12). p. 275

neurotransmitters Chemical substances stored in the axon terminals that are released into the synapse when the neuron fires. Neurotransmitters then influence activity in postsynaptic neurons (Chapter 3). p. 42

nicotine poisoning A consequence of nicotine overdose characterized by palpitations, dizziness, sweating, nausea, or vomiting (Chapter 7). p. 150

norepinephrine A neurotransmitter in the brain that is involved in activity of the sympathetic branch of the autonomic nervous system (Chapter 3). p. 47

O

opium poppy A plant cultivated for centuries—primarily in Eurasia—for opium, a narcotic that acts as a central nervous system depressant (Chapter 2). p. 23

opium The dried sap produced by the poppy plant (Chapter 11). p. 250

P

paranoid schizophrenia A type of schizophrenia distinguished by systematic delusions or auditory hallucinations related to one theme (Chapter 12). p. 282

parasympathetic branch Branch of the ANS that is responsible for lowering heart rate and blood pressure (Chapter 3). p. 52

Parkinson's disease A progressive disease causing the deterioration of motor control (Chapter 3). p. 47

patent medicines Drugs or combination of drugs that were sold, most often in the 19th century, as medicines that would cure a host of illnesses and diseases (Chapter 2). p. 25

peripheral nervous system (PNS) Sensory nerves, motor nerves, and the automatic nervous system (Chapter 3). p. 51

personality disorders Longstanding patterns of behaviour that frequently create distress for individuals due to their personal or social consequences; usually recognizable from adolescence or earlier (Chapter 14). p. 369

pharmacodynamics The branch of pharmacology that concerns the biochemical and physiological effects of drugs and their mechanisms of action (Chapter 4). p. 62

pharmacokinetics The branch of pharmacology that concerns the absorption, distribution, biotransformation, and excretion of drugs (Chapter 4). p. 62

pharmacology The scientific study of drugs concerned with all information about the effects of drugs on living systems (Chapter 1). p. 2

phencyclidine A dissociative anesthetic (Chapter 10). p. 244

placebo In pharmacology, a chemically inactive substance that is used in controlled research to study the effects of expectations or beliefs about a drug's effects (e.g., water or sugar pills) (Chapter 1). p. 9

polydrug use The same person's regular use of more than one drug (Chapter 1). p. 14

pons Hindbrain structure important in the control of sleep and wakefulness (Chapter 3). p. 53

positron emission transaxial tomography (PET) A technique used to measure activity in selected brain regions (Chapter 3). p. 57

prevalence The general occurrence of an event, usually expressed in terms of percentage of a population (Chapter 1). p. 11

primary prevention A prevention strategy that attempts to encourage avoidance of substance use or abuse before it has a chance to occur (Chapter 15). p. 379

progesterone One of the female sex hormones involved in the regulation of ovulation and the menstrual cycle (Chapter 13). p. 315

progestin pill Birth control pill (sometimes called the minipill) that contains only progestin, a synthetic progesterone (Chapter 13). p. 316

prohibition The legislative forbidding of the sale, distribution, or possession of a substance, as in the alcohol Prohibition era in North America during the 1920s–1930s (Chapter 2). p. 31

proof The proportion of alcohol in a beverage, by volume. Proof typically is used in reference to distilled spirits and equals twice the percentage of alcohol (Chapter 6). p. 106

prostaglandins Naturally occurring chemicals blocked by aspirin and related analgesics (Chapter 13). p. 325

pseudoephedrine An over-the-counter decongestant (Chapter 13). p. 325

psilocybin An LSD-like hallucinogen found in mushrooms (Chapter 10). p. 224

psychoactive Pertaining to effects on mood, thinking, and behaviour (Chapter 1). p. 4

psychological set An individual's knowledge, attitudes, expectations, and other thoughts about an object or event, such as a drug (Chapter 1). p. 9

psychological treatment Treatment geared to changing emotions, thoughts, or behaviour without the use of medications or other physical or biological means (Chapter 14). p. 352

psychopharmacology The subarea of pharmacology that is concerned with the effects of drugs on behaviour (Chapter 1). p. 2

psychosurgery Surgery that entails the cutting of fibres connecting particular parts of the brain or the removal or destruction of areas of brain tissue with the goal of modifying severe behavioural or emotional disturbances (Chapter 12). p. 275

psychotherapeutic Exerting a special or unique action on psychological functioning (Chapter 12). p. 274

psychotherapy Typically, conversation between a specially trained individual (therapist) and another person (or family) that is intended to change patterns of behaviour, thoughts, or feelings in that person (or family) (Chapter 14). p. 352

Q

qualitative The kind, as opposed to the quantity, of effect (Chapter 4). p. 81

R

rebound insomnia Inability to sleep produced as a withdrawal symptom associated with some depressant drugs (Chapter 12). p. 298

receptor sites Specialized structures located on dendrites and cell bodies for neurons that are activated by neurotransmitters (Chapter 3). p. 43

recovery In the addictions field, changes back to health in physical, psychological, spiritual, and social functioning. It generally is believed that recovery is a lifetime process that requires total abstinence from alcohol and nonprescribed drugs (Chapter 14). p. 342

relapse A term from physical disease; return to a previous state of illness from one of health. As applied to smoking, it means the smoker resumes smoking after having abstained for some amount of time (Chapter 7). p. 166

REM rebound An increase in the rapid eye movement or REM stage of sleep when withdrawing from drugs that suppress REM time (Chapter 12). p. 299

REM sleep Acronym for "rapid eye movements," which are associated with dream activity and are one stage in a cycle of sleep (Chapter 6). p. 120

reticular activating system Pathway running through the medulla and pons that regulates alertness and arousal (Chapter 3). p. 53

reuptake One process by which neurotransmitters are inactivated. Neurotransmitter molecules are taken back up into the axon terminal that released them (Chapter 3). p. 44

reverse tolerance or sensitization It is the reversal of the side effects from a drug, such as a user of an ATS becomes more aware of the effects of the drug the longer the usage (Chapter 5). p. 99

route of drug administration The way that drugs enter the body (e.g., oral, or intravenous) (Chapter 1). p. 7

S

scopolamine An anticholinergic hallucinogen found in certain plants (Chapter 10). p. 243

secondary prevention Interventions designed to prevent substance-use problems just as the early signs of abuse begin to appear (Chapter 15). p. 380

sedative-hypnotic effects The calming and sleep-inducing effects of some drugs (Chapter 12). p. 293

self-medication The idea that some people prescribe their own medication, in the form of alcohol or illicit drugs, to alleviate psychological difficulties such as anxiety or depression (Chapter 14). p. 369

sensation seeking The need for varied, novel, and complex sensations and experiences and the willingness to take physical and social risks for the sake of such experience (Chapter 1). p. 8

serotonergic hallucinogens A class of drugs that includes LSD and drugs with similar effects and mechanisms of actions (Chapter 10). p. 224

serotonin A neurotransmitter in the brain that is involved with sleep and mood (Chapter 3). p. 47

short-term memory Memory for recent events, which is thought to differ from long-term memory in several important ways (Chapter 6). p. 121

sociopathy Personality disorder characterized by a lack of concern for social obligations or rules, a lack of feelings for others, and a tendency toward violence (Chapter 14). p. 369

solubility The ease with which a compound can be dissolved or entered into a solution (Chapter 4). p. 69

speakeasies A slang expression used to describe saloons operating without a licence; popularly used during Prohibition (Chapter 2). p. 32

spontaneous remission Resolution of a problem without the help of formal treatment (Chapter 14). p. 337

standard drink The alcohol equivalent in a drink of beer, wine, or distilled spirits. A standard drink equals 0.5 ounce of alcohol—about the alcohol content in 12 ounces of beer, four ounces of table wine, or one ounce of 90- to 100-proof whiskey (Chapter 6). p. 114

state-dependent learning When learning under the influence of a drug is best recalled when one is in the same "state" (Chapter 5). p. 96

stimulant psychosis Paranoid delusions and disorientation resembling the symptoms of paranoid schizophrenia, caused by prolonged use or overdose of cocaine and/or amphetamine (Chapter 5). p. 90

substantia nigra Literally "black substance," this basal ganglia structure is darkly pigmented; produces dopamine. Damage to this area produces Parkinson's disease (Chapter 3). p. 53

summary conviction A minor offence under the Criminal Code of Canada, punishable under the CDSA, which does not result in a criminal record (Chapter 2). p. 35

superior colliculi Midbrain structures that control visual localization (Chapter 3). p. 53

suspended When a drug's particles are dispersed in solution but not dissolved in it (Chapter 4). p. 64

sympathetic branch Branch of the ANS that is activated during emotional arousal and is responsible for such physiological changes as increased heart and respiratory rate, increased blood pressure, and pupil dilation (Chapter 3). p. 52

sympathomimetic Drugs such as cocaine and amphetamines that produce the physiological effects of sympathetic activity (Chapter 3 and Chapter 5). p. 52; p. 95

synapse The junction between neurons (Chapter 3). p. 42

syndrome In medicine, a number of symptoms that occur together and characterize a specific illness or disease (Chapter 1). p. 6

synergism (potentiation) Any enhancing drug interaction (Chapter 4). p. 79

synesthesia An effect sometimes produced by hallucinogens that is characterized by the perception of a stimulus in a modality other than the one in which it was presented (for example, a subject may report "seeing" music) (Chapter 10). p. 234

T

taboos A custom that prohibits or restricts a practice of openly addressing an issue, event, person, or object (Chapter 15). p. 382

tardive dyskinesia An extrapyramidal complication characterized by involuntary movements of the mouth and tongue, trunk, and extremities; a side effect of long-term (two or more years) use of antipsychotic drugs (Chapter 12). p. 284

tea-pads Historically, places where people gathered to smoke marijuana. The sites could be anything from a rented room to a hotel suite (Chapter 9). p. 197

teratogenic Producing abnormalities in the fetus (Chapter 12). p. 310

teratogens Any chemical or environmental factor that negatively effects the development of an embryo or fetus during pregnancy (Chapter 6). p. 130

tertiary prevention Treatment interventions with people well beyond the early stages of substance abuse or dependence (Chapter 15). p. 380

testosterone The male sex hormone; anabolic steroids are basically synthetic versions of testosterone (Chapter 13). p. 318

thalamus Forebrain structure that organizes sensory input (Chapter 3). p. 54

therapeutic index A measure of a drug's safety in medical care; it is computed as a ratio: LD 50/ED 50 (Chapter 4). p. 77

tolerance Generally, increased amounts of a drug needed to achieve intoxication, or a diminished drug effect with continued use of the same amount of a drug (Chapter 1). p. 5

treatment Planned activities designed to change some pattern of behaviour(s) of individuals or their families (Chapter 14). p. 337

treatment effects The results of experiencing a treatment, usually measured in different areas of functioning, such as substance use, family functioning, and vocational functioning (Chapter 14). p. 368

treatment outcome research Research designed to show a causal relationship between undergoing a treatment and some physical, psychological, or social change (Chapter 14). p. 355

V

values clarification A common component of affect-oriented prevention programs, which typically involves exploration of one's own needs and beliefs regarding drugs (Chapter 15). p. 390

vesicles Tiny sacs in axon terminals that store neurotransmitters (Chapter 3). p. 43

W

whippets Small containers of pressurized nitrous oxide, most commonly used in household and kitchen products in pressurized cans (Chapter 13). p. 330

withdrawal A definable illness that occurs with a cessation or decrease in use of a drug (Chapter 1). p. 6

REFERENCES

Aaron, P., & Musto, D. (1981). Temperance and prohibition in America: A historical overview. In M. H. Moore & D. R. Gerstein (Eds.), *Alcohol and public policy* (pp. 127–181). Washington, DC: Academy Press.

Abbott, P. J. (1986). Caffeine: A toxicological overview. *The Medical Journal of Australia, 145,* 518–521.

Abel, E. L. (1971). Marihuana and memory: Acquisition or retrieval? *Science, 173,* 1038–1040.

Abel, E. L. (1980). *Marijuana: The first twelve thousand years.* New York: Plenum Press.

Abel, E. L. (1985). *Psychoactive drugs and sex.* New York: Plenum Press.

Abraham, H. D., Aldridge, A. M., & Gogia, P. (1996). The psychopharmacology of hallucinogens. *Neuropsychopharmacology, 14,* 285–298.

Abrahamov, A., Abrahamov, A., & Mechoulam, R. (1995). An efficient new cannabinoid anti-emetic in pediatric oncology. *Life Sciences, 56,* 2097–2102.

Abrams, D. B., & Wilson, G. T. (1986). Habit disorders: Alcohol and tobacco dependence. In A. J. Frances & R. E. Hales (Eds.), *American Psychiatric Association annual review* (Vol. 5, pp. 606–626). Washington, DC: American Psychiatric Press.

Abrams, D. I., Hilton, J. F., Leiser, R. J., Shade, S. B., Elbeik, T. A., Aweeks, F. T., Benowitz, N. L., Bredt, B. M., Korel, B., Aberg, J. A., Deeks, S. G., Mitchell, T. F., Mulligan, K., Baccheti, P., McCune, J. M., & Schambelan, M. (2003). Short-term effects of cannabinoids in patients with HIV-1 infection: A randomized placebo-controlled clinical trial. *Annals of Internal Medicine, 139,* 258–266.

Adams, I. B., & Martin, B. R. (1996). Cannabis: Pharmacology and toxicology in animals and humans. *Addiction, 91,* 1585–1614.

Adams, W. L., Yuan, Z., Barboriak, J. J., & Rimm, A. A. (1993). Alcohol-related hospitalizations of elderly people. *Journal of the American Medical Association, 270,* 1222–1225.

Adesso, V. J. (1985). Cognitive factors in alcohol and drug use. In M. Galizio & S. A. Maisto (Eds.), *Determinants of substance abuse* (pp. 179–208). New York: Plenum Press.

Adlaf, E. M., Begin, P., & Sawka, E. (Eds.). (2005). *Canadian Addiction Survey (CAS): A national survey of Canadians' use of alcohol and other drugs: Prevalence of use and related harms: Detailed report.* Ottawa: Canadian Centre of Substance Abuse.

Adler, I., & Kandel, D. (1981). Crosscultural perspectives on developmental stages in adolescent drug use. *Journal of Studies on Alcohol, 42,* 701–715.

Agurell, S., Halldin, M., Lindgren, J. R., Ohlsson, A., Widman, M., Gillespie, H., & Hollister, L. (1986). Pharmacokinetics and metabolism of tetrahydrocannabinol and other cannabinoids with emphasis on man. *Pharmacological Reviews, 38,* 21–43.

Alasuutari, P. (1992). *A cultural theory of alcoholism.* Albany: State University of New York Press.

Alcohol Drug Rehab Canada. (2011). Canada outpatient drug & alcohol addiction programs. Available at http://www.canadadrugrehab.ca/Canada-Outpatient-Alcohol-Drug-Rehab-Programs.html.

Alcoholics Anonymous. (1972). *If you are a professional, A.A. wants to work with you.* New York: Alcoholics Anonymous World Services.

Alcoholics Anonymous. (1983). *Questions and answers on sponsorship.* New York: Alcoholics Anonymous World Services.

Alcoholics Anonymous. (2011). Estimates of A.A. Groups and Members. Available at http://www.aa.org/subpage.cfm?page=74.

The Alcoholism Report. (1993). Drug czar calls for treatment of drug addicted criminals. *The Alcoholism Report, 21,* 6–7.

Alda, M., Hajek, T., Calkin, C., & O'Donovan, C. (2009). Treatment of bipolar disorder: New perspectives. *Annals of Medicine, 41,* 186–196.

Aldrich, M. R. (1977). Tantric cannabis use in India. *Journal of Psychedelic Drugs, 9,* 227–233.

Allison, M., & Hubbard, R. L. (1985). Drug abuse treatment process: A review of the literature. *International Journal of the Addictions, 20,* 1321–1345.

Alvik, A., Haldorsen, T., & Lindermann, R. (2005). Consistency of reported alcohol use by pregnant women: Anonymous versus confidential questionnaires with item response differences. *Alcoholism: Clinical and Experimental Research, 29,* 1444–1449.

Alzheimer's Society. (2010). Key facts about Alzheimer's disease and related dementia. Available at http://www.alzheimer.ca/english/disease/stats-intro.htm.

Amar, M. B. (2006). Cannabinoids in medicine: A review of their therapeutic potential. *Journal of Ethnopharmacology, 105,* 1–25.

American Psychiatric Association (APA). (1987). *Diagnostic and statistical manual of mental disorders* (3rd ed., rev. ed.). Washington, DC: Author.

American Psychiatric Association. (1994). *Diagnostic and statistical manual of mental disorders* (4th ed.). Washington, DC: Author.

American Psychiatric Association. (2000a). *Diagnostic and statistical manual of mental disorders* (4th ed., rev.). Washington, DC: Author.

American Psychiatric Association. (2000b). *Practice guidelines for the treatment of psychiatric disorders.* Washington, DC: Author.

Anderson, D., Beckerleg, S., Hailu, D., & Klein, A. (2007). *The khat controversy: Stimulating the debate on drugs.* Oxford: Berg Press.

Anderson, T. L., & Levy, J. A. (2003). Marginality among older injectors in today's illicit drug culture: Assessing the impact of aging. *Addiction, 98,* 761–770.

Andrain-McGovern, J., Tercyak, K. P., Shields, A. E., Bush, A., Espinel, C. F., & Leman, C. (2003). Which adolescents are most receptive to tobacco industry marketing? Implications for counter advertising campaigns. *Health Communication, 15,* 490–513.

Andrews, J. M., & Nemeroff, C. B. (1994). Contemporary management of depression. *American Journal of Medicine, 97* (Supplement 6A), 24S–32S.

Annis, H. M. (1986). A relapse prevention model for treatment of alcoholics. In W. R. Miller & N. Heather (Eds.), *Treating addictive behaviors* (pp. 407–433). New York: Plenum Press.

Anthosinen, N. R., Skeans, M. A., Wise, R. A., Manfreda, J., Kanner, R. E., & Connett, R. E., for the Lung Health Study Research Group. (2005). The effects of a smoking cessation intervention on 14.5-year mortality. *Annals of Internal Medicine, 142,* 233–239.

Anton, R. F., et al. (2006). Combined pharmacotherapies and behavioral interventions for alcohol dependence. *Journal of the American Medical Association, 295,* 2003–2017.

Arango, V., & Mann, J. J. (2009). Abnormalities of brain structure and function in mood disorders. In D. S. Charney & E. J. Nestler (Eds.), *Neurobiology of mental illness* (3rd ed., pp. 515–529). New York: Oxford University Press.

Armor, D. J., Polich, J. M., & Stambul, H. B. (1976). *Alcoholism and treatment.* Report prepared for the National Institute on Alcohol Abuse and Alcoholism (R-1739-NIAAA). Santa Monica, CA: Rand Corporation.

Ashley, R. (1975). *Cocaine: Its history, uses, and effects.* New York: Warner.

Ashton, R. (2002). *This is heroin.* London: Sanctuary Publishing LTD.

Austin, S. B., & Gortmaker, S. L. (2001). Dieting and smoking initiation in early adolescent girls and boys: A prospective study. *American Journal of Public Health, 91,* 446–450.

Australian Drug Law Reform Foundation. (1996). *Drug love: The questioning of our current drug law.* Canberra: Author.

Backgrounder on the Canadian Tobacco Industry and its market. (2008). Available at http://www.nsra-adnf.ca/cms/file/pdf/Backgrounder2007_2008.pdf.

Baer, J. S., Kivlahan, D. R., Blume, A. W., McKnight, P., & Marlatt, G. A. (2001). Brief intervention for heavy drinking college students: 4-year follow-up and natural history. *American Journal of Public Health, 91,* 1310–1316.

Baer, J. S., Kivlahan, D. R., Fromme, K., & Marlatt, G. A. (1994). Secondary prevention of alcohol abuse with college student populations: A skills-training approach. In G. Howard & P. E. Nathan (Eds.), *Alcohol use and misuse by young adults* (pp. 83–108). Notre Dame, IN: Notre Dame University Press.

Bailey, S. (2003). Man hailed by some as genius cannot be forcibly drugged for mental illness. Canadian Press. Available at http://www.cognitiveliberty.org/neuro/Starson_wins.html.

Bak, A. A., & Grobbee, D. E. (1989). The effect on serum cholesterol levels of coffee brewed by filtering or boiling. *New England Journal of Medicine, 321,* 1432–1437.

Baker, A., Boggs, T. G., & Lewin, T. J. (2001). Randomized controlled trial of brief cognitive-behavioral interventions among regular users of amphetamine. *Addiction, 96,* 1279–1287.

Balazs, R., Bridges, R. J., & Cotman, C. W. (2006). *Excitatory amino acid transmission in health and disease.* Oxford, UK: Oxford University Press.

Baldessarini, R. J. (1985). *Chemotherapy in psychiatry: Principles and practice* (rev. ed.). Cambridge, MA: Harvard University Press.

Ball, J. C., Meyers, C. P., & Friedman, S. R. (1988). Reducing the risk of AIDS through methadone maintenance treatment. *Journal of Health and Social Behavior, 29,* 214–226.

Bambicoa, F., Nguyena, N., Katza, N., Gobbi, G. (2009). Chronic exposure to cannabinoids during adolescence but not during adulthood impairs emotional behaviour and monoaminergic neurotransmission. *Neurobiology of Disease, 37,* 641–655.

Bangert-Drowns, R. L. (1988). The effects of school-based substance abuse education: A meta-analysis. *Journal of Drug Education, 18,* 243–264.

Barkley, R. A. (2001). Foreword. In L. L. Weyandt (Ed.), *An ADHD primer* (pp. ix–x). Boston: Allyn & Bacon.

Barnes, G. E. (1979). The alcoholic personality: A reanalysis of the literature. *Journal of Studies on Alcohol, 40,* 571–634.

Baron, A., & Galizio, M. (2005). Positive and negative reinforcement: Should the distinction be preserved? *The Behavior Analyst, 28,* 85–99.

Barone, J. J., & Roberts, H. R. (1996). Caffeine consumption. *Food and Chemical Toxicology, 34,* 119–129.

Barr, H. M., & Streissguth, A. P. (2001). Identifying maternal self-reported alcohol use associated with fetal alcohol spectrum disorders. *Alcoholism: Clinical and Experimental Research, 25,* 283–287.

Barrett, R. J. (1985). Behavioral approaches to individual differences in substance abuse. In M. Galizio & S. A.

Maisto (Eds.), *Determinants of substance abuse: Biological, psychological, and environmental factors* (pp. 125–175). New York: Plenum Press.

Barrett-Connor, E., Chang, J. C., & Edelstein, S. L. (1994). Coffee-associated osteoporosis offset by daily milk consumption. *Journal of the American Medical Association, 271,* 280–283.

Bartholow, B. D., & Heinz, A. (2006). Alcohol and aggression without consumption. *Psychological Science, 17,* 30–37.

Bartolet, J., & Levine, S. (2001). The holy men of heroin. In H. T. Wilson (Ed.), *Drugs, society and behavior* (pp. 85–86). Guilford, CT: McGraw-Hill/Dushkin.

Bauman, M. H., Wang, X., & Rothman, R. B. (2007). 3,4-methylinedioxymethamphetamine (MDMA) neurotoxicity in rats: A reappraisal of past and present findings. *Psychopharmacology, 189,* 407–424.

Baur, J. A., & Sinclair, D. A. (2006). Therapeutic potential of resveratrol: The in vivo evidence. *Nature Reviews Drug Discovery, 5,* 493–506.

Beardsley, P. M., Balster, R. L., & Harris, L. S. (1996). Evaluation of the discriminative stimulus and reinforcing effects of gammahydroxybutyrate (GHB). *Psychopharmacology, 127,* 315–322.

Beauvais, F., Wayman, J., Jumper-Thurman, P., Plested, B, & Helm, H. (2002). Inhalant abuse among American Indian, Mexican American and Non-Latino White adolescents. *American Journal of Drug & Alcohol Abuse, 28,* 477–495.

Becker, C. E., Roe, R. L., & Scott, R. A. (1975). *Alcohol as a drug.* New York: Medcom Press.

Becker, H. S. (1953). Becoming a marihuana user. *American Journal of Sociology, 59,* 235–242.

Becker, H. S. (1963). *Outsiders: Studies in the sociology of deviance.* New York: Free Press.

Belluzzi, J. D., Lee, A. G., Oliff, H. S., & Leslie, F. M. (2004). Age-dependent effects of nicotine on locomotor activity and conditioned place preference in rats. *Psychopharmacology, 174,* 389–395.

Benet, L. Z., Mitchell, J. R., & Sheiner, L. B. (1990a). General principles. In A. G. Gilman, T. W. Rall, A. S. Nies, & P. Taylor (Eds.), *Goodman and Gilman's The pharmacological basis for therapeutics* (8th ed., pp. 1–2). New York: Pergamon Press.

Benet, L. Z., Mitchell, J. R., & Sheiner, L. B. (1990b). Pharmacokinetics: The dynamics of drug absorption, distribution, and elimination. In A. G. Gilman, T. W. Rall, A. S. Nies, & P. Taylor (Eds.), *Goodman and Gilman's The pharmacological basis of therapeutics* (8th ed., pp. 3–32). New York: Pergamon Press.

Benowitz, N. L., Hall, S. M., & Modin, G. (1989). Persistent increase in caffeine concentrations in people who stop smoking. *British Medical Journal, 298,* 1075–1076.

Benowitz, N. L., Porchet, H., Sheiner, L., & Jacob, P. (1988). Nicotine absorption and cardiovascular effects with smokeless tobacco use: Companion with cigarettes and nicotine gum. *Clinical Pharmacology and Therapeutics, 44,* 23–28.

Berild, D., & Hasselbalch, H. (1981). Survival after a blood alcohol of 1127 mg/dl. *Lancet, 2*(8242), 363.

Berman, R. M., Sporn, J., Charney, D. S., & Matthew, S. J. (2009). Principles of the pharmacotherapy of depression. In D. S. Charney & E. J. Nestler (Eds.), *Neurobiology of mental illness* (3rd ed., pp. 491–514). New York: Oxford University Press.

Berridge, K. C., & Robinson, T. E. (1998). What is the role of dopamine in reward: Hedonic impact, reward learning or incentive salience? *Brain Research Reviews, 28,* 309–369.

Bhana, N., Foster, R. H., Olney, R., & Plosker, G. L. (2001). Olanzapine: An updated review of its use in the management of schizophrenia. *Drugs, 61,* 111–161.

Bickel, W. K., & DeGrandpre, R. J. (1995). Price and alternatives: Suggestions for drug policy from psychology. *International Journal of Drug Policy, 6,* 93–105.

Bickel, W. K., Amass, L., Higgins, S. T., Badger, G. J., & Esch, R. A. (1997). Effects of adding behavioral treatment to opioid detoxification with buprenorphine. *Journal of Consulting and Clinical Psychology, 65,* 803–810.

Bickel, W. K., DeGrandpre, R. J., & Higgins, S. T. (1995). The behavioral economics of concurrent drug reinforcers: A review and reanalysis of drug self-administration research. *Psychopharmacology, 118,* 250–259.

Bina, C. (1998). Drug testing 101: Detecting tainted samples. *Corrections Today, 60,* 122–128.

Bishara, D., & Taylor, D. (2008). Upcoming agents for the treatment of schizophrenia. *Drugs, 68,* 2269–2292.

Blane, H. T. (1976). Education and the prevention of alcoholism. In B. Kissin & H. Begleiter (Eds.), *The biology of alcoholism: Vol. 4. Social aspects of alcoholism* (pp. 519–578). New York: Plenum Press.

Blane, H. T. (1988). Research on mass communications and alcohol. *Contemporary Drug Problems, 15,* 7–20.

Bloomquist, E. R. (1971). *Marijuana: The second trip* (rev. ed.). Beverly Hills, CA: Glencoe Press.

Blum, K. (1984). *Handbook of abusable drugs.* New York: Gardner Press.

Bofetta, P., Hecht, S., Gray, N., Gupta, P., & Staif, K. (2008). Smokeless tobacco and cancer. *Lancet Oncology, 9,* 667–675.

Bonham, C., & Abbott, C. (2008). Are second generation antipsychotics a distinct class? *Journal of Psychiatric Practice, 14,* 225–231.

Borelli, B., Spring, B., Niaura, R., Hitsman, B., & Papandonatos, G. (2001). Influences of gender and weight gain on short-term relapse to smoking in a cessation trial. *Journal of Consulting and Clinical Psychology, 69,* 511–515.

Botvin, G. J. (1999). Adolescent drug abuse prevention: Current findings and future directions. In M. D. Glantz & C. R. Hartel (Eds.), *Drug abuse: Origins and interventions* (pp. 285–308). Washington, DC: American Psychological Association.

Botvin, G. J., & Botvin, E. M. (1992). School-based and community-based prevention approaches. In J. H. Lowinson, P. Ruiz, & R. B. Millman (Eds.), *Substance abuse: A comprehensive textbook* (2nd ed., pp. 910–927). Baltimore, MD: Williams & Wilkins.

Botvin, G. J., & Griffin, K. W. (2003). Drug abuse prevention curricula in schools. In Z. Sloboda & W. J. Bukoski (Eds.), *Handbook of drug abuse prevention: Theory, science, and practice* (pp. 45–74). New York: Kluwer Academic/Plenum Publishers.

Bouso, J. C., Boblin, R., Farre, M., Alcazar, M. A., & Gomez-Jarabo, G. (2008). MDMA-assisted psychotherapy using low doses in a small sample of women with chronic posttraumatic stress disorder. *Journal of Psychoactive Drugs, 40,* 225–236.

Boutros, N. N., & Bowers, M. B. (1996). Chronic substance-induced psychotic disorders: State of the literature. *Journal of Neuropsychiatry and Clinical Neurosciences, 8,* 262–269.

Boys, A., Marsden, J., & Strang, J. (2001). Understanding reasons for drug use amongst young people: A functional perspective. *Health Education Research, 16,* 457–469.

Bozarth, M. A. (Ed.). (1987). *Methods of assessing the reinforcing properties of drugs.* New York: Springer-Verlag.

Bozarth, M. A., & Wise, R. A. (1985). Toxicity associated with long-term intravenous heroin and cocaine self-administration in the rat. *Journal of the American Medical Association, 254,* 81–83.

Bradley, K. A., Donovan, D. M., & Larson, E. B. (1993). How much is too much? Advising patients about safe levels of alcohol consumption. *Archives of Internal Medicine, 153,* 2734–2740.

Brandon, T. H., Juliano, L. M., & Copeland A. L. (1999). Expectancies for tobacco smoking. In I. Kirsch (Ed.), *How expectancies shape experience* (pp. 263–300). Washington, DC: American Psychological Association.

Brands, B., Sproule, B., & Marshman, J. (Eds.). (1998). *Drugs and drug abuse* (3rd ed.). Toronto: Addiction Research Foundation.

Brecher, E. M. (1972). *Licit and illicit drugs.* Boston: Little, Brown.

Brecher, E. M. (1986). Drug laws and drug law enforcement: A review and evaluation based on 111 years of experience. *Drugs and Society, 1,* 1–27.

Breggin, P. R. (2001). Questioning the treatment for ADHD. *Science, 291,* 595.

Breslau, N., & Peterson, E. L. (1996). Smoking cessation in young adults: Age at initiation of cigarette smoking and other suspected influences. *American Journal of Public Health, 86,* 214–220.

Brewer, C. (1996). On the specific effectiveness and under-valuing of pharmacological treatments for addiction: A comparison of methadone, naltrexone and disulfiram with psychosocial interventions. *Addiction Research, 3,* 297–313.

Brick, J. (1990). *Marijuana.* New Brunswick, NJ: Rutgers University Center of Alcohol Studies.

Brody, A. L., Mandelkern, M. A., Cosyello, M. R., Abrams, A. L., Scheibal, D. Farahi, J., London, E. D., Olmstead, R. E., Rose, J. E., & Mukhin, A. G. (2008). Brain nicotinic acetylcholine receptor occupancy: Effect of smoking a denicotinized cigarette. *The International Journal of Neuropsychopharmacology,* DOI: 10.1017/S146114570800922X.

Brody, A. L., Mandelkern, M. A., London, E. D., Olmstead, R. E., Farahi, J., Scheibal, D., Jou, J., Allen, V., Tiongson, E., Chefer, S. I., Koren, A. O., & Mukhin, A. G. (2006). Cigarette smoking saturates brain $\alpha4\beta2$ nicotinic acetylcholine receptors. *Archives of General Psychiatry, 63,* 907–915.

Brown, B. A., Christiansen, B. A., & Goldman, M. S. (1987). The Alcohol Expectancy Questionnaire: An instrument for the assessment of adolescent and adult alcohol expectancies. *Journal of Studies on Alcohol, 48,* 483–491.

Brown, L., Kroon, P. A., Das, D. K., Samarjit, D., Tosaki, A., Chan, V., Singer, M. V., & Feick, P. (2009). The biological responses to resveratrol and other polyphenols from alcoholic beverages. *Alcoholism: Clinical and Experimental Research, 33,* 1–11.

Brown, R. T., Amler, R. W., Freeman, W. S., Perrin, J. M., Stein, M. T., Feldman, H. M., et al. (2005). Treatment of attention-deficit disorder: Overview of the evidence. *Pediatrics, 115,* 749–757.

Bruce, M., Scott, N., Shine, P., & Lader, M. (1992). Angiogenic effect of caffeine in patients with anxiety disorders. *Archives of General Psychiatry, 49,* 867–869.

Bryan, C. (1930). *The ancient Egyptian medicine: The papyrus ebers.* Chicago, IL: Ares Publishing.

Budney, A. J., & Higgins, S. T. (1998, April). *A community reinforcement approach to treating cocaine addiction.* NIDA publication No. 98–4309.

Budney, A. J., Hughes, J. R., Moore, B. A., & Vandrey, R. (2004). Review of the validity and significance of cannabis withdrawal syndrome. *The American Journal of Psychiatry, 161,* 1967–1977.

Budney, A. J., Moore, B. A., & Vandrey, R. (2004). Health consequences of marijuana use. In J. Brick (Ed.), *Handbook of the medical consequences of alcohol and drug abuse* (pp. 171–217). New York: The Haworth Press.

Bukoski, W. J. (2003). The emerging science of drug abuse prevention. In Z. Sloboda & W. J. Bukoski

(Eds.), *Handbook of drug abuse prevention: Theory, science, and practice* (pp. 3–24). New York: Kluwer Academic/Plenum Publishers.

Burke, L. M. (2008). Caffeine and sports performance. *Applied Physiology, Nutrition, and Metabolism, 33,* 1319–1334.

Burroughs, W. S. (1953). *Junky.* Middlesex, England: Penguin Books.

Burstein, S. H., Karst, M., Schneider, U., & Zurier, R. B. (2004). Ajulemic acid: A novel cannabinoid produces analgesia without a "high." *Life Sciences, 75,* 1513–1522.

Bushman, B. J., & Cooper, H. M. (1990). Effects of alcohol on human aggression: An integrative research review. *Psychological Bulletin, 107,* 341–354.

Butelman, E. R., Prisinzano, T. E., Deng, H., Rus, S., & Kreek, M. J. (2009). *The Journal of Pharmacology and Experimental Therapeutics, 328,* 588–597.

Butts, J. D. (1978). Altered states of consciousness. *Journal of the National Medical Association, 70* (10), 743–744.

Byck, R. (Ed.). (1974). *Cocaine papers by Sigmund Freud.* New York: Stonehill Publishing Company.

Cairney, S., Maruff, P., Burns, C. B., Currie, J., & Currie, B. J. (2005). Neurological and cognitive recovery following abstinence from petrol sniffing. *Neuropsychopharmacology, 30,* 1019–1027.

Cairney, S., Maruff, P., Burns, C., & Currie, B. (2002). The neurobehavioral consequences of petrol (gasoline) sniffing. *Neuroscience and Biobehavioral Reviews, 26,* 81–89.

Caldwell, A. E. (1970). *Origins of psychopharmacology—From CPZ to LSD.* Springfield, IL: Charles Thomas.

Caldwell, A. E. (1978). History of psychopharmacology. In W. G. Clark & J. del Guidice (Eds.), *Principles of psychopharmacology* (2nd ed., pp. 9–30). New York: Academic Press.

Caligiuri, M. P., & Buitenhuys, C. (2005). Do preclinical findings of methamphetamine-induced motor abnormalities translate to an observable clinical phenotype? *Neuropsychopharmacology, 30,* 2125–2134.

Canada Online. (2011). Decriminalization of marijuana in Canada. Available at http://canadaonline.about.com/library/issues/blimj.htm.

Canadian Alcohol and Drug Use Monitoring Survey (CADUMS). (2010). Available at http://www.hc-sc.gc.ca/hc-ps/drugs-drogues/stat/_2009/summary-sommaire-eng.php.

Canadian Cancer Society (2009). Get the facts: Frequently asked questions about marijuana and cancer risks of long-term recreational smoking of marijuana. Available at http://tinyurl.com/o4ob6r.

Canadian Centre for Ethics in Sport. (2011). Performance enhancing drugs pose a significant health risk for athletes, children and youth: Final report. Available at http://www.cces.ca/files/pdfs/CCES-TaskForceFootballFinalReport-E-WEB.pdf; accessed October 3, 2011.

Canadian Council for Tobacco Control. (2007). Available at http://www.cctc.ca.

Canadian Encyclopedia. (2011). Prohibition. Available at http://www.thecanadianencyclopedia.com/index.cfm?PgNm=TCE&Params=A1ARTA0006515; accessed September 24, 2011.

Canadian Gazette. (2011). Department of Health: Controlled Drugs and Substances Act. Available at http://gazette.gc.ca/rp-pr/p1/2011/2011-02-19/html/notice-avis-eng.html.

Canadian Harm Reduction Network (2011). Learning from each other: Enhancing community-based harm reduction programs and practices in Canada. Available at http://www.canadianharmreduction.com/project/.

Canadian Human Rights Commission. (2002). Policy on alcohol and drug testing. Available at http://www.chrc-ccdp.ca/pdf/poldrgalceng.pdf; accessed August 5, 2011.

Canadian Medical Association. (2005). Vioxx: Lessons for Health Canada and the FDA. *Canadian Medical Association Journal, 172* (1). Available at http://www.cmaj.ca/content/172/1/5.full.

Canadian Tobacco Use Monitoring Survey. (2009). Available at http://www.hc-sc.gc.ca/hc-ps/tobac-tabac/research-recherche/stat/ctums-esutc_2009-eng.php.

Cannabis Culture. (2011). Available at http://www.cannabisculture.com.

Cappell, H. D., Sellers, E. M., & Busto, U. (1986). Benzodiazepines as drugs of abuse and dependence. In H. D. Cappell, F. B. Glaser, Y. Israel, H. Kalant, W. Schmidt, E. M. Sellers, & R. C. Smart (Eds.), *Research advances in alcohol and drug problems* (Vol. 9, pp. 53–126). New York: Plenum Press.

Carlin, A. S., Bakker, C. B., Halpern, L., & Post, R. D. (1972). Social facilitation of marijuana intoxication: Impact of social set and pharmacological activity. *Journal of Abnormal Psychology, 80,* 132–140.

Carlson, N. R. (2001). *Physiology of behavior* (7th ed.). Boston: Allyn & Bacon.

Carlson, N.R. (2008). *Foundations of physiological psychology* (7th ed.). Boston: Pearson.

Carroll, J. F. X., Malloy, T. E., & Kenrick, F. M. (1977). Drug abuse by alcoholics and problem drinkers: A literature review and evaluation. *American Journal of Drug and Alcohol Abuse, 4,* 317–341.

Carroll, K. M. (1996). Relapse prevention as a psychosocial treatment: A review of controlled clinical trials. *Experimental and Clinical Psychopharmacology, 4,* 46–54.

Carroll, K. M., Sinha, R., Nich, C., Babuscio, T., & Rounsaville, B. (2002). Contingency management to enhance naltrexone treatment of opioid dependence: A randomized clinical trial of reinforcement magnitude. *Experimental and Clinical Psychopharmacology, 10,* 54–63.

Carroll, M. E. (1990). PCP and hallucinogens. *Advances in Alcohol and Substance Abuse, 9,* 167–190.

Carter, W. E. (1980). *Cannabis in Costa Rica.* Philadelphia: Institute for the Study of Human Issues.

Carter, W. E., & Doughty, P. L. (1976). Social and cultural aspects of cannabis use in Costa Rica. *Annals of the New York Academy of Sciences, 282,* 2–16.

Castrillon, E., Cairns, B., Ernberg, M., Wang, K., Sessle, B., Arendt-Nielsen, L., & Svensson, P. (2008). Glutamate-evoked jaw muscle pain as a model of persistent myofascial TMD pain? *Archives of Oral Biology, 53,* 666–676.

CBC News. (2011). A legal history of smoking in Canada. Available at http://www.cbc.ca/news/health/story/2011/07/29/f-smoking-laws-timeline.html.

CBC. (2005). Dark crystal. *The Fifth Estate.* Report aired March 23.

CBC. (2010). Drug implant treats opioid addiction. Available at http://www.cbc.ca/news/health/story/2010/10/13/opiate-addiction-implantable-drug.html.

Cellucci, T. (1984). The prevention of alcohol problems: Conceptual and methodological issues. In P. M. Miller & T. D. Nirenberg (Eds.), *Prevention of alcohol abuse* (pp. 15–53). New York: Plenum Press.

Center for AIDS Prevention Studies. (1998). *Does needle exchange work?* Chicago: American Medical Association.

Center for Disease Control and Prevention. (1993). Mortality trends for selected smoking-related and breast cancer in the United States, 1950–1990. *Morbidity and Mortality Weekly Report, 42,* 857, 863–866.

Center for Disease Control and Prevention. (2006). Unintended pregnancy prevention: Contraception. Retrieved February 26, 2006, from http://www.cdc.gov/reproductivehealth/UnintendedPregnancy/Contraception.htm.

Center for Substance Abuse Treatment. (1997). *The National treatment improvement evaluation: Final report.* Washington, DC: Author.

Centre of Addition and Mental Health. (2009). About marijuana. Available at http://www.camh.net/About_Addiction_Mental_Health/Drug_and_Addiction_Information/about_marijuana.html.

Centre for Addiction and Mental Health. (2009). Contraband cigarettes are big in teen market. Available at http://www.camh.net/News_events/News_releases_and_media_advisories_and_backgrounders/contraband_cigarette_study_calla.html.

Cepada-Benito, A., Reynoso, J. T., & Erath, S. (2004). Meta-analysis of the efficacy of nicotine replacement therapy for smoking cessation: Differences between men and women. *Journal of Consulting and Clinical Psychology, 72,* 712–722.

Chait, L. D., & Pierri, J. (1992). Effects of smoked marijuana on human performance: A critical review. In L. Murphy & A. Bartke (Eds.), *Marijuana/cannabinoids: Neurobiology and neurophysiology* (pp. 387–423). Boca Raton, FL: CRC Press.

Chakos, M. H., Mayerhoff, D. I., Loebel, A. D., Alvir, J. M., & Lieberman, J. A. (1992). Incidence and correlates of acute extrapyramidal symptoms in first episode of schizophrenia. *Psychopharmacology Bulletin, 28,* 81–86.

Charness, M. E. (1993). Brain lesions in alcoholics. *Alcoholism: Clinical and Experimental Research, 17,* 2–11.

Chen, T. T. L., & Winder, A. E. (1986). When is the critical moment to provide smoking education at schools? *Journal of Drug Education, 16,* 121–134.

Cherek, D. R., Roache, J. D., Egli, M., Davis, C., Spiga, R., & Cowan, K. (1993). Acute effects of marijuana smoking on aggressive, escape, and point-maintained responding of male drug users. *Psychopharmacology, 111,* 163–168.

Childress, A. R., Mozley, P. D., McElgin, W., Fitzgerald, J., Reivich, M., & O'Brien, C. P. (1999). Limbic activation during cue-induced cocaine craving. *American Journal of Psychiatry, 156,* 11–18.

Chopra, R. N. (1933). *Indigenous drugs of India.* India: Academic Publishers.

Chou, S. P., Grant, B. F., Dawson, D. A., Stinson, F. S., Saha, T., & Pickering, R. P. (2006). Twelve-month prevalence and changes in drinking after driving. *Alcohol Research and Health, 29,* 143–151.

Cicero, T. J. (1980). Alcohol self-administration, tolerance, and withdrawal in humans and animals: Theoretical and methodological issues. In H. Rigter & J. Crabbe Jr. (Eds.), *Alcohol tolerance and dependence* (pp. 1–50). Amsterdam: Elsevier/North-Holland Biomedical Press.

Cicero, T. J., Inciardi, J. A., & Munoz, A. (2005). Trends in abuse of Oxycontin and other opioid analgesics in the United States: 2002–2004. *Journal of Pain, 6,* 662–672.

Ciraulo, D. A., Barnhill, J. G., Greenblatt, D. J., Shader, R. I., Ciraulo, A. M., Tarmey, M. F., et al. (1988). Abuse liability and clinical pharmacokinetics of alprazolam in alcoholic men. *Journal of Clinical Psychiatry, 49,* 333–337.

Clapton, E. (2007). *Clapton: The autobiography.* New York: Random House.

Clark, W. G., Brater, D. C., & Johnson, A. R. (Eds.). (1988). *Goth's medical pharmacology* (12th ed.). St. Louis: C. V. Mosby.

Clinger, O. W., & Johnson, N. A. (1951). Purposeful inhalation of gasoline vapors. *Psychiatric Quarterly, 25,* 557–567.

Cobain, K. (2002). *Journals.* New York: Riverhead Books.

Coffee Association of Canada. (2003). Highlights: 2003 Canadian coffee drinking study. http://www.coffeeassoc.com/coffeeincanada.htm.

Cohen, L. J. (1997). Rational drug use in the treatment of depression. *Pharmacotherapy, 17,* 45–61.

Cohen, M. M., & Marmillo, M. J. (1967). Chromosome damage in human leukocytes induced by lysergic acid diethylamide. *Science, 155,* 1417–1419.

Cohen, R. S. (1998). *The love drug: Dancing to the beat of ecstasy.* Binghamton, NY: Haworth Press.

Cohen, S. (1981). *The substance abuse problems.* Binghamton, NY: Haworth Press.

Cohen, S., & Andrysiak, T. (1982). *The therapeutic potential of marijuana's components.* Rockville, MD: American Council on Marijuana and Other Psychoactive Drugs.

Colder, C. R., Mehta, P., Balanda, K., Campbell, R. T., Mayhew, K. P., Stanton, W. R., et al. (2001). Identifying trajectories of adolescent smoking: An application of latent growth mixture modeling. *Health Psychology, 20,* 127–135.

Collins, J. J., Jr. (Ed.). (1980). *Alcohol use and criminal behavior: An empirical, theoretical, and methodological overview.* New York: Guilford Press.

Collishaw, N. (2009). History of tobacco control in Canada. Available at http://www.smokefree.ca/pdf_1/2009/History%20of%20tobacco%20control%20in%20Canada.pdf.

Colpaert, F. C. (1987). Drug discrimination: Methods of manipulation, measurement, and analysis. In M. A. Bozarth (Ed.), *Methods of assessing the reinforcing properties of drugs* (pp. 341–372). New York: Springer-Verlag.

Comer, S. D., Haney, M., Foltin, R. W., & Fischman, M. W. (1997). Effects of caffeine withdrawal on humans living in a residential laboratory. *Experimental and Clinical Psychopharmacology, 5,* 399–403.

Comer, S. D., Hart, C. L., Ward, A.S., et al (2001). Effects of repeated oral methamphetamine administration in humans. *Psychopharmacology, 155,* 397–404.

Comer, S. M., & Zacny, J. P. (2005). Subjective effects of opioids. In M. Earlywine (Ed.), *Mind-altering drugs: The science of subjective experience* (pp. 217–239). London: Oxford Press.

Comitas, L. (1976). Cannabis and work in Jamaica: A refutation of the amotivational syndrome. *Annals of New York Academy of Sciences, 282,* 24–32.

Community Epidemiology Work Group (2009). *Epidemiological trends in substance abuse: Highlights and executive summary.* Bethesda, MD: National Institute on Drug Abuse. http://www.drugabuse.gov/PDF/CEWG/CEWGJan09508Compliant.pdf.

Compton, D. R., Harris, L. S., Lichtman, A. H., & Martin, B. R. (1996). Marijuana. In C. R. Schuster & M. J. Kuhar (Eds.), *Pharmacological aspects of drug dependence: Toward an integrated neurobehavioral approach* (pp. 83–158). New York: Springer-Verlag.

Compton, W. M., & Volkow, N. D. (2006). Major increases in opioid analgesic abuse in the United States: Concerns and strategies. *Drug and Alcohol Dependence, 81,* 103–107.

Connecticut Clearing House. (2001). *Qs and As on drug testing.* Plainville, CT: Author.

Connors, G. J., Donovan, D. M., & DiClemente, C. C. (2001). *Substance abuse treatment and the stages of change.* New York: Guilford Press.

Connors, G. J., Maisto, S. A., & Donovan, D. M. (1996). Conceptualization of relapse: A summary of psychological and psychobiological models. *Addiction, 91* (Supplement), S5–S14.

Consumer Affairs (2011). Canada pulls Adderall after 20 deaths. Retrieved on October 2011 from http://www.consumeraffairs.com/news04/2005/adderall.html.

Cook, R. F. (2003). Drug abuse prevention in the workplace. In Z. Sloboda & W. J. Bukoski (Eds.), *Handbook of drug abuse prevention: Theory, science, and practice* (pp. 157–172). New York: Kluwer Academic/Plenum Publishers.

Cooper, Z. D., & Haney, M. (2009). Comparison of subjective, pharmacokinetic, and physiological effects of marijuana smoked as joints and blunts. *Drug and Alcohol Dependence, 103,* 107–113.

Cooperrider, C. (1988). Antidepressants. In G. W. Lawson & C. A. Cooperrider (Eds.), *Clinical psychopharmacology* (pp. 91–108). Rockville, MD: Aspen Publishers.

Coplan, J. D., Wolk, S. I., & Klein, D. F. (1995). Anxiety and the serotonin 1A receptor. In F. E. Bloom & D. J. Kupfer (Eds.), *Psychopharmacology: The fourth generation of progress* (pp. 1301–1310). New York: Raven Press.

Cornelis, M. C., El-Sohemy, A., Kabagambe, E. K., & Campos, H. (2006). Coffee, CYP1A2 genotype, and risk of myocardial infarction. *Journal of the American Medical Association, 295,* 1135–1141.

Coryell, W., & Winokur, G. (1982). Course and outcome. In E. S. Paykel (Ed.), *Handbook of affective disorders.* New York: Guilford Press.

Cose, E. (2009). Closing the gap: Obama could fix cocaine sentencing. *Newsweek,* July 20, pp. 25.

Costa, E., Guidotti, A., & Mao, C. C. (1975). Evidence for involvement of GABA in the action of benzodiazepines. Studies on rat cerebellum. In E. Costa & P. Greengard (Eds.), *Mechanism of action of benzodiazepines* (pp. 113–130). New York: Raven Press.

Cotton, P. (1993). Low tar cigarettes come under fire. *Journal of the American Medical Association, 270,* 1399.

Coultas, D. B., Stidley, C. A., & Samet, J. M. (1993). Cigarette yields of tar and nicotine and markers of exposure to tobacco smoke. *American Review of Respiratory Disease, 148,* 435–440.

Council on Scientific Affairs. (1984). Caffeine labeling. *Journal of the American Medical Association, 252,* 803–806.

Cox, E. R., Halloran, D. R., Homan, S. M., Welliver, S. & Mager, D. E. (2008). Trends in the prevalence of chronic medication use in children: 2002–2005. *Pediatrics, 122,* 1053–1061.

Cox, W. M. (1986). *The addictive personality.* New York: Chelsea.

Craft, R. M., & Lee, D. A. (2005). NMDA antagonist modulation of morphine antinociception in female vs. male rats. *Pharmacology, Biochemistry & Behavior, 80,* 639–649.

Croft, R. J., Mackay, A. J., Mills, A. T. D., & Gruzelier, J. G. H. (2001). The relative contributions of ecstasy and cannabis to cognitive impairment. *Psychopharmacology, 153,* 373–379.

Crowley, T. J. (1981). The reinforcers for drug abuse: Why people take drugs. In H. Shaffer & M. E. Burglass (Eds.), *Classic contributions in the addictions* (pp. 367–381). New York: Brunner/Mazel.

CTV News. (2003). Marijuana backgrounder: Marijuana timeline. Available at http://www.ctv.ca/generic/WebSpecials/marijuana/index_timeline.html.

Cunningham, J. A. (2009). Internet evidence-based treatments. In P. M. Miller (Ed.), *Evidence-based addiction treatment* (pp. 379–398). Boston: Elsevier.

Cunningham, J. K., & Liu, L. M. (2005). Impacts of federal precursor chemical regulations on methamphetamine arrests. *Addiction, 100,* 479–488.

Curatolo, P. W., & Robertson, D. (1983). The health consequences of caffeine. *Annals of Internal Medicine, 98,* 641–653.

Curry, S. J., Wagner, E. H., & Grothaus, L. C. (1990). Intrinsic and extrinsic motivation for smoking cessation. *Journal of Consulting and Clinical Psychology, 58,* 310–316.

D'Amicis, A., & Viani, R. (1993). The consumption of coffee. In S. Garattini (Ed.), *Caffeine, coffee, and health* (pp. 1–16). New York: Raven Press.

Dackis, C. A., & Gold, M. S. (1985). New concepts in cocaine addiction: The dopamine depletion hypothesis. *Neuroscience and Biobehavioral Reviews, 9,* 469–477.

Dafters, R. I. (2006). Chronic ecstasy (MDMA) use is associated with deficits in task-switching but not inhibition or memory updating executive functions. *Drug and Alcohol Dependence, 83,* 181–184.

Dafters, R. I., Hoshi, R., & Talbot, A. C. (2004). Contribution of cannabis and MDMA ("ecstasy") to cognitive changes in long-term polydrug users. *Psychopharmacology, 173,* 405–410.

Dal Cason, T. A., & Franzosa, E. S. (2003). Occurrences and forms of the hallucinogens. In R. Laing (Ed.), *Hallucinogens: A forensic drug handbook* (pp. 37–66). London: Academic Press.

Daly, J. W., & Fredholm, B. B. (2004). Mechanisms of action of caffeine on the nervous system. In A. Nehlig (Ed.), *Coffee, tea, chocolate, and the brain* (pp. 1–11). Boca Raton, FL: CRC Press.

Damasio, A. R. (1994). *Descartes' error: Emotion, reason and the human brain.* New York: Avon Books.

Daumann, J., Fischermann, T., Heekeren, K., Henke, K., Thron, A., & Gouzoulis-Mayfrank, E. (2005). *Psychopharmacology, 180,* 607–611.

Daumann, J., Hensen, G., Thimm, B., Rezk, M., Till, B., & Gouzoulis-Mayfrank, E. (2004). *Psychopharmacology, 173,* 398–404.

David, G. L., Koh, W.-P., Lee, H.-P., Yu, M. C., & London, S. J. (2005). Childhood exposure to environmental tobacco smoke and chronic respiratory symptoms in nonsmoking adults: The Singapore Chinese health study. *Thorax,* DOI: 10.1136/thx.2005.042960.

Davis, J. M., & Schlemmer, R. F. (1980). The amphetamine psychosis. In J. Caldwell & S. J. Mule (Eds.), *Amphetamines and related stimulants: Chemical, biological, clinical, and sociological aspects* (pp. 161–174). Boca Raton, FL: CRC Press.

Davis, W. (1988). *Passage of darkness: The ethnobiology of the Haitian zombie.* Chapel Hill: University of North Carolina Press.

Davis, W. R., Johnson, B. D., Randolph, D., & Liberty, H. J. (2006). Risks for HIV infection among users and sellers of crack, powder cocaine and heroin in central Harlem: Implications for interventions. *AIDS Care, 18,* 158–165.

Dawson, D. A. (2000). U.S. low-risk drinking guideline: An examination of four alternatives. *Alcoholism: Clinical and Experimental Research, 2000,* 1820–1829.

Day, N. L., & Richardson, G. A. (1991). Prenatal marijuana use: Epidemiology, methodological issues, and infant outcome. *Chemical Dependency and Pregnancy, 18,* 77–91.

De Fonseca, F. R., & Schneider, M. (2008). The endogenous cannabinoid system and drug addiction: 20 years after the discovery of the CBI receptor. *Addiction Biology, 13,* 143–146.

de Sola, S., Tarancon, T., Pena-Casanova, J., Espadaler, J. M., Langohr, K., Poudevida, S., Farre, M., Verdejo-Garcia, A., & de la Torre, R. (2008). Auditory event-related potentials (P3) and cognitive performance in recreational ecstasy polydrug users: Evidence from a 12-month longitudinal study. *Psychopharmacology, 200,* 425–437.

Deahl, M. (1991). Cannabis and memory loss. *British Journal of Addiction, 86,* 249–252.

DeGrandpre, R. J., Bickle, W. K., Hughes, J. R., & Higgins, S. T. (1992). Behavioral economics of drug self-administration, III. A reanalysis of the nicotine regulation hypothesis. *Psychopharmacology, 108,* 1–10.

Djousse, L., Lee, I-M., Buring, J. E., & Gaziano, J. M. (2009). Alcohol consumption and risk of cardiovascular disease and death in women. Potential mediating mechanisms. *Circulation, 120,* 237-244.

Delaney, J. (2010). Doda, or poor man's heroin: A growing problem in Canada. *The Epoch Times.* Available at http://www.theepochtimes.com/n2/world/doda-or-poor-mans-heroin-a-growing-problem-in-canada-32553.html.

DeLeon, G. (1984). *The therapeutic community: Study of effectiveness.* NIDA Treatment Research Monograph 84. Rockville, MD: National Institute on Drug Abuse.

DeLeon, G. (1995). Therapeutic communities for addictions: A theoretical framework. *International Journal of the Addictions, 30,* 1603–1645.

DeLisi, L. E. (2008). The effect of cannabis on the brain: can it cause brain anomalies that lead to increased risk for schizophrenia? *Current Opinion in Psychiatry, 21,* 140–150.

DeLong, F. L., & Levy, B. I. (1974). A model of attention describing the cognitive effects of marijuana. In L. L. Miller (Ed.), *Marijuana: Effects on human behavior* (pp. 103–120). New York: Academic Press.

Deniker, P. (1983). Discovery of the clinical use of neuroleptics. In M. J. Parnham & J. Bruinvels (Eds.), *Discoveries in pharmacology (Vol. 1): Psycho- and neuropharmacology* (pp. 163–180). New York: Elsevier.

Denissenko, M. F., Pao, A., Tang, M., & Pfeiffer, G. P. (1996). Preferential formation of benzo[*a*]pyrene adducts at lung cancer mutational hotspots in *P53. Science, 274,* 430–432.

Dennehy, C. E., Tsourounis, C., & Miller, A. E. (2005). Evaluation of herbal dietary supplements marketed on the Internet for recreational use. *Annals of Pharmacotherapy, 39,* 1634–1639.

Deutsch, A. Y., & Roth, R. H. (2009). Neurochemical systems in the central nervous system. In D. S. Charney & E. J. Nestler (Eds.), *Neurobiology of mental illness* (3rd ed., pp. 12–28). New York: Oxford University Press.

Devane, W. A., Dysarz, F. A., Johnson, R., Melvin, L. S., & Howlett, A. C. (1988). Determination and characterization of a cannabinoid receptor in the rat brain. *Molecular Pharmacology, 34,* 605–613.

Devane, W. A., Hanus, L., Breuer, A., Pertwee, R. G., Stevenson, L. A., Griffin, G., et al. (1992). Isolation and structure of a brain constituent that binds to the cannabinoid receptor. *Science, 258,* 1946–1949.

Dews, P. B., Curtis, G. L., Hanford, K. J., & O'Brien, C. P. (1999). The frequency of caffeine withdrawal in a population-based survey and in a controlled, blinded experiment. *Journal of Clinical Pharmacology, 39,* 1221–1232.

Dews, P. B., O'Brien, C. P., & Bergman, J. (2002). Caffeine: Behavioral effects of withdrawal and related issues. *Food and Chemical Toxicology, 40,* 1257–1261.

Dhawan, B.N., Cesselin, F., Raghubir, R., Reisine T., Bradley, P.B., Portoghese, P.S., Hamon, M. (1996). Classification of opioid receptors. *Pharmacological Review, 48,* 567–592.

Di Forti, M., Morrison, P. D., Butt, A., & Murray, R. M. (2007). Cannabis use and psychiatric and cognitive disorders: The chicken or the egg? *Current Opinion in Psychiatry, 20,* 228–234.

Diem, S. J., Blackwell, T. L., Stone, K. L., Yaffe, K., Haney, E. M., Bliziotes, M. M., & Ensrud, K. E. (2007). Use of antidepressants and rates of hip bone loss in older women: The study of osteoporotic fractures. *Archives of Internal Medicine, 167,* 1240–1245.

Djousse, L., Lee, I-M., Buring, J. E., & Gaziano, J. M. (2009). Alcohol consumption and risk of cardiovascular disease and death in women. Potential mediating mechanisms. *Circulation, 120,* 237–244.

Dolan, K., Rouen, D., & Kimber, J. (2004). An overview of the use of urine, hair, sweat, and saliva to detect drug use. *Drug and Alcohol Reviews, 23,* 213–217.

Doll, R. (1998). The benefit of alcohol in moderation. *Drug and Alcohol Review, 17,* 353–363.

Droomers, M., Schrijvers, C. T. M., & Mackenbach, J. P. (2002). Why do lower educated people continue smoking? Explanations from the longitudinal GLOBE study. *Health Psychology, 21,* 263–272.

Drug Abuse Warning Network. (1996). Retrieved from http://www.samhsa.gov.

Duman, R. S. (2004). Depression: A case of neuronal life and death? *Biological Psychiatry, 56,* 140–145.

Duman, R. S. (2009). Neurochemical theories of depression: Preclinical studies. In D. S. Charney & E. J. Nestler (Eds.), *Neurobiology of mental illness* (3rd ed., pp. 413–434). New York: Oxford University Press.

Duman, R. S., Nakagawa, S., & Malberg, J. (2001). Regulation of adult neurogenesis by antidepressant treatment. *Neuropsychopharmacology, 25,* 836–844.

Duncan, D. F. (1987). Lifetime prevalence of "amotivational syndrome" among users and nonusers of hashish. *Psychology of Addictive Behaviors, 1,* 114–119.

Duncan, J. R., Paterson, D. S.M., Hoffman, J. M., Mokler, D. J., Boresnstein, N. S., Belliveau, R. A., Krous, H. F., Hass, E. A., Stanley, C., Nattie, E. E.,

Trachtenberg, F. L., Kinney, H. C. (2010). Brainstem serotonergic deficiency in Sudden Infant Death Syndrome. *Journal of American Medical Association, 303* (5): 430–437.

Dunn, M. E., & Goldman, M. S. (1996). Empirical modeling of an alcohol expectancy network in elementary-school children as a function of grade. *Experimental and Clinical Psychopharmacology, 4,* 209–217.

DuPont, R. L. (1980). The future of primary prevention: Parent power. *Journal of Drug Education, 10,* 1–5.

Durrant, R., & Thakker, J. (2003). *Substance use and abuse: Cultural and historical perspectives.* Thousand Oaks, CA: Sage Press.

Earleywine, M. (1994). Personality risk for alcoholism and alcohol expectancies. *Addictive Behaviors, 19,* 577–582.

Earleywine, M. (2002). *Understanding marijuana: A new look at the scientific evidence.* New York: Oxford University Press.

Ebmeier, K. P., Donaghey, C., & Steele, J. D. (2006). Recent developments and current controversies in depression. *The Lancet, 367,* 153–167.

Edwards, D. D. (1986). Nicotine: A drug of choice? *Science News, 129,* 44–45.

Eede, H. V., Montenij, L. J., Touw, D. J., & Norris, E. M. (2009). Rhabdomyolysis in MDMA intoxication: A rapid and underestimated killer. *Journal of Emergency Medicine*, June 3, [epub ahead of print].

Efron, S. (2005). Drug war fails to dent U.S. supply. *Los Angeles Times*, June 29.

Ehrenkranz, J. R. L., & Hembree, W. C. (1986). Effects of marijuana on male reproductive function. *Psychiatric Annals, 16,* 243–248.

Eissenberg, T., Ward, K. D., Smith-Simone, S., & Maziak, W. (2008). Waterpipe tobacco smoking on a U.S. college campus: Prevalence and correlates. *Journal of Adolescent Health, 42,* 526–529.

El Sohly, M. A. (2002). Chemical constituents of cannabis. In F. Grotenhermen & E. Russo (Eds.), *Cannabis and cannabinoids: Pharmacology, toxicology and therapeutic potential* (pp. 27–36). London: Haworth Press.

El Sohly, M. A., Ross, S. A., Mehmedic, Z., Arafat, R., Yi, B., & Banahan, B. F. (2000). Potency trends of delta(9)-THC and other cannabinoids in confiscated marijuana from 1980–1997. *Journal of Forensic Sciences, 45,* 24–30.

Eliopoulos, C., Klein, J., Phan, M., Knie, B., Greenwald, M., Chitayat, D., et al. (1994). Hair concentrations of nicotine and cotinine in women and their newborn infants. *Journal of the American Medical Association, 271,* 621–623.

Emrick, C. D. (1975). A review of the psychologically oriented treatment of alcoholism, II. The relative effectiveness of different treatment approaches and the effectiveness of treatment vs. no treatment. *Journal of Studies on Alcohol, 36,* 88–108.

Emrick, C. D. (1989). Alcoholics Anonymous: Membership characteristics and effectiveness as treatment. In M. Galanter (Ed.), *Recent developments in alcoholism* (Vol. 7, pp. 37–53). New York: Plenum Press.

Emrick, C. D., Lassen, C. L., & Edwards, M. T. (1977). Nonprofessional peers as therapeutic agents. In A. S. Gurman & A. M. Razin (Eds.), *Effective psychotherapy: A handbook of research* (pp. 120–161). New York: Pergamon Press.

Emrick, C. D., Tonigan, J. S., Montgomery, H., & Little, L. (1993). Alcoholics Anonymous: What is currently known? In B. S. McCrady & W. R. Miller (Eds.), *Research on Alcoholics Anonymous: Opportunities and alternatives* (pp. 41–76). New Brunswick, NJ: Rutgers Center of Alcohol Studies.

Endo, O., Matsumoto, M., Inaba, Y., Sugita, K., Nakajima, D., Goto, S., Ogata, H., & Susuki, G. (2009). Nicotine, tar, and mutagenicity of mainstream smoke generated by machine smoking with International Organization for Standardization and Health Canada Intense regimens of major Japanese cigarette brands. *Journal of Health Science, 55,* 421–427.

Engs, R. C., Diebold, B. A., & Hansen, D. J. (1996). The drinking patterns and problems of a national sample of college students, 1994. *Journal of Alcohol and Drug Education, 41,* 13–33.

Ennett, S. T., Tobler, N. S., Ringwalt, C. L., & Flewelling, R. L. (1994). How effective is drug abuse resistance education? A meta-analysis of Project DARE outcome. *American Journal of Public Health, 84,* 1394–1401.

Erenhart, C. B. (1991). Clinical correlations between ethanol intake and fetal alcohol syndrome. In M. Galanter (Ed.), *Recent developments in alcoholism* (Vol. 9, pp. 127–150). New York: Plenum Press.

Erickson, P. G. (1992). Recent trends in Canadian drug policy: The decline and resurgence of prohibitionism. *Daedalus, 121,* 239–267.

Ernster, V. L. (1993). Women and smoking. *American Journal of Public Health, 83,* 1202–1203.

Eskelinen, M. H., Ngandu, T., Tuomilehto, J., Soininen, H., & Kivipelto, M. (2009). Midlife coffee and tea drinking and the risk of late-life dementia: A population-based CAIDE study. *Journal of Alzheimer's Disease, 16,* 85–91.

Etheridge, R. M., Hubbard, R. L., Anderson, J., Craddock, S. G., & Flynn, P. M. (1997). Treatment structure and program services in the Drug Abuse Treatment Outcome Study (DATOS). *Psychology of Addictive Behaviors, 11,* 244–260.

Euromonitor. (2011). Cigars. Available at http://www.euromonitor.com/cigars.

European Monitoring Centre for Drugs and Drug Addiction. (2004). Available at http://www.drugsandalcohol.ie/11599/.

Evans, A. M., & Griffiths, R. R. (1999). Caffeine withdrawal: A parametric analysis of caffeine dosing conditions. *The Journal of Pharmacology and Experimental Therapeutics, 289,* 285–294.

Exum, M. L. (2006). Alcohol and aggression: An integration of findings from experimental studies. *Journal of Criminal Justice, 34,* 131–145.

Ezzati, M., & Lopez, A. D. (2003). Estimates of global mortality attributable to smoking in 2000. *The Lancet, 362,* 847–852.

Fainaru-Wada, M., & Williams, L. (2006). *Game of shadows.* New York: Gotham Books.

Fait, M. L., Wise, M. G., Jachna, J. S., Lane, R. D., & Gelenberg, A. J. (2002). Psychopharmacology. In M. Wise & J. R. Rundell (Eds.), *Textbook of consultation-liaison psychiatry* (2nd ed., pp. 939–987). Washington, DC: American Psychiatric Publishing.

Fallon, J. H., Keator, D., Mbgori, J., & Potkin, S. G. (2004). Hostility differentiates the brain metabolic effects of nicotine. *Cognitive Brain Research, 18,* 142–148.

FAO. (2011). Coffee and cocoa. Available at http://www.fao.org/economic/est/est-commodities/coffee-cocoa/en/.

Farre, M., Teran, M., & Cami, J. (1996). A comparison of the acute behavioral effects of flunitrazepam and triazolam in healthy volunteers. *Psychopharmacology, 125,* 1–12.

FDA. (2009). Organ-specific warnings; internal analgesic, antipyretic, and antirheumatic drug products for over-the-counter human use. *Federal Register,* 74, April 29, 2009.

Federal Trade Commission. (2001). *"Tar," nicotine, and carbon monoxide of the smoke of 1294 varieties of domestic cigarettes for the year 1998.* Washington, DC: Author.

Fein, G., Torres, J., Price, L. J., & Sclafani, V. D. (2006). Cognitive performance in long-term abstinent alcoholic individuals. *Alcoholism: Clinical and Experimental Research, 30,* 1538–1544.

Feldman, H. W., Agar, M. H., & Beschner, G. M. (1979). *Angel dust.* Lexington, MA: Lexington Books.

Feldman, R. S., Meyer, J. S., & Quenzer, L. F. (1997). *Principles of neuropsychopharmacology.* Sunderland, MA: Sinauer Associates.

Fell, J. C., Fisher, D. A., Voas, R. B., Blackman, K., & Tippetts, A. S. (2009). The impact of underage drinking laws on alcohol-related fatal crashes of young drivers. *Alcoholism: Clinical and Experimental Research, 33,* 1208–1219.

Fergusson, D. M., & Horwood, L. J. (2000). Does cannabis use encourage other forms of illicit drug use? *Addiction, 95,* 505–520.

Fergusson, D. M., Boden, J. M., & Horwood, L. J. (2006). Cannabis use and other illicit drug use: Testing the cannabis gateway hypothesis. *Addiction, 101,* 556–569.

Ferreira, S. E., Tulio de Mello, M., Pompeia, S., & Oliveira de Souza-Formigoni, M. L. (2006). Effects of energy drink ingestion on alcohol intoxication. *Alcoholism: Clinical and Experimental Research, 30,* 598–605.

Field, T. (2008). Breastfeeding and antidepressants. *Infant Behavior and Development, 31,* 481–487.

Fieve, R. R. (1976). Therapeutic uses of lithium and rubidium. In L. L. Simpson (Ed.), *Drug treatment of mental disorders* (pp. 193–208). New York: Raven Press.

Fillmore, K. M., et al. (2006). Moderate alcohol use and reduced mortality risk: Systematic error in prospective studies. *Addiction Theory and Research, 14,* 101–132.

Fillmore, M. T., & Vogel-Sprott, M. (1996). Evidence that expectancies mediate behavioral impairment under alcohol. *Journal of Studies on Alcohol, 57,* 598–603.

Fiorentine, R. (1997). After drug treatment: Are 12-step programs effective in maintaining abstinence? *American Journal of Drug and Alcohol Abuse, 25,* 93–116.

Fiori, M. G., Keller, P. A., & Curry, S. J. (2007). Health system changes to facilitate the delivery of tobacco dependence treatment. *American Journal of Preventive Medicine, 33,* S349–S356.

First Nations Centre/Des Premieres Nations. (May 2006). Discussion Paper: The emerging issue of crystal meth use in First Nations Communities. Available at http://www.naho.ca/documents/fnc/english/FNC_CrystalMethamphetamineDiscussionPaper.pdf; accessed August 25, 2011.

Fischer, B. D., Miller, L. L., Henry, F. E., Picker, M. J., & Dykstra, L. A. (2008). Increased efficacy of micro-opioid agonist induced antinociception by metabotropic glutamate receptor antagonists in C57BL/6 mice: comparison with 6-phosphonomethyl-deca-hydroisoquinoline-3-carboxylic acid (LY235959). *Psychopharmacology, 198,* 271–278.

Fischer, B., Rehm, J., Patra, J., & Cruz, M. F. (2006). Changes in illicit opioid use across Canada. *Canadian Medical Association Journal, 175,* 1385.

Fischman, M. W. (1984). The behavioral pharmacology of cocaine in humans. In J. Grabowski (Ed.), *Cocaine: Pharmacology, effects and treatment of abuse.* Research Monograph 50. Washington, DC: National Institute on Drug Abuse.

Fisher, L. M. (1992, October 6). New drugs by process of elimination. *The New York Times,* pp. D1, D13.

Fisone, G., Borgkvist, A., & Usiello, A. (2004). Caffeine as a psychomotor stimulant: Mechanism of action. *Cellular and Molecular Life Sciences, 61*, 857–872.

Flay, B. R. (1985). What we know about the social influences to smoking prevention: Review and recommendations. In C. Bell & R. Battjes (Eds.), *Prevention research: Deterring drug abuse among children and adolescents* (pp. 67–112). Rockville, MD: National Institute on Drug Abuse.

Fleming, M. F., Barry, K. L., Manwell, L. B., Johnson, K., & London, R. (1997). Brief physician advice for problem alcohol drinkers. *Journal of the American Medical Association, 277,* 1039–1045.

Fletcher, A. M. (2001). *Sober for good.* Boston: Houghton Mifflin.

Fletcher, B. W., Tims, F. M., & Brown, B. S. (1997). Drug Abuse Treatment Outcome Study (DATOS): Treatment evaluation research in the United States. *Psychology of Addictive Behaviors, 11,* 216–229.

Foltin, R. W., & Fischman, M. W. (1992). The cardiovascular and subjective effects of intravenous cocaine and morphine combinations in humans. *Journal of Pharmacology and Experimental Therapeutics, 261,* 623–632.

Foltin, R. W., & Fischman, M. W. (1993). Self-administration of smoked cocaine by humans. In L. Harris (Ed.), *Problems of drug dependence, 1992.* Research Monograph 132 (p. 63). Washington, DC: National Institute on Drug Abuse.

Foltin, R. W., Fischman, M. W., Brady, J. V., Bernstein, D. J., Capriotti, R. M., Nellis, M. J., et al. (1990). Motivational effects of smoked marijuana: Behavioral contingencies and low-probability activities. *Journal of the Experimental Analysis of Behavior, 53,* 5–19.

Foltin, R. W., Fischman, M. W., Brady, J. V., Kelly, T. H., Bernstein, D. J., & Nellis, M. J. (1989). Motivational effects of smoked marijuana: Behavioral contingencies and high-probability recreational activities. *Pharmacology, Biochemistry, and Behavior, 34,* 871–877.

Fong, G. T., Hammond, D., Laux, F. L., et al. (2004). The near-universal experience of regret among smokers in four countries: Findings from the International Tobacco Control Policy Evaluation Survey. *Nicotine and Tobacco Research, 6* (Suppl. 3), S341–S351.

Food and Drug Administration (FDA). (2002). FDA approves Xyrem for cataplexy attacks in patients with narcolepsy. FDA Talk Paper, July 17.

Fortuna, R., Vaz, M. A., Youssef, A. R., Longino, D., Herzog, W. (2011). Changes in contractile properties of muscles receiving repeat injections of botulinum toxin (Botox). *Journal of Biomechanics, 4*, 44 (1), 39–44.

Franck, P. H. (1983). "If you drink, don't drive" motto now applies to hangovers as well. *Journal of the American Medical Association, 250,* 1657–1658.

Franey, C., & Ashton, M. (2002). The grand design lessons from DATOS. *Drug and Alcohol Findings, 7,* 4–19.

Frary, C. D., Johnson, R. K., & Wang, M. Q. (2005). Food sources and intakes of caffeine in the diets of persons in the United States. *Journal of the American Dietetic Association, 105,* 110–113.

Fredholm, B. B., Battig, K., Holmen, J., Nehlig, A., & Zvartau, E. E. (1999). Actions of caffeine in the brain with special reference to factors that contribute to its widespread use. *Pharmacological Reviews, 51,* 83–133.

Freedman, R. R., Johanson, C., & Tancer, M. E. (2005). Thermoregulatory effects of 3,4-methylenedioxymethamphetamine (MDMA) in humans. *Psychopharmacology, 183,* 248–256.

French, M. T., & McGeary, K. A. (1997). Estimating the cost of substance abuse treatment. *Health Economics Letters, 6,* 1–6.

Frezza, M., di Padova, C., Pozzato, G., Terpin, M., Baraona, E., & Lieber, C. S. (1990). High blood alcohol levels in women: The role of decreased gastric alcohol dehydrogenase activity and first pass metabolism. *New England Journal of Medicine, 322,* 95–99.

Fried, P. A. (1986). Marijuana and human pregnancy. In I. J. Chasnoff (Ed.), *Drug use in pregnancy: Mother and child* (pp. 64–74). Lancaster, PA: MTP Press.

Fried, P. A., Watkinson, B., & Gray, R. (1992). A follow-up study of attentional behavior in 6-year-old children exposed prenatally to marijuana, cigarettes, and alcohol. *Neurotoxicology and Teratology, 14,* 299–311.

Friedl, K. E. (2000a). Effect of anabolic steroid use on body composition and physical performance. In C. E. Yesalis (Ed.), *Anabolic steroids in sport and exercise* (2nd ed., pp. 139–174). Champaign, IL: Human Kinetics Press.

Friedl, K. E. (2000b). Effects of anabolic steroid use on physical health. In C. E. Yesalis (Ed.), *Anabolic steroids in sport and exercise* (2nd ed., pp. 175–224). Champaign, IL: Human Kinetics Press.

Frunkel, E. N., Kanner, J., German, J. B., Parks, E., & Kinsella, J. E. (1993). Inhibition of oxidation of human low-density lipoprotein by phenolic substances in red wine. *Lancet, 341,* 454–457.

Gable, R. S. (2006). The toxicity of recreational drugs, *American Scientist,* (May/June), 206–208.

Galenberg, A. J. (1991). Psychoses. In A. J. Galenberg, E. L. Bussuk, & S. C. Schoonover (Eds.), *The practitioner's guide to psychoactive drugs* (3rd ed., pp. 125–178). New York: Plenum Medical Book Company.

Galenberg, A. J., & Schoonover, S. C. (1991). Depression. In A. J. Galenberg, E. L. Bussuk, & S. C. Schoonover (Eds.), *The practitioner's guide to psychoactive drugs* (3rd ed., pp. 23–89). New York: Plenum Medical Book Company.

Galizio, M., & Maisto, S. A. (Eds.). (1985). *Determinants of substance abuse.* New York: Plenum Press.

Galizio, M., Keith, J. R., Mansfield, W., & Pitts, R. C. (2003). Repeated spatial acquisition: Effects of NMDA antagonists and morphine. *Experimental and Clinical Psychopharmacology, 11,* 79–90.

Galloway, G. P., Frederick-Osborne, S. L., Seymour, R., Contini, S. E., & Smith, D. E. (2000). Abuse and therapeutic potential of gamma-hydroxybutyric acid. *Alcohol, 20,* 263–269.

Ganio, M. S., Klau, J. F., Casa, D. J., Armstrong, L. E., & Maresh, C. M. (2009). Effect of caffeine on sport-specific endurance performance: A systematic review. *Journal of Strength and Conditioning Research, 23,* 315–324.

Gaoni, Y., & Mechoulam, R. (1964). Isolation, structure, and partial synthesis of an active constituent of hashish. *Journal of the American Chemical Society, 86,* 1646–1647.

Garbutt, J. C., West, S. L., Carey, T. S., Lohr, K. N., & Crews, F. T. (1999). Pharmacological treatment of alcohol dependence: A review of the evidence. *Journal of the American Medical Association, 281,* 1318–1325.

Gardner, D. M., Baldessarini, R. J., & Waraich, P. (2005). Modern antipsychotic drugs: A critical overview. *CMAJ, 172,* 1703–1711.

Garriguet, D. (2008). Beverage consumption of Canadian adults. *Health Reports.* Ottawa: Statistics Canada. Available at http://www.statcan.gc.ca/pub/82-003-x/2008004/article/6500821-eng.pdf.

Gastfriend, D. R. (Ed.). (2003). *Addiction treatment matching.* New York: Haworth Medical Press.

Gautier, T. (1844/1966). Le club des hachichins. In D. Solomon (Ed.), *The marijuana papers* (pp. 121–135). New York: Bobbs-Merrill.

Gauvin, D. V., Cheng, E. Y., & Holloway, F. A. (1993). Biobehavioral correlates. In M. Gallanter (Ed.), *Recent developments in alcoholism* (Vol. 11, pp. 281–304). New York: Plenum Press.

Gavaghan, C. (2009). "You can't handle the truth"; Medical paternalism and prenatal alcohol use. *Journal of Medical Ethics, 35,* 300–303.

Gay, G. R., & Way, E. L. (1972). Pharmacology of the opiate narcotics. In D. E. Smith & G. R. Way (Eds.), *It's so good, don't even try it once* (pp. 32–44). Englewood Cliffs, NJ: Prentice Hall.

Gaziano, J. M., et al. (1993). Moderate alcohol intake, increased levels of high-density lipoprotein and its subfractions, and decreased risk of myocardial infarction. *New England Journal of Medicine, 329,* 1829–1834.

Geller, E. S., Russ, N. W., & Delphos, W. A. (1987). Does server intervention training make a difference? *Alcohol Health and Research World, 11,* 64–69.

Ghatol, A., & Kazory, A. (2009). Ecstasy-associated acute severe hyponatremia and cerebral edema: A role for osmotic diuresis? *Journal of Emergency Medicine,* June 3, [epub ahead of print].

Gilbert, R. M. (1976). Caffeine as a drug of abuse. In R. J. Gibbins, Y. Israel, H. Kalant, R. E. Popham, W. Schmidt, & R. G. Smart (Eds.), *Research advances in alcohol and drug problems* (Vol. 3, pp. 49–176). New York: John Wiley.

Gilbert, R. M. (1984). Caffeine consumption. *Progress in Clinical Biological Research, 158,* 185–213.

Gill, S., Veinot, J. P., Kavanagh, M., & Pulido, O. (2007). Human heart glutamate receptors: Implications for toxicology, food safety and drug discovery. *Toxicologic Pathology, 35,* 411–417.

Gitlin, M. J. (1990). *The psychotherapist's guide to psychopharmacology.* New York: Free Press.

Glantz, S. A., & Parmley, W. W. (1991). Passive smoking and heart disease. *Circulation, 83,* 1–12.

Gliksman, L., McKenzie, D., Single, E., Douglas, R., Brunet, S., & Moffatt, K. (1993). The role of alcohol providers in prevention: An evaluation of a server intervention programme. *Addiction, 88,* 1195–1203.

Golan, D. (2005, Summer 2005 Special Edition). Building better medicines. *Newsweek,* pp. 37–39.

Goldman, A. (1971). *Ladies and gentlemen, Lenny Bruce!* New York: Random House.

Goldman, M. S., Darkes, J., & Del Boca, F. K. (1999). Expectancy mediation of biopsychosocial risk for alcohol use and alcoholism. In I. Kirsch (Ed.), *How expectancies shape experience* (pp. 263–300). Washington, DC: American Psychological Association.

Goldschmidt, L., Day, N. L., & Richardson, G. A. (2000). Effects of prenatal marijuana exposure on child behavior problems at age 10. *Neurotoxicology and Teratology, 22,* 325–336.

Goldstein, A. (2001). *Addiction: From biology to social policy* (2nd ed.). New York: Oxford University Press.

Goldstein, A. S., Kaizer, S., & Whitby, O. (1969). Psychotropic effects of caffeine in man. IV. Quantitative and qualitative differences associated with habituation to coffee. *Clinical and Pharmacological Therapeutics, 10,* 489–497.

Goldstein, A., & Wallace, M. E. (1997). Caffeine dependence in school children? *Experimental and Clinical Psychopharmacology, 5,* 388–392.

Goldstein, J. W., & Sappington, J. T. (1977). Personality characteristics of students who became heavy drug users: An MMPI study of an avant garde. *American Journal of Drug and Alcohol Abuse, 4,* 401–412.

Goode, E. (1972). *Drugs in American society.* New York: Alfred A. Knopf.

Goode, E. (1993). *Drugs in American society* (4th ed.). New York: McGraw-Hill.

Gordon, B. (1979). *I'm dancing as fast as I can.* New York: Bantam Books.

Gorman, D. M. (1995). The changing role of mass media in preventing excessive alcohol use. *Drugs: Education, Prevention, and Policy, 2,* 77–84.

Gould, E., Reeves, A. J., Graziano, M. S., & Gross, C. G. (1999). Neurogenesis in the neocortex of adult primates. *Science, 286,* 548–552.

Government of Canada (2011). National anti-drug strategy. Available at http://www.nationalantidrug-strategy.gc.ca/back-fich/doc2008_11_17b.html; accessed October 9, 2011.

Government Printing Office (GPO). (1972). *Drug abuse: Games without winners.* Washington, DC: Author.

Graham, D. M. (1978). Caffeine: Its identity, dietary sources, intake and biological effects. *Nutrition Reviews, 36,* 97–102.

Graham, K., Leonard, K. E., Room, R., Wild, C., Pihl, R. O., Boiss, C., et al. (1998). Current directions in research on understanding and preventing intoxicated aggression. *Addiction, 93,* 659–676.

Grant, B. F., & Dawson, D.A. (1998). Age of onset of drug use and its association with DSM-IV drug abuse and dependence: Results from the National Longitudinal Alcohol Epidemiologic Survey. *Journal of Substance Abuse, 10,* 163–173.

Grant, I., Gonzalez, R., Carey, C.L., Natarajan, L., & Wolfson, T. (2003). Non-acute (residual) neurocognitive effects of cannabis use: a meta-analytic study. *Journal of the International Neuropsychological Society, 9,* 679–689.

Grant, S. G. (2005). Qualitatively and quantitatively similar effects of active and passive maternal tobacco smoke exposure on in utero mutagenesis at the HPRT locus. *BMC Pediatrics,* DOI:10.1186/ 1471-2431-5-20.

Greden, J. F. (1974). Anxiety or caffeinism: A diagnostic dilemma. *American Journal of Psychiatry, 131,* 1089–1092.

Greden, J. F., & Walters, A. (1992). Caffeine. In J. H. Lowinson, P. Ruiz, & R. B. Millman (Eds.), *Substance abuse: A comprehensive textbook* (2nd ed., pp. 357–370). Baltimore, MD: Williams & Wilkins.

Greeley, J., & Oei, T. (1999). Alcohol and tension reduction. In K. E. Leonard & H. T. Blane (Eds.), *Psychological theories of drinking and alcoholism* (2nd ed., pp. 14–53). New York: Guilford Press.

Green, T. C., Serrano, J. M. G., Licari, A., Budman, S. H., & Butler, S. (2009). Women who abuse prescription opioids: Findings from the Addiction Severity Index-Multimedia Version Connect prescription opioid database. *Drug and Alcohol Dependence, 103,* 65–73.

Griffiths, R. R., & Woodson, D. P. (1988b). Reinforcing properties of caffeine: Studies in human and laboratory animals. *Pharmacology, Biochemistry, and Behavior, 28,* 419–427.

Griffiths, R. R., & Woodson, P. P. (1988a). Caffeine physical dependence: A review of human and animal laboratory studies. *Psychopharmacology, 94,* 437–451.

Griffiths, R. R., Bigelow, G. E., Liebson, I., & Kaliszak, J. E. (1980). Drug preference in humans: Double-blind choice comparison of pentobarbital, diazepam, and placebo. *Journal of Pharmacology and Experimental Therapeutics, 215,* 649–661.

Griffiths, R. R., McLeod, E. R., Bigelow, G. E., Liebson, I. A., & Roache, J. D. (1984). Relative abuse liability of diazepam and oxazepam: Behavior and subjective dose effects. *Psychopharmacology, 84,* 147–154.

Griffiths, R. R., McLeod, E. R., Bigelow, G. E., Liebson, I. A., Roache, J. D., & Nowowieski, P. (1984). Comparison of diazepam and oxazepam: Preference liking and extent of abuse. *Journal of Pharmacology and Experimental Therapeutics, 229,* 501–508.

Grilly, D. M. (2002). *Drugs and human behavior.* Boston: Allyn & Bacon.

Grinspoon, L., & Bakalar, J. B. (1976). *Cocaine: A drug and its social evolution.* New York: Harper Books.

Grinspoon, L., & Bakalar, J. B. (1979). *Psychedelic drugs reconsidered.* New York: Basic Books.

Grinspoon, L., & Bakalar, J. B. (1983). *Psychedelic reflections.* New York: Human Sciences Press.

Gritz, E. R., Ksir, C., & McCarthy, W. J. (1985). Smokeless tobacco use in the United States: Present and future trends. *Annals of Behavioral Medicine, 7,* 24–27.

Grobbee, D., Rimm, E., Giovannucci, E., Colditz, G., Stampfer, M., & Willett, W. (1990). Coffee, caffeine, and cardiovascular disease in men. *New England Journal of Medicine, 323,* 1026–1032.

Grogan, F. J. (1987). *The pharmacist's prescription.* New York: Rawson Associates.

Gronbaek, M., Deis, A., Sorensen, T. I. A., Becker, U., Schnohr, P., & Jensen, G. (1995). Mortality associated with moderate intake of wine, beer, or spirits. *British Medical Journal, 310,* 1165–1169.

Grotenhermen, F. (2007). The toxicology of cannabis and cannabis prohibition. *Chemistry & Biodiversity, 4,* 1744–1769.

Grufferman, S., Schwartz, A. G., Ruymann, F. B., & Maurer, H. M. (1993). Parent's use of cocaine and marijuana and increased risk of rhabdomyosarcoma in their children. *Cancer Causes Control, 4,* 217–224.

Grunder, G., Hippius, H., & Carlsson, A. (2009). The 'atypicality' of antipsychotics: A concept re-examined and re-defined. *Nature Reviews, 8,* 197–202.

Gutjahr, E., Gmel, G., & Rehm, J. (2001). Relation between average alcohol consumption and disease: An overview. *Addiction Research, 7,* 117–127.

Haans, D. (1994). *Is there a 'war on drugs?'.* Retrieved on October 2011 from http://www.druglibrary.org/schaffer/Misc/haans1.htm.

Hajek, P., West, R., Foulds, J., Nilsson, F., Burrow, S., & Meadow, A. (1999). Randomized comparative trials of nicotine polacrilex, a transdermal patch, nasal spray, and inhaler. *Archives of Internal Medicine, 159,* 2033–2038.

Halkitis, P. N. (2009). *Methamphetamine addiction: Biological foundations, psychological factors, and social consequences.* Washington: American Psychological Association Press.

Hall, K. M., Irwin, M. M., Bowman, K. A., Frankenberger, W., & Jewett, D. C. (2005). Illicit use of prescribed stimulant medication among college students. *Journal of American College Health, 53,* 167–174.

Hall, W. D., & Lynskey, M. (2005). Is cannabis a gateway drug? Testing hypotheses about the relationship between cannabis use and the use of other illicit drugs. *Drug and Alcohol Review, 24,* 39–48.

Halpern, J. H., & Pope, H. G. (1999). Do hallucinogens cause residual neuropsychological toxicity? *Drug and Alcohol Dependence, 53,* 247–256.

Halpern, J. H., & Pope, H. G. (2003). Hallucinogen persisting perception disorder: What do we know after 50 years? *Drug and Alcohol Dependence, 69,* 109–119.

Halpern, J. H., Pope, H. G., Sherwood, A. R., Barry, S., Hudson, J. I., & Yurgelin-Todd, D. (2004). Residual neuropsychological effects of illicit 3,4-methylenedioxymethamphetamine (MDMA) in individuals with minimal exposure to other drugs. *Drug and Alcohol Dependence, 75,* 135–147.

Hamilton, G., Cross, D., Resnicow, K., & Hall, M. (2005). A school-based harm minimization smoking intervention trial: Outcome results. *Addiction, 100,* 689–700.

Han, J. S., & Terenius, L. (1982). Neurochemical basis of acupuncture analgesia. *Annual Review of Pharmacology and Toxicology, 22,* 193–220.

Harris, G. (2004, December 6). At FDA, strong drug ties and less monitoring. *The New York Times,* pp. A1, A20.

Harris, G. (2007). Potentially incompatible goals at the FDA. *The New York Times*, June 11, 2007.

Harris, L. S., Dewey, W. L., & Razdan, R. K. (1977). Cannabis: Its chemistry, pharmacology, and toxicology. In W. R. Martin (Ed.), *Drug addiction II: Amphetamine, psychotogen, and marihuana dependence* (pp. 371–429). New York: Springer-Verlag.

Hart, C. L., Gunderson, E. W., Perez, A., Kirkpatrick, M. G., Thurmond, A., Comer, S. D., & Foltin, R. W. (2008). Acute physiological and behavioral effects of intranasal methamphetamine in humans. *Neuropsychopharmacology, 33*, 1847–1855.

Harvey, S. C. (1980). Hypnotics and sedatives. In A. G. Gilman, L. S. Goodman, & A. Gilman (Eds.), *Goodman and Gilman's The pharmacological basis of therapeutics* (6th ed., pp. 339–379). London: Macmillan.

Harwood, H., Fountain, D., & Livermore, G. (1998). *The economic costs of alcohol and drug abuse in the United States—1992.* Rockville, MD: U.S. Department of Health and Human Services.

Hathaway, A., Comeau, N., & Erikson, P. (2011). Cannabis normalization and stigma: Contemporary practices of moral regulation. *Criminology and Criminal Justice, 11*, 451–469.

Hatzidimitriou, G., McCann, U. D., & Ricaurte, G. A. (1999). Altered serotonin innervation patterns in the forebrain of monkeys treated with (1/2)-3, 4-methylenedioxymethamphetamine seven years previously: Factors influencing abnormal recovery. *Journal of Neuroscience, 19,* 5096–5107.

Hawks, R. L., & Chiang, C. N. (1986). *Urine testing for drugs of abuse.* Research Monograph 73. Washington, DC: National Institute on Drug Abuse.

Hayden, J. W. (1991). Passive inhalation of marijuana smoke: A critical review. *Journal of Substance Abuse, 3,* 85–90.

Haydon, E., & Fisher, B. (2005). Crack use as a public health problem in Canada: Call for an evaluation of safer crack use kits. *Canadian Journal of Public Health, 96* (3), 185–188.

Health Canada (2005). About natural health products. Retrieved on December 9, 2011 from http://www.hc-sc.gc.ca/dhp-mps/prodnatur/about-apropos/cons-eng.php.

Health Canada. (1999). Women's health strategy. Available at http://www.hc-sc.gc.ca/ahc-asc/pubs/_women-femmes/1999-strateg/index-eng.php.

Health Canada. (2008). Best practices—Methadone maintenance treatment. Available at http://www.hc-sc.gc.ca/hc-ps/pubs/adp-apd/methadone-bp-mp/index-eng.php.

Health Canada. (2009). How are opioid medications regulated? Available at http://www.hc-sc.gc.ca/hl-vs/iyh-vsv/med/opioid-faq-opioides-eng.php#a13.

Health Canada. (2009). Opiate pain medications: Frequently asked questions. Available at http://hc-sc.gc.ca/hl-vs/iyh-vsv/med/opioid-faq-opioides-eng.php.

Health Canada. (2009). Summary of results of the 2008–09 Youth Smoking Survey. Available at http://www.hc-sc.gc.ca/hc-ps/tobac-tabac/research-recherche/stat/_survey-sondage_2008-2009/result-eng.php.

Health Canada. (2010). Canadian Alcohol and Drug Use Monitoring Survey. Available at http://www.hc-sc.gc.ca/hc-ps/drugs-drogues/stat/_2009/summary-sommaire-eng.php.

Health Canada. (2010). Tobacco product labelling. Available at http://www.hc-sc.gc.ca/hc-ps/tobac-tabac/legislation/label-etiquette/index-eng.php.

Health Canada. (2011). Caffeine in food. Available at http://www.hc-sc.gc.ca/fn-an/securit/addit/caf/food-caf-aliments-eng.php.

Health Canada. (2011). Caffeine. Available at http://www.hc-sc.gc.ca/hl-vs/iyh-vsv/food-aliment/caffeine-eng.php.

Health Canada. (2011). Marijuana for medicinal purposes: Statistics (January, 2010). Available at http://www.hc-sc.gc.ca/dhp-mps/marihuana/stat/_2010/jan-eng.php; accessed September 24, 2011.

Health Canada. (2011). Medical use of marijuana. Available at http://www.hc-sc.gc.ca/dhp-mps/marihuana/index-eng.php.

Health Canada. (2011). *Salvia divinorum*. Available at http://www.hc-sc.gc.ca/hl-vs/iyh-vsv/life-vie/salvia-eng.php.

Hecht, A. (1985). *Addictive behavior: Drug and alcohol abuse*. Englewood, CO: Morton Publishing.

Hegadoren, K. M., Baker, G. B., & Bourin, M. (1999). 3,4-methyl-enedioxy analogues of amphetamine: Defining the risks to humans. *Neuroscience and Biobehavioral Reviews, 23,* 539–553.

Heishman, S. J., Taylor, R. C., & Henningfield, J. E. (1994). Nicotine and smoking: A review of effects on human performance. *Experimental and Clinical Psychopharmacology, 2,* 345–395.

Henningfield, J. E., Lukas, S. E., & Bigelow, G. E. (1986). Human studies of drugs as reinforcers. In S. R. Goldberg & I. P. Stolerman (Eds.), *Behavioral analysis of drug dependence* (pp. 69–122). New York: Academic Press.

Henningfield, J. E., Santora, P. S., & Stillman, F. A. (2005). Exploitation by design—could tobacco industry documents guide more effective smoking prevention and cessation in women? *Addiction, 100,* 715–716.

Hepler, R. S., & Petrus, R. J. (1976). Experiences with administration of marijuana to glaucoma patients. In S. Cohen & R. C. Stillman (Eds.), *The therapeutic aspects of marijuana* (pp. 63–75). New York: Plenum Press.

Hepple, J., & Robson, P. (1996). The effect of caffeine on cue exposure responses in ex-smokers. *Addiction, 91,* 269–273.

Herkenham, M., Lynn, A. B., Little, M. D., Johnson, M. R., Melvin, L. S., deCosta, B. R., et al. (1990). Cannabinoid receptor localization in the brain. *National Academy of Science, 87,* 1932–1936.

Hester, R. K., & Delaney, H. D. (1997). Behavioral self-control program for Windows: Results of a controlled clinical trial. *Journal of Consulting and Clinical Psychology, 65,* 683–693.

Hester, R. K., & Miller, W. R. (Eds.). (1989). *Handbook of alcoholism treatment approaches: Effective alternatives*. Elmsford, NY: Pergamon Press.

Hewitt, L. E. (1982). Current status of alcohol education programs for youth. In *Special Population Issues,* Alcohol and Health Monograph 4 (pp. 227–260). Rockville, MD: National Institute on Alcohol Abuse and Alcoholism.

Higdon, J.V., & Frei, B. (2006). Coffee and health: A review of recent human research. *Critical Reviews in Food Science and Nutrition, 46,* 101–123.

Higgins, S. T., & Stitzer, M. L. (1988). Time allocation in a concurrent schedule of social interaction and monetary reinforcement: Effects of *d*-amphetamine. *Pharmacology, Biochemistry, and Behavior, 31,* 227–231.

Higgins, S. T., Budney, A. J., Bickel, W. K., Hughes, J. R., Foerg, F., & Badger, G. (1993). Achieving cocaine abstinence with a behavioral approach. *American Journal of Psychiatry, 150,* 763–769.

Higgins, S. T., Delaney, D. D., Budney, A. J., Bickel, W. K., Hughes, J. R., Foerg, F., et al. (1991). A behavioral approach to achieving initial cocaine abstinence. *American Journal of Psychiatry, 148,* 1218–1224.

Higuchi, S., Parrish, K. M., Dufour, M. C., Towle, L., & Harford, T. C. (1992). The relationship between three types of the flushing response and DSM-III alcohol abuse in Japanese. *Journal of Studies on Alcohol, 53,* 553–560.

Hill, S. Y., Wang, S., Kostelnik, B., Carter, H., Holmes, B., McDermott, M., Zezza, N., Stiffler, S., & Keshavan, M. S. (2009). Disruption of orbitofrontal cortex laterality in offspring from multiplex alcohol dependence families. *Biological Psychiatry, 65,* 129–136.

Hilton, M. E. (1993). An overview of recent findings on alcohol beverage warning labels. *Journal of Public Policy Marketing, 12,* 1–9.

Hindmarch, I., Rigney, U., Stanley, N., Quinlan, P., Rycroft, J., & Lane, J. (2000). A naturalistic investigation of the effects of daylong consumption of tea, coffee, and water on alertness, sleep onset, and sleep quality. *Psychopharmacology, 149,* 203–216.

Hingson, R. W., Heeren, T., Winter, M., & Wechsler, H. (2005). Magnitude of alcohol-related mortality and morbidity among U.S. college students ages 18–24. *Annual Review of Public Health, 26,* 259–279.

Hingson, R. W., Heeren, T., Zakocs, R. C., Kopstein, A., & Wechsler, H. (2002). Magnitude of alcohol-related mortality and morbidity among U.S. college students ages 18–24. *Journal of Studies on Alcohol, 63,* 136–144.

Hinson, R. E. (1985). Individual differences in tolerance and relapse: A Pavlovian conditioning perspective. In M. Galizio & S. A. Maisto (Eds.), *Determinants of substance abuse: Biological, psychological, and environmental factors* (pp. 101–124). New York: Plenum Press.

Ho, A. K. S., & Allen, J. P. (1981). Alcohol and the opiate receptor: Interactions with the endogenous opiates. *Advances in Alcohol & Substance Abuse, 1,* 53–75.

Hofmann, A. (1980). *LSD: My problem child*. New York: McGraw-Hill.

Hofmann, F. G. (1975). *A handbook on drug and alcohol abuse*. New York: Oxford University Press.

Hogan, E. H., Hornick, B. A., & Bouchoux, A. (2002). Communicating the message: Clarifying the controversies about caffeine. *Nutrition Today, 37,* 28–36.

Hogervorst, E., Bandelow, S., Schmitt, J., Jentjens, R., Oliveira, M., Allgrove, J., Carter, T., & Gleeson, M. (2008). Caffeine improves physical and cognitive performance during exhaustive exercise. *Medicine & Science in Sports & Exercise, 40,* 1841–1851.

Holder, H. D., & Blose, J. D. (1991). Typical patterns and cost of alcoholism treatment across a variety of populations and providers. *Alcoholism: Clinical and Experimental Research, 15,* 190–195.

Holland, J. (2001). The history of MDMA. In J. Holland (Ed.), *Ecstasy: The complete guide.* Rochester, VT: Park Street Press.

Hollis, J. F., et al. (2005). Teen Reach: Outcomes from a randomized, controlled trial of a tobacco reduction program for teens seen in primary medical care. *Pediatrics, 115,* 981–989.

Hollister, L. E., Richards, R. K., & Gillespie, H. K. (1968). Comparison of tetrahydrocannabinol and synhexyl in man. *Clinical Pharmacology and Therapeutics, 9,* 783–791.

Hopfer, C., Mendelson, B., Van Leeuwen, J. M., Kelly, S., & Hooks, S. (2006). Club drug use among youths in treatment for substance abuse. *American Journal on Addictions, 15,* 94–99.

Hossick, K. (1956). Canada's senate committee on the traffic in narcotic drugs. *United Nations Office on Drugs and Crime (UNODC), Issue 2, V1,* p. 2.

House of Lords Select Committee on Science and Technology. (1988). *Cannabis: The scientific and medical evidence* (HL Paper 151). London: HMSO.

Howland, R. H. (2009). Prescribing psychotropic medications during pregnancy and lactation: Principles and guidelines. *Journal of Psychosocial Nursing, 47,* 19–23.

Hrobjartsson, A., & Gotzsche, P. C. (2001). Is the placebo powerless? An analysis of clinical trials comparing placebo with no treatment. *New England Journal of Medicine, 344,* 1594–1603.

Hser, Y-I., Hoffman, V., Grella, C. E., & Anglin, M. D. (2001). A 33-year follow-up of narcotics addicts. *Archives of General Psychiatry, 58,* 503–508.

Hubbard, R. L., Marsden, M. E., Rachal, J. V., Harwood, H. J., Cavanaugh, E. R., & Ginzburg, H. M. (1989). *Drug abuse treatment: A national study of effectiveness.* Chapel Hill: University of North Carolina Press.

Hudson, G. M., Green, J. M., Bishop, P. A., & Richardson, M. T. (2008). Effects of caffeine and aspirin on light resistance training performance, perceived exertion, and pain perception. *Journal of Strength and Conditioning Research, 22,* 1950–1957.

Hughes, C. E., Pitts, R. C., & Branch, M. N. (1996). Cocaine and food deprivation: Effects on food-reinforced fixed ratio performance in pigeons. *Journal of the Experimental Analysis of Behavior, 65,* 145–158.

Hughes, J. C., & Cook, C. H. (1997). The efficacy of disulfiram: A review of outcome studies. *Addiction, 92,* 381–395.

Hughes, J. R. (1993). Pharmacotherapy for smoking cessation: Unvalidated assumptions, anomalies, and suggestions for future research. *Journal of Consulting and Clinical Psychology, 61,* 751–760.

Hughes, J. R. (1996). The future of smoking cessation therapy in the United States. *Addiction, 91,* 1797–1802.

Hughes, J. R., & Carpenter, M. J. (2006). Does smoking reduction increase future cessation and decrease disease risk? A qualitative review. *Nicotine and Tobacco Research, 6,* 739–749.

Hughes, J. R., & Hale, K. L. (1998). Behavioral effects of caffeine and other methylxanthines on children. *Experimental and Clinical Psychopharmacology, 6,* 87–95.

Hughes, J. R., Goldstein, M. G., Hurt, R. D., & Shiffman, S. (1999). Recent advances in the pharmacotherapy of smoking. *Journal of the American Medical Association, 281,* 72–75.

Hughes, J. R., Grist, S. W., & Pechacek, T. F. (1987). Prevalence of tobacco dependence and withdrawal. *American Journal of Psychiatry, 144,* 205–208.

Hughes, J. R., Oliveto, A. H., Helzer, J. E., Higgins, S. T., & Bickel, W. K. (1992). Should caffeine abuse, dependence or withdrawal be added to DSM-IV or ICD-10? *American Journal of Psychiatry, 149,* 33–40.

Hull, J. G., & Bond, C. F. (1986). Social and behavioral consequences of alcohol consumption: A meta analysis. *Psychological Bulletin, 99,* 347–360.

Humphreys, K., Wing, S., McCarty, D., Chappel, J., Gallant, L., Haberle, B., et al. (2004). Self-help organizations for alcohol and drug problems: Toward evidence-based practice and policy. *Journal of Substance Abuse Treatment, 26,* 151–158.

Hunt, G. M., & Azrin, N. H. (1973). A community reinforcement approach to alcoholism. *Behavior Research and Therapy, 11,* 91–104.

Hunt, W. A., Barnett, L. W., & Branch, L. G. (1971). Relapse rates in addiction programs. *Journal of Clinical Psychology, 27,* 455–456.

Huxley, A. (1954). *The doors of perception.* New York: Harper.

Huxley, R., Jamrozik, T. H., Lam, T. H., Barzi, F., Ansary-Moghaddam, A., Jiamg, C. Q., Suh, I., & Woodward, M., on behalf of the Asia Pacific Cohort Studies Collaboration. (2007). Impact of smoking and smoking cessation on lung cancer mortality in the Asia-Pacific region. *American Journal of Epidemiology, 165,* 1280–1286.

Hyde, J. S., & DeLamater, J. D. (2006). *Understanding human sexuality* (9th ed.). New York: McGraw-Hill.

Hypericum Depression Trial Study Group. (2002). Effect of *Hypericum perforatum* (St. John's wort) in major depressive disorder: A randomized controlled trial. *Journal of the American Medical Association, 287,* 1807–1814.

Ichiyama, M. A., Fairlie, A. M., Wood, M. D., Turrisi, R., Francies, D. P., Ray, A. E., & Stanger, L. A. (2009). A randomized trial of a parent-based intervention on drinking behavior among incoming college freshmen. *Journal of Studies on Alcohol and Drugs, Supplement, 16,* 67–76.

Iguchi, M. Y., Belding, M. A., Morral, A. R., Lamb, R. J., & Husband, S. D. (1997). Reinforcing operants other than abstinence in drug abuse treatment: An effective alternative for reducing drug use. *Journal of Consulting and Clinical Psychology, 65,* 421–428.

Inciardi, J. A. (2002). *The war on drugs III: The continuing saga of the mysteries and miseries of intoxication, addiction, crime, and public policy.* Boston: Allyn & Bacon.

Infante-Rivard, C., Fernandez, A., Gauthier, R., David, M., & Rivard, G. E. (1993). Fetal loss associated with caffeine intake before and during pregnancy. *Journal of the American Medical Association, 270,* 2940–2943.

Institute of Medicine. (1982). *Marijuana and health.* Washington, DC: National Academy Press.

Institute of Medicine. (1990a). *Broadening the base of treatment for alcohol problems.* Washington, DC: National Academy Press.

Institute of Medicine. (1990b). *Treating drug problems* (Vol. 1). Washington, DC: National Academy Press.

Institute of Medicine. (2001). *Caffeine for the sustainment of mental task performance: Formulations for military operations.* Washington, DC: National Academy of Sciences.

Iversen, L. L. (2000). *The science of marijuana.* New York: Oxford University Press.

Iversen, L. L. (2003). Cannabis and the brain. *Brain, 126,* 1252–1270.

Iversen, L. L. (2008). *Speed, ecstasy, Ritalin: The science of amphetamines.* Oxford: Oxford University Press.

Iversen, L. L., Iversen, S. D., Bloom, F. E., & Roth, R. H. (2009). *Introduction to neuropsychopharmacology.* New York: Oxford University Press.

Jacobs, B. L. (2004). Depression: The brain finally gets into the act. *Current Directions in Psychological Science, 13,* 103–106.

Jacobs, M. R., & Fehr, K. O'Brien. (1987). *Drugs and drug abuse: A reference text* (2nd ed.). Toronto: Addiction Research Foundation.

Jacobson, J. L., Jacobson, S. W., Sokol, R. J., Martier, S. S., Ager, J. W., & Kaplan-Estrin, G. (1993). Teratogenic effects of alcohol on infant development. *Alcoholism: Clinical and Experimental Research, 17,* 174–183.

Jaffe, J. H. (1990). Drug addiction and drug abuse. In A. G. Gilman, T. W. Rall, A. S. Nies, & P. Taylor (Eds.), *The pharmacological basis of therapeutics* (8th ed., pp. 522–573). New York: Pergamon Press.

Jaffe, J. H., & Martin, W. R. (1990). Opioid analgesics and antagonists. In A. G. Gilman, T. W. Rall, A. S. Nies, & P. Taylor (Eds.), *Goodman and Gilman's The pharmacological basis of therapeutics* (8th ed., pp. 485–521). New York: Pergamon Press.

Jahoda, G., & Cramond, J. (1972). *Children and alcohol.* London: HMSO.

James, J. E. (1991). *Caffeine and health.* New York: Academic Press.

James, W. H., & Johnson, S. L. (1996). *Doin' drugs: Patterns of African American addiction.* Austin: University of Texas Press.

Jansen, K. (2004). *Ketamine: Dreams and realities.* Sarasota, FL: Multidisciplinary Association for Psychedelic Studies.

Jarvik, M. E., Madsen, D. C., Olmstead, R. E., Iwamoto-Schapp, P. N., Elins, J. L., & Benowitz, N. L. (2000). Nicotine blood levels and subjective craving for cigarettes. *Pharmacology, Biochemistry, and Behavior, 66,* 553–558.

Jefferson, D. J. (2005, August). America's most dangerous drug. *Newsweek.*

Jiang, W., Zhang, Y., Xiao, L,, Cleemput, J., Van, J., Shao-Pint, B., & Zhang, X. (2005). Cannabinoids promote embryonic and adult hippocampus neurogeneis and produce anxiolytic and antidepressant-like effects. *Journal of Clinical Investigation, 115,* 3104–3116.

Johanson, C. E. (1992). Biochemical mechanisms and pharmacological principles of drug action. In J. Grabowski & G. R. VandenBos (Eds.), *Master lecture series. Psychopharmacology: Basic mechanisms and applied interventions* (pp. 11–58). Washington, DC: American Psychological Association.

Johanson, C. E., & Uhlenhuth, E. H. (1978). Drug self-administration in humans. In N. A. Krasnegor (Ed.), *Self-administration of abused substances: Methods for study.* NIDA Research Monograph 20 (pp. 68–87). Washington, DC: U.S. Government Printing Office.

Johnson, B. D. (1973). *Marihuana users and drug subcultures.* New York: John Wiley.

Johnson, C., Drgon, T., Liu, O. R., Walther, D., Edenberg, H., Rice, J., Foroud, T., & Uhl, G. R. (2006). Pooled association genome scanning for alcohol dependence using 104,268 SNPs: Validation and use to identify alcoholism vulnerability lici in unrelated individuals from the collaborative study on the genetics of alcoholism. *American Journal of Medical*

Genetics. Part B, Neuropsychiatric Genetics, 141B, 844–853.

Johnston, L. D., O'Malley, P. M., Bachman, J. G., & Schulenberg, J. E. (2009a). *Monitoring the future national results on adolescent drug use: Overview of key findings, 2008.* Bethesda, MD: National Institute on Drug Abuse.

Johnston, L. D., O'Malley, P. M., Bachman, J. G., & Schulenberg, J. E. (2009b). *Monitoring the future national results on adolescent drug use, 1975–2008. Volume 1: Secondary school students.* Bethesda, MD: National Institute on Drug Abuse.

Jones, G. (2008). Caffeine and other sympathomimetic stimulants: Modes of action and effects on sports performance. *Essays in Biochemistry, 44,* 109–123.

Jones, K. L., Smith, D. W., Ulleland, C. N., & Streissguth, P. (1973). Pattern of malformation in offspring of chronic alcoholic mothers. *Lancet, 1 (7815),* 1267–1271.

Jones, R. T. (1980). Human effects: An overview. In R. C. Peterson (Ed.), *Marijuana research findings: 1980* (pp. 54–80). Rockville, MD: National Institute on Drug Abuse.

Jones, R. T. (1987a). The psychopharmacology of cocaine. In A. M. Washton & M. S. Gold (Eds.), *Cocaine: A clinician's handbook* (pp. 55–72). New York: Guilford Press.

Jones, R. T. (1987b). Tobacco dependence. In H. Y. Meltzer (Ed.), *Psychopharmacology: The third generation of progress* (pp. 1589–1595). New York: Raven Press.

Joy, J. E., Watson, S. J., & Benson, J. A. (1999). *Marijuana and medicine: Assessing the science base.* Washington, DC: National Academy Press.

Juliano, L. M., & Brandon, T. H. (2002). Effects of nicotine dose, instructional set, and outcome expectancies on the subjective effects of smoking in the presence of a stressor. *Journal of Abnormal Psychology, 111,* 88–97.

Juliano, L. M., & Griffiths, R. R. (2001). Is caffeine a drug of dependence? *Psychiatric Times,* 18.

Juliano, L. M., & Griffiths, R. R. (2004). A critical review of caffeine withdrawal: Empirical validation of symptoms and signs, incidence, severity, and associated features. *Psychopharmacology, 176,* 1–29.

Julien, R. M. (1996). *A primer of drug action* (7th ed.). New York: W. H. Freeman.

Julien, R. M. (1998). *A primer of drug action* (8th ed.). New York: W. H. Freeman.

Julien, R. M. (2001). *A primer of drug action* (9th ed.). New York: W. H. Freeman.

Julien, R. M. (2005). *A primer of drug action* (10th ed.). New York: Worth Publishers.

Julien, R. M., Advokat, C. D., & Comaty, J. E. (2008). *A primer of drug action* (11th ed). New York: Worth Publishers.

Jung, J. (2001). *Psychology of alcohol and other drugs: A research perspective.* Thousand Oaks, CA: Sage Publications.

Kalant, H. (1996). Current state of knowledge about the mechanisms of alcohol tolerance. *Addiction Biology, 1,* 133–141.

Kalant, H., LeBlanc, A. E., & Gibbins, R. J. (1971). Tolerance to, and dependence on, some nonopiate psychotropic drugs. *Pharmacological Reviews, 23,* 135–191.

Kalat, J. W. (2009). *Biological psychology* (10th ed.). Belmont, CA: Wadsworth.

Kalivas, P. W., & Volkow, N. D. (2005). The neural basis of addiction: A pathology of motivation and choice. *American Journal of Psychiatry, 162,* 1403–1413.

Kalus, O., Asnis, G. M., & van Praag, H. M. (1989). The role of serotonin in depression. *Psychiatric Annals, 19,* 348–353.

Kanayama, G. Hudson, J. I. & Pope, H. G. (2009). Features of men with anabolic-androgenic steroid dependence: A comparison with nondependent AAS users and with AAS nonusers. *Drug and Alcohol Dependence, 102,* 130–137.

Kanayama, G. Hudson, J. I., & Pope, H. G. (2008). Long-term psychiatric and medical consequences of anabolic-androgenic steroid abuse: A looming public health concern? *Drug and Alcohol Dependence, 98,* 1–12.

Kandel, D. (1975). Stages in adolescent involvement in drug use. *Science, 190,* 912–914.

Kandel, D., & Yamaguchi, K. (1993). From beer to crack: Developmental patterns of drug involvement. *American Journal of Public Health, 83,* 851–855.

Kapoun, J. (1998). Teaching undergrads web evaluation: A guide for library instruction. *College and Research Library News, 59,* 522–523.

Karch, S. B. (2000). Ma huang and the ephedra alkaloids. In M. J. Cupp (Ed.), *Toxicology and clinical pharmacology of herbal products* (pp. 11–30). Totowa, NJ: Humana Press.

Karlmangla, A. S., Sarkisian, C. A., Kado, D. M., Dedes, H., Liao, D. H., Kim, S., Reuben, D. B., Greendale, G. A., & Moore, A. A. (2009). Light to moderate alcohol consumption and disability: Variable benefits by health status. *American Journal of Epidemiology, 169,* 96–104.

Karst, M., Salim, K., Burstein, S., Conrad, I., Hoy, L., & Schneider, U. (2003). Analgesic effect of the synthetic cannabinoid CT-3 on chronic neuropathic pain. A randomized controlled trial. *Journal of the American Medical Association, 290,* 1757–1762.

Karst, M., Salim, K., Burstein, S., Conrad, I., Hoy, L., & Schneider, U. (2003). Analgesic effect of the synthetic cannabinoid CT-3 on chronic neuropathic pain: A randomized controlled trial. *Journal of the American Medical Association, 290,* 1757–1762.

Katcher, B. S. (1993). Benjamin Russh's educational campaign against hard drinking. *Journal of Public Health, 83,* 273–281.

Katz, E. C., Robles-Sotelo, E., Correia, C. J., Silverman, K., Stitzer, M. L., & Bigelow, G. (2002). The brief abstinence test: Effects of continued incentive availability on cocaine abstinence. *Experimental and Clinical Psychopharmacology, 10,* 10–17.

Kawachi, I., Colditz, G. A., Speizer, F. E., Manson, J. E., Stampfer, M. J., Willett, W. C., et al. (1997). A prospective study of passive smoking and coronary heart disease. *Circulation, 95,* 2374–2379.

Kaweionnehta Human Resources Group. (1993). *First Nations and Inuit Community Youth Solvent Abuse Survey and Study.* Ottawa: National Native Alcohol and Drug Abuse Program.

Keh-Ming, L., Smith, M., & Ortiz, V. (2001). Culture and psychopharmacology. *Cultural Psychiatry: International Perspectives, 24,* 523–538.

Keller, M. (1979). A historical overview of alcohol and alcoholism. *Cancer Research, 39,* 2822–2829.

Kelly, T. H., Foltin, R. W., & Fischman, M. W. (1993). Effects of smoked marijuana on heart rate, drug ratings and task performance by humans. *Behavioural Pharmacology, 4,* 167–178.

Kelly, Y., Sacker, A., Gray, R., Kelly, J., Wolke, D., & Quigley, M. A. (2009). Light drinking in pregnancy, a risk for behavioral problems and cognitive deficits at 3 years of age? *International Journal of Epidemiology, 38,* 129–140.

Kendler, K. S., Heath, A. C., Neale, M. C., Kessler, R. C., & Eaves, L. J. (1992). A population-based twin study of alcoholism in women. *Journal of the American Medical Association, 268,* 1877–1882.

Kennedy, J. (1985). *Coca exotica.* Cranbury, NJ: Associated University Presses.

Kenny, M., & Darragh, A. (1985). Central effects of caffeine in man. In S. D. Iversen (Ed.), *Psychopharmacology: Recent advances and future prospects* (pp. 278–288). Oxford: Oxford University Press.

Kerns, L. L., & Davis, G. P. (1986). Psychotropic drugs in pregnancy. In I. J. Chasnoff (Ed.), *Drug use in pregnancy: Mother and child* (pp. 81–93). Lancaster, PA: MTP Press.

Kesselheim, A. S., Misono, A. S., Lee, J. L., Stedman, M. R., Brookhart, M. A., Choudhry, N. K., & Shrank, W. H. (2008). Clinical equivalence of generic and brand-name drugs used in cardiovascular disease: A systematic review and meta-analysis. *Journal of the American Medical Association, 300,* 2514–2526.

Kessler, R. C., Aguilar-Gaxiola, S., Bergland, P., Caraveo-Anduaga, J. J., DeWit, D. J., Greenfield, S. F., et al. (2001). Patterns and predictors of treatment seeking after the onset of a substance use disorder. *Archives of General Psychiatry, 58,* 1065–1071.

Kessler, R. C., Berglund, P., Demler, O., Jin, R., & Walters, E. E. (2005). Lifetime prevalence and age-of-onset distributions of DSM-IV disorders in the national comorbidity survey replication. *Archives of General Psychiatry, 62,* 593–602.

Kessler, R. C., Chiu, W. T., Demler, O., & Walters, E. E. (2005). Prevalence, severity, and comorbidity of 12-month DSM-IV disorders in the national comorbidity survey replication. *Archives of General Psychiatry, 62,* 617–627.

Kieffer B. L. (1999). Opioids: First lessons from knock-out mice. *Trends in Pharmacological Science,* 20, 19–26.

Kimmel, C. K. (1976). A prevention program with punch: The national PTA's Alcohol Education Project. *Journal of School Health, 46,* 208–210.

Kinder, B. N., Pape, N. E., & Walfish, S. (1980). Drug and alcohol education programs: A review of outcome studies. *International Journal of the Addictions, 15,* 1035–1054.

King, M. B. (1994). Long-term benzodiazepine users—a mixed bag. *Addiction, 89,* 1367–1370.

Kirsch, I., & Sapirstein, G. (1999). Listening to Prozac but hearing placebo: A meta-analysis of antidepressant medications. In I. Kirsch (Ed.), *How expectancies shape experience* (pp. 303–320). Washington, DC: American Psychological Association.

Kirsch, M. M. (1986). *Designer drugs.* Minneapolis: Comp-Care Publications.

Kitano, H. H. L. (1989). Alcohol and the Asian American. In T. D. Watts & R. Wright, Jr. (Eds.), *Alcoholism in minority populations* (pp. 143–158). Springfield, IL: Charles C. Thomas.

Kivlahan, D. R., Marlatt, G. A., Fromme, K., Coppel, D. B., & Williams, E. (1990). Secondary prevention with college drinkers: Evaluation of an alcohol skills training program. *Journal of Consulting and Clinical Psychology, 58,* 805–810.

Klatsky, A. L., Morton, C., Udaltsova, N., & Friedman, G. D. (2006). Coffee, cirrhosis, and transaminase enzymes. *Archives of Internal Medicine, 166,* 1190–1195.

Knight, J. R., Wechsler, H., Kuo, M., Seibring, M., Weitzman, E. R., & Schuckit, M. (2002). Alcohol abuse and dependence among U.S. college students. *Journal of Studies on Alcohol, 63,* 263–270.

Kollins, S. (2005). Subjective effects of methylphenidate. In M. Earlywine (Ed.), *Mind-altering drugs: The science of subjective experience* (pp. 275–304), London: Oxford Press.

Kollins, S. H., & Rush, C. R. (2002). Sensitization to the cardiovascular but not subject-rated effects of oral cocaine in humans. *Biological Psychiatry, 51,* 143–150.

Koob, G. F., & Bloom, F. E. (1988). Cellular and molecular mechanisms of drug dependence. *Science, 242,* 715–723.

Koob, G. F., & Le Moal, M. (2006). *Neurobiology of addiction*. London: Academic Press.

Koob, G. F., Lloyd, G., & Mason, B. J. (2009). Development of pharmacotherapies for drug addiction: A Rosetta Stone approach. *Nature Reviews. Drug Discovery, 8,* 500–515.

Koslowski, L. T., Henningfield, R. M., Keenan, R. M., Lei, H., Leigh, G., Jelinek, L. C., et al. (1993). Patterns of alcohol, cigarette, and caffeine and other drug use in two drug-abusing populations. *Journal of Substance Abuse Treatment, 10,* 171–179.

Kramer, J. C. (1972). A brief history of heroin addiction in America. In D. E. Smith & G. R. Gay (Eds.), *It's so good, don't even try it once* (pp. 12–31). Englewood Cliffs, NJ: Prentice Hall.

Kranzler, H. R., & Van Kirk, J. (2001). Efficacy of naltrexone and acamprosate for alcoholism treatment: A meta-analysis. *Alcoholism: Clinical and Experimental Research, 25,* 1335–1341.

Krogh, D. (1991). *Smoking: The artificial passion*. New York: W. H. Freeman.

Kypri, K., Voas, R. B., Langley, J. D., Stephenson, S. C. R., Begg, D. J., Tippetts, A. S., & Davie, G. S. (2006). Minimum purchasing age for alcohol and traffic crash injuries among 15- to 19-year-olds in New Zealand. *American Journal of Public Health, 96,* 126–131.

Lacey, M. (2009). The Drug (Statistics) War: Is cocaine getting more expensive? http://economix.blogs.nytimes.com/2009/04/17/the-drug-statistics-war-cocaine-prices/.

LaCroix, A. Z., Lang, J., Scherr, P., Wallace, R. B., Cornoni-Huntley, J., Berkman, L., et al. (1991). Smoking and mortality among older men and women in three communities. *New England Journal of Medicine, 324,* 1619–1625.

Lakins, N. E., LaVallee, R., Williams, G. D., & Yi, H. (2008). Apparent per capita alcohol consumption: National, state, and regional trends, 1977–2006. *Surveillance Report #85,* National Institute on Alcohol Abuse and Alcoholism.

Lam, T. H., He, Y., Sun, L., Liang, L. S., He, F. S., & Liang, B. Q. (1997). Mortality attributable to cigarette smoking in China. *Journal of the American Medical Association, 278,* 1505–1508.

Lang, A. R., Searles, J., Lauerman, R., & Adesso, V. (1980). Expectancy, alcohol, and sex guilt as determinants of interest in and reaction to sexual stimuli. *Journal of Abnormal Psychology, 60,* 285–293.

Langenbucher, J. Hildebrandt, T. & Carr, S. J. (2008). Medical consequences of anabolic steroids. In J. Brick (Ed.), *Handbook of the medical consequences of alcohol and drug abuse* (pp. 385–421). New York: Haworth Press.

Langlieb, A. M., & Kahn, J. P. (2005). How much does quality mental health care profit employers? *Journal of Occupational and Environmental Medicine, 47,* 1099–1109.

Langston, J. W. (2002). The impact of MPTP on Parkinson's disease research: Past, present, and future. In S. A. Factor & W. J. Weiner (Eds.), *Parkinson's disease: Diagnosis and clinical management*. New York: Demos Medical Publishing.

Largent-Milnes, T. M., Guo, W., Wang, H. Y., Burns, L. H. & Vanderah, T. W. (2008). Oxycodone plus ultra-low-dose naltrexone attenuates neuropathic pain and associated mu-opioid receptor Gs coupling. *Journal of Pain, 9,* 700–713.

Larimer, M. E., & Cronce, J. M. (2007). Identification, prevention, and treatment revisited: Individual-focused college drinking prevention strategies 1999–2006. *Addictive Behaviors, 32,* 2439–2468.

Laties, V. G., & Weiss, B. (1981). The amphetamine margin in sports. *Federation Proceedings, 40,* 2689–2692.

Latimer, D., & Goldberg, J. (1981). *Flowers in the blood: The story of opium*. New York: Franklin Watts.

Laviolette, S. R., Nader, K., & van der Kooy, D. (2002) Motivational state determines the functional role of the mesolimbic dopamine system in the mediation of opiate reward process. *Behavioral Brain Research, 129,* 17–29.

Lawvere, S., & Mahoney, M. C. (2005). St. John's wort. *American Family Physician, 72,* 2249–2254.

Leach, B., & Norris, J. L. (1977). Factors in the development of Alcoholics Anonymous (AA). In B. Kissin & H. Begleiter (Eds.), *The biology of alcoholism* (Vol. 5, pp. 441–544). New York: Plenum Press.

Leavitt, F. (1982). *Drugs and behavior* (2nd ed.). New York: John Wiley.

LeDain Commission. (1972). *A report of the Commission of Inquiry into the non-medical use of drugs*. Ottawa: Information Canada.

Lee, S. J., Sudore, R. L., Williams, B. A., Lindquist, K., Chen, H. L., & Covinsky, K. E. (2009). Functional limitations, socioeconomic status, and all-cause mortality in moderate alcohol drinkers. *Journal of the American Geriatric Society, 57,* 955–962.

Lehmann, H.E. (n.d.). Introduction of chlorpromazine treatment of mental illness in North America. Available at http://www.chrcrm.org/en/salute-excellence/introduction-chlorpromazine-treatment-mental-illness-north-america.

Lender, M. E., & Martin, J. K. (1982). *Drinking in America*. New York: Free Press.

Leonard, T. K., Watson, R. R., & Mohs, M. E. (1987). The effects of caffeine in various body systems: A review. *Journal of the American Dietetic Association, 87,* 1048–1053.

Lerner, M., & Wigal, T. (2008). Long-term safety of stimulant medications used to treat children with ADHD. *Journal of Psychosocial Nursing, 46*, 38–48.

Leshner, A. I. (1999). Science-based views of drug addiction and its treatment. *Journal of the American Medical Association, 282*, 1314–1318.

Leuchter, A. F., Cook, I. A., Witte, E. A., Morgan, M., & Abrams, M. (2002). Changes in brain function of depressed subjects during treatment with placebo. *American Journal of Psychiatry, 159*, 122–129.

Levenson, H. S., & Bick, E. C. (1977). Psychopharmacology of caffeine. In M. E. Jarvic (Ed.), *Psychopharmacology in the practice of medicine* (pp. 451–463). New York: Appleton-Century-Crofts.

Levine, J. M., Kramer, G. G., & Levine, E. N. (1975). Effects of alcohol on human performance: An integration of research findings based on an abilities classification. *Journal of Applied Psychology, 89*, 644–653.

Lewin, L. (1964). *Phantastica—narcotic and stimulating drugs: Their use and abuse.* London: Routledge & Kegan Paul.

Lewine, R. R. J. (1988). Gender and schizophrenia. In M. T. Tsuang & J. C. Simpson (Eds.), *Handbook of schizophrenia (Vol. 3): Nosology, epidemiology, and genetics of schizophrenia.* Amsterdam: Elsevier.

Lewis, J. A. (1991). Alcohol abuse prevention in industrial settings. In B. Forster & J. C. Salloway (Eds.), *Preventions and treatments of alcohol and drug abuse* (pp. 137–152). Lewiston, NY: Edwin Mellen Press.

Lichtenstein, E. (1982). The smoking problem: A behavioral perspective. *Journal of Consulting and Clinical Psychology, 50*, 804–819.

Lieberman, J. A., Stroup, T. S., McEvoy, J. P., Swartz, M. S., Rosenheck, R. A., Perkins, D. O., et al. (2005). Effectiveness of antipsychotic drugs in patients with chronic schizophrenia. *New England Journal of Medicine, 353*, 1209–1223.

Liechti, M. E., Kunz, I., Greminger, P., Speich, R., & Kupferschmidt, H. (2006). Clinical features of gamma-hydroxybutyrate and gamma-butyrolactone toxicity and concomitant drug and alcohol use. *Drug and Alcohol Dependence, 8*, 323–326.

Liguori, A., Hughes, J. R., & Grass, J. A. (1997). Absorption and subjective effects of caffeine from coffee, cola, and capsules. *Pharmacology, Biochemistry, and Behavior, 58*, 721–726.

Lim, H. K., Pae, C. U., Joo, R. H, Yoo, S. S., Choi, B. G., Kim, D. J., et al. (2005). fMRI investigation on cue-induced smoking craving. *Journal of Psychiatric Research, 39*, 333–335.

Lin, K. M., & Poland R. E. (1995). Ethnicity, culture and psychopharmacology. In F. E. Bloom & D. J. Kupfer (Eds.), *Psychopharmacology: The fourth generation of progress* (pp. 1907–1917). NY: American College of Neuropsychopharmacology.

Linde, K., Berner, M. M., Kriston, L. (2008). St. John's wort for major depression. *Cochrane Database of Systematic Reviews*, Issue 4.

Linder, R. L., Lerner, S. E., & Burns, R. S. (1981). *PCP: The devil's dust.* Belmont, CA: Wadsworth.

Lingford-Hughes, A. R., Welch, S., & Nutt, D. J. (2004). Evidence-based guidelines for the pharmacological management of substance misuse, addiction, and co-morbidity: Recommendations from the British Association for Psychopharmacology. *Journal of Psychopharmacology, 18*, 293–335.

Lingford-Hughes, A., & Nutt, D. (2003). Neurobiology of addiction and implications for treatment. *The British Journal of Psychiatry, 182*, 97–100.

Linszen, D., & van Amelsvoort, T. (2007). Cannabis and psychosis: An update on course and biological plausible mechanisms. *Current Opinion in Psychiatry, 20*, 116–120.

Litman, G. K. (1986). Alcoholism survival: The prevention of relapse. In W. R. Miller & N. Heather (Eds.), *Treating addictive behaviors* (pp. 391–405). New York: Plenum Press.

Litten, R. Z., & Allen, J. P. (1999). Medications for alcohol, illicit drug, and tobacco dependence: An update of research findings. *Journal of Substance Abuse Treatment, 16*, 105–112.

Lloyd, T., Johnson-Rollings, N., Eggli, D. F., Kieselhorst, K., Mauger, E. A., & Cusatis, D. C. (2000). Bone status among postmenopausal women with different habitual caffeine intakes: A longitudinal investigation. *Journal of the American College of Nutrition, 19*, 256–261.

Lopez, A. D. (1998). Counting the dead in China. *British Medical Journal, 317*, 1399–1400.

Lorist, M. M., & Tops, M. (2003). Caffeine, fatigue, and cognition. *Brain and Cognition, 53*, 82–94.

Lowe, G. (1988). State-dependent retrieval effects with social drugs. *British Journal of Addiction, 83*, 99–103.

Luby, J. L., Si, X., Belden, A. C., Tandom, M., & Spitznagel, E. (2009). Preschool depression: Homotypic continuity and course over 24 months. *Archives of General Psychiatry, 66*, 897–905.

Luce, J. (1972). End of the road: A case study. In D. E. Smith & G. R. Gay (Eds.), *It's so good, don't even try it once* (pp. 143–147). Englewood Cliffs, NJ: Prentice Hall.

Ludlow, F. H. (1857/1979). *The hasheesh eater, being passages from the life of a Pythagorean.* San Francisco: City Lights Books.

Ludwig, A. M., & Wikler, A. (1974). "Craving" and relapse to drink. *Quarterly Journal of Studies on Alcohol, 35*, 108–130.

Lyketsos, C. G., Garrett, E., Liang, K. Y., & Anthony, J. C. (1999). Cannabis use and cognitive decline in persons under 65 years of age. *American Journal of Epidemiology, 149*, 794–800.

Lynam, D. R., Milich, R., Zimmerman, R., Novak, S. P., Logan, T. K., Martin, C., et al. (1999). Project DARE: No effects at 10-year follow-up. *Journal of Consulting and Clinical Psychology, 67,* 590–593.

MacAndrew, C., & Edgerton, R. B. (1969). *Drunken comportment.* Chicago: Aldine.

Macdonald, S., Csiernik, R., Durand, P, et al. (2006). The prevalence and factors related to Canadian workplace health programs. *Canadian Journal of Public Health, 97* (2), 121–125.

Mackay, A. V. P. (1982). Antischizophrenic drugs. In P. J. Tyrer (Ed.), *Drugs in psychiatric practice.* London: Butterworths.

MacKinnon, D. P. (1995). Review of the effects of the alcohol warning label. In R. R. Watson (Ed.), *Drug and alcohol abuse reviews: Vol. 7. Alcohol, cocaine, and accidents* (pp. 131–161). Totowa, NJ: Humana Press.

Maertens, R. M., White, P. A., Rickert, W., Levasseur, G., Douglas, G. R., Bellier, P. V., McNamee, J. P., Thuppal, V., Walker, M., & Desjardins, S. (2009). The genotoxicity of mainstream and side-stream marijuana and tobacco smoke condensates. *Chemical Research in Toxicology, 22* (8), 1406–1414.

Magliozzi, J. R., & Schaffer, C. B. (1988). Psychosis. In J. P. Tupin, R. I. Shader, & D. S. Harnett (Eds.), *Handbook of clinical psychopharmacology* (2nd ed., pp. 1–48). Northvale, NJ: Jason Aronson.

Maitre, M., Andriamampandry, C., Kemmel, V., Schmidt, C., Hode, Y., Hechler, V., et al. (2000). Gamma-hydroxybutyric acid as a signaling molecule in brain. *Alcohol, 20,* 277–283.

Malberg, J. E., Eisch, A. J., Nestler, E. J., & Duman, R. S. (2000). Chronic antidepressant treatment increases neurogenesis in adult rat hippocampus. *Journal of Neuroscience, 20,* 9104–9110.

Malsch, U., & Kieser, M. (2001). Efficacy of kava-kava in the treatment of non-psychotic anxiety following pretreatment with benzodiazepines. *Psychopharmacology, 157,* 277–283.

Marks, V., & Kelly, J. F. (1973). Absorption of caffeine from tea, coffee, and Coca Cola. *Lancet, 3,* 827.

Marlatt, G. A., & Gordon, J. R. (Eds.). (1985). *Relapse prevention.* New York: Guilford Press.

Marlatt, G. A., & Witkiewitz, K. (2005). Relapse prevention for alcohol and drug problems. In G. A. Marlatt & D. M. Donovan (Eds.), *Relapse prevention* (2nd ed., pp. 1–44). New York: Guilford Press.

Marlatt, G. A., Bowen, S. W., & Witkiewitz, K. (2009). Relapse prevention: Evidence base and future. In P. M. Miller (Ed.), *Evidence-based addiction treatment* (pp. 215–232). Boston: Elsevier.

Marlatt, G. A., Larimer, M. E., Baer, J. S., & Quigley, L. A. (1993). Harm reduction for alcohol problems: Moving beyond the controlled drinking controversy. *Behavior Therapy, 24,* 461–504.

Marmot, M. G. (2001). Alcohol and coronary heart disease. *International Journal of Epidemiology, 30,* 724–729.

Marona-Lewicka, D., Thisted, R. A., & Nichols, D. E. (2005). Distinct temporal phases in the behavioral pharmacology of LSD: Dopamine D2 receptor-mediated effects in the rat and implications for psychosis. *Psychopharmacology, 180,* 427–435.

Marshal, M. P., Friedman, M. S., Stall, R. S., King, K. M., Miles, J., Gold, M. A., Bukstein, O. G., & Morse, J. Q. (2008). Sexual orientation and adolescent substance use: A meta-analysis and methodological review. *Addiction, 103,* 546–556.

Marshall, E. (1988). The drug of champions. *Science, 242,* 183–184.

Martin, B. R., Cabral, G., Childers, S. R., Deadwyler, S., Mechoulam, R., & Reggio, P. (1993). International Cannabis Research Society meeting summary, Keystone, CO (June 19–20, 1992). *Drug and Alcohol Dependence, 31,* 219–227.

Martin-Soelch, C., Leenders, K. L., Chevalley, A. F., Missemer, J., Kuenig, G., Magyar, S., et al. (2001). Reward mechanisms in the brain and their role in dependence: Evidence from neurophysiological and neuroimaging studies. *Brain Research Reviews, 36,* 139–149.

Mathew, S. J. (2008). Treatment-resistant depression: Recent developments and future directions. *Depression and Anxiety, 25,* 989–992.

Matsuda, L., Lolait, S. J., Brownstein, J. J., Young, A. C., & Bonner, T. I. (1990). Structure of a cannabinoid receptor and functional expression of the cloned cDNA. *Nature, 346,* 561–564.

Matthew, R. J., Wilson, W. H., Coleman, R. E., Turkington, T. G., & DeGrado, T. R. (1997). Marijuana intoxication and brain activation in marijuana smokers. *Life Sciences, 60,* 2075–2089.

Mayeda, A. (2011). Supreme Court says Canada doesn't share liability for tobacco health costs. *Bloomberg.com.* Available at http://www.bloomberg.com/news/2011-07-29/supreme-court-says-canada-doesn-t-share-tobacco-cost-liability.html.

Mayor LaGuardia's Committee on Marihuana. (1944). *The marihuana problem in the city of New York.* Lancaster, PA: Jacques Cattell Press. Reprinted by Scarecrow Reprint Corporation, Metuchen, NJ, 1983.

Mayo-Smith, M. F. (1997). Pharmacological management of alcohol withdrawal. *Journal of the American Medical Association, 278,* 144–151.

Maziak, W. (2008). The waterpipe: Time for action. *Addiction, 103,* 1763–1767.

Mazis, M. B., Morris, L. A., & Swasy, J. L. (1991). An evaluation of the alcohol warning label: Initial survey results. *Journal of Public Policy and Marketing, 10,* 229–241.

McBride, C. M., Pollak, K. L., Lyna, P., Lipkus, I. M., Samsa, G. P., & Beplor, G. (2001). Reasons for quitting smoking among low-income African American smokers. *Health Psychology, 20,* 334–340.

McBride, N., Farringdon, F., Midford, R., Meuleners, & Phillips, M. (2004). Harm minimization in school drug education: Final results of the School Health and Alcohol Harm Reduction Project (SHAHRP). *Addiction, 99,* 278–291.

McCann, U. D., Szabo, Z., Seckin, E., Rosenblatt, P., Mathews, W. B., Ravert, H. T., et al. (2005). Quantitative PET studies of the serotonin transporter in MDMA users and controls using [11C]McN5652 and [11C] DASB. *Neuropsychopharmacology, 30,* 1741–1750.

McCarthy, D. M., Kroll, L. S., & Smith, G. T. (2001). Integrating disinhibition and learning risk for alcohol use. *Experimental and Clinical Psychopharmacology, 9,* 389–398.

McCarty, D. (1985). Environmental factors in substance abuse: The microsetting. In M. Galizio & S. A. Maisto (Eds.), *Determinants of substance abuse: Biological, psychological, and environmental factors* (pp. 247–282). New York: Plenum Press.

McCloskey, J., & Bailes, J. (2005). *When winning costs too much: Steroids, supplements and scandal in today's sports.* Lanham, MD: Taylor Trade Publishing Group Inc.

McCrady, B. S., & Langenbucher, J. W. (1996). Alcohol treatment and health care system reform. *Archives of General Psychiatry, 53,* 737–746.

McCrady, B. S., & Ziedonis, D. (2001). American Psychiatric Association practice guideline for substance use disorders. *Behavior Therapy, 32,* 309–336.

McGlothlin, W. H., & West, L. J. (1968). The marihuana problem: An overview. *American Journal of Psychiatry, 125,* 370–378.

McGovern, M. P., & Carroll, K. M. (2003). Evidence-based practices for substance use disorders. *Psychiatric Clinics of North America, 26,* 991–1010.

McGregor, C., Srisurapanont, M., Jittiwutikarn, J., Laobhripatr, S., Wongtan, T., & White, J. (2005). The nature, time course, and severity of methamphetamine withdrawal. *Addiction, 100,* 1320–1329.

McKay, J. R., Murphy, R. T., & Longabaugh, R. (1991). The effectiveness of alcoholism treatment: Evidence from outcome studies. In S. M. Mirin, J. T. Gossett, & M. C. Grob (Eds.), *Psychiatric treatment: Advances in outcome research* (pp. 143–158). Washington, DC: American Psychiatric Press.

McKee, S. A., O'Malley, S. S., Salovey, P., Krishnan-Sarin, S., & Mazure, C. M. (2005). Perceived risks and benefits of smoking cessation: Gender-specific predictors of motivation and treatment outcome. *Addictive Behaviors, 30,* 423–435.

McKenna, T. (1992). *Food of the gods: The search for the original tree of knowledge.* New York: Bantam Books.

McKim, W. A. (2000). *Drugs and behavior* (4th ed.). Upper Saddle River, NJ: Prentice Hall.

McLaren, J., Swift, W., Dillon, P., & Allsop, S. (2008). Cannabis potency and contamination: A review of the literature. *Addiction, 10,* 1100–1109.

McLellan, A. T., Luborsky, L., Woody, G. E., O'Brien, C. P., & Druley, K. A. (1983). Increased effectiveness of substance abuse treatment: A prospective study of patient treatment matching. *Journal of Nervous and Mental Disease, 171,* 597–605.

McLellan, T., Lewis, D. C., O'Brien, C. P., & Kleber, H. D. (2000). Drug dependence, a chronic medical illness: Implications for treatment, insurance, and outcomes evaluation. *Journal of the American Medical Association, 284,* 1689–1695.

McMurran, M. (1994). *Psychology of addiction.* Bristol, PA: USA Taylor & Francis Inc.

Mechoulam, R. (1973). Cannabinoid chemistry. In R. Mechoulam (Ed.), *Marijuana: Chemistry, pharmacology, metabolism, and clinical effects* (pp. 2–99). New York: Academic Press.

Meichun, K., Adlaf, E., Lee, H., Gliksman, L., Demers, A., & Wechsler, H. (2002). More Canadian students drink but American students drink more: comparing college alcohol use in two countries. *Addiction, 97,* 1583–1592.

Mellaart, J. (1967). *Catal Huyuk: A Neolithic town in Anatolia.* New York: McGraw-Hill.

Mello, N. K. (1987). Alcohol abuse and alcoholism: 1978–1987. In H. Y. Meltzer (Ed.), *Psychopharmacology: The third generation of progress* (pp. 1515–1520). New York: Raven Press.

Mello, N. K., & Griffiths, R. R. (1987). Alcoholism and drug abuse: An overview. In H. Y. Meltzer (Ed.), *Psychopharmacology: The third generation of progress* (pp. 1511–1514). New York: Raven Press.

Mendelson, J. H., & Mello, N. K. (1985). *Alcohol: Use and abuse in America.* Boston: Little, Brown.

Mendelson, W. B. (1980). *The use and misuse of sleeping pills: A clinical guide.* New York: Plenum Press.

Merritt, J. C., Crawford, W. J., Alexander, P. C., Anduze, A. L., & Gelbart, S. S. (1980). Effect of marihuana on intraocular and blood pressure in glaucoma. *Ophthalmology, 87,* 222–228.

Messinis, L., Kyprianidou, A., Malefaki, S., & Papathanasopoulos, P. (2006). Neuropsychological deficits in long-term frequent cannabis users. *Neurology, 66,* 737–739.

Meyer, J. S., & Quenzer, L. F. (2005). Psychopharmacology: Drugs, the brain, and behavior. Sunderland, MA: Sinauer Associates Inc.

Meyer, R. E., & Mirin, S. M. (1979). *The heroin stimulus: Implications for a theory of addiction.* New York: Plenum Press.

Midanik, L. T., & Room, R. R. (1992). The epidemiology of alcohol consumption. *Alcohol Health and Research World, 16,* 183–190.

Miller, K. E. (2008). Energy drinks, race, and problem behaviors among college students. *Journal of Adolescent Health, 43,* 490–497.

Miller, L. G., & Greenblatt, D. J. (1996). Benzodiazepine discontinuation syndromes: Clinical and experimental aspects. In C. R. Schuster & M. J. Kuhar (Eds.), *Pharmacological aspects of drug dependence: Toward an integrated neurobehavioral approach* (pp. 53–82). Berlin: Springer-Verlag.

Miller, N. S. (1991). *The pharmacology of alcohol and drugs of abuse/addiction.* New York: Springer-Verlag.

Miller, W. R., & C'de Baca, J. (2001). *Quantum change.* New York: Guilford Press.

Miller, W. R., & Hester, R. K. (1980). Treating the problem drinker: Modern approaches. In W. R. Miller (Ed.), *The addictive behaviors: Treatment of alcoholism, drug abuse, smoking, and obesity* (pp. 11–141). New York: Plenum Press.

Miller, W. R., & Hester, R. K. (1986). Inpatient alcoholism treatment: Who benefits? *American Psychologist, 41,* 794–805.

Miller, W. R., & Hester, R. K. (1989). Treating alcohol problems: Toward an informed eclecticism. In R. K. Hester & W. R. Miller (Eds.), *Handbook of alcoholism treatment approaches* (pp. 3–14). New York: Pergamon Press.

Miller, W. R., & Hester, R. K. (1995). Treatment for alcohol problems: Toward an informed eclecticism. In R. K. Hester & W. R. Miller (Eds.), *Handbook of alcoholism treatment approaches* (2nd ed., pp. 1–11). Needham Heights, MA: Allyn & Bacon.

Miller, W. R., & Hester, R. K. (2002). Treating alcohol problems: Toward an informed eclecticism. In R. K. Hester & W. R. Miller (Eds.), *Handbook of alcoholism treatment approaches* (3rd ed., pp. 1–12). Boston: Allyn & Bacon.

Mills, J. L., Holmes, L. B., Aarons, J. H., Simpson, J. L., Brown, A. A., Jovanovic-Peterson, L. G., et al. (1993). Moderate caffeine use and the risk of spontaneous abortion on intrauterine growth retardation. *Journal of the American Medical Association, 269,* 593–597.

Millson, P. E., Challacombe, L., Villeneuve, P. J., Fischer, B., Strike, C. J., Myers, T., Shore, R., Hopkins, S., Raftis, S., & Pearson, M. (2004). Self-perceived health among Canadian opiate users: a comparison to the general population and to other chronic disease populations. *Canadian Journal of Public Health,* 95, 99–103.

Mintzer, M. Z., Copersino, M. L., & Stitzer, M. L. (2005). Opioid abuse and cognitive performance. *Drug and Alcohol Dependence, 78,* 225–230.

Mintzer, M. Z., Guarino, J., Kirk, T., Roache, J. D., & Griffiths, R. R. (1997). Ethanol and pentobarbital: Comparison of behavioral and subjective effects in sedative drug abusers. *Experimental and Clinical Psychopharmacology, 5,* 203–215.

Modell, J. G. (1997). Protracted benzodiazepine withdrawal syndrome mimicking psychotic depression. *Psychosomatics, 38,* 160–161.

Möhler, H., & Okada, T. (1977). Benzodiazepine receptor: Demonstration in the central nervous system. *Science, 198,* 849–851.

Moir, D., Rickert, W., Levasseur, G., Larose, Y., Maertens, R., White, P., & Desjardins, S. (2007). A comparison of mainstream and side-stream marijuana and tobacco cigarette smoke produced under two machine smoking conditions. *Chemical Research in Toxicology, 21,* 494–502. Available at http://www.ukcia.org/research/ComparisonOfSmoke.pdf.

Molarus, A., Parsons, R. W., Dobson, A. J., Evans, A., Fortmann, S. P., Jamrozik, K., et al. (2001). Trends in cigarette smoking in 36 populations from the early 1980s to the mid-1990s: Findings from the WHO MONICA project. *American Journal of Public Health, 91,* 206–212.

Moncrieff, J., & Kirsch, I. (2005). Education and debate. *BMJ, 331,* 155–159.

Montana Meth Project (2008, May 3). *The Economist,* 36.

Mood Disorders Society of Canada (MDSC). (2009). *Quick facts on mental illness and addictions in Canada,* 3rd edn. Available at http://www.mooddisorderscanada.ca/documents/Media%20Room/Quick%20Facts%203rd%20Edition%20Eng%20Nov%2012%2009.pdf.

Moore, T. H. M., Zammit, S., Lingford-Hughes, A., Barnes, T. R. E., Jones, P. B., Burke, M., & Lewis, G. (2007). Cannabis use and risk of psychotic or affective mental health outcomes: a systematic review. *The Lancet, 370,* 319–328.

Moreau, R. (2009, August 3). America's new nightmare. *Newsweek,* 38–42.

Morgan, C. J. A., Riccelli, M., Maitland, C. H., & Curran, H. V. (2004). Long-term effects of ketamine: Evidence for a persisting impairment of source memory in recreational users. *Drug and Alcohol Dependence, 75,* 301–308.

Morgan, H. W. (1981). *Drugs in America: A social history, 1800–1980.* Syracuse, NY: Syracuse University Press.

Morgenstern, J., Labouvie, E., McCrady, B. S., Kahler, C. W., & Frey, R. M. (1997). Affiliation with Alcoholics Anonymous after treatment: A study of its therapeutic effects and mechanisms of action. *Journal of Consulting and Clinical Psychology, 65,* 768–777.

Morland, J., Bugge, A., Skuterud, B., Steen, A., Wethe, G.H., & Kjeldsen, T. (1985). Cannabinoids in blood and urine after passive inhalation of cannabis smoke. *Journal of Forensic Science, 30,* 997–1002.

Morral, A. R., McCaffrey, D. F., & Paddock, S. M. (2002). Reassessing the marijuana gateway effect. *Addiction, 97,* 1493–1504.

Mortimer, W. G. (1901). *Peru: History of coca, "the divine plant" of the Incas.* New York: J. H. Vail.

Morton, J. (2005). Ecstasy: Pharmacology and neurotoxicity. *Current Opinion in Pharmacology, 5,* 79–86.

Mosher, J. F., & Colman, V. J. (1986). Prevention research: The model Dram Shop Act of 1985. *Alcohol Health and Research World, 10,* 4–11.

Mumford, G. K., Rush, C. R., & Griffiths, R. R. (1995). Alprazolam and DN-2327 (Pazinaclone) in humans: Psychomotor, memory, subjective, and reinforcing effects. *Experimental and Clinical Psychopharmacology, 3,* 39–48.

Munro, S., Thomas, K. L., & Abu-Shaar, M. (1993). Molecular characterization of a peripheral receptor for cannabinoids. *Nature, 365,* 61–65.

Murphy, E. (1922). *The black candle.* Toronto: Thomas Allen.

Myrick, H., Anton, R. F., Li, X., Henderson, S., Drobes, D., Voronin, K. et al. (2004). Differential brain activity in alcoholics and social drinkers to alcohol cues: Relationship to craving. *Neuropsychopharmacology, 29,* 393–402.

Nace, E. P., & Isbell, P. G. (1991). Alcohol. In R. J. Francis & S. I. Miller (Eds.), *Clinical textbook of addictive disorders* (pp. 43–68). New York: Guilford Press.

Nadelmann, E. A. (1989). Drug prohibition in the United States: Costs, consequences, and alternatives. *Science, 245,* 939–947.

Nahas, G. G. (1973). *Marijuana—Deceptive weed.* New York: Raven Press.

Nakken, C. (1996). *The addictive personality.* New York: Hazelden.

Naqvi, N. H., Rudrauf, D., Demasioo, H., & Bechara, A. (2007). Damage to the insula disrupts addiction to cigarette smoking. *Science, 315,* 531–534.

Naranjo, C. (2001). Experience with the interpersonal psychedelics. In J. Holland (Ed.), *Ecstasy: The complete guide: A comprehensive look at the risks and benefits of MDMA* (pp. 208–221). Rochester, VT: Park Street Press.

Narconon. (1999–2011). History of cocaine. Available at http://www.narconon.org/drug-information/cocaine-history.html; accessed August 25, 2011.

Nathan, P. E. (1984). Alcoholism prevention in the workplace: Three examples. In P. M. Miller & T. D. Nirenberg (Eds.), *Prevention of alcohol abuse* (pp. 387–405). New York: Plenum Press.

Nathan, P. E., & Niaura, R. S. (1987). Prevention of alcohol problems. In W. M. Cox (Ed.), *Treatment and prevention of alcohol problems: A resource manual* (pp. 333–354). New York: Academic Press.

National Advisory Council on Alcohol Abuse and Alcoholism. (2002). *A call to action: Changing the culture of drinking at U.S. colleges.* (NIH Publication No. 02-5010). Bethesda, MD: National Institute on Alcohol Abuse and Alcoholism.

National Cancer Council of Australia. (2006). *National cancer prevention policy: 2004–2006.* New South Wales: Author.

National Drug Intelligence Center. (2009). MDMA. Available at http://www.justice.gov/ndic/pubs31/31379/mdma.htm.

National Institute on Alcohol Abuse and Alcoholism (NIAAA). (1993). *Eighth special report to the U.S. Congress on alcohol and health.* Washington, DC: U.S. Department of Health and Human Services.

National Institute on Drug Abuse (NIDA). (1982). *Marijuana and health: Ninth annual report to the U.S. Congress from the Secretary of Health and Human Services.* Rockville, MD: Author.

National Institutes of Health. (2000, January). *Cirrhosis of the liver.* NIH Publication No. 00-1134.

Neal, D. J., & Fromme, K. (2007). Event-level covariation of alcohol intoxication and behavioral risks during the first year of college. *Journal of Consulting and Clinical Psychology, 75,* 294–306.

Nehlig, A. (2004). Dependence upon coffee and caffeine: An update. In A. Nehlig (Ed.), *Coffee, tea, chocolate, and the brain* (pp. 133–146). Boca Raton, FL: CRC Press.

Nestler, E. J. (2009). Cellular and molecular mechanisms of drug addiction. In D. S. Charney & E. J. Nestler (Eds.), *Neurobiology of mental illness* (3rd ed., pp. 775–786). New York: Oxford University Press.

NeuroScience Canada. (2005). UBC scientists create protein to block addiction cravings. Available at http://braincanada.ca/en/WangNewsRelease_en.

Newsweek. (1989, January 16). A tide of drug killing.

Newsweek. (1993, December 12). Death on the spot: The end of a drug king.

Newsweek. (1996, March 18). Mother's little helper.

Newsweek. (1997a, March 31). White storm warning.

Newsweek. (1997b, October 27). Death of the party.

Newsweek. (2001, May 14). Painkiller crackdown.

Newton, T. F., De La Garza, R., Kalechstein, A. D., & Nestor, L. (2005). Cocaine and methamphetamine produce different patterns of subjective and cardiovascular effects. *Pharmacology, Biochemistry and Behavior, 82,* 90–97.

NIAAA. (1999). Brief interventions for alcohol problems. *Alcohol Alert, No. 43.*

NIAAA. (2000). *Tenth special report to the U.S. Congress on alcohol and health.* Washington, DC: U.S. Department of Health and Human Services.

NIAAA. (2001, July). Cognitive impairment and recovery from alcoholism. *Alcohol Alert,* No. 53.

NIAAA. (2002). *A call to action: Changing the culture of drinking at U.S. colleges.* Washington, DC: U.S. Department of Health and Human Services.

NIAAA. (2005). *Helping patients who drink too much.* Bethesda, MD: National Institutes of Health.

NIAAA. (2008). *Research findings on college drinking and the minimum drinking age.* Bethesda, MD: Author.

Nichols, D. E. (2004). Hallucinogens. *Pharmacology and Therapeutics, 101,* 131–181.

NIDA. (1991). *Annual emergency room data: 1990.* Washington, DC: Author.

NIDA. (2002). *Research report series: Nicotine addiction.* Bethesda, MD: Author.

NIDA. (2003). *Preventing drug abuse among children and adolescents: A research-based guide for parents, educators, and community leaders* (2nd ed.). Bethesda, MD: Author.

NIDA. (2005). *HIV/AIDS.* NIDA Research Report, Bethesda, MD.

Nies, A. S. (2001). Principles of therapeutics. In J. G. Hardman & L. E. Limbird (Eds.), *Goodman & Gilman's The pharmacological basis of therapeutics* (10th ed., pp. 45–66). New York: McGraw-Hill.

Nirenberg, T. D., & Miller, P. M. (1984). History and overview of the prevention of alcohol abuse. In P. M. Miller & T. D. Nirenberg (Eds.), *Prevention of alcohol abuse* (pp. 3–14). New York: Plenum Press.

Nkondjock, A. (2009). Coffee consumption and the risk of cancer: An overview. *Cancer Letters, 277(Issue 2),* 121–125.

Nolen-Hoeksema, S. (2004). Gender differences in risk factors and consequences for alcohol use and problems. *Clinical Psychology Review, 24,* 981–1010.

O'Brien, C. (1995). *Nicotine dependence.* University of Pennsylvania Health System, Internet Alcohol Recovery Center.

O'Brien, C. P. (1996). Recent developments in the pharmacotherapy of substance abuse. *Journal of Consulting and Clinical Psychology, 64,* 677–686.

O'Brien, C. P. (2001). Drug addiction and drug abuse. In J. G. Hardman & L. E. Limbird (Eds.), *Goodman & Gilman's The pharmacological basis of therapeutics* (10th ed., pp. 621–643). New York: McGraw-Hill.

O'Brien, R., & Cohen, S. (1984). *The encyclopedia of drug abuse.* New York: Facts on File.

O'Hanlon, J. F., & de Gier, J. J. (1986). *Drugs and driving.* London: Taylor & Francis.

O'Loughlin, J., Gervais, A., Dugas, E., & Meshefedjian, G. (2009). Milestones in the process of cessation among novice adolescent smokers. *American Journal of Public Health, 99,* 499–504.

O'Loughlin, J., Karp, I., Henderson, M., Gray-Dobald, K. (2008). Does cigarette use influence adiposity or height in adolescence? *Annals of Epidemiology, 18,* 395–402.

O'Malley, P. M., & Johnston, L. D. (2002). Epidemiology of alcohol and other drug use among American college students. *Journal of Studies on Alcohol,* Supplement 14, 23–39.

O'Malley, S. S., Jaffe, A. J., Chang, G., Schottenfeld, R. S., Meyer, R. E., & Rounsaville, B. (1992). Naltrexone and coping skills therapy for alcohol dependence. *Archives of General Psychiatry, 49,* 881–887.

Olds, J., & Milner, P. (1954). Positive reinforcement produced by electrical stimulation of septal area and other regions of rat brains. *Journal of Comparative and Physiological Psychology, 47,* 419–427.

Olfson, M., & Marcus, S. C. (2009). National patterns in antidepressant medication treatment. *Archives of General Psychiatry, 66,* 848–856.

Ontario Addiction Hotline (2011). History of cocaine use and distribution. Retrieved on August 25, 2011 from http://www.ontario-drug-rehab.com/history-and-distribution.html.

Ontario Tobacco Research Unit. (2002). Monitoring the Ontario tobacco strategy. Available at http://www.otru.org/pdf/8mr/8mr_eng_part3.pdf.

Orcutt, J. D. (1987). Differential association and marijuana use: A closer look at Sutherland (with a little help from Becker). *Criminology, 25,* 341–358.

Orford, J. (1985). *Excessive appetites: A psychological view of addictions.* Chichester, England: John Wiley.

Ouardouz, M., Malek, S., Coderre, E., Stys, P. K. (2006). Complex interplay between glutamate receptors and intracellular Ca2+ stores during ischaemia in rat spinal cord white matter. *Journal of Physiology,* 15, 191–204.

Oviedeo-Joekes, E., Brissette, S., Marsh, D. C., Lauzon, P., Guh, D., Anis, A., & Schechter, M. T. (2009). Diacetylmorphine versus Methadone for the treatment of opioid addiction. *The New England Journal of Medicine, 361,* 777–786.

Owen, F. (2007). *No speed limit: The highs and lows of meth.* New York: St. Martins Press.

Page, J. B. (1983). The amotivational syndrome hypothesis and the Costa Rica study: Relationship between methods and results. *Journal of Psychoactive Drugs, 15,* 261–267.

Palmgreen, P., & Donohew, L. (2003). Effective mass media strategies for drug abuse prevention campaigns. In Z. Sloboda & W. J. Bukoski (Eds.), *Handbook of drug abuse prevention: Theory, science, and practice* (pp. 27–43). New York: Kluwer Academic/Plenum Publishers.

Parkinson Society Canada. (2011). What is Parkinson's? Available at http://www.parkinson.ca/site/c.kgLNIWODKpF/b.5184077/k.CDD1/What_is_Parkinsons.htm.

Parrino, L., & Terzano, M. G. (1996). Polysomnographic effects of hypnotic drugs. *Psychopharmacology, 126,* 1–16.

Parrott, A. C. (1998). Nesbitt's paradox revisited? Stress and arousal modulation during cigarette smoking. *Addiction, 93,* 27–39.

Parrott, A. C. (2004). Is ecstasy MDMA? A review of the proportion of ecstasy tablets containing MDMA, their dosage levels, and the changing perceptions of purity. *Psychopharmacology, 173,* 234–241.

Parrott, A. C., Milani, R. M., Parmar, R., & Turner, J. J. D. (2001). Recreational ecstasy/MDMA and other drug users from the UK and Italy: Psychiatric symptoms and psychobiological problems. *Psychopharmacology, 159,* 77–82.

Parrott, D. J., & Giancola, P. R. (2004). A further examination of the relation between trait anger and alcohol-related aggression: The role of anger control. *Alcoholism: Clinical and Experimental Research, 28,* 855–864.

Parsons, O. A. (1986). Alcoholics' neuropsychological impairment: Current findings and conclusions. *Annals of Behavioral Medicine, 8,* 13–19.

Paton, W. D. M., & Pertwee, R. G. (1973). The actions of cannabis in man. In R. Mechoulam (Ed.), *Marijuana: Chemistry, pharmacology, metabolism, and clinical effects* (pp. 288–333). New York: Academic Press.

Peachey, J. E., & Annis, J. (1985). New strategies for using the alcohol-sensitizing drugs. In C. A. Naranjo & E. M. Sellers (Eds.), *Research advances in new psychopharmacological treatments for alcoholism* (pp. 199–216). Amsterdam: Elsevier Science Publishers.

Peele, S. (1985). *The meaning of addiction.* New York: Oxford.

Peele, S. (1996). Assumptions about drugs and the marketing of drug policies. In W. K. Bickel & R. J. DeGrandpre (Eds.), *Drug policy and human nature* (pp. 199–220). New York: Plenum Press.

Perez-Reyes, M., Hicks, R. E., Bumberry, J., Jeffcoat, A. R., & Cook, C. E. (1988). Interaction between marijuana and ethanol: Effect on psychomotor performance. *Alcoholism: Clinical and Experimental Research, 12,* 268–276.

Perkins, H. W. (2002). Social norms and the prevention of alcohol misuse in collegiate contexts. *Journal of Studies on Alcohol,* Supplement 14, 164–172.

Perkins, H. W. (2007). Misperceptions of peer drinking norms in Canada: Another look at the "reign of terror" and its consequences among college students. *Addictive Behaviors, 32,* 2645–2656.

Perkins, K. A. (1996). Sex differences in nicotine versus nonnicotine reinforcement as determinants of tobacco smoking. *Experimental and Clinical Psychopharmacology, 4,* 166–177.

Perkins, K. A., Fonte, C., Ashcom, J., Broge, M., & Wilson, A. (2001). Subjective responses to nicotine in smokers may be associated with responses to caffeine and to alcohol. *Experimental and Clinical Psychopharmacology, 9,* 91–100.

Perrine, D. M. (1996). *The chemistry of mind-altering drugs. History, pharmacology, and cultural context.* Washington, DC: American Chemical Society.

Pert, C., & Snyder, S. H. (1973). Opiate receptor: Demonstration in nervous system tissue. *Science, 179,* 1011–1014.

Pertwee, R. (2002). Sites and mechanism of action. In F. Grotenhermen & E. Russo (Eds.), *Cannabis and cannabinoids: Pharmacology, toxicology and therapeutic potential* (pp. 73–88). London: Haworth.

Petersen, R. C. (1977). History of cocaine. In R. C. Petersen & R. C. Stillman (Eds.), *Cocaine: 1977.* Research Monograph 13 (pp. 17–34). Washington, DC: National Institute on Drug Abuse.

Petersson, A., Garle, M., Holmgren, P., Druid, H., Krantz, P., & Thiblin, I. (2006). Toxicological findings and manner of death in autopsied users of anabolic androgenic steroids. *Drug and Alcohol Dependence, 81,* 241–250.

Petrovic, P., Kalso, E., Petersson, K. M., & Ingvar, M. (2002). Placebo and opioid analgesia: Imaging a shared neuronal network. *Science, 295,* 1737–1740.

Peugh, J., & Belenko, S. (2001). Alcohol, drugs, and sexual function: A review. *Journal of Psychoactive Drugs, 33,* 223–232.

Physicians for a Smoke Free Canada (n.d.). Available at http://www.smoke-free.ca/pdf_1/lightregs.pdf.

Pierce, J. P., & Gilpin, E. A. (1995). A historical analysis of tobacco marketing and the uptake of smoking by youth in the United States: 1890–1977. *Health Psychology, 14,* 500–508.

Pijlman, F. T., Rigter, S. M., Hoek, J., Goldschmidt, H. M. J., & Niesink, R. J. M. (2005). Strong increase in total delta-THC in cannabis preparations sold in Dutch coffee shops. *Addiction Biology, 10,* 171–180.

Pisinger, C., & Godtfredsen, N. S. (2007). Is there a health benefit of reduced tobacco consumption? A systematic review. *Nicotine and Tobacco Research, 9,* 631–646.

Pittler, M. H., Verster, J. C., & Ernst, E. (2005). Interventions for preventing or treating alcohol hangover: Systematic review of randomized controlled trials. *British Medical Journal, 331,* 1515–1517.

Plasse, T. F., Gorter, R. W., Krasnow, S. H., Lane, M., Shepard, K. V., & Wadleigh, R. G. (1991). Recent clinical experience with Dronabinol. *Pharmacology, Biochemistry, and Behavior, 40,* 695–700.

Pliner, P., & Cappell, H. (1974). Modification of affective consequences of alcohol: A comparison of social and solitary drinking. *Journal of Abnormal Psychology, 89,* 224–233.

Poling, A., & Cross, J. (1993). State-dependent learning. In F. van Haaren (Ed.), *Methods in behavioral pharmacology* (pp. 245–256). Amsterdam: Elsevier.

Pomerleau, C. S. (1997). Co-factors for smoking and evolutionary psychobiology. *Addiction, 92,* 397–408.

Pomerleau, C. S., & Saules, K. (2007). Body image, body satisfaction, and eating patterns in normal-weight and overweight/obese women current smokers and never-smokers. *Addictive Behaviors, 32,* 2329–2334.

Pope, H. G., Jr., & Katz, D. L. (1988). Affective and psychotic symptoms associated with anabolic steroid use. *American Journal of Psychiatry, 145,* 487–490.

Pope, H. G., Jr., Gruber, A. J., Hudson, J. I., Huestis, M. A., & Yurgelun-Todd, D. (2001). Neuropsychological performance in long-term cannabis users. *Archives of General Psychiatry, 58,* 909–915.

Porjesz, B., & Begleiter, H. (1995). Event-related potentials and cognitive function in alcoholism. *Alcohol Health and Research World, 19,* 108–113.

Poulin, C. (2001). Medical and nonmedical stimulant use among adolescents: From sanctioned to unsanctioned use. *Canadian Medical Association Journal, 165,* 1039–1044.

Prasad, S., Arellano, J., Steer, C., & Libretto, S. E. (2009). Assessing the value of atomoxetine in treating children and adolescents with ADHD in the UK. *International Journal of Clinical Practice, 63,* 1031–1040.

Presley, C. A., Leichliter, M. A., & Meilman, P. W. (1998). *Alcohol and drugs on American college campuses: A report to college presidents: Third in a series, 1995, 1996, 1997.* Carbondale: Core Institute, Southern Illinois University.

Presley, C. A., Meilman, P. W., & Cashin, J. R. (1996). *Alcohol and drugs on American college campuses: Use, consequences, and perceptions of the campus environment, Vol. IV: 1992–1994.* Carbondale: Core Institute, Southern Illinois University.

Presley, C. A., Meilman, P. W., Cashin, J. R., & Lyerla, R. (1996). *Alcohol and drugs on American college campuses: Use, consequences, and perceptions of the campus environment, Vol. III: 1991–1993.* Carbondale: Core Institute, Southern Illinois University.

Press Release, College Alcohol Study, Harvard School of Public Health. (2005). Highlights from the first national comparison of alcohol use among U.S. and Canadian college students. Available at http://www.hsph.harvard.edu/cas/Documents/Canadian1-pressRelease/; accessed September 30, 2011.

Primack, B. A., Gold, M. A., Land, S. R., & Fine, M. J. (2006). Association of cigarette smoking and media literacy about smoking among adolescents. *Journal of Adolescent Health, 39,* 465–472.

Prochaska, J. O., DiClemente, C. C., & Norcross, J. C. (1992). In search of how people change. Applications to addictive behaviors. *American Psychologist, 47,* 1102–1114.

Project MATCH Research Group. (1997). Matching alcoholism treatments to client heterogeneity: Project MATCH posttreatment drinking outcomes. *Journal of Studies on Alcohol, 58,* 7–29.

Public Health Agency of Canada (2006). Enhanced surveillance of risk behaviours among injecting drug users in Canada. Available at http://www.phac-aspc.gc.ca/i-track/sr-re-1/index-eng.php.

Public Health Agency of Canada. (2009). Surveillance Report to December 31, 2008. Available at http://www.phac-aspc.gc.ca/aids-sida/publication/survreport/2008/dec/index-eng.php.

Quaglio, G., Lugoboni, F., Pattaro, C., Melara, B. Mezzelani, P., & Des Jarlais, D. C. (2008). Erectile dysfunction in male heroin users receiving methadone and buprenorphine maintenance treatment. *Drug and Alcohol Dependence, 94,* 12–18.

Queen's Policy Review. (2011). Available at http://www.queensu.ca/sps/qpr/.

Quickfall, J., & Crockford, D. (2006). Brain neuroimaging in cannabis use: A review. *Journal of Neuropsychiatry and Clinical Neurosciences, 18,* 318–332.

Rajacic, N. (1997). Coordinator presents on SMART to social workers. *S.M.A.R.T. Recovery News and Views, III,* 4–5.

Rall, T. W. (1990a). Drugs used in the treatment of asthma. The methylxanthines, cromolyn sodium, and other agents. In A. G. Gilman, T. W. Rall, A. S. Niles, & P. Taylor (Eds.), *Goodman and Gilman's The pharmacological basis of therapeutics* (8th ed., pp. 618–637). New York: Pergamon Press.

Rall, T. W. (1990b). Hypnotics and sedatives; Ethanol. In A. G. Gilman, T. W. Rall, A. S. Nies, & P. Taylor (Eds.), *Goodman and Gilman's The pharmacological basis of therapeutics* (8th ed., pp. 345–382). New York: Pergamon Press.

Ranganathan, M., & D'Souza, D. C. (2006). The acute effects of cannabinoids on memory in humans: A review. *Psychopharmacology, 188,* 425–444.

Rasmussen, C. (2005). Executive functioning and working memory in fetal alcohol spectrum disorder. *Alcoholism: Clinical and Experimental Research, 29,* 1359–1367.

Rathus, S., Veenlivet, S., & Maheu, S. (2012). *PSYCH.* Toronto: Nelson Education Ltd.

Raven, M. A., Necessary, B. D., Danluck, D. A., & Ettenberg, A. (2000). Comparison of the reinforcing and anxiogenic effects of intravenous cocaine and cocaethylene. *Experimental and Clinical Psychopharmacology, 8,* 117–124.

Rawson, R. A. (1990–1991). Chemical dependency treatment: The integration of the alcoholism and drug addiction/use treatment systems. *International Journal of the Addictions, 25,* 1515–1536.

Ray, W. A., Chung, C. P., Murray, K. T., Hall, K., & Stein, M. (2009). Atypical antipsychotic drugs and the risk of sudden cardiac death. *New England Journal of Medicine, 360,* 225–235.

Ream, G. L., Benoit, E., Johnson, B. D., & Dunlap, E. (2008). Smoking tobacco along with marijuana increases symptoms of cannabis dependence. *Drug and Alcohol Dependence, 95,* 199–208.

Reed, S. C., Haney, M., Evans, S. M., Vadhan, N. P., Rubin, E. & Foltin, R. W. (2009). Cardiovascular and subjective effects of repeated smoked cocaine administration in experienced cocaine users. *Drug and Alcohol Dependence, 102,* 102–107.

Rees, V., & Connolly, G. N. (2006). Measuring air quality to protect children from second smoke in cars. *American Journal of Preventive Medicine, 31,* 363–368.

Regier, D. A., Narrow, W. E., Rae, D. S., Manderscherd, R. W., Locke, B. Z., & Goodwin, R. K. (1993). The de facto U.S. mental and addictive disorders service system. *Archives of General Psychiatry, 50,* 85–94.

Rehm, J., Mathers, C., Popova, S., Thavorncharoensap, M., Teerawattananon, Y., & Patra, J. (2009). Global burden of disease and injury and economic cost attributable to alcohol use and alcohol-use disorders. *Lancet, 373,* 2223–2233.

Reissig, C. J., Strain, E. C., & Griffiths, R. R. (2009). Caffeinated energy drinks—A growing problem. *Drug and Alcohol Dependence, 99,* 1–10.

Renaud, S., & deLorgerd, M. (1992). Wine, alcohol, platelets, and the French paradox for coronary heart disease. *The Lancet, 339,* 1523–1526.

Rezvani, A. H., Overstreet, D. H., Perfumi, M., & Massi, M. (2003). Plant derivatives in the treatment of alcohol dependency. *Pharmacology, Biochemistry & Behavior. 75,* 593–606.

Riba, J., Rodriguez-Fornells, A., Urbano, G., Morte, A., Antonijoan, R., Montero, M., et al. (2001). Subjective effects and tolerability of the South American psychoactive beverage Ayahuasca in healthy volunteers. *Psychopharmacology, 154,* 85–95.

Ricaurte, G., Bryan, G., Strauss, L., Seiden, L., & Schuster, C. (1985). Hallucinogenic amphetamine selectively destroys brain serotonin nerve terminals. *Science, 299,* 986–988.

Rich, J. D., McKenzie, M., Macalino, G. E., Taylor, L. E., Sanford-Colby, S., Wolf, F., et al. (2004). A syringe protection program to prevent infectious disease and improve health of injection drug users. *Journal of Urban Health, 81,* 122–134.

Richards, J. B., Papaioannou, A., Adachi, J. D., Joseph, L., Whitson, H. E., Prior, J. C., & Goltzman, D., for the Canadian Multicentre Osteoporosis Study (CaMos) Research Group. (2007). Effect of selective serotonin reuptake inhibitors on the risk of fracture. *Archives of Internal Medicine, 167,* 188–194.

Richmond, L. B. (1977, Winter). Decisions and drinking: A prevention approach. *Alcohol Health and Research World,* 22–26.

Ridenour, T. A., Bray, B. C., & Cottler, L. B. (2007). Reliability of use abuse, and dependence of four types of inhalants in adolescents and young adults. *Drug and Alcohol Dependence, 91,* 40–49.

Riedlinger, J., & Montagne, M. (2001). Using MDMA in the treatment of depression. In J. Holland (Ed.), *Ecstasy: The complete guide: A comprehensive look at the risks and benefits of MDMA* (pp. 261–272). Rochester, VT: Park Street Press.

Riley, D. (1998). Drugs and drug policy in Canada: A brief review and commentary, a report prepared for the Canadian Senate Special Committee on Illegal Drugs. Available online at: http://www.parl.gc.ca/37/1/parlbus/commbus/senate/com-e/ille -e/library-e/riley-e.htm.

Rimm, E. B. (2000). Moderate alcohol intake and lower risk of coronary heart disease: Meta-analysis of effects on lipids and homeostatic factors. *Journal of the American Medical Association, 319,* 1523–1528.

Rinaldi, R. C., Steindler, E. M., Wilford, B. B., & Goodwin, D. (1988). Clarification and standardization of substance abuse terminology. *Journal of the American Medical Association, 259,* 555–557.

Ritchie, J. M. (1985). The aliphatic alcohols. In A. G. Gilman, L. S. Goodman, T. W. Rall, & F. Murod (Eds.), *Goodman and Gilman's The pharmacological basis of therapeutics* (7th ed., pp. 372–386). New York: Macmillan.

Robins, L. N., Helzer, J. E., & Davis, D. H. (1975). Narcotic use in Southeast Asia and afterward. *Archives of General Psychiatry, 32,* 955–961.

Robinson, T. E., & Berridge, K. C. (2003). Addiction. *Annual Review of Psychology, 54,* 25–53.

Robison, L. L., Buckley, J. D., Daigle, A. E., Wells, R., Benjamin, D., Arthur, D. C., et al. (1989). Maternal drug use and risk of childhood non-lymphoblastic leukemia among offspring. *Cancer, 63,* 1904–1911.

Robson, P. (2001). Therapeutic aspects of cannabis and cannabinoids. *British Journal of Psychiatry, 178,* 107–115.

Roine, R., Gentry, R. T., Hernández-Muñoz, R., Baraona, E., & Leiber, C. S. (1990). Aspirin increases blood alcohol concentration in humans after ingestion of ethanol. *Journal of the American Medical Association, 264,* 2406–2408.

Roiser, J. P., & Sahakian, B. J. (2004). Relationship between ecstasy use and depression: A study controlling for poly-drug use. *Psychopharmacology, 173,* 411–417.

Roldan, M. (1999). Colombia: Cocaine and the "miracle" of modernity in Medellin. In P. Gootenberg (Ed.), *Cocaine: Global histories* (pp. 165–182). London: Routledge Press.

Rollnick, S., & Heather, N. (1982). The application of Bandura's self-efficacy theory to abstinence-oriented alcoholism treatment. *Addictive Behaviors, 7,* 243–250.

Rose, A. H. (1977). History and scientific basis of alcoholic beverage production. In A. H. Rose (Ed.), *Alcoholic beverages* (pp. 1–41). New York: Academic Press.

Rose, J. E. (1991). Transdermal nicotine and nasal nicotine administration as smoking cessation treatments. In J. A. Cocores (Ed.), *The clinical management of nicotine dependence* (pp. 196–207). New York: Springer-Verlag.

Rosenberg, H. (1993). Prediction of controlled drinking by alcoholics and problem drinkers. *Psychological Bulletin, 113,* 129–139.

Rosenberg, N. L., & Sharp, C. W. (1992). Solvent toxicity: A neurological focus. In C. W. Sharp, F. Beauvais, & R. Spence (Eds.), *Inhalant abuse: A volatile research agenda.* Research Monograph 129 (pp. 117–171). Rockville, MD: National Institute on Drug Abuse.

Ross, E. M., & Gilman, A. G. (1985). Pharmacodynamics: Mechanisms of drug action and the relationship between drug concentration and effect. In A. G. Gilman, L. S. Goodman, T. W. Rall, & F. Murod (Eds.), *Goodman and Gilman's The pharmacological basis of therapeutics* (7th ed., pp. 35–48). New York: Macmillan.

Rosso, A., Mossey, J., & Lippa, C. F. (2008). Caffeine: Neuroprotective functions in cognition and Alzheimer's disease. *American Journal of Alzheimer's Disease & Other Dementias, 23,* 417–422.

Rowberg, R. E. (2001). *Pharmaceutical research and development: A description and analysis of the process: A CRS report for Congress.* Washington, DC: Library of Congress.

Rush, B., & Gliksman, L. (1986). The distribution of consumption approach to the prevention of alcohol-related damage: An overview of relevant research and current issues. *Advances in Alcohol and Substance Abuse, 5,* 9–32.

Rush, C. R., & Griffiths, R. R. (1996). Zolpidem, triazolam, and temazepam: Behavioral and subject-rated effects in normal volunteers. *Journal of Clinical Psychopharmacology, 16,* 146–157.

Rush, C. R., & Griffiths, R. R. (1997). Acute participant-rated and behavioral effects of alprazolam and buspirone, alone and in combination with ethanol in normal volunteers. *Experimental and Clinical Psychopharmacology, 5,* 28–38.

Rush, C. R., Roll, J. M., & Higgins, S. T. (1998). Controlled laboratory studies on the effects of cocaine in combination with other commonly abused drugs in humans. In S. T. Higgins & J. L. Katz (Eds.), *Cocaine abuse: Behavior, pharmacology, and clinical applications* (pp. 239–264). San Diego: Academic Press.

Russell, M. A. H. (1976). Tobacco smoking and nicotine dependence. In R. J. Gibbins, Y. Israel, H. Kalant, R. E. Popham, W. Schmidt, & R. G. Smart (Eds.), *Research advances in alcohol and drug problems* (Vol. 3, pp. 1–47). New York: John Wiley.

Ryan, R. M., Plant, R. W., & O'Malley, S. S. (1995). Initial motivations for alcohol treatment: Relations with patient characteristics, treatment involvement, and dropout. *Addictive Behaviors, 20,* 279–297.

Sack, R. L., & DeFraites, E. (1977). Lithium and the treatment of mania. In J. D. Barchas, P. A. Berger, R. D. Ciaranello, & G. R. Elliott (Eds.), *Psychopharmacology: From theory to practice.* New York: Oxford University Press.

Saitz, R. (2005). Unhealthy alcohol use. *New England Journal of Medicine, 352,* 596–607.

Salzman, C. (1992). Behavioral side effects of benzodiazepines. In J. M. Kane & J. A. Lieberman (Eds.), *Adverse effects of psychotropic drugs* (pp. 139–152). New York: Guilford Press.

Sanchez-Craig, M., Wilkinson, A., & Davila, R. (1995). Empirically based guidelines for moderate drinking: 1-year results from three studies with problem drinkers. *American Journal of Public Health, 85,* 823–828.

Sanger, D., Willner, P., & Bergman, J. (2003). Applications of behavioral pharmacology in drug discovery. *Behavioral Pharmacology, 14,* 363–367.

Santarelli, L., Saxe, M., Gross, C., Surget, A., Battaglia, F., Dulawa, S., et al. (2003). Requirement of hippocampal neurogenesis for the behavioral effects of antidepressants. *Science, 301,* 805–809.

Saul, S. (2007). More generics slow the surge in drug prices. *The New York Times,* August 8, 2007.

Sawa, A., & Snyder, S. H. (2002). Schizophrenia: Diverse approaches to a complex disease. *Science, 296,* 692–695.

Sawyer, D. A., Julia, H. L., & Turin, A. C. (1982). Caffeine and human behavior: Arousal, anxiety, and performance effects. *Journal of Behavioral Medicine, 5,* 415–439.

Sayette, M. A., Kirchner, T. R., Moreland, R. L., Levine, J. M., & Travis, T. (2004). Effects of alcohol on risk-seeking behavior: A group-level analysis. *Psychology of Addictive Behaviors, 18,* 190–193.

Scammon, D. L., Mayer, R. N., & Smith, K. R. (1991). Alcohol warnings: How do you know when you have had one too many? *Journal of Public Policy and Marketing, 10,* 214–228.

Schaffer Library of Drug Policy. (1998). Chapter 12: The national legislative context: From 1960 to the LeDain Commission, the search for reasons. In D. Riley,

Drugs & Drug Policy in Canada. Ottawa: Canadian Foundation for Drug Policy. Available at http://www.cfdp.ca/sen8ex1.htm.

Schama, K. F., Howell, L. L., & Byrd, L. D. (1998). Prenatal exposure to cocaine. In S. T. Higgins & J. L. Katz (Eds.), *Cocaine abuse: Behavior, pharmacology, and clinical applications* (pp. 159–180). San Diego: Academic Press.

Scheffler, R. M., Brown, T. T., Fulton, R. D., Hinshaw, S. P., Levine, P. & Stone, S. (2009). Positive association between attention-deficit/hyperactivity disorder medication use and academic achievement during elementary school. *Pediatrics, 123,* 1273–1279.

Schifano, F. (2004). A bitter pill. Overview of ecstasy (MDMA, MDA) related fatalities. *Psychopharmacology, 173,* 242–248.

Schivelbusch, W. (1992). *Taste of paradise.* New York: Pantheon Books.

Schizophrenia Society of Canada (SSC). (2011). Cannabis and psychosis. Available at http://www.cannabisandpsychosis.ca/index.php?id=31.

Schlieffer, H. (1973). *Sacred narcotic plants of the New World Indians.* New York: Hafner Press.

Schmidt, W., & Popham, R. E. (1978). The single distribution theory of alcohol consumption. *Journal of Studies on Alcohol, 39,* 400–419.

Schneider Institute for Health Policy. (2001). *Substance abuse: The nation's number one health problem.* Waltham, MA: Heller Graduate School, Brandeis University.

Schuckit, M. A. (1987). Biology of risk of alcoholism. In H. Y. Meltzer (Ed.), *Psychopharmacology: The third generation of progress* (pp. 1527–1533). New York: Raven Press.

Schuckit, M. A. (1994). The treatment of stimulant dependence. *Addiction, 89,* 1559–1563.

Schuckit, M. A. (1995). *Drug and alcohol abuse: A clinical guide to diagnosis and treatment* (4th ed.). New York: Plenum Press.

Schuckit, M. A. (1996). Recent developments in the pharmacotherapy of alcohol dependence. *Journal of Consulting and Clinical Psychology, 64,* 669–676.

Schuckit, M. A. (2000). *Drug and alcohol abuse: A clinical guide to diagnosis and treatment* (5th ed.). New York: Kluwer Academic/ Plenum Publishers.

Schuckit, M. A., Smith, T. L., & Kalmijn, J. (2004). The search for genes contributing to the low level of response to alcohol: Patterns of findings across studies. *Alcoholism: Clinical and Experimental Research, 28,* 1449–1458.

Schultes, R. E. (1976). *Hallucinogenic plants.* New York: Golden Press.

Scott, J. M. (1969). *The white poppy: A history of opium.* New York: Funk & Wagnalls.

Seligman, J., & King, P. (1996). Roofies: The date rape drug. *Newsweek,* February 26, p. 54.

Selvaraj, S., Hoshi, R., Bhagwagar, Z., Murthy, N. V., Hinz, R., Cowen, P., Curran, H. V., & Grasby, P. (2009). Brain serotonin transporter binding in former users of MDMA (ecstasy). *British Journal of Psychiatry, 194,* 355–359.

Senate Special Committee on Illegal Drugs. (2002). *Cannabis: Our position for a Canadian public policy.* Ottawa: Senate of Canada.

Sevak. R. J., Stoops, W. W., Hays, L. R., & Rush, C. R. (2009). Discriminative-stimulus and subject-rated effects of methamphetamine, d-amphetamine, methylphenidate and triazolam in methamphetamine trained humans. *The Journal of Pharmacology and Experimental Therapeutics, 328,* 1007–1018.

Sharp, C. W. (1992). Introduction to inhalant abuse. In C. W. Sharp, F. Beauvais, & R. Spence (Eds.), *Inhalant abuse: A volatile research agenda.* Research Monograph 129 (pp. 1–12). Rockville, MD: National Institute on Drug Abuse.

Sheilds, J. (2007). Christ and the cactus: A study of peyotism among the Canadian Sioux. Available at http://tinyurl.com/d7msp5c.

Shelton, R. C., Keller, M. B., Gelenberg, A., Dunner, D., Hirschfeld, R., Thase, M. E., et al. (2001). Effectiveness of St. John's wort in major depression: A randomized controlled trial. *Journal of the American Medical Association, 285,* 1978–1986.

Shenfeld, H. (2006). The best high they've ever had. *Newsweek,* June 12.

Sher, K. J. (1987). Stress response dampening. In H. T. Blane & K. E. Leonard (Eds.), *Psychological theories of drinking and alcoholism* (pp. 227–271). New York: Guilford Press.

Sher, K. J., & Levenson, R. W. (1982). Risk for alcoholism and individual differences in the stress-dampening effect of alcohol. *Journal of Abnormal Psychology, 91,* 350–368.

Shiffman, S. (1993). Smoking cessation treatment: Any progress? *Journal of Consulting and Clinical Psychology, 61,* 718–722.

Shiffman, S., Gnys, M., Richards, T. J., Paty, J. A., Hickcox, M., & Kassel, J. D. (1996). Temptations to smoke after quitting: A comparison of lapsers and maintainers. *Health Psychology, 15,* 455–461.

Siegel, R. K. (1984). The natural history of hallucinogens. In B. L. Jacobs (Ed.), *Hallucinogens: Neurochemical, behavioral, and clinical perspectives* (pp. 1–19). New York: Raven Press.

Siegel, R. K. (1985). New patterns of cocaine use: Changing doses and routes. In N. J. Kozel & E. H. Adams (Eds.), *Cocaine use in America: Epidemiological and clinical perspectives* (pp. 204–220). NIDA Research Monograph 61.

Siegel, R. K. (1992). *Fire in the brain: Clinical tales of hallucination.* New York: Dutton.

Single, E. (1995). Harm reduction and alcohol. *International Journal of Drug Policy, 6,* 26–30.

Sisson, R., & Azrin, N. (1989). The community reinforcement approach. In R. K. Hester & W. R. Miller (Eds.), *Handbook of alcoholism treatment approaches* (pp. 242–258). New York: Pergamon Press.

Skirrow, J., & Sawka, E. (1987). Alcohol and drug abuse prevention strategies: An overview. *Contemporary Drug Problems, 14,* 147–241.

Skog, O. J. (1985). The collectivity of drinking cultures: A theory of the distribution of alcohol consumption. *British Journal of Addiction, 80,* 83–99.

SMART Recovery. (2011). Available at http://blog.smartrecovery.org/?m=201105.

Smart, R. (1988). Crack cocaine use in Canada: New epidemic. *American Journal of Epidemiology, 127* (6), 1315–1317.

Smit, H. J., & Rogers, P. J. (2000). Effects of low doses of caffeine on cognitive performance, mood, and thirst in low and higher caffeine consumers. *Psychopharmacology, 152,* 167–173.

Smith, A. (2002). Effects of caffeine on human behavior. *Food and Chemical Toxicology, 40,* 1243–1255.

Smith, C. A. H. (1927). The discovery of anesthesia. *The Scientific Monthly, 24,* 64–70.

Smith, D. E. (1968). Acute and chronic toxicity of marijuana. *Journal of Psychoactive Drugs, 2,* 37–47.

Smith, D. E., & Gay, G. R. (1972). *It's so good, don't even try it once.* Englewood Cliffs, NJ: Prentice Hall.

Smith, N. T. (2002). A review of the published literature into cannabis withdrawal symptoms in human users. *Addiction, 97,* 621–632.

Smith, P. (2004). The influence of St. John's wort on the pharmacokinetics of protein binding of imatinib mesylate. *Pharmacotherapy, 24,* 1508–1514.

Smith, T. C., Cooperman, L. H., & Wollman, H. (1980). The therapeutic gases. In A. G. Gilman, L. S. Goodman, & A. Gilman (Eds.), *Goodman and Gilman's The pharmacological basis of therapeutics* (6th ed., pp. 321–338). London: Macmillan.

Snel, J., Tieges, Z., & Lorist, M. M. (2004). Effects of cocaine on sleep and wakefulness: An update. In A. Nehlig (Ed.), *Coffee, tea, chocolate, and the brain* (pp. 13–33). Boca Raton, FL: CRC Press.

Snyder, S. H. (1989). *Brainstorming: The science and politics of opiate research.* Cambridge, MA: Harvard University Press.

Snyder, S. H., & Largent, B. L. (1989). Receptor mechanisms in antipsychotic drug action: Focus on sigma receptors. *Journal of Neuropsychiatry, 1,* 7–15.

Snyder, S. H., & Sklar, P. (1984). Behavioral and molecular actions of caffeine: Focus on adenosine. *Journal of Psychiatric Research, 18,* 91–106.

Snyder, S. H., Burt, D. R., & Creese, I. (1976). Dopamine receptor of mammalian brain: Direct demonstration of binding to agonist and antagonist states. *Neuroscience Symposia, 1,* 28–49.

Sobell, L. C., Sobell, M. B., Toneatto, T., & Leo, G. I. (1993). What triggers the resolution of alcohol problems without treatment? *Alcoholism: Clinical and Experimental Research, 17,* 217–224.

Sobell, M. B., & Sobell, L. C. (1981). *Alcohol abuse curriculum guide for psychology faculty.* Rockville, MD: U.S. Department of Health and Human Services.

Sobell, M. B., & Sobell, L. C. (1993). *Problem drinkers: Guided self-change treatment.* New York: Guilford Press.

Sobell, M. B., & Sobell, L. C. (2000). Stepped care as a heuristic approach to the treatment of alcohol problems. *Journal of Consulting and Clinical Psychology, 68,* 573–579.

Sokolow, L., Welte, J., Hynes, G., & Lyons, J. (1981). Multiple substance use by alcoholics. *British Journal of Addiction, 76,* 147–158.

Soloman, R., & Green, M. (1988). The first century: The history of non-medical opiate use and control policies in Canada, 1870–1970. In J. Blackwell and P. Erikson (Eds.), *Illicit drugs in Canada: A risky business.* Scarborough: Nelson Canada.

Solomon, D. (Ed.). (1966). *The marijuana papers.* New York: Bobbs-Merrill.

Solomon, R. (1980). The opponent process theory of acquired motivation: The costs of pleasure and the benefits of pain. *American Psychologist, 35,* 691–712.

Solomon, R. L., & Corbit, J. D. (1974). An opponent-process theory of motivation: I. Temporal dynamics of affect. *Psychological Review, 81,* 119–145.

Solowij, N. (1998). *Cannabis and cognitive functioning.* Cambridge, England: Cambridge University Press.

Sommers, I., Baskin, D., & Baskin-Sommers, A. (2006). Methamphetamine use among young adults: Health and social consequences. *Addictive Behaviors, 31,* 1469–1476.

Sorer, H. (1992). *Acute cocaine intoxication: Current methods of treatment.* Research Monograph 123. Washington, DC: National Institute on Drug Abuse.

Spector, I. (1985). AMP: A new form of marijuana. *Journal of Clinical Psychiatry, 46,* 498–499.

Spicer, L. (2002). Historical and cultural uses of cannabis and the Canadian "marijuana clash." Ottawa: Parliament of Canada. Available at http://www.parl.gc.ca/Content/SEN/Committee/371/ille/library/Spicer-e.htm.

Spiegel, R., & Aebi, H. (1983). *Psychopharmacology.* New York: John Wiley.

Spillane, J. F. (2000). *Cocaine: From medical marvel to modern menace in the United States, 1884–1920.* Baltimore, MD: Johns Hopkins Press.

Spinella, M. (2001). *The psychopharmacology of herbal medicine.* Cambridge, MA: MIT Press.

Spitzer, R. L., Gibbon, M., Skodol, A. E., Williams, J. B. W., & First, M. B. (1989). *DSM-III-R case book.* Washington, DC: American Psychiatric Press.

Spitzer, R. L., Skodol, A. E., Gibbon, M., & Williams, J. B. W. (1981). *DSM–III case book.* Washington, DC: American Psychiatric Press.

Spoth, R. L., Randall, G. K., Trudeau, L., Shin, C., & Redmond, C. (2008). Substance use outcomes 5 ½ years past baseline for partnership-based family-school preventive interventions. *Drug and Alcohol Dependence, 96,* 57–68.

Squires, R. F., & Braestrup, C. (1977). Benzodiazepine receptors in rat brain. *Nature, 266,* 732–734.

Stanton, M. D., & Shadish, W. R. (1997). Outcome, attrition, and family-couples treatment for drug abuse: A meta-analysis and review of controlled, comparative studies. *Psychological Bulletin, 122,* 170–191.

Statistics Canada. (2008). The control and sale of alcoholic beverages in Canada, 2007. Ottawa, ON: Statistics Canada. Available at http://www.statcan.gc.ca/pub/63-202-x/63-202-x2007000-eng.pdf.

Steenland, K., Thun, M., Lally, C., & Heath, C., Jr. (1996). Environmental tobacco smoke and coronary heart disease in the American Cancer Society CPS-II cohort. *Circulation, 94,* 622–628.

Stephens, R. S., Roffman, R. A., & Curtin, L. (2000). Comparison of extended versus brief treatments for marijuana use. *Journal of Consulting and Clinical Psychology, 68,* 898–908.

Stephens, R. S., Roffman, R. A., & Simpson, E. E. (1994). Treating adult marijuana dependence: A test of the relapse prevention model. *Journal of Consulting and Clinical Psychology, 62,* 92–99.

Steptoe, A., & Wardle, J. (1999). Mood and drinking: A naturalistic diary study of alcohol, coffee, and tea. *Psychopharmacology, 141,* 315–321.

Sternbach, L. H. (1983). The discovery of CNS active 1,4-benzodiazepines. In E. Costa (Ed.), *The benzodiazepines: From molecular biology to clinical practice* (pp. 1–6). New York: Raven Press.

Stevens, J. (1987). *Storming heaven: LSD and the American dream.* New York: Atlantic Monthly Press.

Stewart, G. C. (1967). A history of the medical use of tobacco. *Medical History, 11,* 228–268.

Stewart, O. C. (1987). *Peyote religion: A history.* Norman: University of Oklahoma Press.

Stinson, F. S., Grant, B. F., & Dufour, M. C. (2001). The critical dimension of ethnicity in liver cirrhosis mortality statistics. *Alcoholism: Clinical and Experimental Research, 25,* 1181–1187.

Stitzer, M. L., Iguchi, M. Y., & Felch, L. J. (1992). Contingent take-home incentive: Effects on drug use in methadone maintenance patients. *Journal of Consulting and Clinical Psychology, 60,* 927–934.

Stock, S. H. (1986). Synthetic drugs: A history of ups and downs—Part 2. *PharmChem Newsletter, 15–5,* 1–6.

Stonehenge. (2011). Available at http://www.stonehengetc.com/news.aspx.

Strain, E. C., Mumford, G. K., Silverman, K., & Griffiths, R. R. (1994). Caffeine dependence syndrome: Evidence from case histories and experimental evaluations. *Journal of the American Medical Association, 272,* 1043–1048.

Strassman, R. (2005). Hallucinogens. In M. Earlywine (Ed.), *Mind-altering drugs: The science of subjective experience* (pp. 49–85), Oxford, UK: Oxford University Press.

Streatfeild, D. (2001). *Cocaine: An unauthorized biography.* New York: St. Martins Press.

Stuart, R. B. (1974). Teaching facts about drugs: Pushing or preventing. *Journal of Educational Psychology, 66,* 189–201.

Subramaniam, G. A., & Stitzer, M. A. (2009). Clinical characteristics of treatment-seeking prescription opioid vs. heroin-using adolescents with opioid use disorder. *Drug and Alcohol Dependence, 101,* 13–19.

Substance Abuse and Mental Health Services Administration (SAMHSA). (2008). National Survey on Drug Use & Health. Retrieved from http://www.oas.samhsa.gov/NSDUHlatest.htm.

Substance Abuse and Mental Health Services Administration (SAMHSA). (2008). Results from the 2007 National Survey on Drug Use and Health: National findings. Rockville, MD: SAMHSA Office of Applied Studies.

Sugiura, T., Kondo, S., Kishimoto, S., Miyashita, T., Nakan, S., Kodaka, T., et al. (2000). Evidence that 2-arachidonoylglycerol but no *N*-palmitoylethanolamine or anandamide is the physiological ligand for the cannabinoid CB2 receptor. Comparison of the agonistic activities of various cannabinoid receptor ligands in HL-60 cells. *Journal of Biological Chemistry, 275,* 605–612.

Sullivan, E. V., Rosenbloom, M. J., & Pfefferbaum, A. (2000). Pattern of motor and cognitive deficits in detoxified alcoholic men. *Alcoholism: Clinical and Experimental Research, 24,* 611–621.

Sussman, S., Stacy, A. W., Dent, C. W., Simon, T. R., & Johnson, C. A. (1996). Marijuana use: Current issues and new research directions. *Journal of Drug Issues, 26,* 695–733.

Suter, P. M., Schutz, Y., & Jequier, E. (1992). The effect of ethanol on fat storage in healthy subjects. *New England Journal of Medicine, 326,* 983–987.

Swift, R., & Leggio, L. (2009). Adjunctive pharmacotherapies in the treatment of alcohol and drug dependence. In P. M. Miller (Ed.), *Evidence-based addiction treatment* (pp. 287–310). Boston: Elsevier.

Syed, I. B. (1976). The effects of caffeine. *Journal of the American Pharmaceutical Association, 16,* 568–572.

Tancer, M., & Johanson, C. (2003). Reinforcing, subjective, and physiological effects of MDMA in humans: A comparison with d-amphetamine and mCPP. *Drug and Alcohol Dependence, 72,* 33–44.

Taylor, P. (2001). Anticholinesterase agents. In J. G. Hamilton & L. E. Limbird (Eds.), *Goodman & Gilman's The pharmacological basis of therapeutics* (10th ed., pp. 175–192). New York: McGraw-Hill.

Temple, J. L. (2009). Caffeine use in children: What we know, what we have left to learn, and why we should worry. *Neuroscience and Biobehavioral Reviews, 33,* 793–806.

Thompson, H. S. (1971). *Fear and loathing in Las Vegas.* New York: Random House.

Ticku, M. K., Burch, T. P., & Davis, W. C. (1983). The interactions of ethanol with the benzodiazepine-GABA receptor-ionophore complex. *Pharmacology, Biochemistry, and Behavior, 18,* 15–18.

Tiffany, S. T. (1990). A cognitive model of drug urges and drug use behavior: Role of automatic and nonautomatic processes. *Psychological Review, 97,* 147–168.

Tiffany, S. T. (1992). A critique of contemporary urge and craving research: Methodological, psychometric, and theoretical issues. *Advances in Behavior Research and Therapy, 14,* 123–139.

Tilashalski, K., Rodu, B., & Cole, P. (2005). Seven-year follow-up of smoking cessation with smokeless tobacco. *Journal of Psychoactive Drugs, 37,* 105–108.

Time. (1993). Cyberpunk. *Time, 141*(6), pp. 58–65.

Tobacco Research Unit. (2011). Available at http://www.otru.org.

Tobler, N. S. (1986). Meta-analysis of 143 adolescent drug prevention programs: Quantitative outcome results of program participants compared to a control or comparison group. *Journal of Drug Issues, 16,* 537–567.

Todd, M. (2004). Daily processes in stress and smoking: Effects of negative events, nicotine dependence, and gender. *Psychology of Addictive Behaviors, 18,* 31–39.

Tolman, S. A. (2005). The Oxycontin epidemic. *The Boston Globe,* June 30.

Tolstrup, J., Jensen, M. K., Tjanneland, A., Overvad, K., Mukamel, M. J., & Granbaak, M. (2006). Prospective study of alcohol drinking and coronary heart disease in women and men. *British Medical Journal, 332,* 1244–1248.

Tonigan, J. S., Toscova, R., & Miller, W. R. (1995). Meta-analysis of the literature on Alcoholics Anonymous: Sample and study characteristics moderate findings. *Journal of Studies on Alcohol, 57,* 65–72.

Tooley, J. (1999). Demon drugs and holy wars: Canadian drug policy as symbolic action. MA thesis, University of New Brunswick.

Transport Canada (2008). A quick look at alcohol-related crashes in Canada. Fact Sheet. Retrieved on October 2011 from http://www.tc.gc.ca/eng/roadsafety/tp-tp2436-rs200809-menu-397.htm.

Trimpey, J. (1992). *Rational recovery from alcoholism* (4th ed.). New York: Delacorte Press.

Troisi, J. R., II, Critchfield, T. S., & Griffiths, R. R. (1993). Buspirone and lorazapam abuse liability in humans: Behavioral effects, subjective effects, and choice. *Behavioural Pharmacology, 4,* 217–230.

Tuchfeld, B. (1981). Spontaneous remission in alcoholics: Empirical observation and theoretical implications. *Journal of Studies on Alcohol, 42,* 626–641.

Tunnicliff, G., Eison, A., & Taylor, D. (1991). *Buspirone: Mechanisms and clinical aspects.* Orlando, FL: Academic Press.

Tyler, L. (2000). *Understanding alternative medicine: New health paths in America.* New York: Haworth Herbal Press.

Tyre, P. (2005). A problem in the brain. *Newsweek,* October 17.

Tyrer, P. J. (1982a). Evaluation of psychotropic drugs. In P. J. Tyrer (Ed.), *Drugs in psychiatric practice* (pp. 31–44). London: Butterworths.

Tyrer, P. J. (Ed.). (1982b). *Drugs in psychiatric practice.* London: Butterworths.

Tyrer, S., & Shaw, D. M. (1982). Lithium carbonate. In P. J. Tyrer (Ed.), *Drugs in psychiatric practice.* London: Butterworths.

U.S. Department of Health and Human Services (USDHHS). (1984). *Drug abuse and drug abuse research.* Washington, DC: U.S. Government Printing Office.

U.S. Drug Enforcement Agency (2009). Meth clandestine laboratory incidents. http://www.usdoj.gov/dea/concern/map_lab_seizures.html.

U.S. National Highway Traffic Safety Administration (USNHTSA). (1997). Setting limits, saving lives. The case for .08 BAC laws. Washington, DC: U.S. Department of Transportation.

Uhl, G. R., Liu, Q-R., Drgon, T., Johnson, C., Walther, D., Rose, J. E., David, S. P., Niaura, R., & Lerman, C. (2008). Molecular genetics of successful smoking cessation. *Archives of General Psychiatry, 65,* 683–693.

United Nations Office on Drugs and Crime. (2009a). *Global illicit drug trends: 2009.* Vienna: Author.

United Nations Office on Drugs and Crime. (2009b). *World drug report: 2009.* Vienna: Author.

University of California–Irvine Transdisciplinary Tobacco Use Research Center (UCI TTURC). (2005). *Closing the gap on youth tobacco use.* Irvine, CA: Author.

Urgert, R., Meyboom, S., Kuilman, M., Rexwinkel, H., Vissers, M. N., Klerk, M., et al. (1996). Comparison of effect of cafetiere and filtered coffee on serum concentrations of liver aminotransferases and lipids: A six-month randomized controlled trial. *British Medical Journal, 313,* 1362–1366.

USDHHS. (1987a). *Alcohol and health.* Rockville, MD: Author.

USDHHS. (1987b). *Smoking, tobacco, and health. A fact book.* Rockville, MD: U.S. Public Health Service.

USDHHS. (1989). *Reducing the health consequences of smoking: 25 years of progress.* Rockville, MD: U.S. Public Health Service.

USDHHS. (1990). *Alcohol and health.* Rockville, MD: Author.

USDHHS. (1993). *Alcohol and health.* Bethesda, MD: National Institutes of Health.

USDHHS (2001). *Women and smoking: A report to the Surgeon General.* Rockville, MD: Author.

USDHHS (2008). *Treating tobacco use and dependence: 2008 update.* Rockville, MD: Author.

Uttal, W. R. (2001). *The new phrenology.* Cambridge, MA: MIT Press.

Valenstein, E. S. (2005). *The war of the soups and the sparks: The discovery of neurotransmitters and the dispute over how nerves communicate.* New York: Columbia University Press.

Van Amsterdam, J. G. C., van der Laan, J. W., & Slangen, J. L. (1996). *Residual effects of prolonged heavy cannabis use.* National Institute of Public Health and the Environment, Report No. 318902003. Bilthoven, Netherlands.

van Dam, R. M. (2008). Coffee consumption and risk of type 2 diabetes, cardiovascular diseases, and cancer. *Applied Physiology, Nutrition, and Metabolism, 33,* 1269–1283.

van Laar, M., van Dorsselaer, S., Monshouwer, K., & de Graaf, R. (2007). Does cannabis use predict the first incidence of mood and anxiety disorders in the adult population? *Addiction, 102,* 1251–1260.

Vastag, B. (2005). Ibogaine therapy: A "vast uncontrolled experiment." *Science, 308,* 345–346.

Vega, W. A., et al. (2002). Prevalence and age of onset for drug use in seven international sites: Results from the international consortium of psychiatric epidemiology. *Drug and Alcohol Dependence, 68,* 285–297.

Verstraete, A. (2004). Detection time of drugs of abuse in blood, urine, and oral fluids. *Therapeutic Drug Monitoring, 26* (2): 200–205.

Viscusi, W. K. (1992). *Smoking: Making the risky decision.* New York: Oxford University Press.

Vocci, F. J., Acri, J., & Elkashef, A. (2005). Medication development for addictive disorders: The state of the science. *American Journal of Psychiatry, 162,* 1432–1440.

Vogel-Sprott, M. (1992). *Alcohol tolerance and social drinking: Learning the consequences.* New York: Guilford Press.

Vogel-Sprott, M., & Fillmore, M. T. (1999). Expectancy and behavioral effects of socially used drugs. In I. Kirsch (Ed.), *How expectancies shape experience* (pp. 215–232). Washington, DC: American Psychological Association.

Volkow, N. D., Chang, L., Wang, G. J., Fowler, J. S., Leonido-Yee, M., Franceschi, D., Sedler, M., Gatley, R., Hitzemann, R., & Ding, Y. S (2001). Association of dopamine transporter reduction with psychomotor impairment in methamphetamine abusers. *American Journal of Psychiatry, 158,* 377–382.

Volpicelli, J. R., Alterman, A. I., Hayashida, M., & O'Brien, C. P. (1992). Naltrexone in the treatment of alcohol dependence. *Archives of General Psychiatry, 49,* 876–880.

Vuchinich, R. E., & Tucker, J. A. (1988). Contributions from behavioral theories of choice to an analysis of alcohol abuse. *Journal of Abnormal Psychology, 97,* 181–195.

Wagenaar, A. C., & Toomey, T. L. (2002). Effects of minimum drinking age laws: Review and analyses of the literature from 1960 to 2000. *Journal of Studies on Alcohol, Supplement No. 14,* 206–225.

Walker, D. J., & Zacny, J. P. (2005). Subjective effects of nitrous oxide. In M. Earlywine (Ed.). *Mind-altering drugs: The science of subjective experience* (pp. 305–337). Oxford, UK: Oxford University Press.

Walsh, B. T., Seidman, S. N., Sysko, R., & Gould, M. (2002). Placebo response in studies of major depression: Variable, substantial, and growing. *Journal of the American Medical Association, 287,* 1840–1847.

Walsh, D. C., Hingson, R. W., Merrigan, D. M., Levenson, S. M., Cupples, A., Heeren, T., et al. (1991). A randomized trial of treatment options for alcohol abusing workers. *New England Journal of Medicine, 325,* 775–782.

Walters, P. G. (1992). FDA's new drug evaluation process: A general overview. *Journal of Public Health and Dentistry, 52,* 333–337.

Wang, P. S., Berglund, P., Olfson, M., Pincus, H. A., Wells, K. B., & Kessler, R. C. (2005). Failure and delay in initial treatment contact after first onset of mental disorders in the national comorbidity survey replication. *Archives of General Psychiatry, 62,* 603–613.

Wang, P. S., Lane, M., Olfson, M., Pincus, H. A., Wells, K. B., & Kessler, R. C. (2005). Twelve-month use of mental health services in the United States. *Archives of General Psychiatry, 62,* 629–640.

Wansink, B., & van Ittersum, K. (2005). Shape of glass and amount of alcohol poured: Comparative study of effect of practice and concentration. *British Medical Journal, 331,* 1512–1514.

Ward, A. S., Haney, M., Fischman, M. W., & Foltin, R. W. (1997). Binge cocaine self-administration in humans: Intravenous cocaine. *Psychopharmacology, 132,* 375–381.

Ware, M., Wang, T., Shapiro, S., Robinson, A., Ducruet, T., Huynh, T., Gamsa, A., Bennett, G., & Collet, J-P. (2010). Smoked cannabis for chronic neuropathic pain. *Canadian Medical Association Journal, 182* (14), E694–E701.

Warner, J. (1997). Shifting categories of the social harms associated with alcohol: Examples from late medieval and early modern England. *American Journal of Public Health, 87,* 1788–1797.

Warner, K. E., Slade, J., & Sweanor, L. L. B. (1997). The emerging market for long-term nicotine maintenance. *Journal of the American Medical Association, 278,* 1087–1092.

Washton, A. M. (1990). Structured outpatient treatment of alcohol vs. drug dependence. In M. Galanter (Ed.), *Recent developments in alcoholism* (Vol. 8, pp. 285–304). New York: Plenum Press.

Washton, A. M. (Ed.). (1995). *Psychotherapy and substance abuse.* New York: Guilford Press.

Wasson, R. G. (1979). Fly agaric and man. In D. H. Efron, B. Holmstedt, & N. S. Kline (Eds.), *Ethnopharmacologic search for psychoactive drugs* (pp. 505–514). New York: Raven Press.

Webb, G., Shakeshaft, A., Sanson-Fisher, R., & Havard, A. (2009). A systematic review of work-place interventions for alcohol-related problems. *Addiction, 104,* 365–377.

Webster, L. R. (2007). Oxytrex: An oxycodone and ultra-low-dose naltrexone formulation. *Expert Opinions and Investigations on Drugs, 16,* 1277–1283.

Wechsler, H., Lee, J. E., Kuo, M., Seibring, M., Nelson, T. F., & Lee, H. P. (2002). Trends in college binge drinking during a period of increased prevention efforts: Findings from four Harvard School of Public Health study surveys, 1993–2001. *Journal of American College Health, 50,* 203–217.

Wechsler, H., Moeykens, B., Davenport, A., Castillo, S., & Hansen, J. (1995). The adverse impact of heavy episodic drinkers on other college students. *Journal of Studies on Alcohol, 56,* 628–634.

Wechsler, H., Nelson, T. F., Lee, J. E., Seibring, M., Lewis, C., & Keeling, R. P. (2003). Perception and reality: A national evaluation of social norms marketing interventions to reduce college students' heavy alcohol use. *Journal of Studies on Alcohol, 64,* 484–494.

Weil, A., & Rosen, W. (1983). *From chocolate to morphine.* Boston: Houghton Mifflin.

Weiss, K. J., & Greenfield, D. P. (1986). Prescription drug abuse. *Psychiatric Clinics of North America, 9,* 475–490.

Weiss, R. D., & Mirin, S. M. (1987). *Cocaine.* Washington, DC: American Psychiatric Press.

Welte, J. W., & Barnes, G. M. (1985). Alcohol: The gateway to other drug use among secondary-school students. *Journal of Youth and Adolescence, 14,* 487–498.

West, R. J., & Russell, M. A. H. (1985). Nicotine pharmacology and smoking dependence. In S. D. Iverson (Ed.), *Psychopharmacology: Recent advances and future prospects* (pp. 303–314). Oxford, UK: Oxford University Press.

West, S. L., & O'Neal, K. K. (2004). Project D.A.R.E. outcome effectiveness revisited. *American Journal of Public Health, 94,* 1027–1029.

Wester, R. C., & Maibach, H. I. (1983). Cutaneous pharmacokinetics: 10 steps to percutaneous absorption. *Drug Metabolism Reviews, 14,* 169–205.

Westin, A. A. & Slordal, L. (2009). Passive inhalation of cannabis smoke—is it detectable? *Tidsskr Nor Laegeforen,* 15, 109–113.

Wetter, D. W., Kenford, S. L., Welsch, S. K., Smith, S. S., Fouladi, R. T., Fiori, M. C., et al. (2004). Prevalence and predictors of transitions in smoking behavior among college students. *Health Psychology, 23,* 168–177.

Wexler, B. E., Gottschalk, C. H., Fulbright, R. K., Prohovnik, I., Lacadie, C. M., Rounsaville, R. J., et al. (2001). Functional magnetic resonance imaging of cocaine craving. *American Journal of Psychiatry, 158,* 86–95.

Whitaker, B. (1987). *The global connection: The crisis of drug addiction.* London: Jonathan Cade.

White, J. M. (1991). *Drug dependence.* Englewood Cliffs, NJ: Prentice Hall.

Whitehead, P. C. (1975). Prevention of alcoholism: Divergences and convergences of two approaches. *Addictive Diseases, 7,* 431–443.

WHO. (1999). Press releases 1999. *Cigars and pipes as lethal as cigarettes, says new European study.* Geneva, Switzerland: Author.

Wiegand, T., Thai, D., & Benowitz, N. (2008). Medical consequences of the use of hallucinogens: LSD, mescaline, PCP and MDMA (ecstasy). In J. Brick (Ed.), *Handbook of the medical consequences of alcohol and drug abuse* (2nd ed., pp. 461–490). New York: Haworth Press.

Wilens, T. E., Faraone, S. V., Biederman, J., & Gunawardene, S. (2003). Does stimulant therapy of attention-deficit/hyperactivity disorder beget later substance abuse? A meta-analytic review of the literature. *Pediatrics, 111,* 179–185.

Wilkinson, J. (1986). *Tobacco: The facts behind the smoke screen.* Middlesex, England: Penguin Books.

Wilkinson, R. (1970). *The prevention of drinking problems: Alcohol control and cultural influences.* New York: Oxford University Press.

Williams, G. C., Gagne, M., Ryan, R. M., & Deci, E. L. (2002). Facilitating autonomous motivation for smoking cessation. *Health Psychology, 21,* 40–50.

Williams, N. (1996). How the ancient Egyptians brewed beer. *Science, 273,* 432.

Wilsnack, S. C., Klassen, A. D., & Wilsnack, R. W. (1984). Drinking and reproductive dysfunction among women in a 1981 national survey. *Alcoholism: Clinical and Experimental Research, 8,* 451–458.

Windle, M., Barnes, G. M., & Welte, J. (1989). Causal models of adolescent substance use: An examination of gender differences using distribution-free estimators. *Journal of Personality and Social Psychology, 56,* 132–142.

Winickoff, J. P., Friebely, J., Tanski, S. E., Sherrod, C., Matt, G. E., Hovell, M. F., & McMillen, R. C. (2009). Beliefs about the health effects of "third hand" smoke and home smoking bans. *Pediatrics, 123,* e74–e79.

Winkelmayer, W. C., Stampfer, M. J., Willett, W. C., & Curhan, G. C. (2005). Habitual caffeine intake and the risk of hypertension in women. *Journal of the American Medical Association, 294,* 2330–2335.

Wise, R. A. (1988). The neurobiology of craving: Implications for the understanding and treatment of addiction. *Journal of Abnormal Psychology, 97,* 118–132.

Witkiewitz, K., & Marlatt, G. A. (2004). Relapse prevention for alcohol and drugs: That was Zen, this is Tao. *American Psychologist, 59,* 224–235.

Wolfe, T. (1969). *The electric Kool-Aid acid test.* New York: Bantam Books.

Woloshin, S., Schwartz, L. M., & Welch, H. G. (2002). Risk charts: Putting cancer in context. *Journal of the National Cancer Institute, 94,* 799–804.

Women for Sobriety. (2011). 13 Affirmations. Available at http://womenforsobriety.

Women for Sobriety. (April 1985). *Sobering thoughts.* Quakertown, PA: Author.

Woods, J. H., & Winger, G. (1997). Abuse liability of flunitrazepam. *Journal of Clinical Psychopharmacology, 17* (Supplement 2), 1–57.

Woodward, B. (1984). *Wired: The short life and fast times of John Belushi.* New York: Pocket Books.

Workshop on the Medical Utility of Marijuana. (1997). *Report to the Director, National Institutes of Health, by the Ad Hoc group of experts.* Washington, DC: National Institutes of Health.

World Health Organization (WHO). (1981). Nomenclature and classification of drugs and alcohol-related problems: A WHO memorandum. *Bulletin of the World Health Organization, 59,* 225–242.

Wray, L. A., Herzog, A. R., Willis, R. J., & Wallace, R. B. (1998). The impact of education and heart attack on smoking cessation among middle-aged adults. *Journal of Health and Social Behavior, 39,* 271–294.

Wu, L., Pilowsky, D. J., & Patkar, A. A. (2008). Non-prescribed use of pain relievers among adolescents in the United States. *Drug and Alcohol Dependence, 94,* 1–11.

Yang, S. (2005). Researchers find that passive smoking kills as many women as active smoking in China. Retrieved October 2005, from http://www.berkeley.edu/news/media/releases/2005/09/04_smoking.shtml.

Yesalis, C. E., Bahrke, M. S., Kopstein, A. M., & Barsukiewicz, C. K. (2000). Incidence of anabolic steroid use: A discussion of methodological issues. In C. E. Yesalis (Ed.), *Anabolic steroids in sport and exercise* (2nd ed., pp. 73–116). Champaign, IL: Human Kinetics Press.

Young, A. M., & Herling, S. (1986). Drugs as reinforcers: Studies in laboratory animals. In S. R. Goldberg & I. Stolerman (Eds.), *Behavioral analysis of drug dependence* (pp. 9–68). Orlando, FL: Academic Press.

Young, A. M., McCabe, S. E., & Boyd, C. J. (2007). Adolescents' sexual inferences about girls who consume alcohol. *Psychology of Women Quarterly, 31,* 229–240.

Young, C. R. (1997). Sertraline treatment of hallucinogen persisting perception disorder. *Journal of Clinical Psychiatry, 58,* 85.

Young, T., Lawson, G. W., & Gacono, C. B. (1987). Clinical aspects of phencyclidine (PCP). *The International Journal of the Addictions, 22,* 1–15.

Yuan J., Hatzidimitriou, G., Suthar, P., Mueller, M., McCann, U., & Ricaurte, G. (2006). Relationship between temperature, dopaminergic neurotoxicity, and plasma drug concentrations in methamphetamine-treated squirrel monkeys. *Journal of Pharmacology and Experimental Therapeutics, 316,* 1210–1218.

Zacny, J. P. (1995). A review of the effects of opioids on psychomotor and cognitive functioning in humans. *Experimental and Clinical Psychopharmacology, 3,* 432–466.

Zador, P. L. (1991). Alcohol-related relative risk of fatal driver injuries in relation to driver age and sex. *Journal of Studies on Alcohol, 52,* 302–310.

Zhdanova, I. V., & Friedman, L. (2002). Melatonin for sleep disorders. In D. Mischoulon & J. F. Rosenbaum (Eds.), *Natural medications for psychiatric disorders* (pp. 147–171). Philadelphia: Lippincott, Williams & Wilkins.

Zimmer, L., & Morgan, J. P. (1997). *Marijuana myths, marijuana facts.* New York: Lindesmith Center.

Zinberg, N. E. (1984). *Drug, set, and setting.* New Haven, CT: Yale University Press.

Zubieta, J. K., & Stohler, C. S. (2009). Neurobiological mechanisms of placebo responses. *Annals of the New York Academy of Sciences, 1156,* 198–210.

Zubieta, J. K., Bueller, J. A., Jackson, L. R., Scott, D. J., Xu, Y., Koeppe, R. A., et al. (2005). Placebo effects mediated by endogenous opioid activity on μ-opioid receptors. *The Journal of Neuroscience, 25,* 7754–7762.

Zubieta, J., Greenwald, M. K., Lombardi, U., et al. (2000). Buprenorphine-induced changes in mu-opioid receptor availability in male heroin-dependent volunteers: A preliminary study. *Neuropsychopharmacology, 23,* 326–334.

Zucker, R. A., Kincaid, S. B., Fitzgerald, H. E., & Bingham, R. C. (1996). Alcohol schema acquisition in preschoolers: Differences between children of alcoholics and children of nonalcoholics. *Alcoholism: Clinical and Experimental Research, 19,* 1011–1017.

Zuckerman, B., Frank, D. A., & Mayes, L. (2002). Cocaine-exposed infants and developmental outcomes. *Journal of the American Medical Association, 287,* 1990–1991.

Zuckerman, M. (1979). *Sensation seeking: Beyond the optimal level of arousal.* New York: John Wiley.

Zusy, A. (1987). For smokers, ways to quit are many, but the goal is elusive. *The New York Times,* July 15, pp. C1, C10.

INDEX

Note: Page numbers followed by f or t denote figures and tables, respectively.
Page numbers italicized denote photos/illustrations.

D

E

N

Q

R